Contents

KU-386-556

Sponsor's Foreword

International gourmets and travellers will be delighted to see the new *Egon Ronay's Seagram Guide 1995 Europe*. This definitive guide to good eating and fine living reveals some of today's best restaurants and hotels. It covers a broad range of establishments and is designed to meet differing budgets and occasions and individual tastes.

The new association between Egon Ronay's Guides and Seagram stems from a simple and shared belief that fine cuisine and premium spirits and wines enhance the quality of life and are best appreciated and enjoyed in the right environment.

Seagram has an unrivalled portfolio of prestigious distilled spirits and wines, suitable for any such occasion. Chivas Regal, the world's leading premium Scotch whisky, continues to win international acclaim, while our two very distinctive single malt Scotch whiskies, The Glenlivet and Glen Grant, remain favourites among whisky connoisseurs. We also have Four Roses Bourbon, with its distinctive, all-American whisky style and flavour. From Martell, the oldest of the major Cognac Houses, we offer a fine range of quality Cognacs, including Martell's unique flagship marque, Cordon Bleu. We are also extremely proud to be able to offer Absolut Vodka, the world's number one premium vodka. Our choice of wines is equally extensive. From The House of Sandeman we have a selection of Ports and Sherries, while classic French Wines are available from Barton & Guestier. Finally, should your occasion require added sparkle, Seagram has the perfect answer with two of France's best known Champagnes, Mumm and Perrier-Jouët.

Welcome to *Egon Ronay's Seagram Guide 1995 Europe*. As it divulges, there are many wonderful hotels and restaurants to be found throughout Europe. It simply remains for you to explore this Guide and savour some of the delights it has to offer.

Introduction by Andrew Eliel

While this Guide has been prepared very much with business travellers in mind, and therefore concentrates on the major cities across 30 European countries, we have also included a number of exceptional hotels and restaurants outside these major cities that are well worth a special detour. Some are up to 50 miles away, but in travelling terms this often represents less than an hour's drive, given the excellent motorway links on the Continent.

Heading East
Over the years, we have published individual Guides to Western European countries, so our inspectors have long been *familiar* with the best hotels and restaurants in France, Belgium, Italy, Germany, Switzerland and Spain. Eastern Europe and the Russian Federation are another matter, however, for while some of our inspectors have visited the area privately, we have never as a professional body conducted research in these areas on the Guides' behalf. So it was with trepidation, intrigue and excitement that we set off for countries such as the Russian Federation, Estonia, Bulgaria and Romania. We were reasonably confident about what we would find in cities such as Prague and Budapest, but Bucharest, Sofia, and even Moscow and St Petersburg were (for us) uncharted territories.

Prague, for instance, feels like a 'western' city, chock-a-block with tourists who are pushing up hotel prices, one result of which is that there is little relationship between price and quality. There's a strong Austrian influence in the newer hotels (either ownership or management) – the need now is for more quality hotels in the mid-category. Interestingly, Czech hotels do not generally make a distinction between 'double' and 'twin' rooms, so if you want to be sure of getting a double bed it's best to ask for a 'French' bed. Taxis here can be a bit of a rip-off as some of the operators 'speed up' the meters for the tourists. Most menus are either multi-lingual or come in a separate English version, and most hotels quote prices in US$ (a couple, Austrian schillings) as well as local currency (the same is true for Bucharest and Sofia; although here it is the $ price that is fixed and the local currency price that fluctuates with the exchange rate). There are plenty of private restaurants in the city, but of variable quality, almost none being outstanding. The local Czech cuisine, often listed as Bohemian on menus (the historic name for the area), features the ubiquitous dumpling, both sweet and savoury, plus the likes of stuffed quail, and pheasant in creamy sauce. The traditional way to start is to be offered a tray of hors d'oeuvre with stuffed eggs and tomatoes, and ham-wrapped tinned asparagus the most common items. More 'fashionable' cooking is beginning to filter through – notably at Parnas and Vinárna V Zátiśí – where one might find the likes of grilled prawns with polenta and tomato salsa, home-made pasta with pesto or grilled fresh tuna.

Bucharest doesn't seem to have caught up with Western practices and there is little evidence of foreign investment other than the new Sofitel Hotel, which is part of a new World Trade Centre (by far the best place in town to stay) and another being refurbished by an international group. The rather drab, dated but acceptable Inter-Continental dates from the early 70s, although there is talk of refurbishment and a tie-up with a foreign partner. Restaurants tend to concentrate on the luxury of the surroundings rather than the quality of the food, most usually making a very poor attempt at 'international' cuisine.

Sofia is less bleak than Bucharest as a city centre – there are a few sidewalk cafés, green spots and some buildings of interest. With few exceptions hotel and restaurant staff have yet to learn the art of hospitality and the value of a smile of welcome, most having no concept of service, if only for the reason that it might be a good idea to look after the customer, who now ultimately pays their wages. A communist mentality remains, and things are improving only slowly. As in Bucharest there is no real evidence of foreign investment, just a vague rumour that a Hilton hotel might be in the offing. However, the restaurant scene here is a little more encouraging – the local cuisine makes much use of offal (brains appeared on virtually every menu), but most places also had a good selection of salads, the traditional start to a Bulgarian meal, which might make a safer choice for the faint-hearted. Dishes with a more international flavour are also now starting to feature on menus.

Moscow

The good news is that things are a lot better now than they used to be – and they are getting better all the time. The bad news is that they are still pretty awful. There are more and more restaurants and cafés in Moscow, with new ones sprouting up like mushrooms every week, but few merit a second glance, let alone a visit. If you arrive expecting expensive, bad food, with slow, sloppy and charmless service, then at least you won't be disappointed – though every now and then you could be in for a pleasant surprise. We've managed to find a handful where you should be able to get a decent meal. As with all large cities, there are basic ground rules. First, try not carry large sums of money around. Avoid taxis if possible: none have meters and all charge astronomical fares. If you have to take a cab, agree a fare in advance. Otherwise, take the excellent metro – or, in the city centre at least, walk – it's probably quicker anyway, due to frequent traffic jams. There are a huge number of nightclubs and casinos, but some are not safe and should be avoided – the safest places are in the international hotels, but for the more adventurous, there are a growing number of other opportunities – with bars and cafés easy to find at any time of day.

Comparisons

It would be naive and rather pointless to compare standards we found in the East with those in the West. The former, only now awakening from a suppressed past, is in the embryonic stage as far as investment, training and accepted levels of service are concerned, and though there are moves in the right direction in these areas, it will be some time before it catches up with the West. Nowhere is this more evident than in the standard of cooking in restaurants, where our inspectors applied their normal objective experience, taking into account how well the restaurant achieved what it set out to do as reflected in the menu, decor, prices, publicity, and atmosphere – factors that add up to some sort of expectation.

Awards

We have awarded our Golden Eurostars to restaurants throughout the Guide. While the quality of cooking is of great importance, it is by no means the only criteria for the award (see How to Use). And, in choosing our six major awards (see pages xxx), we are of course reflecting our own findings – they do not necessarily denote *the* best hotels and restaurants, though naturally they are among the best, but are awarded on the basis of consistent excellence and/or outstanding enterprise. To say, for instance, that *'t Laurierblad* is a better restaurant than, say, *Girardet* or *Robuchon* is akin to saying that red wine is better than white wine. Such comparisons cannot be made in absolute terms.

Your recommendations

In producing our new Seagram Guide to Europe we have endeavoured to cover all the major business areas where our inspectors are satisfied that both the hotels and restaurants visited come up to our standards. Inevitably, there are some gaps, not necessarily because we haven't been there, but because we didn't feel standards merited sending our readers there. During the 37 years of our existence, it has never been our policy to plot entries just to fill gaps: our first insistence is that establishments come up to our standards. We very much look forward to receiving your comments on establishments included in the Guide and recommendations for those you feel should be in the next edition. There are forms at the back of the Guide for this purpose.

Flying the flag

We are grateful to the Guide's overall sponsor Seagram, whose assistance, especially in Eastern Europe, greatly facilitated our inspectors' research, and our thanks also to the Scotch Beef Club who promote this prime product overseas, demonstrating its quality is unsurpassed throughout the world. Wherever you see the bull, you can be assured of the very best Scottish beef.

How to use this Guide

This unique new Guide covers 30 countries throughout Europe, listed in the order shown on the contents page. Each country is preceded by a title page containing useful information for the traveller. Within each country, the capital city (where there are recommended entries) comes first, followed by other featured major towns in alphabetical order. Establishments within a reasonable distance of major locations are listed after those locations, and at the end of some countries is a section 'Elsewhere in .....', listing worthy establishments not very near a major town or city. A 4-page map of locations included in the Guide begins on page 548. We have not attempted to give exhaustive coverage of establishments but to provide a cross-section of hotels and restaurants across the price range.

Order of Entries

Within each location hotels with recommended restaurants (HR), hotels (H) and restaurants (R) are listed in alphabetical order; (RR) denotes a restaurant with rooms. An index to each country's entries will be found at the end of that country (except where the number of entries makes it unnecessary).

Prices

Hotel prices given are per night for a double room with en-suite facilities; prices will often vary considerably according to the season and the length of stay. Meal prices are for two people – three courses (à la carte where offered), a modest bottle of wine, and coffee. In some Eastern European countries prices are listed in US dollars, following local practice. Opening times and closures are liable to alteration, and it's always best to book.

Telephone Numbers

Telephone numbers and area codes shown apply to calls made from the UK. From within the various countries it is often necessary to prefix numbers with 0 when calling another town.

Symbols

The Golden Eurostar [★] symbol denotes the pick of the restaurants in each country. The quality of cooking is not the only consideration (though this is the major factor), as we also take into account factors such as ambience, comfort and service.

The symbol [🐂] at the end of an entry denotes an establishment that is a member of the Scottish Beef Club. A full list of Club members appears at the end of participating countries.

The sign [#] after American Express Travel Service telephone numbers on the country title pages denotes those offering a client mail service.

10

Golden Eurostar List

Austria

| Vienna | Hotel Bristol, Restaurant Korso bei der Oper |
| Vienna | Restaurant Steirereck |

Belgium

Brussels	La Villa Lorraine
Brussels	La Truffe Noire
Brussels	Comme Chez Soi
Brussels	L'Ecailler du Palais Royal
Brussels	La Maison du Cygne
Brussels	Michel
Brussels	Claude Dupont
Antwerp	't Fornuis
Auderghem	La Grignotière
Berlare	't Laurierblad
Bruges	De Karmeliet

Czechoslovakia

| Prague | Vinárna V Zátiší |

Denmark

Copenhagen	Belle Terrasse
Copenhagen	La Crevette
Copenhagen	Kong Hans Kaelder
Copenhagen	Nouvelle
Holte	Søllerød Kro

Finland

| Helsinki | Havis Amanda |

France

Paris	L'Ambroisie
Paris	Amphyclès
Paris	Apicius
Paris	L'Arpège
Paris	Benoit
Paris	Bistrots du Dome
Paris	La Butte Chaillot
Paris	Carré des Feuillants
Paris	Hotel de Crillon, Les Ambassadeurs
Paris	Duquesnoy
Paris	Gérard Besson
Paris	Le Grand Véfour
Paris	Guy Savoy
Paris	Lasserre
Paris	Laurent
Paris	Ledoyen
Paris	Lucas Carton
Paris	Michel Rostang
Paris	Miravile
Paris	L'Oulette
Paris	Joël Robuchon
Paris	Le Pré Catelan
Paris	Taillevent
Paris	La Tour d'Argent
Paris	Vivarois
Les Baux-de-Provence	Oustau de Baumanière
Bordeaux	Jean Ramet
Bordeaux	Le Chapon Fin
Carry-le-Rouet	L'Escale
Chagny	Lameloise
Eugénie-les-Bains	Les Prés d'Eugénie, Michel Guérard
Illhaeusern	Auberge de l'Ill
Lyons	L'Alexandrin
Lyons	Paul Bocuse
Lyons	Léon de Lyon
Mionnay	Alain Chapel
Montrond-les-Bains	Hostellerie La Poularde
Mougins	Le Moulin de Mougins
Nice	Négresco, Restaurant Chantecler
Pont-de-l'Isère	Michel Chabran
Puymirol	l'Aubergade
Reims	Boyer "Les Crayères"
Roanne	Troisgros
St-Père-sous-Vézelay	L'Espérance
Saulieu	Bernard Loiseau La Cote d'Or
St Etienne	Pierre Gagnaire
St-Jean-Pied-de-Port	Les Pyrénées
Strasbourg	Buereheisel
Strasbourg	Le Crocodile
Tours	Jean Bardet
Tours	Charles Barrier
Valence	Le Pic
Vienne	La Pyramide
Vonnas	Georges Blanc

Germany

Aschau	Residenz Heinz Winkler
Baiersbronn	Hotel Traube-Tonbach, Schwarzwaldstube
Berlin	Alt Luxemburg
Berlin	Bamberger Reiter
Berlin	Rockendorf's Restaurant
Cologne	Rino Casati
Dusseldorf	Hummer Stübchen
Dusseldorf	Im Schiffchen
Hamburg	Anna & Sebastiano
Hamburg	Landhaus Scherrer
Hanover	Landhaus Ammann
Munich	Aubergine*
Munich	Hotel Preysing-Keller
Munich	Tantris

Hungary

Budapest	Gundel Restaurant
Budapest	Mátyás Pince Restaurant
Budapest	Robinson Restaurant

Italy

Rome	Checchino dal 1887
Rome	Lord Byron Hotel, Relais Le Jardin
Abbiategrasso	Antica Osteria del Ponte
Castrocaro Terme	La Frasca
Costiglione d'Asti	Da Guido
Erbusco	Gualtiero Marchesi L'Abereta
Florence	Don Chisciotte
Florence	Enoteca Pinchiorri
Milan	L'Ami Berton
Milan	Calajunco
Milan	Bistrot Di Gualtiero Marchesi

Luxembourg

| Geyershaff | La Bergerie |
| Kockelscheuer | Patin d'Or |

Malta
Valletta	The Carriage

Monaco
Monte Carlo	Hotel de Paris, Restaurant Louis XV

Netherlands
Amsterdam	Christophe
Hoorn	De Oude Rosmolen
Leidschendam	Villa Rozenrust
Overveen	De Bokkedoorns

Norway
Oslo	Bagatelle
Oslo	Le Canard
Oslo	Continental Hotel, Restaurant Annen Etage
Oslo	D'Artagnan
Oslo	Feinschmecker

Poland
Warsaw	Bazyliszek
Warsaw	Hotel Bristol, Restaurant Malinowa

Portugal
Lisbon	Casa da Comida

Republic of Ireland
Dublin	Le Coq Hardi
Dublin	Patrick Guilbaud
Dublin	La Stampa
Cork	Arbutus Lodge
Cork	Cliffords
Shanagarry	Ballymaloe House

Romania
Bucharest	Sofitel, Restaurant Darclée

Russian Federation
Moscow	Pirosmani
St Petersburg	Grand Hotel Europe

Spain
Madrid	El Amparo
Madrid	Bajamar
Madrid	Cabo Mayor
Madrid	Casa Lucio
Madrid	Combarro
Madrid	Las Cuatro Estaciones
Madrid	Jockey
Madrid	El Pescador
Madrid	Principe de Viana
Madrid	La Trainera
Madrid	Zalacaín
Barcelona	El Dorado Petit
Barcelona	Florián
Barcelona	Jaume de Provença
Barcelona	Reno
Barcelona	Via Veneto
Marbella	La Hacienda
Marbella	La Fonda
Marbella	La Meridiana
Saint Celoni	El Racó de Can Fabes
San Sebastian	Arzak
Valencia	Rias Gallegas
Valencia	Oscar Torrijos

Sweden
Stockholm	Eriks
Stockholm	Grand Hotel, Restaurant Franska Matsalen
Stockholm	Operakällaren
Stockholm	Paul & Norbert
Stockholm	Wedholms Fisk
Gothenburg	The Place
Gothenburg	Westra Piren

Switzerland
Basle	Stucki Bruderholz
Crissier	Girardet
Gattikon	Sihlhade
Geneva	L'Arlequin
Geneva	La Perle du Lac
Geneva	Parc des Eaux-Vives
Küsnacht	Petermann's Kunstube
Unterengstringen	Witschi's
Vufflens-le-Chateau	Hotel de l'Ermitage
Zurich	Restaurant Agnès Amberg
Zurich	Dolder Grand Hotel

United Kingdom
London	Aubergine
London	The Canteen
London	Chez Nico at Ninety Park Lane
London	The Dorchester, Terrace Restaurant
London	Four Seasons Hotel
London	Le Gavroche
London	Inter-Continental Hotel, Le Soufflé
London	Langan's Brasserie
London	Restaurant Marco Pierre White
London	Les Saveurs
London	The Square
London	La Tante Claire
Bray-on-Thames	The Waterside Inn
Bristol	Restaurant Lettonie
Great Milton	Le Manoir aux Quat'Saisons
Longridge	Paul Heathcote's Restaurant
Shinfield	L'Ortolan
Belfast	Roscoff

WHISKY IS **12** YEARS OLD

AS LONG AS TIME IS
OUR MOST PRIZED POSSESSION...

There will always be a
CHIVAS REGAL.

*Those who appreciate quality
enjoy it responsibly.*

Best Hotel Western Europe

Grand Hotel Villa Cora
Florence, Italy

The classical splendour of the villa, originally built as a private house in 1865, is complemented by a stunning setting just south of the city centre. Stucco friezes, beautiful trompe l'oeil frescoes, exquisite marble statuary and colourful mosaic floors are just a few of the very fine details that create an aura of great comfort and tranquillity. Spacious, elegant bedrooms offer a very traditional ambience plus such modern conveniences as air-conditioning. Add to all this exemplary standards of service and civility and you have a hotel of outstanding quality – a real gem.

WHAT HAS AN UNUSUALLY BRIGHT, CLEAR COLOUR?

HAT HAS A CLEAN, DISTINCTIVE TASTE?

GLEN GRANT.
DIFFERENT BY TRADITION. SINCE 1840

Best Hotel Eastern Europe

Grand Hotel Europe
St Petersburg, Russian Federation

Built in 1824 and a hotel since the 1830s, there's both a sense of history and architectural beauty here, backed up by a friendly atmosphere and committed staff. It has been splendidly restored and renovated – note the front facade by Carlo Rossi, stained-glass window by the artist Benoit, the courtyard glass atrium, and Sadko's bar, *the* favourite meeting place of the city. Huge bedrooms, especially the first-floor *belles chambres*, terraced rooms, suites and penthouses, are all handsomely furnished with antiques or in art nouveau style, while the public areas are awash with marble, gilt and grandeur. In addition, there's a health club and good conference facilities – all in all a hotel of character on a par with Europe's best.

12 years ago my daughter was born. She breezed into my life like a miniature hurricane. I celebrated with something new; Malt Whisky.

Has she changed my life? I'll say (You try standing in a hurricane for twelve years.) One thing hasn't changed: I still like that Whisky.

The **GLENLIVET** *Single Malt Scotch Whisky.* **AGED *12* YEARS.**
Definitive Speyside character, remarkably flowery, clean and soft. BODY: *Medium, firm, smooth.*
PALATE: *Fruity, flowery, notes of vanilla. Delicate balance between sweetness and malty dryness.* FINISH: *Long, subtle, gently warming.*
COLOUR: *Pale gold.*

ABSOLUT BRUSSELS.

ABSOLUT VODKA IS THE SUPREME CHOICE ANYWHERE IN EUROPE,
ENJOYED NEAT, ON THE ROCKS, OR IN DRINKS AND COCKTAILS

Best Restaurant Western Europe

't Laurierblad
Berlare, Belgium

Very much part of the local community (villagers come here to buy the large, flat, round loaves that are stacked on wooden racks in the foyer), Guy Van Cauteren has created one of Belgium's finest restaurants out of a collection of buildings (including an original timber-framed building where his grandfather ran a theatre-cum-brasserie) set around a delightful courtyard garden. The cooking has tremendous appeal with sophistication and luxury ingredients combining with a certain *gout du terroir* to great effect. Add a changing art exhibition, an all-day *salon de thé* menu, a characterful conference room (on the upper floor of an old linseed oil mill) and five luxurious bedrooms and one has a thoroughly well-rounded establishment of enormous charm.

ABSOLUT GENEVA.

ABSOLUT VODKA IS THE SUPREME CHOICE ANYWHERE IN EUROPE,
ENJOYED NEAT, ON THE ROCKS, OR IN DRINKS AND COCKTAILS.

ABSOLUT AMSTERDAM.

ABSOLUT VODKA IS THE SUPREME CHOICE ANYWHERE IN EUROPE,
ENJOYED NEAT, ON THE ROCKS, OR IN DRINKS AND COCKTAILS.

Best Restaurant Eastern Europe

Gundel
Budapest, Hungary

With 100 years of history and experience (the restaurant celebrated its centenary in September 1994), there is no better place in which to eat in Eastern Europe than here. The American-Hungarian restaurateur George Lang has brought back its refined cuisine and elegance, and whether you choose chef Kálmán Kalla's quail broth, goose liver and tenderloin of beef, or patissier Béla Borbély's sensational pancakes, all washed down with the restaurant's own wines, you are likely to leave satisfied, having dined well at – to quote Hungary's President Arpád Göncz – "this institution".

THE ART OF DISTINCTION.

Many are called V.S.O.P.,
but only one bears the
rare seal of Louis XIV
and offers a distinctive
marriage of our most
exquisite cognacs: Martell
Medallion V.S.O.P.

MARTELL

SINCE 1715.

COGNAC. L'ART DE MARTELL.

FourRoses

"Seduction is a rare talent."

Four Roses

BOURBON

KENTUCKY STRAIGHT
BOURBON WHISKEY

EST.º 1888

MELLOW
BUT
NEVER
TAME.

The BIG network congratulates the Egon Ronay's Guides Business Hotel of the Year – Western Europe.

For further information on the BIG network call

0800 214000

Best Business Hotel Western Europe

Hotel Bristol
Vienna, Austria

In the heart of Europe, the city of Vienna has always played an important role for business travellers, and nowhere are they better catered for than here. The CIGA-owned hotel combines regal splendour and grandeur with up-to-date facilities and technology. To meet the increasing demands of guests on business, the hotel has created the 'Club Vienna' which incorporates a club floor with preferential room rates, VIP lounge and a Global Business Centre offering secretaries, PCs, fax machines, interpreter and translation services, mobile telephones and the latest financial information from around the world. Gourmets are not forgotten – the hotel's main restaurant *Korso bei der Oper* is one of the best in the country.

cellnet

Using your mobile phone overseas.

In addition to superb voice quality, and enhanced call security, Cellnet's new digital service Primetime Plus enables business users who travel extensively, to keep in touch – and be contactable – throughout the UK, and while travelling overseas.

primetime™
plus

For further information call
0800 214000

Best Business Hotel Eastern Europe

Sheraton Sofia Balkan
Sofia, Bulgaria

Right in the centre of the city, this massive neo-classical hotel combines luxury – glittering chandeliers, grand sweeping staircases, acres of marble – with all the facilities needed by the modern business traveller: fully-fledged business centre, bank, travel agency and even, for the moment, the local British Airways office. A choice of dining, from the very formal Preslav Restaurant with its tail-coated waiters to a Viennese café with pavement terrace, provides for all levels of entertaining, and there are meeting rooms for up to 160 people. A night-club with floor show and a fitness centre cope with off-duty hours.

Business Central Europe

SPECIALLY SELECTED SCOTCH BEEF

THE TRUE TASTE OF QUALITY

Scotland's world-wide reputation for producing prime beef cattle owes much to nature. Favoured with the ideal stock-rearing conditions of a temperate climate, an abundance of grass and pure water, and vast tracts of unspoiled countryside, generations of Scottish farmers have used their skills to produce beef for the discerning tables of the world.

300 YEARS OF TRADITION AND DEVELOPMENT

As far back as the 17th century, the beef from Scottish cattle was in demand, and each year tens of thousands were exported - on foot - to eager English markets.

A century later agricultural improvements enabled whole herds to be fed through the winters, and attention was then turned to improving native cattle breeds. The result, by the early 19th century, was beef breeds which were to become renowned throughout the world.

Until the 19th century Scotch beef cattle continued to be walked to markets in the south, but the introduction of steam navigation, then railways, brought the cattle droving tradition of generations to an end. Prime Scotch beef could now travel to London in peak condition, and the modern meat industry began.

Now, one hundred years on, fleets of refrigerated vehicles daily transport Specially Selected Scotch Beef to the markets of Europe.

REPUTATION FOR EXCELLENCE

Like other products with a reputation for excellence - such as vintage red wine and famous malt whiskies - it takes time and skill to produce Specially Selected Scotch Beef. Generations of experience in cattle rearing, backed by the quality assurance schemes of today, means that Specially Selected Scotch Beef is produced to the highest farming standards throughout. The Scotch meat

industry has its own expertise, and Specially Selected Scotch Beef is matured in the traditional, time-honoured way to maximise the flavour and tenderness for which it is world renowned.

EUROPEAN QUALITY BEEF

The EC recognises the contribution of the Scottish meat industry in setting standards of quality. The use of the European Quality Beef logo signifies that strict EC standards for quality

European Quality Beef

**Specially Selected
SCOTCH
BEEF**

Partially funded by the EC.

control and product traceability from farm to consumer have been adhered to - further enhancing the reputation of Specially Selected Scotch Beef for consistent product quality.

A WHOLE NEW EATING EXPERIENCE

Specially Selected Scotch Beef is recognised as a popular choice for caterers around the world and many top class restaurants have enhanced their reputations with the quality of the Scotch beef they serve.

For the true taste of quality and a whole new eating experience, discover the flavour and tenderness of Specially Selected Scotch Beef at one of the many Scotch Beef Club restaurants in Europe, highlighted throughout this Guide.

WELCOME TO THE SCOTCH BEEF CLUB

An elite club with over 500 members throughout Europe - each one a distinguished restaurant with an international reputation for excellence.

This new Egon Ronay's Guide, recognised for the quality of its listed establishments and an indispensable aid to the discerning diner in Europe, features many of the Scotch Beef Club members.

Chefs demand exacting standards of quality in the beef they buy. Scotch Beef Club members purchase not only one of the world's finest meat products, but a true taste of quality.

This, together with their culinary expertise produces Specially Selected Scotch Beef dishes that enhance their international reputations and confirms their listing in the Guide.

D.S. Cameron

"At Turnberry we cater for the most discerning of both national and international clientele, and are proud to feature the finest of Scotch beef throughout the hotel's three restaurants. The creation of the Scotch Beef Club will continue to ensure that the highest standards are constantly maintained and protected for the future. Turnberry Hotel is proud to be a founder member of this prestigious Club".

D.S. Cameron,
Executive Chef de Cuisine,
Turnberry Hotel.

Look for the Black Bull symbol, and the list at the end of each country, to identify members of the

Scotch Beef Club.

So whether you favour a succulent steak, a tender roast or a more exotic international recipe, visit a Scotch Beef Club member and experience the flavour and tenderness of Specially Selected Scotch Beef for yourself.

The Scotch Beef Club operates in Belgium, France, Germany, Great Britain, Holland, Italy and Spain - and each member restaurant is identified by a distinctive door sticker or plaque.

For a full list of all Scotch Beef Club members, please contact the Scotch Quality Beef and Lamb Association on

031•333 5335

or write to: Scotch Quality Beef and Lamb Association, Rural Centre, West Mains, Ingliston, Newbridge, Midlothian EH28 8NZ, Scotland.

This advertorial is partially funded by the EC.

Go your

You've never seen a Ford like it; you've never driven a Ford like it.

The new Probe from Ford is the real thing – a genuine sports coupe. A coupe that has been designed to set your heart racing the way no souped-up, cut down saloon car ever could.

With the Probe you get the choice of two engines – a sporty, 16-valve, 2.0 litre

Specifications correct at time of going to press.

double-overhead camshaft four cylinder unit, or a silky-smooth, 2.5 litre, 24 valve, four cam V6.

The 5 speed close ratio gearbox is sweet and neat. The ride is right. The engine-sensitive power steering is precise at every speed.

The all disc braking system with ABS fitted as standard, is confidently

own way.

assuring.

Driver and passenger can relax the supportive sports seats with the knowledge that airbags are standard r both.

And everything is protected by e electronic engine immobiliser.

The new Probe from Ford – to drive it to want it.

To discover where you can slip behind the wheel call **0800 111 222** for the address of your nearest Ford Dealer.

The Probe. New from Ford.

Everything we do is driven by you.

AMERICAN EXPRESS TRAVEL SERVICE

If you have purchased your travel arrangements (air ticket, cruise or tour package) with any American Express Travel Service or Representative location, the following services are provided free of office charges under the Worldwide Customer Care facility:

- Reconfirmation of airline tickets
- Facilitation of rerouting/issuing of airline tickets
- Revalidation/changing of reservations
- Hotel reservations
- Car rental reservations
- Sightseeing arrangements
- Travel assistance

Additionally, *most* American Express Travel Service Offices worldwide provide the services listed below to all clients of American Express:

- Client Mail Service
- American Express Travellers Cheques
- Emergency Cheque Encashment Service
- Bureau de Change
- American Express Card emergency replacement facility
- American Express currency & travel cheque dispensers (with PIN)
- Local Sightseeing arrangements
- Car Hire Service

However, in some cases local regulations may require referral to another address (a bank, for example) for a specific service. It is advisable to telephone the office before you visit to make sure that the service you require is available at that address. At most locations, there is a complete local travel service for the purchase of onward transportation, hotel reservations and general travel information. For full details about these services, contact American Express.

American Express offices in Europe are listed on the Title Information Page at the start of each country's section.

It's easy to recognise a good place when you see one.

American Express Cardmembers have been doing it for years.

The secret? Instead of just relying on what they see in the window they look at the door. If there's an American Express Blue Box on it, they know they've found an establishment that cares about high standards.

Whether it's a place to eat, to sleep, to shop, or simply meet, they know they will be warmly welcomed.

So much so, they're rarely taken in by anything else.

Always a good sign.

ABSOLUT ROME.

ABSOLUT VODKA IS THE SUPREME CHOICE ANYWHERE IN EUROPE,
ENJOYED NEAT, ON THE ROCKS, OR IN DRINKS AND COCKTAILS

PASSPORT SCOTCH. A STYLE OF IT'S OWN.

ABSOLUT MADRID.

ABSOLUT VODKA IS THE SUPREME CHOICE ANYWHERE IN EUROPE,
ENJOYED NEAT, ON THE ROCKS, OR IN DRINKS AND COCKTAILS.

SEAGRAM'S 7 CROWN.
THE BEST OF AMERICA.

It was the whiskey which grew up with America. And the real thing is still available today. 7 Crown American Whiskey is made in the traditional way using the finest ingredients for a full bodied taste. A taste which was America's favourite for 40 years.

America's No.1 selling *whiskey.*

ABSOLUT ATHENS.

ABSOLUT VODKA IS THE SUPREME CHOICE ANYWHERE IN EUROPE,
ENJOYED NEAT, ON THE ROCKS, OR IN DRINKS AND COCKTAILS.

Austria

Currency: Austrian Schilling **Exchange Rate** £1 = approx ATS 16.6

International dialling code: 010 43
(Vienna + 1 Salzburg + 662)

Passports/Visas: No visa required by British passport holders.

British Consulate in Vienna Tel: 1-713 1575 Fax: 1-712 7316

TRANSPORT
Airports:
Flughafen Wien (Vienna) Tel: 1-711 100
Salzburg Flughafenbetriebesgesmbh Tel: 662-80 550
Railway Stations:
Vienna: Westbahnhof/Südbahnhof/Franz-Josef-Bahnhof Tel: 1-1717
Salzburg: Hauptbahnhof Tel: 662-1717
Car hire in Vienna:
Avis Tel: 1-587 62 41 / Budget Tel: 1-71 46 565 / Europcar Tel: 1-505
29 47 / Hertz Tel: 1-713 15 96 / Rent-A-Car Tel: 1-714 6717 / Trans
hire Tel: 1-714 6717
Speed limits: 100km/h on trunk roads, 130km/h on motorways,
50km/h in towns.

Banks open: 8am-12.30pm, 1.30-3pm Mon-Wed & Fri, 1-5.30pm
Thur.

Shops open: 8am-6.30pm weekdays, 8am-1pm Sat, 8am-5pm first Sat
every month. Many shops closed 2hrs midday.

National Holidays: New Year's Day, 6 Jan, Easter Monday, 1 May,
Ascension Day, Whit Monday, Corpus Christi, 15 Aug, 26 Oct, 1 Nov,
8 Dec, Christmas Day & Boxing Day.

Tourist Offices:
Austrian Tourist Board in London - Tel: 0171-629 0461
In Austria - Vienna Tel: 1-211 140 / Salzburg Tel: 662-88 9 87

American Express Travel Service Offices:
Vienna - AETS
  21/23 Kaerntnerstrasse
  A-1015
  PO Box 28
  Tel: 1-51540 #
Salzburg - AETS
  5 Mozartplatz
  A-5010
  PO Box 244
  Tel: 662-842501 #

Vienna

Vienna   Altes Presshaus

Tel (1) 32 23 93 Fax (1) 32 23 42 85   **R**

Copenzlegasse 15 1190 Vienna
Seats 500   Meal for 2 approx ATS400

Right in the heart of the city, in Grinzing (Vienna's answer
to Montmartre), this is a vast place spreading through three rooms
and a wine cellar. There is a corner for everyone either in the
large dining room with an open fireplace, or the trophy-filled
room or down in the cellar, where regular wine tastings are
organised. The building itself is a 16th-century convent and
a national monument; and the food inside is as much a monument
to traditional Viennese cooking as one can find anywhere in this
city. Country-style sausages are served with whipped cream and
horseradish sauce; *weinhauer*, another favourite, is a mixed platter
of beef and sausages. A popular feature is the buffet (a typically
Viennese offering of meats and salads). Follow up with pancakes
filled with chocolate cream and whipped cream, and you should
get up from your table well satisfied. *Open 4pm–midnight.*
AMERICAN EXPRESS *Diners, Mastercard, Visa.*

THE APARTMENT SERVICE
Tel in UK: (0181) 748 4207   Fax: (0181) 748 3972
The Apartment Service will find you the right apartment
worldwide to suit your needs, whether you are on a short or
long-term stay. A 96-page colour catalogue is free on request.
All budgets are catered for.

Vienna   Hotel Biedermeier im Sünnhof

Tel (1) 71 67 10 Fax (1) 71 67 15 03   **H**

Landstrasser Haupstrasse 28 1030 Vienna
Rooms 203   Double room from ATS2250

Ten minutes from Vienna Cathedral, in two Biedermeier-style
19th-century buildings linked by a small footbridge, a hotel
offering the traditional Viennese experience. The stone floors and
cherrywood may have remained, but the rooms have been
updated and all have cable TV. Conference facilities comprise five
small seminar rooms with a total capacity of 60. *No room service.*
AMERICAN EXPRESS *Diners, Mastercard, Visa.*

Vienna   Hotel Bristol

Tel (1) 51 51 60 Fax (1) 51 516 550   **HR**

Kärntner Ring 1 1015 Vienna
Rooms 146   Double room from ATS3800

A grand *fin de siècle* CIGA-owned hotel, perfectly positioned
opposite the Vienna State Opera House, filled with Biedermeier
and other treasures. Air-conditioned bedrooms, with their high
ceilings, fine chandeliers and tasteful fabrics, are extremely
luxurious, each having three telephones with direct lines, a fax
connection, safe, mini-bar, and satellite TV, while bathrooms,
mostly in art deco style, are splendidly equipped, providing every

pampering need. The exclusive Bristol Club and penthouse floor (panoramic views from here) is primarily aimed towards business guests, offering more space and larger working desks. For these discriminating executive travellers, the 'CIGA Club Vienna' has been created, incorporating a VIP lounge, offering complimentary refreshments throughout the day and the latest financial information on screen, and a Global Business Centre, earning the hotel the 1995 Guide's award for Best Business Hotel Western Europe (see page 29). Fitness fanatics can use a centre just around the corner free of charge. *24hr room service. Theatre-style conferencce facilities for up to 180.* AMERICANEXPRESS *Diners, Mastercard, Visa.*

Restaurant Korso bei der Oper

Seats 65   Meal for 2 approx ATS1600

A stately dining room, also with its own entrace or Mahlerstrasse, has antique furnishings, fine paintings and sparkling crystal chandeliers, suggesting perhaps classical cooking in the old style. Yet, chef Reinhard Gerer has a light, modern approach to his cooking while incorporating authentic Austrian elements in his daily-changing menus (from ATS440-980) which offer an interesting mixture, say, a lunch menu starting with cream of fennel soup, veal schnitzel with puréed potatoes and salad, and curd plum dumplings. If choosing à la carte, you might be tempted by the terrine of seafood with lobster and caviar cream, roast fillet of pike perch with parsley sauce, ending with pear tartlets and Pear William cream. Good to see many local Austrian wines on the list, some quite reasonably priced. Advisable to book in advance. *L 12-3. D 7-11. Closed L Sat.*

Vienna   Restaurant Eckel

Tel (1) 32 32 18   Fax (1) 32 66 60   R

Sieveringer Strasse 46 1190 Vienna
Seats 150   Meal for 2 approx ATS900

As a teenager, Maria Zarl-Echel trained in this very kitchen, when her father was the chef. Now she is running the show from the old vineyard farmhouse her grandfather built, and her local clientele is large and loyal. Traditional Austrian cuisine has been updated with many inventive touches: brown cap mushrooms with noodles, 'serviette' dumplings, yoghurt-based fruit sorbets, soufflée omelette with chocolate sauce. The restaurant is decorated in old-fashioned Viennese style. Outside eating in fine weather. *Closed Sun, Mon, 24 Dec-24 Jan, 2 weeks mid Aug. Diners.*

Vienna   Restaurant Gottfried

Tel (1) 713 82 56   Fax (1) 713 35 51 30   R

Untere Viaduktgasse 45 1030 Vienna
Seats 70   Meal for 2 approx ATS1600

A fine old town house in typical Viennese style. Joseph Fadinder's cooking is interesting, appetising and lighter than most: crab served on a bed of cucumber salad; roasted goose liver in a salad; freshly baked mushroom lasagne. Desserts are also refreshingly simple with offerings like peach sorbet; or choose something from the cheese trolley. Live piano music three times a week. *L 12-3 D 6-12. Closed Sat, Sun (but open D Sat Sep-May). Public parking.* AMERICANEXPRESS *Visa.*

Vienna   Hotel Imperial

Tel (1) 50 11 00   Fax (1) 501 104 10   H

Kärntner Ring 16 1015 Vienna
Rooms 128   Double room from ATS4700

Austria's leading hotel, now part of the CIGA hotel chain, was
opened by Emperor Franz Joseph in 1873, when Duke Philip
of Würtemberg's former private residence was converted into
a hotel. It retains plenty of regal status and splendour, with ornate
furnishings and marble staircases, and it still regularly hosts official
state visitors in its opulent Royal Suite. At the time of going
to press the hotel was closed for complete renovation.
Cable/satellite TV/fax. Theatre-style conference facilities for up to 200.
AMERICAN EXPRESS *Diners, Mastercard, Visa.*

Vienna   Kervansaray-Hummerbar

Tel (1) 512 88 43   Fax (1) 513 81 30   R

Mahlerstrasse 9 1010 Vienna
Seats 50   Meal for 2 approx ATS800

Kervansaray has several dining rooms, all unpretentiously
decorated, with wooden tables and chairs. Unusually, it is the
Hummerbar upstairs that is more elegant, offering sophiscated
dishes like fresh Irish lobster. Most of the menu in the bar
is dedicated to fish, from poached turbot to baked fillets of sole,
or medallions of tuna served with a herb cream. Lobster is a
speciality, served cold with a cocktail sauce, boiled with garlic
butter, Thermidor or in bouillabaisse. Kervansaray, on the other
hand, has a more Middle Eastern flavour to its cooking, serving
mainly meaty Turkish dishes: *kapama* (baby lamb poached with
fresh vegetables in a light herb sauce and served with potatoes)
and kebab of lamb and veal with rice and aubergine purée are
popular choices. For those looking for a lighter lunch, try one
of the large choice of salads. Desserts are international, but fresh
Turkish figs are on offer along with chocolate mousse served
on an apple sauce. *Open noon-midnight. Closed 24-25 Dec. Public
parking.* AMERICAN EXPRESS *Diners, Mastercard, Visa.*

Vienna   Kuperferdachl

Tel (1) 533 93 81   Fax (1) 533 93 814   R

Schottengasse 7 1010 Vienna
Seats 350   Meal for 2 approx ATS360

Traditional Viennese fare is served in the Kuperferdachl and its
sister restaurant on the same site, the more homely *Zum Leupold.*
Typical dishes are Wiener schnitzel, herrings marinated in red
wine, steak with braised onions, and the popular tafelspitz – boiled
beef with potatoes, root vegetables and various sauces. There are
a few more international dishes like lobster cream soup, quiche
Lorraine and assorted Italian pasta with tomato and basil sauce.
Some Austrian wines complement the mainly all-Austrian menu,
along with some French, Swiss and Italian bottles. *Open 10am-
midnight. Private parking.* AMERICAN EXPRESS *Diners, Mastercard, Visa.*

Vienna　　**Hotel im Palais Schwarzenberg**

Tel (1) 798 45 15   Fax (1) 798 47 14　　　　　　　　　**H**

Schwarzenbergplatz 9 1030 Vienna
Rooms 38　　　　　　　Double room from ATS2200

A family-owned 18th-century Baroque castle complete with eight
hectares of private park, five tennis courts and even a lawn for that
deceptively genteel game, croquet. Rooms have a comfortably old-
fashioned air, even though there is a colour TV and mini-bar in all
of them. A simply splendid place to stay and right in the city
centre. The Palais has a fine collection of paintings and other
works of art, plus vast gardens on four levels of terraces. *24hr room
service. Theatre-style conference facilities for up to 250. Secretarial
services. Translation services on request. 5 tennis courts/croquet Private
parking.* AMERICAN EXPRESS *Diners, Mastercard, Visa.*

Vienna　　**Hotel Sacher**

Tel (1) 51 45 60   Fax (1) 51 457 810　　　　　　　**HR**

Philharmonikerstrasse 4 1010 Vienna
Rooms 116　　　　　　Double room from ATS3550

Almost as renowned as the Vienna State Opera opposite, this place
is famous for inventing the Sachertorte cake and still organises
numerous food festivals. Privately owned by the Gürtler family,
it retains the old Viennese feel with its rococo decor and long-
serving staff, (the head concierge, for example has been here since
1958). Among its many attractions, the hotel boasts a fine
collection of furniture and paintings. The *kaffeehaus* has long been
one of Vienna's most fashionable spots for drinking coffee and
swapping gossip. *24hr room service. Cable/satellite TV/fax. Theatre-
style conference facilities for up to 250. Secretarial/translation services
on request. Private garage.* AMERICAN EXPRESS *Diners, Mastercard, Visa.*

Restaurant Anna Sacher
Seats 42　　　　　　　Meal for 2 approx ATS1500

The Viennese political powers-that-be are often ensconced in the
rich red velvet seats, lunching on perfectly-prepared traditional
Viennese dishes. As at London's Savoy Grill, lunch is a serious
matter, not a casual snacking time. They are famous for their
tafelspitz (boiled beef), but other Viennese specialities abound:
a chicken schnitzel served with potato salad, roasted liver with
onions. But desserts are the fatal attraction here: not only their
sacred Sachertorte topped with whipped cream, but also a plethora
of mousses and fresh apple strudel. *L 12-3 D 6-12.*

To dial overseas from the UK, 010 will change to 00
on 16th April 1995.

Vienna   SAS-Palais-Hotel

Tel (1) 51 51 70   Fax (1) 512 22 16   **H**

Parkring 16 1010 Vienna
Rooms 246   Double room from ATS3800

Opposite the city Stadtpark and only five minutes from the main
railway station, a nine-storey hotel catering almost exclusively for
the business traveller and well equipped to do just that: the Royal
Club lounge has all up-to-date business facilities and a variety
of meeting/conference rooms with a capacity ranging from 20 to
300. The building dates from the 19th century but was
completely renovated as recently as 1993. The style is Biedermeier,
the amenities thoroughly up to date. Bedroom choice runs from
single to doubles, suites and maisonettes. *24hr room service.*
Cable/satellite TV/fax. AMERICAN EXPRESS *Diners, Mastercard, Visa.*

Vienna   Scandic Crown Hotel

Tel (1) 727 77   Fax (1) 727 77 199   **H**

Handelskai 269 1020 Vienna
Rooms 367   Double room from ATS1800

As one would expect from a large Swedish hotel chain, facilities
here are excellent. Two tennis courts compete with the outdoor
swimming pool, gym, sauna and solarium. The large bedrooms
are equally impressive, with cable TV, air-conditioning and king-
size beds. Conference facilities are extensive with a capacity for
up to 300 delegates theatre-style. Right on the Danube, the
building is old (originally a grain store) and typically Viennese,
even though the hotel has only been going for the last six years.
Out by the *prater* (funfair), it is 15 minutes from the centre
of town, but still very much in Vienna, with the airport a 13km
drive away. If you are tired of Austrian cooking, the restaurant
serves a Swedish smörgasbord on Sundays. *24hr room service. Cable*
TV. Conference facilities. Secretarial/translation services on request.
Sports facilities. Free parking for 200 cars. AMERICAN EXPRESS *Diners,*
Visa.

Vienna   Restaurant Steirereck

Tel (1) 713 31 68   Fax (1) 713 516 82   **R**

Rasumofskygasse 2 1030 Vienna
Seats 90   Meal for 2 approx ATS1700

A place priding itself on its internationalism (the dining room
chairs are from Italy, the silver, Christofle, from France) and on its
chef, Helmut Österreicher, a man with lofty international culinary
ambitions, some original Royal menus and even a regular
television slot. He certainly provides a welcome change from the
uniformity of most Viennese restaurants. Lightly smoked veal
sweetbreads, river char served with yellow sorrel noodles and red   ★
beets, and lamb chop along with lamb crepes add a refined note
to the solid city culinary map. Chocolate dumpling with
strawberry sorbet is a signature dessert. The kitchen is also very
friendly: if any dish appeals, Österreicher will give you a copy
of the not-so-secret recipe. *L 11.30-2 D 7-11. Public parking.*
AMERICAN EXPRESS *Visa.*

Vienna **Villa Hans Moser**

Tel (1) 877 474 70   Fax (1) 877 60 50   R

Auhofstrasse 76-78 1130 Vienna
Seats 180   Meal for 2 approx ATS940

Formerly the home of actor Hans Moser, the villa has recently
been totally rebuilt as a restaurant, with only the original outer
walls surviving. But all three floors with their different dining
rooms retain undoubted glamour: fine old paintings line the walls,
plush green carpets cover the floor, and tables are laid with silver
and crystal. Meat and fish dishes share balanced, daily-changing
menus: pike-perch and salmon are served with mango and wild
rice, breast of duckling with caramelised apples and ratatouille,
fillet of venison with dumplings and red cabbage. *L 12-2.30
D 7.30-10.30. Closed Sun, Mon, 24 Dec-4 Jan. Private parking.*
AMERICAN EXPRESS *Diners, Mastercard, Visa.*

Salzburg

Salzburg   **Hotel Dorint**

| Tel (662) 88 20 31   Fax (662) 88 20 319 | **H** |

Sterneckstrasse 20 5020 Salzburg
Rooms 140   Double room from ATS1350

A modern, convenient, no-nonsense hotel, built around an inner
courtyard. The bedrooms, including 20 suites, are bright, practical
and comfortable. On-the-spot leisure amenities comprise a sauna,
solarium and steam bath. *Cable TV. Theatre-style conference
facilities for up to 260.* AMERICAN EXPRESS *Diners, Mastercard, Visa.*

Salzburg   **Hotel Gasthof Brandstätter**

| Tel (662) 43 45 35   Fax (662) 43 45 35 90 | **HR** |

Münchner Bundesstrasse 69 5020 Salzburg
Rooms 36   Double room from ATS1200

A warm countrified place in an old farmhouse on the edge of the
city, quiet but still glamorous enough to attract the Austrian
television station, ORF, here for regular meetings. The rooms are
in keeping with the style of the building, and are decorated with
traditional farmhouse furniture. The hall is lined with rich warm
Persian carpets. Conference facilities for 40 people theatre-style.
*Closed 1-14 Jan, 2 weeks end Jun-Jul. Conference facilities.
Secretarial/translation services. Sauna, solarium, steam bath, indoor
swimming pool. Private parking.* AMERICAN EXPRESS *Diners, Mastercard,
Visa.*

Restaurant
Seats 100   Meal for 2 approx ATS700

Karl Paller in the kitchen trained in Vienna and has been here for
two years. His food is devotedly Austrian (that is a combination
of German and Czech influences). Marinated crab and trout
is served on a bed of summer salad; beef bouillon with liver
dumplings; meat cutlets with a variety of salads and potatoes.
Every day there is also a fresh fish option, perhaps whole char
with lemon and almonds. Open for breakfast, lunch and dinner.
Open 6.30am-midnight. No credit cards.

Salzburg   **Hotel Mercure**

| Tel (662) 881 43 80   Fax (662) 871 111 411 | **H** |

Bayerhamerstrasse 14 5020 Salzburg
Rooms 121   Double room from ATS1400

Fifteen minutes leisurely walk from the old city, this hotel is part
of the international chain, Accor. It is quiet here, partly due to the
small park snugly surrounding it. The modern building has
equally modern rooms, all similarly decorated in white and
subdued red. The tennis court is, at the time of going to press,
in the process of being renovated. *Cable TV. Theatre-style
conference facilities for up to 150. Private garage.* AMERICAN EXPRESS
Diners, Mastercard, Visa.

Salzburg — Hotel Österreichischer Hof

Tel (662) 889 77   Fax (662) 889 77 14   **H**

Schwarzstrasse 5-7 5020 Salzburg
Rooms 120   Double room from ATS2500

Located on a quieter bank of the Salzach river, a family-run hotel
with a pedigree going back to 1866, when their first guests stayed
here. It is still elegant and traditional, with the rooms retaining
a period feel, but with added mod cons like cable and satellite TV,
air-conditioning, safes and mini-bars. Private parking available
at ATS300 per night. The hotel boasts five restaurants and a piano
bar. *Theatre-style conference facilities for up to 80.*
Secretarial/translation services on request. AMERICAN EXPRESS *Diners,*
Mastercard, Visa.

Salzburg — Hotel Radisson Altstadt

Tel (662) 848 57 10   Fax (662) 848 57 16   **H**

Judengasse 15 5020 Salzburg
Rooms 60   Double room from ATS3000

An elegant international hotel set in a 14th-century building that
includes college, synagogue and brewery in its past lives. The
rooms either have original exposed beams, or elegant stucco
ceilings and all have traditional furniture and the expected mod
cons. The hotel is located on the river in a pedestrianised street
in the old town. *Cable/satellite TV/safe. Theatre-style conference*
facilities for up to 150. Secretarial/translation services on request.
Private garage. AMERICAN EXPRESS *Diners, Mastercard, Visa.*

Salzburg — Hotel Rosenberger

Tel (662) 43 55 46   Fax (662) 43 95 10 95   **H**

Bessarabierstrasse 5020 Salzburg
Rooms 120   Double room from ATS1720

Part of a family-run chain of hotels and restaurants, a large hotel
built in 1989 and standing right opposite the exhibition centre, 15
minutes out of the city centre. Bedrooms offer all the expected
accessories, including mini-bar, hairdryer and trouser press. The
conference facilities are large, with eight meeting rooms seating
350 theatre-style. *Cable TV. Conference facilities.*
Secretarial/translation services. Sauna/steam bath. Private garage.
AMERICAN EXPRESS *Diners, Mastercard, Visa.*

> The Golden Eurostar [★] denotes our pick of the
> restaurants. Cooking is the major consideration, but
> other factors are also taken into account, including
> ambience, comfort and service.

Salzburg   **Hotel Schloss Mönchstein**

Tel (662) 8 48 55 50   Fax (662) 84 85 59   **H**

Mönchsberg Park 26 5020 Salzburg
Rooms 17   Double room from ATS2400

A place with a colourful history: Mönchstein Castle was built
in 1358 and became part of the monastic estate of Mülln,
becoming a hotel back in the late 1940s. It is remarkably well
situated, right on the top of the Mönchsburg, one of the three hills
in the centre of Salzburg, with a ten-hectare garden surrounding it.
The bedrooms – singles, doubles, superior doubles and suites – are
grand and comfortable with sturdy furnishings and flowery
fabrics. All have cable and satellite TV and mini bars. Clearly, it is
a splendid place to hold an unusual event, though the largest of the
three salons holds no more than 30. Cultural and musical events
are regularly held in the castle chapel and there are castle concerts
every Saturday and Sunday. *No room service. Conference facilities.
Secretarial/translation services on request. Tennis court. Private
parking.* AMERICAN EXPRESS *Diners, Mastercard.*

Salzburg-Parsch   **Hotel Villa Pace**

Tel (662) 64 15 01   Fax (662) 64 15 01 22   **H**

Sonnleitenweg 9 5020 Salzburg-Parsch
Rooms 13   Double room from ATS3500

At the foot of the Gaisberg, the hotel gardens look over to the
fortress and the 'City of Mozart'; it is only seven minutes from the
city centre and 15 minutes drive from the airport. The 400-year-
old building is full of interest, from the imposing wooden-
ceilinged entrance to the heavy, traditional furnishings which are
a feature throughout. Bedroom pieces are Italian, Spanish
or Austrian in style. *24hr room service. Satellite TV. Outdoor
swimming pool, sauna, solarium, limousine service. Private garage and
parking. Closed 1 Nov-28 Feb.* AMERICAN EXPRESS *Diners, Mastercard,
Visa.*

Around Salzburg

Mondsee   **Hotel Seehof**

Tel (6232) 50 31 Fax (6232) 50 31 51   **H**

Loibichl 5311 Mondsee
Rooms 35   Double room from ATS2000

A country house hotel (partially rebuilt in 1988) surrounded
by acres of park and right beside a lake. It is a delightful rural
retreat, but there is plenty to keep the hyper-active happy,
including waterskiing, windsurfing and tennis. The rooms look
over the lake or grounds, some have their own private terraces,
and all have French and Italian furniture and all mod cons.
Relaxing is the 11th commandment here and even business
meetings are limited to 10 people. *Room service. Cable/satellite
TV/safe/fax (in suites only). Open 10 May-20 Sept. Tennis
court/watersports/sauna/solarium/masssage/beauty salon. Private garage.*
AMERICAN EXPRESS *Visa.*

Hof   **Hotel Schloss Fuschl**

Tel (6229) 2 25 30   Fax 6229 22 53 531   H

5322 Hof
Rooms 84   Double room from ATS2400

The 15th-century castle, 20km from Salzburg, is divided into two
buildings: the tower filled with antiques and the other newer
buildings decorated in quite a modern style. Being out of the city,
sports facilities are excellent with golf, a gym, sauna, tennis courts
and an indoor swimming pool, not to mention a beauty salon for
those in need of a little pampering. There is a free and easy
atmosphere, helped by their quiet, secluded location. *Cable TV.*
Theatre-style conference facilities for up to 250. Sports facilities. Private
garage. AMERICAN EXPRESS *Diners, Mastercard, Visa.*

Austria Index

Belgium

Currency: Belgian Franc   **Exchange Rate:** £1 = approx BFr 50

International dialling code: 010 32
(Antwerp + 3 Brussels + 2 Bruges + 50)

Passports/Visas: No visa required by British passport holders.

British Embassy in Brussels Tel: 2-287 6211   Fax: 2-287 6360

TRANSPORT
Airports:
Brussels National Airport Tel: 2-723 6010 / Deurne Airport Antwerp
Tel: 3-218 1211
Railway Stations:
Brussels Central Tel: 2-224 6010 / Antwerp Central Tel: 3-231 76 90 /
Bruges Tel: 50-38 58 71
Car hire in Brussels:
Auto Rent Tel: 2-217 15 50 / AT Rent-a-Car Tel: 2-230 8989 / Avis
Tel: 2-513 10 51 / Budget Tel: 2-376 85 31 / Europcar Tel: 2-640 94
00 / Luxauto Tel: 2-538 33 21
Speed limits: 90 km/h outside built-up areas, 120 km/h on
motorways, 50 km/h in towns.

Banks open: 9am-12, 2-4pm Mon-Fri.

Shops open: 9am-6pm Mon-Sat. Shops in the main cities are open until
9pm on Fridays.

National Holidays: New Year's Day, Easter Monday, 1 May,
Ascension Day, Whit Monday, 21 July, 15 Aug, 1 Nov, 11 Nov, 15
Nov, Christmas Day & Boxing Day.

Tourist Offices:
Belgian Tourist Board in London - Tel: 0171-629 0230
In Belgium –
Brussels Tel: 2-513 8940 / Antwerp Tel: 3-332 0103 / Bruges Tel: 50-
44 86 86

American Express Travel Service Offices:
Antwerp - AETS
    Frankrijklei 21
    2000
    Tel: 3-2325920
Brussels - AETS
    2 Place Louise
    1050
    Tel: 2-5121740 #

Brussels

Brussels   Amigo

Tel (2) 547 47 47 Fax (2) 513 52 77   **H**

1-3 Rue de l'Amigo 1000 Brussels
Rooms 185   Double room from Fr6750

Since the late 50s, the Amigo has been a superb place. The rooms
are individually designed, with oak furniture and Flemish
tapestries, and now they also have up-to-date facilities (120 rooms
have been renovated in the last three years) with satellite TV and
faxes in 80 rooms. The location, just off the Grand Place, is equally
splendid, with the main railway station five minutes walk away.
Conference facilities are comprehensive. *24hr room service. Theatre-
style conference facilities for up to 300. Laundry/dry cleaning.
Private garage.* AMERICAN EXPRESS *Diners, Mastercard, Visa.*

THE APARTMENT SERVICE
Tel in UK: (0181) 748 4207   Fax: (0181) 748 3972
The Apartment Service will find you the right apartment
worldwide to suit your needs, whether you are on a short or
long-term stay. A 96-page colour catalogue is free on request.
All budgets are catered for.

Brussels   Aux Armes de Bruxelles

Tel (2) 511 55 98   Fax (2) 514 33 81   **R**

13 Rue Bouchers 1000 Brussels
Seats 180   Meal for 2 approx Fr3500

In one of the narrow lanes that surround the Grand Place in the
old part of the city, the 'Armes' has been run by the Veulemans
family since 1921. There are three air-conditioned dining rooms –
one wood-panelled with brass chandelier, another with cool
white decor and the main room in typical brasserie style with
1920s glass and chrome light fittings, parlour plants and banquette
seating down each side – but just one menu set out in traditional
brasserie format. Among chef-patron Jacques Veulemans'
specialities are *waterzooi* dishes (in which either chicken, lobster,
turbot or other fish is cooked in a rich cream sauce with
vegetables), fresh prawn croquettes, carbonnade of beef and
mussels cooked in various ways. The latter are also served from
a long wooden stand-up counter in the cobbled lane outside. There
are several fixed-price options including a good value set lunch
(noon-2, Mon-Fri only) at Fr495. The wine list ranges from some
half-a-dozen wines by the glass to no less than ten different
vintages of Ch Mouton Rothschild. *Set meals: Fr495 (L Mon-Fri
only), Fr995 & Fr1695. Open noon-11.15pm. Closed Mon & one
month Jun/Jul.* AMERICAN EXPRESS *Diners, Mastercard, Visa.*

Brussels   **Astoria**

Tel (2) 217 62 90   Fax (2) 217 11 50   **HR**
103 Rue Royale 1000 Brussels
Rooms 125   Double room from Fr8000

A neo-Victorian hotel with Belle Epoque-style reception rooms,
easily accessible from the main business district. At the time
of going to press there are plans to redecorate half the rooms
by December 1994 and the rest in 1995. At the moment, they are
all equipped with cable TV and filled with antique furniture.
There are seven conference rooms than can cater for a total of 200
people theatre-style. *24hr room service. Conference facilities.*
AMERICAN EXPRESS *Diners, Mastercard, Visa.*

Le Palais Royal
Seats 40   Meal for 2 approx Fr3100

In an art deco-style dining room, lined with wallpaper and filled
with glowing lamps and antique vases, traditional French food
is served. A *consommé double de volaille fermière aux fines herbes*
(double-filtered consommé of free-range wild fowl and fine herbs)
and *terrine de foie gras d'oie Landes, gelée au porto* (a terrine
of Landes goose liver with a port jelly) are typical house
specialities. Other dishes have a more Mediterranean French
influence: *salade de crevettes grises aux agrumes* (salad of prawns and
citrus fruits). The wine list is shorter than many, but all the major
French regions are well represented with the house wine a decent
bordeaux. *L 12-3 D 7-10. Closed L Sat, D Sun. Private parking.*

Brussels   **Les Baguettes Impériales**

Tel & Fax (2) 479 67 32   **R**
70 Avenue Jean Sobieski 1020 Brussels
Seats 30   Meal for 2 approx Fr5000

A rare Oriental jewel in the otherwise predominantly French
culinary crown, the lady chef here carefully prepares an authentic
and traditional Vietnamese menu. Particular house specialities are
crunchy lobster pancakes, duckling baked in spices and
langoustines cooked with peppers and served with a sweet and
sour sauce. Red dragons make the decor as traditional as the
cooking. So for those looking for a little culinary variety, it is well
worth making the ten-minute drive north from the centre of the
city. *L 12-3 D 7-10.30. Closed D Sun, all Tue, Easter, Aug.*
No parking. AMERICAN EXPRESS *Visa.*

Meal prices for 2 are based on à la carte menus.
When set menus are available, prices will often be lower.

Brussels **Bedford**

Tel (2) 512 78 40 Fax (2) 514 17 59 **H**

135 Rue du Midi 1000 Brussels
Rooms 296   Double room from Fr7300

Friendly, privately owned hotel near the historic centre of the
city. Newly refurbished public areas are spacious, comfortable and
smart. The Luxury or new Executive bedrooms are best, being
distinctly larger than the standard rooms, but all come with the
usual modern amenities including more than 25 TV channels.
Some rooms are air-conditioned. *Conferencing for up to 200,
parking in hotel's own multi-storey nearby.* AMERICAN EXPRESS *Diners,
Mastercard, Visa.*

Brussels **Bruneau**

Tel (2) 427 69 78 Fax (2) 425 97 26 **R**

73 Avenue Broustin Ganshoren 1080 Brussels
Seats 80   Meal for 2 approx Fr8000

In the northern suburb of Ganshoren, close to the Sacré Coeur
Basilica. Completely re-modelled in 1992 in a pleasing 'designer'
1920s style and with the addition of air-conditioning and a pretty
terrace for summer eating, the setting now matches the excellence
of Jean Pierre Bruneau's cooking. The menus are essentially
market-driven and Jean Pierre's *menu surprise* continues to be
a popular choice, comprising at least six courses, some taken from
an à la carte that might include such dishes as a 'millefeuille' of veal
tongue and goose liver with a salad of chicory and truffles, fillets
of red mullet with a virgin olive oil and basil dressing, carpaccio
of langoustine à la crème with caviar, Malins chicken stuffed with
morels, and Barbary duck with honey, figs and red wine. If you
find it difficult to choose just one of the tempting desserts
remember that with the *menu surprise* you get a selection
of several. Only the service, which can on occasion be careless and
insensitive, lets the side down. Outstanding wine list. *Set menus:
Fr1870 (L only), Fr2500, Fr3500. L 12-2 D 7-10 Closed D Tues, all
Wed (L Sat & all Mon till March '95), last week May, first two
weeks June & one week Christmas.* AMERICAN EXPRESS *Diners, Mastercard,
Visa.*

Brussels **Claude Dupont**

Tel (2) 426 00 00 Fax (2) 426 65 40 **R**

46 Avenue Vital Riethuisen 1080 Brussels
Seats 30   Meal for 2 approx Fr7000

Right beside the Koekelberg Basilica to the north of the city in
the Ganshoren district, a classical and comfortable town-house
restaurant with a certain 70s charm. It has been family run since
1971 and Monsieur Dupont still cooks his old favourites in the
kitchen: lobster and vegetable stew with light curry, salmon and
sea bass cooked in white wine with a caviar mousse, and perch
fillet cooked in butter and served with asparagus. The menu
changes every month, but sticks mainly to classical cooking and
features a lot of fish. *L 12-2.30 D 7-9.30. Closed Mon, Tue, early
Jul-early Aug. Public parking.* AMERICAN EXPRESS *Diners, Mastercard,
Visa.*

★

Brussels   **Comme Chez Soi**

Tel (2) 512 29 21   Fax (2) 511 80 52   **R**

23 Place Rouppe 1000 Brussels

Seats 60   Meal for 2 approx Fr7000

It is not the sumptous art nouveau decor that has attracted
a pilgrimage of international gourmets to this restaurant over the
last 40 years, but the allure of greater culinary satisfaction than
almost any place, in or out of Belgium, can provide. Pierre
Wynants, the chef, has become an international culinary guru,
with his famous house specialities like fillets of sole with
a mousseline of *crevettes grises* and Riesling, shoulder of lamb
served with a lentil and truffle flan and lobster served *en cardinale*
(in a coral, tomato and cream sauce). The choice is wide and with
set menus starting at Fr1875 can be also be very reasonable,
considering the feast of fine cooking you will experience. Where
you eat is worth thinking about: the choice is a table in the
kitchen, in the main dining room, or in a party in one of the
private dining rooms. *L 12-2 D 7-10. Closed Sun, Mon, 23 Dec-2
Jan, 9 Jul-9 Aug.* AMERICAN EXPRESS *Diners, Mastercard, Visa.*

★

Brussels   **Conrad**

Tel (2) 542 42 42   Fax (2) 542 42 00   **H**

71 Avenue Louise 1050 Brussels

Rooms 269   Double room from Fr7000

Sister to the Hotel Conrad in Chelsea Harbour, London, but quite
unlike its British counterpart. The building was formerly one
of the Royal Family's residences, with the much sought after
address of Avenue Louise, and the facade still remains much the
same. However, inside is extremely modern and plans are afoot
for an indoor swimming pool, gym and health club, but no date
for completing these facilities has yet been finalised. The rooms
have satellite TV and a fax and are conservatively decorated. The
hotel has been open only about a year, so more changes are likely
to be afoot. Conference facilities for up to 650. *24hr room service.*
AMERICAN EXPRESS *Diners, Mastercard, Visa.*

The Golden Eurostar [★] denotes our pick of the
restaurants. Cooking is the major consideration, but
other factors are also taken into account, including
ambience, comfort and service.

Brussels   L'Ecailler du Palais Royal

Tel (2) 512 87 51   Fax (2) 511 99 50   **R**

18 Rue Bodenbroek 1000 Brussels
Seats 30   Meal for 2 approx Fr7000

Very close to the Palais Royal and the museum of Ancient Art,
Attilo Basso has made his restaurant rightly famous for its fresh
fish dishes (the name itself means oyster seller). His lavish creations
are the result of over 45 years cooking experience and, not
surprisingly, there is little to find fault with. Warmed lobster salad
is served with artichokes, escalopes of wild salmon are grilled and
served with asparagus and lobster sabayon and ravioli are filled
with fresh lobster and served with a light curry sauce. Only
seafood dishes are served, expect for a few foie gras specialities.   ★
The fish is international: the salmon comes from Scotland, wild
not farmed, the lobster from Norway and the sea urchins from
France. The wines, though, are limited to French and German.
The rich wood-panelled dining room, still in the style of a 20s
café, is as lavish as the food. All in all, a great place. *L 12-2.30 D 7-
10.30. Closed Sun, National Holidays, Aug, Good Friday for 10 days.
Private parking.* AMERICAN EXPRESS *Diners, Mastercard, Visa.*

Brussels   Hilton Brussels

Tel (2) 504 11 11   Fax (2) 504 21 11   **HR**

38 Boulevard de Waterloo Brussels 1000
Rooms 450   Double room from Fr11,500

Difficult to miss – a 28-storey tower hotel on the inner 'little' ring
road near all the expensive designer shops that congregate around
the junction of the Boulevard de Waterloo and the Avenue Louise.
Rooms and suites high up on the four Executive floors benefit
from fine views over the city as well as a separate check-in desk
with concierge facilities and exclusive lounge offering
complimentary breakfast, drinks and snacks. Numerous meeting
rooms, the largest seating up to 650 theatre-style. *Air-conditioning,
room safe, overnight laundry, sauna, steam room, solarium, secure
underground parking.* AMERICAN EXPRESS *Diners, Mastercard, Visa.*

Maison du Boeuf
Seats 87   Meal for 2 approx Fr4000

Michel Theurel's menu is dominated by fish and beef dishes all
cooked in a modern French way with mainly Belgian ingredients.
Carpaccio of bass is served with chives, Guérande salt and black
pepper; lobster bisque is dressed with sour cream and dill and
freshly minced steak tartare is prepared as a '*maison du boeuf*'
speciality of Theurel. Others dishes have more international
ingredients, with roasted pigeon from the *Vendée*, prime rib of US
beef roasted in a salt crust and a gratin of Belon oysters
in champagne with a parsley mousseline. They boast a healthy
international wine list. *L 12-2.30 D 7-10.* 🐂

Brussels   La Maison du Cygne

Tel (2) 511 82 44   Fax (2) 514 31 48   **R**

9 Grand Place 1000 Brussels
Seats 100   Meal for 2 approx Fr6000

Once a cavorting cabaret venue and then home to a butchers'
Guild, the 16th-century listed building is now a rich wooden-
panelled restaurant. Definitely book a table on the first floor,
so you can admire the other architectural masterpieces around the
Grand Place. The chef, Richard Hahn, has made the cooking
as rich as the surroundings, with house specialities like turbot
braised *à l'américaine* (a fine, complex sauce of pounded lobster,
fish *velouté*, corals and butter blended with brandy and dry white
wine) and Belgian duckling glazed with baby onions. For a light
lunch, try the warmed sweetbread and lobster salad served with
a mild curry sauce, or the prawn and sole salad. There are 50,000
bottles in the cellar, and they are rather proud of their dessert
wines. *L 12-2.30 D 7.30-10. Closed L Sat, all Sun, 1-21 Aug, 24-31
Dec. Private parking.* AMERICAN EXPRESS *Diners, Mastercard, Visa.*

★

Brussels   Manos Stephanie

Tel (2) 539 02 50   Fax (2) 537 57 29   **H**

28 Chaussée de Charleroi 1060 Brussels
Rooms 55   Double room from Fr7350

Slightly off the main tourist track and 20 minutes from the
business centre, a three-year-old hotel in a 19th-century building.
The rooms looking out over the street can be a trifle noisy, despite
the double-glazing, so it would be advisable to insist on a room
at the rear of the building. They are filled with old-fashioned
furniture, but do have all the European mod cons one would
expect. Conference facilities are limited to one small room, fully
equipped, but only able to seat 15 people maximum. Note there
is no restaurant. *Cable TV. Private parking.* AMERICAN EXPRESS *Diners,
Mastercard, Visa.*

Brussels   Mayfair

Tel (2) 649 95 86   Fax (2) 649 22 49   **H**

381 Avenue Louise 1050 Brussels
Rooms 99   Double room from Fr9360

Japanese-owned hotel at the Bois de la Cambre end of Avenue
Louise. Well-appointed bedrooms include four Study rooms –
designed for businessmen with extra work space and very
masculine decor – and four Lady rooms with pretty Laura Ashley-
style furnishings. There are also two Junior and two Full suites.
Bathrooms all come with robes and slippers in addition to a good
range of toiletries. Beds are turned down at night. Public rooms
include a very civilised lounge which opens on to a small patio
garden. *Air-conditioning. Underground parking for 35 cars.*
AMERICAN EXPRESS *Diners, Mastercard, Visa.*

Brussels **Métropole**

Tel (2) 217 23 00   Fax (2) 218 02 20   **H**

31 Place Brouckère 1000 Brussels
Rooms 410   Double room from Fr6000

A traditional turn-of-the century hotel in a busy central location, five minutes from the Grand Place, and right by the main shops, banks and entertainment. Being a large hotel, it tends to have a life all its own, and is not for those looking for a quiet retreat. But they do have excellent facilities: a health centre and ten conference rooms capable of seating 600 theatre-style. The rooms (all doubles) are decorated in art deco style and are very well equipped. *24hr room service. Cable TV/fax. Conference facilities. Secretarial/translation services on request. Sports facilities/massage. Private parking.* AMERICAN EXPRESS *Mastercard, Visa.*

Brussels **Michel**

Tel (2) 466 65 91   Fax (2) 466 90 07   **R**

31 Schepen Gossetlaan Groot-Bijgaarden 1720 Brussels
Seats 45   Meal for 2 approx Fr5500

A detached house in a residential suburb to the west of the city, near the junction of the E40 with the motorway ring road, is home to Michel and Helda Coppens' restaurant with its comfortable sitting area for pre-prandial drinks and light, airy dining room. There is also a small patio for summer dining. Following the seasons and the markets, Michel eschews complicated garnishes, preferring to allow the excellence of the raw materials to speak for themselves in thoroughly enjoyable dishes. Gateau of foie gras *en gelée* with truffles, terrine of sole and smoked salmon, oysters in champagne with tomato and chervil, best end of lamb with seasonal vegetables, saddle of hare with mustard sauce and cabbage and grilled turbot with mousseline sauce show the style. Prices are not excessive and the *menu d'affaires* (Fr1450) is, unusually, also available at night. *Set menus: Fr1450 & Fr2100. L 12-2.30 D 7-9.30. Closed Sun, Mon & Aug.* AMERICAN EXPRESS *Diners, Mastercard, Visa.*

★

Brussels **Montgomery Hotel**

Tel (2) 741 85 11   Fax (2) 741 85 00   **H**

134 Avenue de Tervueren 1150 Brussels
Rooms 64   Double room from Fr11,500

Residential chic fills the air at this townhouse hotel near a large park, but also only ten minutes from the airport and within walking distance from the EU headquarters. The rooms are extremely well equipped, and very original, filled with mahogany furniture (including large desks) from all over Europe and decorated in romantically English, or chic Chinese style as well as having a fax, books and fine toiletries. Excellent personal service. *24hr room service. Cable/satellite TV/fax/safe/library. Restaurant (traditional French). Theatre-style conference facilities for up to 20. Secretarial/translation services on request. Sauna/fitness centre. Private parking.* AMERICAN EXPRESS *Diners, Mastercard, Visa.*

Brussels — Novotel Brussels Airport

Tel (2) 725 30 50   Fax (2) 721 39 58   H

1830 Olmenstraat Diegem Brussels

Rooms 209   Double room from Fr5370

Easy to spot but difficult to reach – follow the Zaventem signs, with the airplane symbol, off the ring road then right at the lights and right again at the first proper crossroads – this 70s-built hotel (the first Novotel outside France) offers functional accommodation close to the airport. Rooms in the 'new block' are best. There are flight information screens in the lobby and a free shuttle bus runs to the terminal every 20 minutes from early morning till late at night. Children under 14 stay free in parents' room. *Air-conditioning, outdoor swimming pool, unsupervised open parking for 250 cars.* AMERICAN EXPRESS *Diners, Mastercard, Visa.*

Brussels — Royal Crown

Tel (2) 220 066 11   Fax (2) 217 84 44   H

250 Rue Royale 1210 Brussels

Rooms 315   Double room from Fr9300

For the last 18 years, this privately-owned hotel, right in the city centre near the Gare du Nord Botanical Gardens, and more importantly the EU building, has been a political hothouse of European debate with international diplomats staying here. Despite being under the Euro-spotlight, the place is in a quiet corner of Brussels, ten minutes in a taxi from the airport. The rooms, modernised in 1990, now have faxes and air-conditioning. As one would expect, the conference facilities are excellent: they can accommodate up to 550 delegates theatre-style. *24hr room service. Conference facilities. Sauna/gym. Private parking.* AMERICAN EXPRESS *Diners, Mastercard, Visa.*

Brussels — Royal Windsor Hotel

Tel (2) 505 55 55   Fax (2) 505 55 00   HR

5 Rue Duquesnoy 1000 Brussels

Rooms 275 ·   Double room from Fr11150

Despite its size there is an intimate feel to this classy hotel conveniently located in the centre of town not far from the Grand Place. Day rooms include the English-style Windsor Arms (all red leather and mahogany), the Waterloo piano bar and a disco night club. Executive rooms are the more spacious but all are stylishly decorated and come with good marble bathrooms and effective air-conditioning. One floor is reserved for non-smokers. *Room safe, sauna, gym, conferencing for up to 230 delegates, secure underground parking for 60 cars.* AMERICAN EXPRESS *Diners, Mastercard, Visa.*   *See over for Restaurant*

Les Quatres Saisons
Seats 50   Meal for 2 approx Fr4600

In this elegant and cosy dining room, guests are served some
splendid dishes, all the creation of one of the city's most renowned
chefs, Dutchman Jan Raven. His specialities include fish and
shellfish: *fricassée de langoustines et d'asperges à l'emincé de truffes,
gateau de saumon tartiné au caviar.* Rich game dishes are on the
menu when they are in season. For a slighter cheaper meal, opt for
the *menu d'affaires*, which offers three courses, with
a comprehensive choice of dishes, for Fr1390. For a longer, more
extravagant dinner, the *menu gourmand* is the obvious choice.
Whatever you decide, the wide choice of French wines will
manage to satisfy most. *L 12-2.30 D 7.30-10.30. Closed L Sat,
20 Jul-20 Aug.*

Brussels   **SAS Royal Hotel**

Tel (2) 219 28 28   Fax (2) 219 62 62   **HR**
47 Rue du Fossé-aux-Loups 1000 Brussels
Rooms 281   Double room from Fr11,900

A few minutes from the Grand Place, in the main commercial
centre of the city, a new art deco style hotel that's popular with
businessmen. The rooms are individually decorated in Italian,
Scandinavian or art deco style. The hotel has a fully equipped
business centre, and the John Harris Fitness Club with its sauna,
jacuzzi, whirlpool and massage is also open to guests. *24hr room
service. Fax. Theatre-style conference facilities for up to 350. Private
parking. Sports facilities. Private parking.* AMERICAN EXPRESS® *Diners,
Mastercard, Visa.*

Sea Grill J. le Divellec   Tel (2) 217 92 25
Seats 80   Meal for 2 approx Fr6000

The chef, Yves Mattagne, trained in Paris with Jacques le Divellec,
who has given his name to this restaurant. Mattagne himself was
elected as the youngest Maitre Cuisinier in Belgium by *Les
Disciples d'Escoffier*. He very much followed in le Divellec's
modern fish footsteps, with dishes like steamed scallops served on a
bed of seaweed and sole soufflée with Brittany crab, lemon liqueur
and ginger butter. But the most spectacular dish is their pressed
lobster; the lobster is chosen from the restaurant's tank and once
the cooked meat has been removed from the tail and back, the
remaining meat and shell are pressed in a rare lobster press in front
of diners. The *Marée de Jour* changes every week(!), while the rest
of the menu changes once a month. *L 12-2.30 D 7-10.30. Closed
L Sat, Sun, 14-23 Apr, 21 Jul-15 Aug.*

Brussels   **Sheraton Brussels Airport**

Tel (2) 725 10 00   Fax (2) 725 11 55   **H**
1930 Zaventem Brussels
Rooms 298   Double room from Fr11,680

The only hotel actually at the airport, just 39 steps from the
terminal building, the Sheraton is a five-year-old atrium hotel
with well-equipped, air-conditioned bedrooms and a full range
of services from 24hr room service to a business centre and
conference facilities for up to 450 delegates. *Air-conditioning,
overnight laundry, keep-fit equipment, unsupervised parking for 77 cars.*
AMERICAN EXPRESS® *Diners, Mastercard, Visa.*

Brussels — **Stanhope**

Tel (2) 506 91 11   Fax (2) 512 17 08   **HR**

9 Rue du Commerce 1040 Brussels

Rooms 50 — Double room from Fr12,500

Relaxed elegance is the motto of this deeply sophiscated, classical place, easy bag-carrying distance from *La Toison d'Or*, the chicest shopping street in Brussels. The whole hotel is decorated like an English country home and filled with British antiques. The rooms are luxuriously furnished, with heavy curtains and grand beds and are lined with fine wallpaper. Reception rooms are filled with old books to peruse and comfortable sofas to relax in. Note that conference facilities extend only to one boardroom, for 15 people. *24hr room service. Air-con/fax. Gym/sauna. Private garage.* AMERICAN EXPRESS *Diners, Mastercard, Visa.*

Brighton Restaurant

Seats 70 — Meal for 2 approx Fr6000

Bathed in soft yellow candle-light with glowing frescoes on the walls, the place has a quiet modern elegance, that suits the subtle gastromic cooking coming from Jean Couture's kitchen. *Médaillons de foie gras de canard chauds aux peches caramélisées* (medallions of warmed duck's liver with caramelised peaches); *cotelettes d'agneau roties, jus parfumé à l'estragon, gratin de pommes boulangère et bouquet de légumes de saison* (roast lamb cutlets seasoned with a tarragon jus and served with potatoes *boulangère* and seasonal fresh vegetables). Couture specialises in French patisserie, so do try one of his interesting desserts. *L 12-2.30 D 8-10. Closed Sat, Sun. 18 Jul-22 Aug (only limited menu).*

Brussels — **Trente Rue de la Paille**

Tel (2) 512 07 15   Fax (2) 514 23 33   **R**

30 Rue de la Paille 1000 Brussels

Seats 40 — Meal for 2 approx Fr5000

André Martiny has now been cooking inventive French food in this 100-year-old restaurant (formerly a haberdasher's shop) for the last 16 years. Turbot, sweetbreads and langoustines are popular house specialities, all cooked in interesting ways: sweetbreads are braised with cider vinegar, honey, cream and fresh herbs, while langoustine tails are roasted with almonds and served as a salad with strips of fried duck's liver. Desserts are delicately presented, with 'Monsieur' and 'Madame' written across the plate in chocolate cream. *L 12-2.30 D 7-11. Closed Jul, 2 weeks Dec. Public parking.* AMERICAN EXPRESS *Diners, Mastercard, Visa.*

> Opening times are often liable to change at short notice, so it's always best to book.

Brussels   La Truffe Noire

Tel (2) 640 44 22   Fax (2) 647 97 04   R

12 Boulevard de la Cambre 1050 Brussels
Seats 45   Meal for 2 approx Fr6500

The modern French cooking, touched with a light Italian feel and
always strongly laced with white and black truffles, owes a lot
to their two chefs, Aziz Rehman and Erik Lindelauf, who have
come from *Comme Chez Soi*, elsewhere in Brussels. A warm salad
of asparagus is served with truffles, fillet of John Dory is stuffed
with truffles and served with leeks, and black chocolate truffles are
encased in sugar. So you know what to order here, but it's not *all*
truffles, and there are some interesting lamb and fish dishes on the   ★
menu dégustation. The wine list is almost as impressive as the
truffles, with 500 references. The restaurant is away from the
tourist trade near the Bois de la Cambre. *L 12-2.15 D 7-11. Closed
L Sat, all Sun, 22-27 Dec, Easter, 1-15 Aug. Valet parking.*
AMERICAN EXPRESS *Diners, Mastercard, Visa.*

Brussels   La Villa Lorraine

Tel (2) 374 31 63   Fax (2) 372 01 95   R

75 Avenue du Vivier d'Oie 1180 Brussels
Seats 100   Meal for 2 approx Fr6500

On the edge of the vast *Foret des Soignes*, La Villa Lorraine has
wined and dined guests for over 125 years. In days gone by it was
controlled by culinary maestro Marcel Kreusch, who then handed
it down to his protégés, Henri Van Ranst and chef Freddy Van
de Casserie. The team may be new, but the restaurant has lost
none of its early originality, culinary or otherwise: chandeliers
hang from the trees outside, decorating the terrace. The menus   ★
(beautifully illustrated) have plenty of interesting dishes to choose
from: millefeuille of sweetbreads, wild mushrooms and crayfish,
rack of lamb coated in parsley and served with seasonal vegetables
and desserts like iced soufflé of figs and chestnuts. There is an
impressive list of champagnes. *L 12-2 D 7-9.30. Closed Sun, 7-31
Jul. Private parking.* AMERICAN EXPRESS *Diners, Mastercard, Visa.*

Around Brussels

Auderghem   La Grignotière

Tel & Fax (2) 672 81 85   R

2041 Chaussée de Wavre 1160 Auderghem
Seats 30   Meal for 2 approx Fr4500

Augustin Chanson professes to be heavily influenced by his
internationally renowned and revered friend, Pierre Wynants,
of *Comme Chez Soi* (qv) – much to his credit. For the last 42
years, he has followed the great gourmets, but consistently tried
to keep his prices as modest as his small restaurant. Game, fish and
poultry are all served in fine sauces seasoned with fresh herbs.
Now working with his son in the kitchen, he changes his menu   ★
every two weeks, but the modest French wine list remains the
same. Eight kilometres out the city centre on the edge of the
Soigné forest, the dining room is surrounded by a flower-filled
garden. *Open 12-9.30. Closed Sun, Mon, 1-15 Aug, 24 Dec-1 Jan.
Private parking.* AMERICAN EXPRESS *Diners, Mastercard, Visa.*

Genval   **Le Manoir du Lac**

Tel (2) 655 63 11   Fax (2) 655 64 55   **H**

4 Avenue Hoover 1332 Genval

Rooms 16   Double room from Fr8900

Chateau du Lac is 100m away, but otherwise there is only the lake
and a few windsurfers to break the secluded calm. 13 bedrooms
are in the actual Manoir itself, while the other three are in another
villa. All are doubles and all have cable TV. It is a real country
retreat with simple wooden furniture, floral carpets and curtains
and a relaxed rustic air, unspoilt by any overt modernisation,
except the outdoor swimming pool, sauna and Turkish bath.
Private parking. AMERICAN EXPRESS *Diners, Visa.*

Genval   **Le Trèfle à Quatre**

Tel (2) 654 07 98   Fax (2) 653 31 31   **R**

Chateau de Lac 87 Avenue de Lac 1332 Genval

Seats 60   Meal for 2 approx Fr4000

John Martin manages a collection of Belgian hotels and restaurants
along with this one-time Schweppes bottling factory. However,
it is Michel Haquin, the chef here for the last nine years, who has
made it a splendid and undoubtedly special place, only 20 minutes
from Brussels by car. Sharp cooking comes in the shape of oven-
roasted turbot, croque monsieur with goose liver paté and a cider
sauce and Bresse chicken baked in salt. Desserts are equally
tantalising, with a choice of imaginative dishes like cinnamon ice
cream with a cherry purée. Set menus start at Fr1450 for the
business *carte*. The restaurant is part of the luxurious 38-
bedroomed Chateau du Lac, Tel: (2) 654 11 22. *L 12-2.30 D 7-
9.30. Closed Mon, Tue, mid Jan-mid Feb. Private car park.*
AMERICAN EXPRESS *Diners, Mastercard, Visa.*

Antwerp

Antwerp   Alfa De Keyser

Tel (3) 234 01 35   Fax (3) 232 39 70   **H**

66-70 De Keyserlei 2018 Antwerp

Rooms 123   Double room from Fr8400

Only seconds from the railway station and right next to the shopping arcade and diamond centre, this is a well-equipped hotel, with a great health and fitness centre containing a sauna, Turkish bath, whirlpool, indoor swimming pool, solarium and gym. The rooms, the majority of which are doubles, are also the model of modernity with all the usual amenities in place. The conference facilities are small – just three modestly-sized meeting rooms, but they are all fully-equipped. *24hr room service. Cable TV. Theatre-style conference facilities for up to 50. Secretarial/translation services on request. Valet/public parking.* AMERICAN EXPRESS *Diners, Mastercard, Visa.*

Antwerp   Firean

Tel (3) 237 02 60   Fax (3) 238 11 68   **H**

6 Karel Oomsstraat 2018 Antwerp

Rooms 17   Double room from Fr5500

An art deco architectural attraction built in the 20s, it became a family-run hotel back in 1986. A new wing was added in 1993, giving it six more bedrooms. They all have cable and satellite TV and air-conditioning, and two of the suites are also equipped with faxes. All feature antiques, crystal chandeliers and beautiful stained-glass windows. Quiet and undisturbed by the residential district around, the hotel is still only ten minutes from Antwerp Airport and the same distance from the main railway station. *Cable/satellite TV/air-con. Laundry/dry cleaning. Closed 29 Jul-21 Aug, 23 Dec-9 Jan. Private garage.* AMERICAN EXPRESS *Diners, Mastercard, Visa.*

Antwerp   't Fornuis

Tel (3) 233 62 70   Fax (3) 233 99 03   **R**

24 Reyndersstraat 2000 Antwerp

Seats 30   Meal for 2 approx Fr8000

Old-fashioned cooking comes to the small tables of this rustic restaurant under the watchful eye of chef Johan Segers, who bursts out of the kitchen to suggest what his guests should eat and to explain the day's specials. His cooking is as spontaneous as his manner, with plenty of modern French fish dishes, like fillet of salmon cooked with honey and sole baked with fresh rhubarb. Vegetarians can consult with Segers and concoct any creation they desire. Do not be fooled by the relaxed, intimate atmosphere into thinking this place is cheap; wines start at Fr650 and the dishes are also quite expensive. The restaurant, renovated by Segers himself, is in the heart of the old town. *Closed Sat, Sun, 7-31 Aug, 22-29 Dec.* AMERICAN EXPRESS *Diners, Mastercard, Visa.*

Antwerp   De Kerselaar

Tel (3) 233 59 69   Fax (3) 233 11 49   **R**

22 Grote Pieter Potstraat 2000 Antwerp
Seats 30   Meal for 2 approx Fr5000

Yves Michiels, the owner and chef at this opulent restaurant,
trained under Joël Robuchon and Roger Vergé and his *nouvelle-
légère* cooking owes a lot to both their influences: *queues
de langoustines roties aux dix poussières d'épices, sa sauce au curry doux
et ses pates fraiches à la ficelle de légumes* (lobster tails roasted with
ten different spices and served with a light curry sauce and fresh
pasta and vegetables), *pigeonneau laqué au miel* (baby pigeon coated
in honey). The *menu dégustation* changes every month, with a new
collection of wines to accompany the dishes; however, the à la
carte menu changes only slightly with the seasons. The
comprehensive wine list is classically French; a perfect
complement to the modern culinary extravaganzas created in the
kitchen, all only 100m from the Grand Place and Cathedral.
*Closed L Mon & Sat, all Sun, 21-28 Mar, 22 Jul-9 Aug, 22-25 Dec.
Public parking.* AMERICAN EXPRESS *Diners, Visa.*

Antwerp   De Rosier

Tel (3) 225 01 40   Fax (3) 231 41 11   **H**

21-23 Rosier 2000 Antwerp
Rooms 12   Double room from Fr6500

A few minutes walk away from the Grand Place and Cathedral,
De Rosier is more like a 17th-century private home than a hotel.
The same family have been running it for 22 years and fill the
rooms with interesting antiques, which not only decorate the
rooms, but can also be bought. So the rooms are constantly
redecorated as their English and French furniture is sold to guests,
and new collectable pieces bought. Despite its Old World feel,
there have been some renovations: an indoor swimming pool was
recently installed and all the rooms have cable TV and a beer-only
mini-bar. It is really too small a place for conferences, but board
meetings can be arranged in the President's Room for up to 18
people. *Indoor swimming pool, sauna. Private parking.* AMERICAN EXPRESS
Diners, Mastercard, Visa.

Antwerp   Vateli

Tel (3) 238 72 52   Fax (3) 238 25 88   **R**

31 Vanputlay 2018 Antwerp
Seats 65   Meal for 2 approx Fr6000

Belgian chef, Jacques Slap has been here for 20 years preparing
a classical, traditional Belgian menu, which changes with the
seasons. The set menus vary dramatically in price, from the
lunchtime special at Fr1450 to the more extravagant Fr3500 one.
The house specialities are all fish and poultry: turbot is simply
grilled and foie gras is sautéed and served with caramelised apples.
They bottle their own wine, as well as serving many a renowned
French label. Vateli is a ten-minute drive south of the city centre
in a quiet residential suburb. *L 12-2.30 D 6-9. Closed D Sat, all
Sun, National Holidays, 17-31 Jul. Private parking.* AMERICAN EXPRESS
Diners, Visa.

Around Antwerp

Hostellerie Kasteelhoeve Groeninghe

Tel (3) 457 95 86   Fax (3) 458 13 68   **HR**

78 Kontichsesteenweg 2630 Aartselaar
Rooms 7   Double room from Fr5250

The bedrooms in this old farmhouse by Groeninghe Castle are
very much secondary to the restaurant, but they too have their
attractions, being well equipped and furnished with antiques. It's
only a small place and it's the little touches that appeal: Antwerp
Cathedral (6km away) was restored a couple of years ago and the
old stone steps were brought here and made into a staircase
leading up to the rooms. Though limited in accommodation space
the *hostellerie* can host a conference for up to 250 people theatre-
style. *Closed 22-31 Jul, 24-31 Dec. Private parking.* AMERICAN EXPRESS
Diners, Mastercard, Visa.

Restaurant
Seats 30   Meal for 2 approx Fr6000

Light, well-balanced French food, with a healthy choice of meat,
fish and vegetables, is served on various menus, starting with the
lunch menu at Fr1550 (which also changes every day). Scottish
salmon is grilled with celery and served with a mustard sauce;
fillet of lamb and Roquefort-filled ravioli come with a tarragon
sauce; escalope of goose liver is sautéed with mangos. As well
as serving 300 different French wines, they bottle their own
Bordeaux house wine. *L 12-2.30 D 6.30-9.30. Closed L Sat, all
Sun, 22-31 Jul, 24-31 Dec. Private parking.*

De Schone van Boskoop

Tel (3) 454 19 31   **R**

10 Appelkanstraat 2530 Boechout
Seats 30   Meal for 2 approx Fr2700

Opened only a year or so ago, this small, friendly, family-run place
is just a 15-minute drive from the city's bustle (with terrace tables
outside). The menu is traditional and sticks to classics
of consommé, langoustines, lamb, veal and fillet of beef, with the
fresh fish of the day simply grilled. The choice though
is extensive, with a *menu dégustation*, a set menu and the à la carte
menu to choose from. Desserts are quite flamboyant, with dishes
like rhubarb compote served with strawberries and lemon confit.
L 12-3 D 7-10. Closed Sun, Mon, 15 Aug-5 Sept, 1-7 Jan.
AMERICAN EXPRESS *Visa.*

Bruges

Bruges   't Bourgoensche Cruyce

Tel (50) 33 79 26   Fax (50) 34 19 68 .   **R**

41 Wollestraat 8000 Bruges
Seats 30   Meal for 2 approx Fr6500

A 15th-century building converted into a traditional French
restaurant right on the canal, next to the main Market Square.
Lightly-smoked terrine of goose liver paté with Gewurztraminer
and a side salad dressed with walnut oil and tarragon, and
Zeebrugge shrimps in a mango and horseradish sauce are two
of the popular house specialities. All the dishes, however, have
their own inimitable touch: baby pigeon is served with a light
truffle sauce and preserved turnip sauerkraut. The à la carte menu
changes seasonally, but the lunch dishes change every week. *L 12-
2 D 7-9.30. Closed L Wed, all Tues, 3 weeks Feb & Nov.
No parking.* AMERICAN EXPRESS *Diners, Mastercard, Visa.*

Bruges   Hermitage

Tel (50) 34 41 73   **R**

18 Ezelstraat 8000 Bruges
Seats 24   Meal for 2 approx Fr6500

A small team runs this splendid little place, a 17th-century house
converted by owners M and Mme Dryepondt. Dryepondt trained
in Belgium, but he cooks very traditional French food. The menu
is well balanced, offering a wide variety of meat, fish and poultry
served in a cosy dining room decorated like an English living
room. The restaurant is very accessible, being right by the market
place. *D only 7-9.30. Closed Sun, Mon, Jul, Aug. Public parking.
Diners, Mastercard, Visa.*

Bruges   Hostellerie Pannenhuis

Tel (50) 31 19 07   Fax (50) 31 77 66   **HR**

2 Zandstraat 8200 Bruges
Rooms 18   Double room from Fr2950

A relaxed, friendly and informal hotel, most of whose staff have
been here almost 20 years. It's surrounded by a large garden and
seven of the bedrooms look out over it (four of them with their
own private terraces). But no matter which room you stay in,
it will be secluded, despite being 500m from the city centre. The
rooms are classically decorated in English style, and have all the
necessary mod cons. *Cable TV. Theatre-style conference facilities for
up to 30. Secretarial/translation services on request. Closed 15-30 Jan.
Private parking.* AMERICAN EXPRESS *Diners, Mastercard, Visa.*

Restaurant
Seats 60   Meal for 2 approx Fr5000

Chef Verhaeghe, also a long-standing member of staff, loves
to cook fish, and most of the menu is devoted to his passion.
Monkfish cooked with leeks, bone marrow and green beans is a
particular speciality of his. But for those less keen on fish, the
menu also has some interesting meat dishes: saddle of lamb
is roasted with tarragon and thyme fresh from their garden and
carved in front of diners. Sabayon is also cooked at the table.
L 12-2 D 7-8.30. Closed Wed, D Tue, 15-30 Jan, 1-15 Jul.

Bruges   De Karmeliet

Tel (50) 33 82 59   Fax (50) 33 10 11   **R**

19 Langestraat 8000 Bruges
Seats 80   Meal for 2 approx Fr6000

Once the weekend home of a local baron, it was converted into
a restaurant by Geert Van Hecke 12 years ago. His menu owes
a lot to the enlightening times he spent working with Alain
Chapel and the Roux brothers and is very much *cuisine recherché*.
Roasted Bresse pigeon served in a millefeuille of thinly-sliced
potatoes and escalope of goose liver and truffles presented on a bed
of mashed potatoes with a crunchy herb salad are two of the
delights in store. Large baked potatoes stuffed with small grey
snails served with duck cooked in its own juices and a herb salad   ★
with balsamic vinegar is among the house specialities. Presentation
is, Van Hecke feels, his passport to culinary success, so he often
adds ingredients for their colour and symmetrical effect: his
chartreuse of mackerel is dressed with a quail's egg and caviar.
Wines are as French as the menu. *L 12-2.30 D 7-9.30. Closed
D Sun, all Mon, 1-14 Feb, 15-31 Aug. Private parking. Garden.*
AMERICAN EXPRESS *Diners, Mastercard, Visa.*

Bruges   De Snippe

Tel (50) 33 70 70   Fax (50) 33 76 62   **RR**

53 Nieuwe Gentweg 8000 Bruges
Seats 60   Meal for 2 approx Fr7000

Primarily a restaurant (though they do have nine rooms for
gourmets wanting to stay), in a 17th-century residence on the
banks of the canal, seven minutes walk from the main Market
Square. Luc Huysentruyt has been cooking inventive French fish
dishes here for the last 16 years, getting his fish fresh from the
local markets – perhaps *gratin de homard, julienne d'artichauts et
truffes*, followed by *escalope de foie d'oie aux champiguous sauvages*.
For dessert, try the *dégustation* plate. It is rather relaxing to start
your evening with an aperitif in the small salon, decorated with
old landscapes. In the summer, the covered Winter Garden's roof
opens up, or alternatively, you can sit on the terrace. *L 12-3 D 7-
10. Closed L Mon, all Sun, 23-30 Nov, 19 Feb-17 Mar.*
AMERICAN EXPRESS *Diners, Mastercard, Visa.*

Bruges   Die Swaene

Tel (50) 34 27 98   Fax (50) 33 33 66 74   **HR**

1 Steenhouwersdijk 8000 Bruges
Rooms 22   Double room from Fr6350

Looking out over the Cathedral and down on to the canal, Die
Swaene, set in an old Butchers' Guild building, is one of the many
idyllic spots right in the centre of this picture postcard city. The
building itself is surrounded by a small garden, and there are
plenty of narrow streets and tiny squares to discover in the
neighbourhood. The rooms have recently renovated bathrooms
and are very cosy with antique armchairs, four-poster canopied
beds and even – in some rooms – large open fires. The reception
rooms are equally individualistic: delicate chandeliers hang from
the ceilings, walnut bookcases line the walls with silk wall

hangings up above. Conference facilities, however, are limited to one meeting room able to seat 20 people, at a pinch. An indoor swimming pool was, at the time of going to press, in the middle of being built. *24hr room service. Cable TV. Private/valet parking.* AMERICAN EXPRESS® *Diners, Mastercard, Visa.*

Restaurant
Seats 36   Meal for 2 approx Fr6000

The chef has been here since it opened, after a spell working at *La Tour d'Argent* in Paris; and his dishes are largely loyal to his French *haute cuisine* experience. The menu is dominated by game and fish, appearing in their seasons. Asparagus soup is served with scallops and sea bass is served on thinly-sliced potatoes with a tomato and sauternes sauce. Another delicate house speciality is escalope of goose liver paté on a bed of marinated apples and grapes, in a passion fruit sauce. Wines are international. *L 12-2.15 D 7-9.15. Closed L Thur, all Wed, 1-14 Jul, 14-31 Jan.* 🐂

Bruges   Vasquez   R

| Tel (50) 34 08 45   Fax (50) 33 52 41 |

38 Zilverstraat 8000 Bruges
Seats 50   Meal for 2 approx Fr5000

The Private Secretary to Isabelle of Portugal built a house back in 1418 and for centuries it was the home of bishops, situated as it is right opposite the Cathedral. Now, the neo-Gothic vaulted ceilings and wooden-panelled rooms have become a classic French restaurant with a definite Mediterranean influence and plenty of dishes laced with spices and fresh herbs. Desserts are equally sumptuous – note hot chocolate ravioli served with chicory ice cream. Set menus start at Fr975. Wines are eclectically international. *L 12-2 D 7-9.30. Closed L Thur, all Wed, 1-14 Jul, 1-7 Jan. Public parking.* AMERICAN EXPRESS® *Mastercard, Visa.*

Elsewhere in Belgium

Berlare   't Laurierblad

| Tel (52) 42 48 01   Fax (52) 42 59 97 | RR |

4 Dorp 9290 Berlare
Seats 65   Meal for 2 approx Fr7000

Guy Van Cauteren's grandfather ran a community theatre-cum-brasserie here, his father a butcher's shop and now Guy has created one of Belgium's finest restaurants (our Restaurant of the Year for Western Europe) out of this jumble of old buildings half an hour's drive from Brussels. The original galleried theatre with its exposed timbers and bare brick walls is on one side of a delightful water garden opposite an old linseed oil mill (the top floor of which is now a characterful conference room); the two are joined by a more modern section with a Mediterranean feel where there is a changing art exhibition. Just as the old and new elements of the decor are unified by a great sense of style, so Guy's cooking is a happy combination of sophistication and luxury ingredients with a certain *gout du terroir*; a rémoulade of lobster with chunky slices of carrot, turnip and haricots verts surrounded by a refined *sauce nantua*; a baby baked potato, the inside mixed with smoked salmon and soured cream, the whole topped with a little mountain of Sevruga caviar; hot foie gras with an onion confit and peppercorns. There's plenty of choice, with a longish carte and several set menus including one for vegetarians. A separate list of local specialities requires 48hrs notice. Throughout the day there is a *salon de thé* menu with a selection of some 50 teas. An outstanding wine list strongly favours Bordeaux over Burgundy. *Set meals: Fr1315 (L only), Fr1500, Fr1800, Fr2425 & Fr3135. L 12-2.30 D 7-9.30* AMERICAN EXPRESS *Diners, Mastercard, Visa.*

★

Rooms   Double room from Fr3470

Five letting bedrooms were nearing completion when we visited in the summer of '94. Bathrooms in particular promise to be most luxurious.

Tongeren   Clos St Denis

| Tel (12) 23 60 96   Fax (12) 26 32 07 | R |

Grimmertingenstraat 24 Tongeren
Seats 50   Meal for 2 approx Fr6000

Christian Denis bought a 17th-century former chateau-farmhouse with his wife in 1982 and they have been running the Clos St Denis ever since. The spot is idyllic, with a huge stone terrace stretching round the house with trees and potted plants and white canvas umbrellas. His menu, though, is hardly provincial, with delicate dishes like braised turbot with celery and truffles, fillet of beef with black truffles and baby pigeon roasted with exotic spices. Desserts are delicious: try the banana sabayon decorated with grilled almonds. The business lunch (Wed to Fri only) starts at Fr1850 including wine – all French. *L 12-2 D 7-9.30. Closed Mon, Tue, 26 Dec-5 Jan, 1 week Easter, 19-31 Jul.* AMERICAN EXPRESS *Diners, Mastercard, Visa.*

Scotch Beef Club Members: Belgium

ANTWERPEN
ANTWERP: Country Grill
ANTWERP: Holiday Inn
ANTWERP: Petrus
ANTWERP: La Rade
ANTWERP: La Sirene
ANTWERP: Ten Carvery
ANTWERP: Vateli
BRASSCHAAT: De Notelaar
HERENTALS: Snepkenshoeve
KONTICH: Careme
MOL: Hippocampus
SCHOTEN: Kleine Barreel

BRABANT
ASSE: De Pauw
BLANDEN: Chateau de Namur
BRUSSELS: Alban Chambon
BRUSSELS: Bécasse Blanche
BRUSSELS: Hotel Bedford
BRUSSELS: Belle Maraichère
BRUSSELS: Boerenhesp
BRUSSELS: Brasseries Georges
BRUSSELS: Bruneau
BRUSSELS: Cabrils
BRUSSELS: Critérion
BRUSSELS: La Farigoule
BRUSSELS: Henri I
BRUSSELS: I Trolli
BRUSSELS: 't Kelderke
BRUSSELS: Maison du Boeuf (Hilton)
BRUSSELS: Meiser
BRUSSELS: 't Misverstand
BRUSSELS: Pergola
BRUSSELS: Les Petits Oignons
BRUSSELS: Prince de Liège
BRUSSELS: Roma
BRUSSELS: La Réserve
BRUSSELS: La Roue d'Or
BRUSSELS: Les 4 Saisons (Royal Windsor)
BRUSSELS: Serge et Anne
BRUSSELS: Sterkerlapatte
BRUSSELS: Les 3 Tilleuls
BRUSSELS: Le Vieux Pannenhuis
BRUSSELS: La Villette
CORROY LE GRAND: Le Pin Pignon
DIEGEM: Holiday Inn (Airport)
GENVAL: l'Argentine
GENVAL: Le Trèfle à 4
GROOT-BIJGAARDEN: De Bijgaarden
GROOT-BIJGAARDEN: Michel
HALLE: Les Eleveurs
HALLE: Mario
HERNE: Kokejane
HOEILAART: Le Bollewinkel

HOEILAART: Romeyer
HUIZINGEN: Terborght
ITTRE: La Valette
KESSEL LO: In Den Mol
KOBBEGEM: Chalet Rose
LIMELETTE: Chateau de Limelette
MELSBROECK: Kasteel Boetfort
OPHAIN: Cheval Fou
OVERIJSE: Barbizon
VILVOORDE: 't Riddershof
VLEZENBEEK: Philippe Verbaeys
WATERLOO: La Maison du Seigneur
WEMMEL: De Kam
WEZEMBEEK: l'Auberge Saint-Pierre

HAINAUT
CHARLEROI: Square Sud
DOTTIGNIES: La Chaumière de l'E3
FELUY: Les Peupliers
FLEURUS: Les Tilleuls
GOSSELIES: Saint-Exupéry
MAFFLE: Le Chauffour
MONS: Chez John
MONS: Devos

LIEGE
FRAIPONT: Auberge de Halinsart
HAMOIR: Hotel Restaurant du Commerce
LIEGE: Au Vieux Liège
LIEGE: Chez Max
LIEGE: Le Duc d'Anjou
LIEGE: Le Lion Dodu
ST VITH: Zur Post

LIMBOURG
BOCHOLT: Kristoffel
HOUTHALEN: De Barrier
KORTESSEM: Clos Saint-Denis

NAMUR
CRUPET: Les Ramiers
DINANT: Le Moulin de Lisogne
GEMBLOUX: St Guibert
LAVAUX ST ANNE: Lavaux
PHILIPPEVILLE: La Cote d'Or
ROCHEFORT: Le Luxembourg
SOMME-LEUZE: Le Charolais

OOST-VLAANDEREN
BERLARE: 't Laurierblad
DEINZE: d'Hulhaeghe
DEINZE: Wallebeke
DE PINTE: Te Lande
GENT: Amadeus
GENT: Caphorn
GENT: Reinaert
KRUISHOUTEM: Yzerberghoeve
LAARNE: Gasthof van het Kasteel

LOCHRISTI: De Lozen Boer
MASSEMEN: Geuzenhof
NINOVE: De Hommel
OOSTAKKER: Sint-Bavo
ST NIKLAAS: Begijnhofke
SINT-MARTENS-LATEM: Auberge du Pecheur
ZAFFELARE: Kasteel van Saffelaere

WEST-VLAANDEREN
BRUGES: Die Swaene
DAMME: Gulden Kogge
IEPER: Rallye Grill
IEPER: Regina
IEPER: Yperley
KNOKKE: Ter Dycken
KOKSIJDE: Le Régent
KORTRIJK: Broel Central Hotel
OOSTENDE: 't Genoegen
OOSTDUINKERKE: Bécassine
ROESELARE: Savarin
ST IDESBALD: l'Aquilon
TIELT: De Wildeman
VEURNE: De Kloeffe
ZWEVEGEM: De Muishond
ZWEVEGEM: Gambrinus

Belgium Index

Bulgaria

Currency: Bulgarian Lev   **Exchange Rate:** £1 = approx lev 96

International dialling code: 010 359
(Sofia + 2)

Passports/Visas: Visa required by British passport holders.
(Bulgarian Embassy in London - 188 Queen's Gate SW7 5HL Tel:
0171-584 9400)

British Embassy Sofia Tel: 2-88 53 61

TRANSPORT
Airports:
Sofia Airport Tel: 2-84 44 33
Railway Stations:
Central Railway Station Tel: 2-31 111
Car hire in Sofia:
Avis Varco Rent-a-Car Tel: 2-873 412 / Budget Tel: 2-706 148 / Hertz
Tel: 2-791 506 (airport) 2-723 957 (Hotel Pliska)
Speed limits: 80km/h on trunk roads, 120km/h on motorways,
60km/h in towns.

Banks open: 8am-12.30pm & 1-3pm Mon-Fri, 8am-2pm Sat.

Shops open: 8am-5pm (some shops until 8pm) Mon-Fri, 8am-2pm Sat.

National Holidays: New Year's Day, 3 Mar, May Day, 24 May,
Christmas Day.

Tourist Offices:
Bulgarian Tourist Board in London - Tel: 0171-499 6988
In Sofia - Balkantourist Tel: 2-43 331

American Express Travel Service Offices or Representative (R):
Sofia - Megatours (R)
   Levski Str.1
   Tel: 2-872567/808889 #

Sofia

Sofia   **Colibri**

`Tel (2) 442 581`   **R**

Oborishete Str 18 Sofia

Seats 35   Meal for 2 approx lev1000

Quite a smart little galleried restaurant with air-conditioning, pink upholstery, white walls and brass fittings. Hot towels arrive with the menu, which has a *meze* with salami, cheese and smoked pork traditionally served with the drinks. The usual salads and hot starters plus omelettes, pasta and stuffed vine leaves precede cosmopolitan main dishes ranging from chicken *à la paysanne*, Provençal-style mussels and steak béarnaise. There are also some Bulgarian specialities; *kavarma* (pork cooked in a special earthenware dish) and *giuveche* (tongue in butter with mushrooms and cooked cheese). Desserts include *mlechna banitza* (sweet egg custard in filo pastry). In the summer eat at the pavement tables. *Open noon-11pm. No credit cards.*

THE APARTMENT SERVICE
Tel in UK: (0181) 748 4207   Fax: (0181) 748 3972
The Apartment Service will find you the right apartment worldwide to suit your needs, whether you are on a short or long-term stay. A 96-page colour catalogue is free on request.
All budgets are catered for.

Sofia   **Diplomatic Club**

`Tel (2) 442 948`   **R**

27 Veliko Tamovo Sofia

Seats 60   Meal for 2 approx lev1200

In the heart of the embassy district, this restaurant was, until recently, the exclusive preserve of diplomats; however, it now attracts the new movers and shakers from both government and business. The menu reflects the restaurant's origins, with French onion soup, langoustine Americano, Wiener schnitzel and chicken wings in a Chinese-style sauce all prepared with varying degrees of authenticity. Bulgarian specialities like brain fritters and stuffed battered peppers add some local colour. Several separate rooms allow for discreet business lunches. In the summer, tables are set out under an awning in the courtyard. *Open noon-11pm.*
AMERICAN EXPRESS *Diners, Mastercard, Visa.*

Sofia   Rusalka

Tel (2) 437 679   **R**

47 Tcherkovna St 1505 Sofia
Seats 80   Meal for 2 approx lev800

In a leafy suburb to the south of the city centre, the restaurant
is rather chic, with mauve damask French reproduction chairs
sitting genteelly on marble floors in a galleried interior; while
outside, a pretty covered terrace overlooks a courtyard with more
marble and a fountain. Both lunch and dinner are accompanied
by a just slightly out-of-tune upright piano. The menu is currently
predominantly Bulgarian, but there are plans to introduce more
Western dishes, while retaining the more popular local ones. *Open
noon-1am.* AMERICAN EXPRESS *Diners, Mastercard, Visa.*

Sofia   Sheraton Sofia Balkan

Tel (2) 876 541   Fax (2) 871 038   **HR**

5 Sveta Nedelya Square 1000 Sofia
Rooms 188   Double room from lev13,000

Right in the centre of town, this 50s-built neo-classical pile was
completely refurbished on becoming a Sheraton hotel eight years
ago. It is rather grand, with lots of chandeliers, pillars and marble,
including a long staircase reaching right up to the top of the
building. Good-sized, high-ceilinged bedrooms feature darkwood
furniture and all modern conveniences like air-conditioning but,
oddly, only the deluxe rooms have a remote control for the TV.
In addition to the breakfast buffet there's a short-order cook
on hand, to prepare eggs the way you like them cooked. Just
about every need has been catered for: a fitness centre, shop, night
club, bank and travel agent. The local British Airways office
is also located here at the moment. Winner of our Best Business
Hotel Eastern Europe award (see page 33). *24hr room service.
Satellite TV. Theatre-style conference facilities for up to 160. Business
centre. Sauna, spa baths, sunbeds, hairdresser. Private parking.*
AMERICAN EXPRESS *Diners, Mastercard, Visa.*

Restaurant Preslav

Seats 50   Meal for 2 approx lev4800

Opulence shimmers throughout the place, with glittering
chandeliers, a rich red decor and tail-coated waiters offering
formal, if rather cold service. A short (about eight main dishes)
à la carte menu of fairly straightforward French-inspired dishes
is typified by warm salad of sautéed scallops with balsamic
vinaigrette, duck liver terrine with king prawn tails served with
a ginger and walnut dressing, roast duck breast with peach-
flavoured Cointreau cream, rack of lamb on boulangère potatoes
and steamed salmon filled with scallop mousse. Imported wines
are pricey – the starting price for champagne is about lev13,130 –
but local wines are much more reasonable and very drinkable.
L 12-3 D 6-11. Closed Sat, Sun.

Sofia   33 Chairs

Tel (2) 442 981	R

14 Prof Asen Zlatarov Sofia

Seats 33   Meal for 2 approx lev1000

Set in a period house in the diplomatic district of town, this
restaurant has exactly 33 chairs, so reservations are essential. It is
smart, fashionable and popular with local 'celebrities'. The chef
boasts a repertoire of some 1000 different dishes of which a good
selection appear on each daily-changing menu written using the
Cyrillic alphabet (invented by two Bulgarians), but thankfully
with accurate English translations. Hors d'oeuvre offer a variety
of sausages and cheeses and a couple of dozen salads (the traditional
start to a Bulgarian meal) such as aubergine purée with walnuts
and mayonnaise, Chinese salad with celery, bamboo shoots and
shrimps, or African with maize, beans, leeks and tomatoes. Hot
starters include a rather good soufflé with shrimps and globe
artichokes. Main dishes come along the lines of chicken grilled
with honey, a roulade of pork filled with ham, cheese and herbs
and grilled Black Sea herrings. Desserts are variations on the
theme of fruit and ice cream. *Open noon-midnight. No credit cards.*

Sofia   Vitosha

Tel (2) 62 511 Fax (2) 681 225	HR

100 James Bourchier Boulevard 1407 Sofia

Rooms 467   Double room from lev10,550

Still under state ownership as we went to press (though
privatisation seems to be well on the way), the hotel is modern
and high-rise, on the southern outskirts of the city. The spacious,
comfortable bedrooms have every modern amenity (except for
international direct dialling, which will shortly be installed) and
good-sized bathrooms all with showers over the tub. The public
areas are smart and extensive: with a sunken marble day-bar in the
lobby area, numerous restaurants, including a hard-currency-only
Japanese timber affair, sitting on its own ornamental lake, eight
lanes of ten-pin bowling, and a good leisure centre, with both
indoor and outdoor tennis courts. *24hr room service. Satellite
TV/air con. Theatre-style conference facilities for up to 150. Tennis
courts (1 inside, 2 outside), indoor swimming pool, sauna, steam room,
sunbed, gym. Hairdresser, beauty salon. Bank, shops, travel offices.
Business centre. Private parking.* AMERICAN EXPRESS *Diners, Mastercard,
Visa.*

Restaurant Lozenetz

Seats 80   Meal for 2 approx lev2800

Rustic Bulgarian decor adds to the ambience in this Italian
restaurant, with a terrace outside adjacent to the main restaurant,
where a folk music group plays each evening. The classical Italian
cuisine is the work of an Italian chef, whose short menu includes
carpaccio, gnocchi, minestrone, spaghetti carbonara, rigatoni
bolognese, veal stewed with gin and juniper berries and salmon
with mustard and cream. Desserts include traditional tiramisu.
Sound, authentic cooking and some Italian wines from about
lev875 a bottle. *D only 6-11.30. Closed Sun.*

Bulgaria Index

Recommended by

EGON RONAY'S GUIDES

1995

Hotels & Restaurants	Pubs & Inns
Europe	Just a Bite
Family Hotels & Restaurants	Paris
Oriental Restaurants	Ireland
New Zealand & South Pacific	Australia

Cyprus

Currency: Cyprus Pound   **Exchange Rate:** £1 = approx CY£ 0.7

International dialling code: 010 357
(Larnaca + 4 Nicosia + 2 Paphos + 6 Limassol + 5)

Passports/Visas: No visa required by British passport holders.

UK British High Commission in Nicosia Tel: 2-476100
Fax: 2-459571

TRANSPORT
Airports:
Larnaca International airport Tel: 4-643000 / Paphos International
airport Tel: 6-422833
Car hire:
Avis Tel: Larnaca 4-657132 (airport 4-643120) / Nicosia: 2-472062 /
Budget Tel: Larnaca (airport) 4-657850 / Nicosia 2-352457 / Paphos
(airport) 6-245146 / Limassol 5-323672
Speed limits: 100km/h on motorways, 80km/h on other roads unless a
lower one is indicated.

Banks open: 8.15am-12.30pm Mon-Fri, centrally located banks
provide "afternoon tourist services" Tue-Fri.

Shops open: 8am-1pm, 2.30-5.30pm (4-7pm in summer) Mon, Tue,
Thur, Fri, 8am-1pm Wed & Sat.

National Holidays: New Year's Day, 6 Jan, 6 Mar, 25 Mar, 1, 21 &
23 Apr, 1 May, 12 Jun, 15 Aug, 1 Oct, 28 Oct, Christmas Day &
Boxing Day.

Tourist Offices:
Cyprus Tourist Board in London - Tel: 0171-734 9822
In Cyprus - Nicosia Tel: 2-444264 / Limassol Tel: 5-362756 / Larnaca
Tel: 4-654322 / Paphos Tel: 6-232841

American Express Travel Service Offices or Representative (R):
Nicosia - A.L Mantovani & Sons Ltd (R)
   130 Spyrou Araouzou Str
   PO Box 1127
   Tel: 2-443777 #
Larnaca - A.L Mantovani & Sons Ltd (R)
   King Paul Square
   PO Box 109
   Tel: 4-652022

Nicosia

Nicosia   Le Chateau

Tel (2) 46 48 21   **R**

25 Metochiou Street Nicosia
Seats 40   Meal for 2 approx CY£20

In the last year this old colonial building has developed from
a low-lit French bistro into one of Nicosia's best Far Eastern
restaurants. The traditional Thai and modern Japanese food
is served in three connecting dining rooms, and also in the garden.
Favourites are sushi and stir-fries, green curries and fragrant soup
laced with lemon grass. A popular dish, and one to try, is fresh fish
of the day simply cooked with ginger. The French and Italian
wines on offer are not in as much demand than their own wines
from Limassol, and of course, the good bottles of sake they serve.
Open 11am-midnight. Closed 25 & 26 Dec. AMERICAN EXPRESS *Diners,
Mastercard, Visa.*

Nicosia   Churchill Nicosia

Tel (2) 44 88 58   Fax (2) 44 55 06   **HR**

1 Achaeans Street P0 Box 4145 Nicosia
Rooms 52   Double room from CY£58

The Churchill's exclusivity has, in recent years, been rather
overshadowed. However, situated in a smart, chic residential
district in central Nicosia, it is still a good place to stay and
popular for business conferences and art exhibitions. Like its sister
hotel in Limassol, it has plenty of sports facilities, flowery modern
bedrooms and relaxed, cosy reception rooms. *24hr room service.
Fax/air-con. Conference facilities. Secretarial/translation/valet/courier
services on request.* AMERICAN EXPRESS *Diners, Mastercard, Visa.*

Restaurant
Seats 80   Meal for 2 approx CY£12

The two Scottish chefs pride themselves on their cunning
combination of French *nouvelle cuisine* and Cypriot specialities.
And despite the rather uneasy mix, customers seem to like it.
Stifado (braised chicken with tomatoes, onion, garlic and olive oil),
and lamb *souvlaki* can be found alongside Scottish smoked salmon
and fresh trout. The wine list ranges from regional Keo, Etko and
SODAP to French Bordeaux and burgundies. *L 1-3 D 7-11.*

THE APARTMENT SERVICE
Tel in UK: (0181) 748 4207   Fax: (0181) 748 3972
The Apartment Service will find you the right apartment
worldwide to suit your needs, whether you are on a short or
long-term stay. A 96-page colour catalogue is free on request.
All budgets are catered for.

Nicosia   Date Club

Tel (2) 37 67 37   **R**

2 Agaphons Street Nicosia

Seats 120   Meal for 2 approx CY £18

Businessmen may flock to this restaurant with the promise
of 'haute cuisine', but the menu actually adheres strongly to its
Cypriot roots. The menu consists largely of traditional lamb and
beef stews, grilled steaks and also red mullet and shrimps when the
market allows. But this family-run place is still causing a stir ten
years after opening, because of its delicate use of raw ingredients,
and attentive service in chic, air-conditioned surroundings. *L 12-3
D 7-11. Closed Easter, 25 & 26 Dec.* AMERICAN EXPRESS *Mastercard, Visa.*

Nicosia   Excelsior

Tel (2) 36 85 85   **H**

4 Photiou Stavrou Pitta Street Nicosia

Rooms 36   Double room from CY £37

A five-floor, family-run hotel, the Excelsior is a 60s building
in the centre of Nicosia, which can be rather noisy. The rooms
(most have balconies) are simply furnished in plain colours and
redecorated every few years. The atmosphere is relaxed, with
'buffet nights' guaranteed to break down any amount of British
reserve. *Fax services on request.* AMERICAN EXPRESS *Mastercard, Visa.*

Nicosia   Executive

Tel (2) 45 90 59   **R**

1 Goudiou Street Nicosia

Seats 80   Meal for 2 approx CY £15

This 30s sandstone building, with its rich red curtains and pink
walls, comes alive at night when the piano is played and colourful
cocktails are mixed at the long bar. The Armenian owner,
Garabet Adjenian, previously owned a restaurant in England.
He blends together French and Cypriot cuisine, with one chef
who has cooked traditional French food for the UN officers for
25 years and another, a local, who is a fish connoisseur. The result
is grilled *halloumi* (grilled Cypriot goat's cheese) and fish served
alongside grilled steaks with mushrooms and garlic, king prawns
cooked in ouzo and cream and Dover sole. Not an imaginative
menu by Western standards, but proficiently prepared. A drink
can be enjoyed on the veranda before dinner. *D only 8-12.30.
Closed Aug, 1 week Easter, 25 & 26 Dec, 1 Jan.* AMERICAN EXPRESS
Diners, Mastercard, Visa.

> Opening times are often liable to change at short notice,
> so it's always best to book.

Nicosia   Grecos Tavern

`Tel (2) 47 45 66`   **R**

3 Menandros Street Nicosia
Seats 60   Meal for 2 approx CY£7

Owner, Thassos Ioannou's passion for traditional Cypriot cookery
comes from watching his grandmother and mother at work in the
kitchen. Yet, beyond the usual representation of grilled lamb,
stewed pork and beef, he has introduced some fragrant vegetarian
dishes, like mushrooms in a fennel sauce, oven-baked *melitzanes*
(aubergines cooked in garlic and lemon) and a tomato and feta
bake. Plenty of fresh coriander, fennel and lemon add fragrance
to these tasty *meze* dishes. The menu does not include fish. Cypriot
wines (Limassol and Keo) only. *D 8-11.30. Closed Sun.*
No credit cards.

Nicosia   Hilton International Cyprus

`Tel (2) 37 77 77   Fax (2) 37 77 88`   **HR**
Archbishop Makarios III Avenue Nicosia
Rooms 224   Double room from CY£86

This, their very own Hilton, is Cyprus' pride and joy. Its opening
in the late 60s symbolised their rapid economic growth and
increased recognition by Western Europe. Since then, Presidential
and Governmental meetings have been held here and the world's
press, Greek Presidents, even Indira Ghandi have stayed, high
on this hill overlooking Nicosia, minutes away from the city
centre. The rooms are light and airy with plain furnishings and
splendid balcony views of the Troodos Mountains. From January
1995, an extension will give 71 further bedrooms and seven more
conference suites. *24hr room service. Cable TV/air-con. Theatre-style
conference facilities for up to 1000. Secretarial/translation/fax services
on request. Squash, gym, floodlit tennis court, sauna, jacuzzi, indoor
swimming pool, running track, health club. Private parking.*
AMERICAN EXPRESS *Diners, Mastercard, Visa.*

Orangery Restaurant
Seats 35   Meal for 2 approx CY£25

The *nouvelle cuisine* here makes a refreshing change from the
endless traditional and international dishes on offer in most Greek-
Cypriot restaurants. Breast of roast duck with balsamic vinegar
sauce served with a cabbage and apple stew, smoked Alaska black
cod served on a bed of green vegetables, and medallions of veal
in a chanterelle cream sauce are specialities. Californian, Italian and
French wines boost the traditional Cypriot choices. Popular with
parties, diners eat surrounded by foliage under the setting sun
which filters through the skylights. *L 12-3 D 7-12.*

Nicosia   Holiday Inn Nicosia

`Tel (2) 47 51 31`   **H**
70 Regaena Street Nicosia
Rooms 140   Double room from CY£60

At the time of going to press, this hotel was closed for massive
refurbishment but planning to re-open late in 1994. Friendly
family owners have bought the Holiday Inn franchise, and as they

have to match the hotel up to international standards, a new wing with 50 extra bedrooms is being added and complete redecoration carried out. If all goes according to plan, the rooms will be modern and flowery, but hopefully the polite, relaxed atmosphere will remain. *Conference facilities. Fax/secretarial/translation services on request. Indoor pool.* AMERICANEXPRESS *Diners, Mastercard, Visa.*

Nicosia — Ledra Hotel

Tel (2) 35 20 86   Fax (2) 35 19 18   **HR**

Grivas Digenis Ave Engomi Nicosia

Rooms 103   Double room from CY£58

The Ledra's five-floor balconied modern building may not be beautiful, but it offers great views, extensive gardens and is only five minutes from Nicosia. Its tennis courts are used by many of the locals. The rooms are plainly decorated with 60s wooden furniture. Conference facilities include simultaneous translation in up to six languages. *24hr room service. Satellite TV/fax. Secretarial/translation services. Hairdresser. Tennis courts, swimming pool, gym, bowling.* AMERICANEXPRESS *Mastercard, Visa.*

Restaurant

Seats 150   Meal for 2 approx CY£17

The restaurant is also a favourite with the locals. As well as typical Cypriot *meze* dishes (stuffed vine leaves, grilled meat balls, grilled lamb and salad) there is also an à la carte French menu on offer. Wednesday is an important night in Cyprus when lavish dishes are produced. All the fish is fresh from the market. *D only 7-12.*

Nicosia — Philoxenia Hotel

Tel (2) 49 97 00   Fax (2) 49 80 38   **H**

Eylenja Ave Eylenja PO Box 5466 Nicosia

Rooms 34   Double room from CY£50

A modern hotel offering excellent conference facilities. Most of the guests are here on business, not pleasure. The simple wooden furnished rooms were last renovated in 1989, but they were being redecorated at the time of going to press. *Video. Restaurants. Theatre-style conference facilities for up to 600. Fax/secretarial services on request.* AMERICANEXPRESS *Mastercard, Diners, Visa.*

Nicosia — Plaka Tavern

Tel (2) 44 64 98   **R**

6 Makarios Square Engomi Nicosia

Seats 40   Meal for 2 approx CY£6

Traditional *meze* is the order of the day here – all 30 dishes of it. Favourites, like fresh *tsatsiki* and *tahini* (crushed sesame seeds with olive oil) are complemented by lighter dishes of courgettes with scrambled egg or *okra* in tomato sauce. George Frangeskides has been running this taverna in a little square in the centre of Nicosia for 20 years and it is one of the oldest traditional restaurants. The standard remains high, with food consistently well-presented. *D only 8-12. Closed Sun. No credit cards.*

Psarolimano 2

Nicosia

Tel (2) 35 09 90   **R**

59 28th October Street Nicosia
Seats 250   Meal for 2 approx CY£5

George Constantinou's purpose-built restaurant specialises in finely
prepared Mediterranean fish. Most of the fish, like bream, ink fish,
swordfish, and snapper are lightly grilled Greek-Cypriot style,
with a rich Provençal-style cream sauce. A sumptuous fish buffet
is laid out on Wednesday, Friday and Saturday. A smattering
of German, Italian and French wines stand out among the local
village vineyard bottles. *Open 11am-midnight. Closed 2 days Easter.
Private parking.* AMERICAN EXPRESS *Mastercard, Visa.*

Skaraveos

Nicosia

Tel (2) 46 49 95   **R**

4 Nikokreontos Street Nicosia
Seats 170   Meal for 2 approx CY£13

Since it opened eight years ago, Skaraveos has been sought out
by businessmen who lunch. Right in the heart of a busy, old
residential area of Nicosia, the large sandstone building is set back
from the street, surrounded by its own grounds. Inside it is
smarter than most with high ceilings, proper table-cloths, napkins
and upholstered seats. The clientele either choose their meal from
the fish tank: grouper, snapper, red mullet, cuttlefish or octopus,
which is then lightly grilled with plenty of herbs, olive oil and
lemon, or they opt for the fish *meze*. The fish is fresh from the
market, not always the case on the island. French and Italian
bottles balance the Cypriot regional wines on offer. *L 12.30-3
D 8-12. Closed Sun, 24-26 Dec, 31 Dec & 1 Jan, 6 days Easter.*
AMERICAN EXPRESS *Mastercard, Visa.*

Skorpios

Nicosia

Tel (2) 44 59 50   **R**

3 Stassinos Street Engomi Nicosia
Seats 80   Meal for 2 approx CY£24

Good foreign food is at a premium in Cyprus; so this chef was
welcomed with open arms on his return from the gastronomic
capital of the world, France, to his culinarily lesser known
homeland. His repertoire mostly follows the traditional French
examples of *chateaubriand, escargots, foie de poulet* and *steak tartare*,
although he experiments with his own creations such as prawns
cooked in whisky and cranberry sauce. The vegetarian dishes are
basic: vegetable burgers, pasta with cheese and spinach. So,
if possible, it's best to stick to the meaty French dishes. *L 12-3 D 6-
11. Closed Sun, 5 days Easter, 1st 3 weeks Aug.* AMERICAN EXPRESS
Mastercard, Visa.

Nicosia   **V.I.P.S Restaurant**

Tel (2) 31 67 72   R

15 Chiou Street Ay Omoloyites Nicosia

Seats 40   Meal for 2 approx CY£12

The owner-chef, Andreas Karaviopis, has adopted and successfully executed a comprehensive French menu from *moules* and *chateaubriand* to salmon fillets with a subtle sole mousse and light crepes. Most of the fish available in Cyprus is frozen, but here it is flown in fresh from the Gulf – so try the simple grilled fish of the day. The President, ambassadors and businessmen are all regular visitors to this modern, light dining room and its garden. *L 12-2 D 7.30-10.45. Closed 15 days Aug, National holidays, 25 Dec, Easter.* AMERICAN EXPRESS® *Mastercard, Visa.*

Paphos

Paphos   ## Coral Beach Hotel

Tel (6) 62 17 11   Fax (6) 62 11 56   **H**

PO Box 422 Paphos
Rooms 232   Double room from CY£32

Just opened, this hotel is equipped with every conceivable facility.
Although it's new, traditional stone and marble floors run
elegantly throughout the reception rooms with beautiful pottery
lights glistening from the ceilings. The rooms are bright, stylish
and well equipped. *24hr room service. Six restaurants. Theatre-style
conference facilities. Indoor and outdoor swimming pool, golf, tennis
courts, private beach.* AMERICAN EXPRESS *Mastercard, Visa.*

Paphos   ## Panicos Corallo Restaurant

Tel (6) 62 10 52   Fax (6) 62 10 52   **R**

Coral Bay Paphos
Seats 40   Meal for 2 approx CY£24

Old-fashioned woven tablecloths cover the small tables and old
baskets decorate the walls, in this traditional family-run restaurant.
The chef-owner has three other restaurants in Paphos with his two
brothers. This, however, is the best with some particularly good
fish dishes: grilled sole and swordfish with a Provençal sauce and
competently cooked *chateaubriand*, veal dishes and fillet of steak
with a mushroom sauce. Local Limassol and village wines only are
served. Sit under the vined terrace for an authentic local eating
experience. *L 12-3 D 7-12.* AMERICAN EXPRESS *Mastercard, Visa.*

Limassol

Limassol	Sheraton Hotel
Tel (5) 32 11 00 Fax (5) 32 43 94	**H**

PO Box 1064 Limassol

Rooms 215   Double room from CY£84

Situated outside the sticky city centre on a colourful marina, the hotel has great water sport facilities to offer. The light, recently redecorated rooms have great views. *24hr room service. Fax. 4 restaurants. Theatre-style conference facilities for up to 220. Outdoor swimming pools, health club, scuba diving, tennis courts, water sports.* AMERICAN EXPRESS® *Mastercard, Visa.*

Cyprus Index

Czech Republic

Currency: Czech Crown   **Exchange Rate** £1 = approx kc 43

International dialling code: 010 42
(Prague + 2)

Passports/Visas: No visa required by British passport holders.

British Embassy in Prague Tel: 2-24 51 04 39

TRANSPORT
Airports:
Ruzyne airport, Prague Tel: 2-36 77 60
Railway Stations:
Prague Main station Tel: 2-24 21 76 54
Car hire:
Avanticar Tel: 2-316 5204 / Hertz Tel: 2-297 836 (airport 2-312 0717)
/ Europcar Tel: (airport) 2-316 7849
Speed limits: 90km/h on trunk roads, 110 km/h on motorways,
60km/h in towns.

Banks open: 8am-4pm Mon-Sat.

Shops open: Hours vary, but most shops are open 7am-6pm Mon-Fri,
8am-noon Sat (some department stores open until 4pm Sat).

National Holidays: New Year's Day, Easter Monday, 1 May, 5 & 6
July, 28 Oct, Christmas Eve, Christmas Day & Boxing Day.

Tourist Offices:
Czech Tourist Board in London - Tel: 0181-343 4659
In Prague - Information Service Tel: 2-242 12 212

American Express Travel Service Offices:
Prague - AETS
    Vaclavske Namesti 56
    11000-1
    Tel: 2-443777 #

Prague

Prague   **Atrium Praha**

Tel (2) 2484 1111   Fax (2) 2481 1896   H

Pobřežní 1 Prague 8
Rooms 788   Double room from kc6440

The largest hotel in the Republic, built around an 11-storey glass
atrium. The rooms offer all the normal facilities of a mid-range
international hotel including air-conditioning, although the latter
only works, like all the electrics, when you insert your key card
into a slot in the room, so it may take a while to cool down
if you're out all day. Bedroom corridors are only dimly lit, with
some corners quite dark, and some rooms are quite a way from
the lift. Entertainment is big here, ranging from a night club with
floor show and casino to a sports centre with indoor swimming
pool and even indoor tennis courts. *24hr room service. Satellite TV.
Conference facilities for up to 1000. Indoor swimming pool, sauna,
gym, indoor tennis courts. Hairdresser/beauty salon. Private parking.*
AMERICAN EXPRESS *Diners, Mastercard, Visa.*

THE APARTMENT SERVICE
Tel in UK: (0181) 748 4207   Fax: (0181) 748 3972
The Apartment Service will find you the right apartment
worldwide to suit your needs, whether you are on a short or
long-term stay. A 96-page colour catalogue is free on request.
All budgets are catered for.

Prague   **Diplomat**

Tel (2) 2439 4111   Fax (2) 2439 4207   H

15 Evropská 160 00 Prague 6
Rooms 387   Double room from kc7290

Built four years ago, just out of the town centre on the main road
to the airport (it's much favoured by flight crews) and only a few
minutes by train to the city. Spacious, marble-floored public areas
are matched by good-quality bedrooms, each with a couple of easy
chairs and all the usual facilities. Only a handful of rooms have
double beds, the rest being twins, but as Czech hotels habitually
refer to 'twins' as 'doubles' it's best to check carefully when
booking – it's best to ask for a 'French bed' if you want a double.
A night club with dancing to live music and a fitness centre that
is bright and inviting add to the experience. *Satellite TV/air-con.
Theatre-style conference facilities for up to 400. Sauna, spa bath, keep-
fit equipment. Hairdresser/florist. Private garage.* AMERICAN EXPRESS *Diners,
Mastercard, Visa.*

Prague   Esplanade

Tel (2) 2421 1715   Fax (2) 2422 9306   **H**

Washingtonova 19 11000 Prague 1

Rooms 64   Double room from kc6850

Close to the main railway station, only a few steps away from the
museum at the top of Wenceslas Square, the hotel dates from
1925. Bedrooms have recently been refurbished in art deco style
with brass bedsteads – but the purple and mauve carpets may be
something of an acquired taste. Rooms have all the usual modern
facilities, except air-conditioning. Half the new marble bathrooms
have only showers and WC. In the summer of 1994 work was
under way to restore the public areas to their original art deco and
Italianate splendour. *Satellite TV/ safe. Theatre-style conference
facilities for up to 45.* AMERICAN EXPRESS *Diners, Mastercard, Visa.*

Prague   Hotel Forum

Tel (2) 61 19 1111   Fax (2) 420 684   **H**

Kongresová 1 14069 Prague 4

Rooms 531   Double room from kc6500

This late-80s glass tower a couple of Metro stops from the town
centre to the south-east is next to the Palace of Culture conference
centre. The bedrooms are fairly functional in style, but do have
air-conditioning and mini-bars. The most appealing public area
is the recently refurbished lobby with lots of easy seating,
a cocktail bar and no less than three separate water features.
Facilities include a night club, beer and bowling bar (ten-pin, four-
lane) and 25th-floor leisure centre with swimming pool, sauna,
squash court, gym, beauty salon, hairdressing and sun beds. The
largest theatre-style conference room seats up to 250. *24hr room
service. Satellite TV/air-con. Conference facilities. Hairdresser/beauty
salon. Private parking.* AMERICAN EXPRESS *Diners, Mastercard, Visa.*

Prague   Grand Hotel Bohemia

Tel (2) 232 3417   Fax (2) 232 9545   **HR**

Králodvorská 4 CR-11000 Prague 1

Rooms 78   Double room from kc8892

Tucked away in a side street just off Republic Square, the Grand
was built as a private hotel in the 1920s, and later became the
headquarters of the KGB in Prague. Austrian owners have
completely rebuilt the interior to create an exclusive, air-
conditioned business travellers' haven (with a fax machine in every
room). The stunning neo-baroque 'Boccaccio' ballroom in the
basement has the discreet addition of modern theatre-style
conference facilities for up to 140. The bedrooms have lightwood
furnishings and restful green-and-blue decor. Only the single fresh
flower adds a touch of colour to otherwise clinically white
bathrooms. *Satellite TV/ air-con/safe/fax. Conference facilities. Valet
parking.* AMERICAN EXPRESS *Diners, Mastercard, Visa.*

Restaurant
Seats 50   Meal for 2 approx kc1800

The menu includes a section of Bohemian specialities, but
generally the selection of dishes reflects the cosmopolitan clientele
– chicken paté with red onion sauce and green peppers, spaghetti
bolognese, wiener schnitzel, beef stroganoff (a particularly good
dish enhanced with capers on a bed of home-made noodles).
In addition to the à la carte there's a good-value set business lunch.
L 12-2.30 D 7.30-10.30 (D 6-9.30 in winter).

Prague   Hanavský Pavilon
Tel (2) 32 57 92   **R**

Letenské Sady 173 Prague 7
Seats 24   Meal for 2 approx kc2500

Undoubtedly the prettiest restaurant in town, this small pseudo-
baroque pavilion, with its ornate gilt pillars, Arcadian murals and
elaborate wrought iron, was built for an exhibition in 1891 and
later transferred to its present site in the Letenské park – a plateau
commanding a superb view over the city. Diners can drink
aperitifs and coffee on the terrace. A mix and match of Czech
specialities, like roast goose from Southern Bohemia, stuffed quails
and haunch of venison with cream sauce, is served along with
more cosmopolitan dishes such as Burgundy snails, Sicilian
vermicelli, trout *au bleu* and American turkey with two kinds
of stuffing. Freshly baked plum jam-filled pastry tarts are a good
choice to finish. Sound cooking from chef-manager Filip and
friendly, helpful service. *Open noon-11pm. Public parking.*
AMERICAN EXPRESS *Mastercard, Visa.*

Prague   Inter-Continental
Tel (2) 2488 1111   Fax (2) 2481 0071   **H**

Nám Curieových 43/5 11000 Prague 1
Rooms 365   Double room from kc8500

Celebrating its 25th anniversary with a top-to-toe refurbishment
(to be completed by the end of 1994) this medium-rise hotel near
the river is just a couple of minutes walk from the city centre. Air-
conditioned bedrooms have cool marble surfaces and various
facilities including room safes, mini-bars and direct-dial telephones.
The splendid marble bathrooms have hand as well as power
showers over the tub. Junior and full suites make up 30% of the
accommodation, the latter with faxes installed. Trying to target
the business traveller, the conference rooms are large, and there's
a fully-equipped business centre. Sports facilities, complete with
indoor swimming pool, will be on offer from spring 1995. *24hr
room service. Satellite TV. Theatre-style conference facilities for up to
400. Secretarial/translation services. Indoor swimming pool, sauna,
steam room, gym (all spring 1995). Private garage.* AMERICAN EXPRESS
Diners, Mastercard, Visa.

Prague   U Modré Kachničky

`Tel (2) 539 751`   **R**

Nebovidská 6 Mala Strana Prague 1
Seats 45   Meal for 2 approx kc1000

This place has great character, set as it is in a building dating back
to 1613; the name means 'little blue duck' and each table gets one
as decoration. The two dining rooms both have extravagant
murals, while one has a vaulted ceiling, the other beams and
a skylight. There is a separate Bohemian section on the menu:
goulash of wild boar, duck in the 'old Prague style' and some
other more international dishes still with a strong Czech flavour.
Generous, hearty cooking and reasonable prices. *L 12-2.30 D 7-11.
Closed 31 Dec.* AMERICAN EXPRESS *Diners, Visa.*

Prague   Palace Hotel

`Tel (2) 240 93 111   Fax (2) 2422 1240`   **H**

Panská 12 11000 Prague 1
Rooms 125   Double room from kc8900

Probably the most expensive hotel in town, where good-quality,
international-standard bedrooms come with air-conditioning, free
mini-bar (soft drinks and beer), cable TV and white marble
bathrooms that boasts robes, huge bathsheets and lots of toiletries.
The only drawback is that when hand-held showers are fixed
above the tub the water pressure is such that the water could well
spray anywhere. The 1989 refurbishment only hints at the
original (1906) art nouveau style in public areas that are not
notably spacious. Huge crystal chandeliers make a good first
impression in the lobby, off which the lower-ceilinged reception
area provides the only lounge seating other than that in the piano
bar. High levels of service beginning with the top-hatted doorman
with his gold, rope-like sash extend to comprehensive 24-hour
room service and evening turn-down. *Satellite TV/safe. Sauna.
Theatre-style conference facilities for up to 100. Private garage.*
AMERICAN EXPRESS *Diners, Mastercard, Visa.*

Prague   Parnas

`Tel (2) 2422 7614   Fax (2) 2422 8932`   **R**

Smetanovo Nâbřezí 2 Prague 1
Seats 65   Meal for 2 approx kc2200

Overlooking the river on the National Theatre side of the Legü
Bridge, the Parnas has been established since the 1920s – note the
inlaid marquetry – but the menu is surprisingly modern and
varied: green salad with balsamic vinegar and olive oil dressing,
chicken satay with peanut sauce and sweet cucumber and fettucine
with wild mushrooms, saffron and crème fraiche as starters, and
with main courses like grilled prawns with polenta and tomato
salsa, and sautéed duck breast with pumpkin purée. Bohemian
dishes feature among the specialities and there are some interesting
vegetarian options. Decent French bread is served, but you have
to ask for it. Pear crème brulée (made with milk rather than
cream) makes a nice light conclusion. Polite, efficient service
attracts local businessmen. *L 12-2.30 (Sun 11-3) D 5.30-10.30.
Closed 24 Dec.* AMERICAN EXPRESS *Mastercard, Visa.*

Prague   Hotel U Páva

Tel (2) 532 251   Fax (2) 533 379

U Lužického Semianáre 106 Prague 1
Rooms 11   Double room from kc4600

One of Prague's 'Boutique' hotels: intimate, with considerable
charm, this one is on the Lesser Town side of the river, near the
Charles Bridge, a mid-19th-century house, completely renovated
in 1991. There are only eleven rooms, of which five are full suites,
with rug-strewn tiled floors, timber ceilings, crystal chandeliers,
tapestry upholstery and stained-glass windows, some with views
of the Castle. Facilities include satellite TV, mini-bars and good
bathrooms, but telephones are not direct-dial. Reception rooms are
limited to a small restaurant and separate breakfast room. The staff
are a delight. AMERICAN EXPRESS *Mastercard, Visa.*

Prague   Prague Renaissance

Tel (2) 2481 0396   Fax (2) 2481 1687

V Celnici 7 PO Box 726 11000 Prague 1
Rooms 309   Double room from kc6500

A new hotel with a fine central location just off the Republic
Square – one entrance to the Metro station is under the hotel –
offering good standards of service and accommodation. The
spacious marble-floored lobby has a useful little 'café' area and
there is a rustic-themed bar. The well-designed bedrooms have
a personalised welcome message on the TV screen, also offering
hotel information along with numerous channels in various
languages. *Satellite TV/air-con/safe. Conference facilities for up to
370. Indoor swimming pool, sauna, steam room, keep-fit equipment.
Private garage.* AMERICAN EXPRESS *Diners, Mastercard, Visa.*

Prague   Hotel Praha

Tel (2) 2434 1111   Fax (2) 2431 1218

Suïcká 20 166 35 Prague 6
Rooms 124   Double room from kc5880

Out in Prague's poshest suburb towards the airport, the hotel was
built in the early 80s (but the decor has a 70s feel) as a secure hotel
for Communist Party bigwigs. An unusual serpentine, terraced
design means that every single room has its own green terrace and
great views of the city. All the rooms are spacious, if somewhat
functional, with their own entrance lobby and separate loos. The
decor is rather dated but in good condition. Eight of the suites
were designed for Party Secretaries, and are huge. The 20
conference rooms, one being a very comfortable theatre/cinema
with simultaneous translation facilities, offer facilities for up to 200
people. The owners, the City of Prague, are rumoured to be
selling out to a large international chain and refurbishment
is bound to follow. *24hr room service. Satellite TV/air-con.
Translation services. Indoor swimming pool, sauna, tennis courts.
Hairdresser/beauty salon. Private garage.* AMERICAN EXPRESS *Diners,
Mastercard, Visa.*

Prague — **Hotel Savoy**

Tel (2) 2430 2111   Fax (2) 2430 2128   **HR**

Keplerova Ul 6 CR-118 00 Prague 1

Rooms 61   Double room from kc7444

In the government and embassy district, a stone's throw from the
castle, a brand new luxury hotel has been created behind
an original art nouveau facade to cater for top diplomats and
business people. The atmosphere is intimate, with a marble-floored
lobby, elegant library lounge and cosy bar with red banquette
seating. Air-conditioned bedrooms are furnished and equipped to a
high standard with fax and video machines and no less than four
telephones, including one in the separate loo and one in the
coloured bathroom with walk-in shower in addition to the tub.
*24hr room service. Satellite TV/air-con/safe/fax. Conference facilities
for up to 40. Sauna, steam room, spa bath, gym. Hairdresser, beauty
salon. Valet parking.* AMERICAN EXPRESS *Diners, Mastercard, Visa.*

Restaurant

Seats 50   Meal for 2 approx kc2300

At the touch of a button it is possible to make the roof slide open
and the windows sink into the floor to create a semi-alfresco
environment. Austrian management has yet to get to grips with
the service, but for buttering-up government officials and business
contacts this is an ideal spot. Dishes such as a fricassee of green
asparagus and lobster; trout carpaccio with root vegetables and
sour cream; breast of Barbary duck with orange sauce and rack
of lamb (cooked pink, a novelty for Prague) with onion mousse
come in almost nouvelle-sized portions. A small 'gateau' of fresh
figs and Bavarian cream on a strawberry sauce tastes as good as it
looks. *L 12-3.30 D 6-11.*

Prague — **Hotel Sax**

Tel (2) 538 422   Fax (2) 538 498   **H**

Janský Vršek 328-3 Mala Strana Prague 1

Rooms 22   Double room from kc2400

A small, functional, newly built hotel behind a period facade, near
the US Embassy, across the river from the city centre. Public
rooms are limited to a bar counter in the atrium reception and
a breakfast room where a decent cold buffet, plus bacon and eggs,
is included in the room price. Bedrooms are simple and
uncluttered. Doubles (two single beds pushed together) have tubs
in their pristine bathrooms, while the singles (just two) have
showers and WC only. All have mini-bars (but no room service)
and cable TV. Helpful staff speak good English. *Cable/satellite TV.
Private garage.* AMERICAN EXPRESS *Diners, Mastercard, Visa.*

The Golden Eurostar [★] denotes our pick of the
restaurants. Cooking is the major consideration, but
other factors are also taken into account, including
ambience, comfort and service.

Prague   U Sixtů

| Tel (2) 422 5724   Fax (2) 421 1671 | R |

Celetná 2 Prague 1

Seats 50   Meal for 2 approx kc1750

Just off the old town square, this is good place to keep cool, out
of the city's stifling summer heat; it is not only air-conditioned
but located in a medieval cellar with high stone-vaulted ceilings.
The Czech cooking goes beyond the bounds of the usual cold hors
d'oeuvre, offering dishes like saddle of venison in a cream sauce
with bilberries and dumplings, haunch of rabbit with ham, bacon,
mushrooms and a wine sauce, and a particularly tender chicken
steak with apples, almonds and morello cherries, all prepared with
some finesse and care. Pancakes are a good bet for dessert: either
thick (a bit like drop scones) or thin and served with a compote
of fruits and whipped cream. Five set menus supplement the à la
carte. The restaurant is due to close for a couple of months in the
spring of 1995. A ground floor café offers pastries and savoury
snacks from 10am-10pm. *Open 11.30am-midnight.* AMERICAN EXPRESS®
Diners, Mastercard, Visa.

Prague   Villa Voyta

| Tel (2) 472 5511   Fax (2) 472 9426   · | H |

K Novému Duoru 124/54 Lhotka 14200 Prague 4

Rooms 13   Double room from kc5600

In a leafy suburb, a good 15-minute taxi ride south of the city
centre (more if the driver doesn't know the way, and he probably
won't), the house was built in 1912; and restored to its original art
nouveau glory in 1992. In summer there is a bar and barbecue out
in the pretty garden. Bedrooms are also decorated in art nouveau
style, comfortably furnished with proper armchairs and/or sofas
and gold-plated (we were assured) brass bedsteads. Four of the
single rooms have only showers and WC. *24hr room service.*
Satellite TV/air-con/safe. Private parking. AMERICAN EXPRESS® *Diners,*
Mastercard, Visa.

Prague   Vinárna V Zátiší

| Tel (2) 2422 8977   Fax (2) 2422 8932 | R |

Liliová 1 Betlémské Náměstí Prague 1

Seats 58   Meal for 2 approx kc1800

Ask for directions to Bethlehem Square to find this cool white,
greenery-filled restaurant (sister restaurant to Parnas). There are
a couple of Bohemian specialities on the menu but this
is essentially a fairly up-market establishment with relatively
sophisticated modern cooking: carpaccio with mature Parmesan,
freshly-baked vegetable tart with a glaze of hollandaise, home-
made pasta with pesto, grilled fresh tuna with melted butter,
sautéed chicken breast with mustard sauce and rack of lamb (not
as lightly roasted as the menu suggests) coated with mustard crust
and served with a good saffron sauce. Chocolate mousse is a
popular choice for dessert. If you intend a full three-course meal
go for the 'deluxe menu' which offers the full à la carte choice at a
reduced price. *L 12-2.45 D 5.30-10.45. Closed 24 Dec.*
AMERICAN EXPRESS® *Mastercard, Visa.*

★

Prague   U Zlaté Hrušky

Tel (2) 531 133   **R**

Nový Svět 3 Hradčany Prague 1
Seats 85   Meal for 2 approx kc2400

This 17th-century restaurant in the Castle district has several
panelled dining rooms on two floors. The long menu (some 30
main dishes) seems even longer with each dish translated into five
languages: tripe in five guises, four different soups, three snail
dishes, game, fish and poultry. There's even a special section
of dishes 'suitable for gentlemen' and another section 'suitable for
ladies'. Emphasis is put on show – flambéed items and dishes
served sous cloche. Finish off with a cup of their excellent coffee.
Choice rather than subtle cooking is the order of the day but it is
still worth knowing about. A courtyard on the opposite side of the
lane has a cheaper menu for alfresco diners. *L 11.30-3 D 6.30-
midnight. Closed 24 & 25 Dec.* AMERICAN EXPRESS *Diners, Mastercard,
Visa.*

Czech Republic Index

Denmark

Currency: Danish Krone   **Exchange Rate:** £1 = approx DKr 10

International dialling code: 010 45 (for whole country)

Passports/Visas: No visa required by British passport holders.

British Embassy in Copenhagen Tel: 35 26 46 00 Fax: 35 38 10 12

TRANSPORT
Airports:
Copenhagen Tel: 32 50 93 33 / Aarhus Tel: 86 36 36 11 / Billund Tel: 75 33 80 22
Railway Stations:
Copenhagen Tel: 33 14 17 01 / Odense Tel: 66 12 10 13 / Aarhus Tel: 86 18 17 78
Car hire:
Copenhagen - Avis Tel: 31 31 50 20 (airport 31 51 22 99) / Budget Tel: 33 13 39 00 (airport 32 52 39 00)
Aarhus - Budget Tel: (airport) 86 36 39 86
Billund - Budget Tel: (airport) 75 35 39 00
Odense - Budget Tel: (airport) 65 95 50 20
Speed limits: 80 km/h on trunk roads, 110 km/h on motorways, 50 km/h in towns.

Banks open: Mon-Wed & Fri 9.30am-4pm, Thu till 6pm.

Shops open: Mon-Wed 9/10am-5.30/6pm, Thu till 5.30/7pm, Fri till 7/8pm, Sat till 12/2pm (first Saturday of each month, some shops stay open till 5pm).

National Holidays: New Year's Day, 13, 14, 16 & 17 April, 12 & 25 May, 4 & 5 Jun, Christmas Eve, Christmas Day & Boxing Day, New Year's Eve (from noon).

Tourist Offices:
Danish Tourist Board in London - Tel: 0171-259 5959
In Denmark -
Copenhagen Tel: 33 11 13 25 / Aarhus Tel: 86 12 16 00 / Odense Tel: 66 12 75 20 / Aalberg Tel: 98 12 60 22

American Express Travel Service Offices:
Copenhagen - AETS
  Amagertov 18 (Stroget)
  DK 1146
  Tel: 33 12 23 01 #

Copenhagen

Copenhagen   **Belle Terrasse**

Tel 33 12 11 36   Fax 33 15 00 31   **R**

Tivoli Gardens Vesterbrogade 3 1620 Copenhagen V
Seats 250   Meal for 2 approx DKr1000

Sister restaurant to the well-known *Søllerød Kro*, outside
Copenhagen, this place now offers similar gastronomic delights.
Norwegian lobster is baked in puff pastry with herbs and wild
mushrooms, fillet of turbot is cooked with clams and white wine   ★
and served with prawns. Danish fjord prawns are a favourite
house speciality. *Open noon-midnight. Closed 27 Apr-17 Sept. Public
parking.* AMERICAN EXPRESS® *Diners, Mastercard, Visa.*

THE APARTMENT SERVICE
Tel in UK: (0181) 748 4207   Fax: (0181) 748 3972
The Apartment Service will find you the right apartment
worldwide to suit your needs, whether you are on a short or
long-term stay. A 96-page colour catalogue is free on request.
All budgets are catered for.

Copenhagen   **La Crevette**

Tel 33 14 68 47   Fax 33 14 60 06   **R**

Tivoli Gardens Bernstorffsgade 5 1577 Copenhagen V
Seats 60   Meal for 2 approx DKr2000

Paul Bocuse rates René Bolvig as one of the best fish chefs
in Denmark, a reputation he has built up in the five years since
he took over from his parents. His fish is as fresh as can be,
delivered to the door just before lunch and served with all the
elegance of nouvelle cuisine. Turbot is served in a delicate *matelote*
sauce (made with pearl onions, *bouillon* and red wine). The three-   ★
course lunch and four-course dinner change every day, but
a particular house speciality is Dover sole lightly fried in butter.
The French wine list perfectly complements the menu, including
a good dry house white and light red. *Open noon-11. Closed
15 Sept-30 Apr. Public parking.* AMERICAN EXPRESS® *Diners, Mastercard,
Visa.*

Copenhagen   **Divan 2 Tivoli**

Tel 33 12 51 51   Fax 33 91 08 82   **R**

Tivoli Gardens Vesterbrogade 3 1620 Copenhagen V
Seats 200   Meal for 2 approx DKr1500

Surrounded by the lush Tivoli Gardens, this early 19th-century
slated house was built when the gardens were originally laid out.
The restaurant looks over Tivoli Lake and across to the fairytale
Hans Andersen Castle and the Copenhagen Town Hall clock
tower. The menu is French and there isn't a traditional piece
of Danish pork or dumpling in sight here; instead mousseline
of lobster is baked with turbot and served with sautéed asparagus
and a lobster jus and rack of Danish lamb is roasted with garlic
and sage and served with the juices whipped with lemon butter.

Fish is great in Denmark, so try some of their fiord prawns. New World wines make an appearance on the list. *Open noon-midnight. Closed 18 Sept-30 Apr.* ▓▓AMERICANEXPRESS▓▓ *Diners, Mastercard, Visa.*

Copenhagen   **Els**

| Tel 33 14 13 41   Fax 33 91 07 00 | **R** |

Store Strandstrade 3 1255 Copenhagen K

Seats 60   Meal for 2 approx DKr900

Hans Christian Andersen wrote a poem about this place overlooking the Nyhavn canal when it opened as a coffee shop 142 years ago, and he spent many an hour here. Now it is a Danish-cum-French restaurant with traditional Danish decor complete with a proud moose head pinned to the wall. Seafood and fish are favourite dishes: salmon tartare is served with roe and fresh herbs on a bed of tossed salad, trout is steamed in white wine and served on sautéed cabbage with an orange sauce. The menu changes every week, popular choices being caviar, oysters and lobsters. The European wine list is dominated by French vintages. *L 12-3 D 5.30-10. Public parking.* ▓▓AMERICANEXPRESS▓▓ *Diners, Mastercard, Visa.*

Copenhagen   **Ida Davidsen**

| Tel 33 91 36 55   Fax 33 11 36 55 | **R** |

Store Kongensgade 70 1264 Copenhagen K

Seats 85   Meal for 2 approx DKr200

Few restaurants in the world manage to be genuinely original; but this one does. The Davidsen family have been here for 106 years, since Oskar Davidsen started it and passed it down through the female side of the family to the present owner, great-granddaughter, Ida. The female-only kitchen has created the longest open sandwich list in the world (in the *Guinness Book of Records* to prove it) with such extravaganzas as the 'rush hour' sandwich, with 80 to 100 prawns layered on top of each other and a sandwich with a purée of smoked salmon, raw egg yolk, horseradish and onion. For those with more conservative tastes is the brisket of beef with home-made pickles. They smoke their own duck, salmon and lamb, so those sandwiches are also excellent. Another house speciality that is a must is Ida's blackcurrant rum (which can be tasted at all hours due to Denmark's liberal drinking laws). They also boast perhaps the world's smallest bar – it seats two comfortably. *Open 9-5. Closed Sat, Sun, July, Good Fri-Easter Mon, 23 Dec-1 Jan. Public parking. Diners, Mastercard, Visa.*

> Meal prices for 2 are based on à la carte menus.
> When set menus are available, prices will often be lower.

Copenhagen **Restaurant Kommandanten**

Tel 33 12 09 90   Fax 33 93 12 23   **R**

Ny Adelgade 7 1104 Copenhagen K

Seats 45   Meal for 2 approx DKr1100

An old Danish commander built this house for his family in 1698,
and it has been a restaurant since the 1930s. The Danish chef has
worked in Italy and there are Mediterranean influences in his
menu: terrine of foie gras and lobster with a truffle salad, pigeon
sautéed with bacon, cabbage and cherries, and fresh seafood served
in every conceivable way. The desserts are equally appealing:
a cold soufflé of white chocolate is served with a light chocolate
sorbet. Only one menu has a meat main course, the other one just
does fish, while a third 'surprise' menu serves a different glass
of wine with each course. All the menus change daily. French,
Californian and Spanish wines feature on the list. The place is as
interesting as the menu, with 17th-century wooden floors and
beams contrasted by original Warhol modern art on the walls.
L 12-2.30 D 5.30-10. Closed L Sat, all Sun, Jul, 23 Dec-2 Jan.
AMERICAN EXPRESS *Diners, Mastercard, Visa.*

Copenhagen **Kong Frederik Hotel**

Tel 33 12 59 02   Fax 33 93 59 01   **H**

Vester Voldgade 25 1552 Copenhagen V

Rooms 110   Double room from DKr1650

Two hotels side by side used to fight for business, but in 1973 they
merged to form this one place. It is right in the centre of the city,
two minutes from the Tivoli Gardens and the Town Hall Square
and five minutes from the main railway station. The rooms are all
being restored, but keeping their Colonial style, and there will
be a large new conference room. *Room service. Cable/satellite TV.
Private garage.* AMERICAN EXPRESS *Diners, Mastercard, Visa.*

Copenhagen **Kong Hans Kaelder**

Tel 33 11 68 68   Fax 33 32 67 68   **R**

Vingardsstraede 6 1070 Copenhagen K

Seats 40   Meal for 2 approx DKr2000

King Hans of Denmark used to own this cellar, one of the oldest
in Denmark, which is now a typically French restaurant, complete
with two chefs from Alsace. They offer dishes like mussel soup
laced with saffron, confit of duck or coq au vin, rounded off with
crème brulée. A new house speciality is warmed goose liver served   ★
with a raspberry vinaigrette. The wines are exclusively French,
except for one lone Spanish bottle. The Gothic-style, arched
dining room is just off the main Kongens Nytorv Square, near the
Royal Theatre. *D only 6-10. Closed Sun, Jul, 24 Dec-1 Jan.*
AMERICAN EXPRESS *Diners, Mastercard, Visa.*

Copenhagen   **The Mayfair Hotel**

Tel 31 31 48 01   Fax 31 23 96 86   **H**

Helgolandsgade 3 1653 Copenhagen V
Rooms 106   Double room from DKr1095

The Vottrup family have been running this bed and breakfast
in the city centre, next to the main railway station for the last
eight years, along with their restaurant, the Divan 2. Inside, all
is quiet and peaceful as the six floors overlook a small side street.
Ten de luxe rooms on the fifth floor are full of objects from the
Far East. Coffee and tea are always available in the lounge. The
one conference room here is very small and not ideal for anything
more than informal chats. *No room service. Cable/satellite TV/fax.*
Closed 23 Dec-2 Jan. Public parking. AMERICAN EXPRESS *Diners,*
Mastercard, Visa.

Copenhagen   **Neptun Hotel**

Tel 33 13 89 00   Fax 33 14 12 50   **HR**

Sankt Anna Plads 14-20 1250 Copenhagen K
Rooms 133   Double room from DKr1500

Going back to ecological basics, the couple who own this hotel
save electricity, water and waste, with the avid compliance
of their politically correct clients. The rooms are, however, still
well equipped (CNN, mini-bars, hairdryers) and are decorated
in pale, restful colours. Despite being in a small quiet street near
the harbour, the hotel is still close to the shops and the main sights
and only 1km away from Østerport Station. *Theatre-style*
conference facilities for up to 70. Closed 22 Dec-3 Jan. Public parking.
AMERICAN EXPRESS *Diners, Mastercard, Visa.*

Restaurant Gendarmen Café
Seats 40   Meal for 2 approx DKr120

Breaking away from the bland mould of international cuisine
which has swept through Denmark, the restaurant concentrates
on an interesting mix of regional dishes, which rotate according
to the season. In the summer, dishes from Sydfynske or Ohav are
served and in autumn mid-Jutland specialities dominate the menu:
everything from a ragout of small eels in a cream sauce lightly
flavoured with cardamon and ginger, to cabbage pudding – a
layered cake of cabbage stuffed with a pork meatloaf and served
with a traditional parsley sauce. When Northern Jutland is
featured, they serve a plethora of fresh fish: salmon and potato
salad and rissoles (meat balls) and cucumber. Look out for the
honey and chocolate cake on the South Jutland menu (the cake
is based on an early 20th-century recipe). The same ecological
principles are applied in the restaurant as well as in the hotel.
L 12-3 D 6-10.30. Closed Sun, 22 Jul, 22 Dec-2 Jan. Public parking.

To dial overseas from the UK, 010 will change to 00
on 16th April 1995.

Copenhagen   **Nouvelle**

Tel 33 13 50 18   Fax 33 32 07 97   **R**

Gammel Strand 34 1202 Copenhagen K
Seats 50   Meal for 2 approx DKr1200

In a first-floor setting alongside the canal and right opposite the
parliament buildings, there has been a restaurant here since 1830.
The chef, who trained extensively in Belgium, now serves
traditional Danish dishes. Starters like crisp lettuce served with
cold scallops and seaweed and asparagus soup with Brittany oysters
are followed by turbot with mussels in a thyme *bouillon* and fillet
of veal in a truffle sauce with celery purée and peas. Fish is a
speciality, as it is in almost all Danish restaurants, so ask for the
fresh fish of the day. *L 11.30-3 D 5.30-10. Closed Sun, Jul, 22 Dec-
2 Jan. Public parking.* AMERICAN EXPRESS *Diners, Mastercard, Visa.*

★

Copenhagen   **Plaza**

Tel 33 14 92 62   Fax 33 93 93 62   **H**

Bernstorffsgade 4 1577 Copenhagen V
Rooms 93   Double room from DKr1580

Cosy and classical, this early 20th-century hotel is very popular.
It is right in the centre of Copenhagen, minutes away from the
main railway station. The rooms are fairly old-fashioned, with
Laura Ashley prints and heavy wooden furniture. There are only
11 ordinary double rooms, so it is worth checking carefully to see
exactly what you are reserving. *Cable/satellite TV. Closed 16-27
Dec. Private garage.* AMERICAN EXPRESS *Diners, Mastercard, Visa.*

Copenhagen   **SAS Royal**

Tel 33 14 14 12   Fax 33 14 14 21   **H**

Hammerichsgade 1 1611 Copenhagen V
Rooms 255   Double room from DKr1245

Right in the middle of the city and close to the Tivoli Gardens,
this 21-storey hotel can be a little noisy. The rooms are rather
unusual, having been designed by avant-garde architect, Arne
Jakobsen; all have satellite and cable TV and faxes. The 60s
building is simple but sophisticated, with tall mirrors and marble
floors. Theatre-style conference facilities are available for up to
200 people, but sports facilities are limited to just a gym.
*Conference facilities. Business centre:secretarial/translation services.
Private garage.* AMERICAN EXPRESS *Diners, Mastercard, Visa.*

Copenhagen   **71 Nyhavn Romantik Hotel**

Tel 33 11 85 85   Fax 33 93 15 85   **H**

Nyhavn 71 1051 Copenhagen K
Rooms 82   Double room from DKr1350

The city harbour and sailing boats are the view from most of the
bedrooms at this 200-year-old converted warehouse. Inside, it is
still very rustic, as it is a listed building and little can be touched,
and Pomeranian beams, white walls and terracotta floors all add
to the place's charm. The rooms are well equipped, but there are
no proper conference facilities in the hotel (but the next door
Fyrskibet/lighthouse can be used for private functions.)
Cable/satellite TV. AMERICAN EXPRESS *Diners, Mastercard, Visa.*

Around Copenhagen

Holte   **Søllerød Kro**

Tel 42 80 20 05   Fax 42 80 22 70   **R**

Søllerødvej 35 2840 Holte
Seats 50   Meal for 2 approx DKr1000

Some 15 km north, at Søllerød, down a winding village street,
and surrounded by a cobbled courtyard, this 16th-century
thatched inn is an aesthetic and culinary find. The old-fashioned
dining rooms, with antique Danish paintings and objets d'art, offer
some excellent French haute cuisine, from foie gras to suckling
lamb on a bed of saffron ravioli, with a fennel sauce and sun-dried
tomatoes. After the meal, diners retire to a cosy living room for
coffee. *Open 11.30am-midnight. Closed 14-28 Feb, 7-28 Jul. Private
parking.* AMERICAN EXPRESS *Diners, Mastercard, Visa.*

★

Elsewhere in Denmark

Ebeltoft   Mellem Jyder

Tel 86 34 11 23   **R**

Juulsbakke 3 8400 Ebeltoft

Seats 70   Meal for 2 approx DKr300

Way up on the east coast of Jutland, hearty Danish fare is served
in this early 17th-century house. Tables are piled high with boiled
hams, open sandwiches, roasted partridges, herrings and rye bread
and their unique speciality: eel fried in butter and served in a
cream sauce with new potatoes. Traditionally, the Danes have
been known to down a pint or two, finishing off with some
strong schnapps, but these days even the locals stick to French
or German wine in the evening! *Open 10am-9pm. Closed Tue, Feb.
Public parking. Mastercard, Visa.*

Fredensborg   Store Kro Hotel

Tel 42 28 00 47   Fax 42 28 45 61   **H**

Slotsgade 6 3480 Fredensborg

Rooms 50   Double room from DKr1350

In 1723 King Frederick IV built this inn for his guests, next to his
splendid castle residence 40km north of Copenhagen. Despite
attempts at modernisation, bedrooms remain classical with open
fireplaces and valuable paintings on the walls. Like many
Scandinavian establishments, there is a sauna, but no other sports
facilities on the premises (though there is a popular golf course
next door). However, with the biggest lake in Denmark, Esium,
on their doorstep, most people decide to take the more relaxing
option and go for a leisurely row and picnic on the lake. *24hr room
service. Theatre-style conference facilities for up to 170. Closed 23 Dec-
2 Jan.* AMERICAN EXPRESS *Diners, Mastercard, Visa.*

Snekkersten   Scanticon Hotel

Tel 42 22 03 33   Fax 42 22 03 99   **H**

Nørrevej 80 3070 Snekkersten

Rooms 152   Double room from DKr1250

The hotel is located on the northern tip of Zeeland, a slim stretch
of water away from Sweden in an area popular with the citizens
of Copenhagen, who come here to relax using the sauna,
swimming and spa facilities available. Opened in 1989, the hotel
is surrounded by a public park. Scandinavian simplicity meets
modern facilities in the bedrooms and in the many fully-equipped
conference rooms: ergonomically designed conference chairs ease
the discomfort of sitting through painfully long speeches, while
the efficient air-conditioning aids concentration. *Satellite/cable TV.
Theatre-style conference facilities for up to 300. Private car park.*
AMERICAN EXPRESS *Diners, Mastercard, Visa.*

Vejle   **Munkebjerg**

Tel 75 72 35 00   Fax 75 72 08 86

Munkebjergvej 125 7100 Vejle

Rooms 148   Double room from DKr995

Stags and deer graze in the beech forest and the fiord glistens
through the trees, while guests play a few holes of golf, or have
a quick game of tennis. It is idyllic and only a 20-minute taxi ride
away from Vejle city and 35km away from the international
airport. The family who have run it since the 60s constantly add
little touches, like baskets of fruit in the bedrooms. The hotel
is popular with conference parties who use one of the 18 fully-
equipped conference rooms; while stars such as Nana Mouskouri
have wandered down the illuminated paths rehearsing their songs.
Satellite TV. Theatre-style conference facilities for up to 500. Closed
18-28 Dec. Private parking. AMERICAN EXPRESS *Diners, Mastercard, Visa.*

Denmark Index

Estonia

Currency: Estonian Kroon   **Exchange Rate:** £1 = approx EEK 19
EEK 8000 limit to take in or bring out. US dollars/travellers
cheques/DM recommended.

International dialling code: 010 372

Passports/Visas: No visa required by British passport holders for stay
of less than 30 days.

British Embassy in Tallinn Tel: 6-31 3461/2/3 or 6-31 3353

TRANSPORT
Airports:
Tallinn Airport Tel: 2-211 092
Railway Stations:
Tallinn Main Station Tel: 2-624 958
Car hire in Tallinn:
Hertz Tel: 2-421 003 / Avis Tel: 6-31 5930 (airport 2-215 602)
Speed limits: 70 km/h on trunk roads, 110 km/h on motorways,
50 km/h in towns.

Banks open: Hours vary, but banks are generally open between 10am
& 6pm. Exchange bureaus may stay open later.

Shops open: Hours vary, but shops are generally open between 9am &
6pm (some later) and many close for lunch.

National Holidays: New Year's Day, 1 May, 23 & 24 Jun, 16 Nov,
Christmas Day & Boxing Day.

Tourist Offices:
Estonian Embassy in London - Tel: 0171-589 3428
Tourist Board in Tallinn Tel: 2-601 700

(further information available from Intourist London - Tel: 0171-538
8600/538 5965)

American Express Travel Service Offices or Representative (R):
Tallinn - Estonian Tours (R)
    Roosikrantsi 4B
    200106
    Tel: 2-442034 #

Estonia   Tallinn

Tallinn   **Hotel Palace**

Tel (2) 44 47 65   Fax (2) 44 30 98   **H**

Vabaduse Valjak 3 EE0001 Tallinn
Rooms 81   Double room from $390

The hotel dates back to the days of Estonia's previous
independence in the 30s and since then it has played host
to visiting dignitaries such as President Mitterrand and Estonian
politicians. The whole place was renovated in 1989, and a night
club was built on the seventh floor. Most of the rooms have
showers, but only ten have baths. Two of the suites have their
own sauna. The *Linda* restaurant was undergoing renovation at the
time of going to press and will re-open serving European dishes,
but the timing of this is still uncertain. *2 restaurants. Public parking.*
AMERICAN EXPRESS *Mastercard, Visa.*

THE APARTMENT SERVICE
Tel in UK: (0181) 748 4207   Fax: (0181) 748 3972
The Apartment Service will find you the right apartment
worldwide to suit your needs, whether you are on a short or
long-term stay. A 96-page colour catalogue is free on request.
All budgets are catered for.

Finland

Currency: Finnish Marka   **Exchange Rate:** £1 = approx FIM 8

International dialling code: 010 358
(Helsinki + 0, Tampere + 31)

Passports/Visas: No visa required by British passport holders.

British Consulate in Helsinki Tel: 0-66 1293

TRANSPORT
Airports:
Helsinki Airport Tel: 0-81 881/82 771
Railway Stations:
Information Tel: 0-100 122.
Car hire:
Avis Tel: 0-82 2833 / Budget Tel: 0-870 1606 / Europcar Tel: 0-82
6677 / Hertz Tel: 0-82 1052
Speed limits: If no signposts 80km/h. 120km/h on motorways in
summer, 100km/h in winter. 50/60km/h in towns.

Banks open: 9.15am-4.15pm weekdays. Closed Sat, Sun.

Shops open: 9am-5/6pm weekdays, 9am-2/3pm Sat.

National Holidays: New Year's Day, 6 Jan, Good Friday, Easter Mon,
1 Apr, 1, 16 & 26 May, 21 & 22 Jun, 2 Nov, 6 Dec, Christmas Eve,
Christmas Day & Boxing Day.

Tourist Offices:
Finnish Tourist Board in London - Tel: 0171-839 4048
In Helsinki - Tel: 0-169 3757/174 088 or 0-403 011

American Express Travel Service Offices or Representative (R):
Helsinki - Area Travel Agency Ltd (R)
      Kaisaniemenkatu 13A
      Sf-00100
      Tel: 0-18551 #

Helsinki

Helsinki   **Alexander Nevski**

Tel (0) 63 96 10   Fax (0) 61 64 42 52   **R**

Pohjoisesplanadi 17 00170 Helsinki
Seats 100   Meal for 2 approx FIM800

The Finnish chef here has, for the last few years, specialised
in classical Russian cooking with dishes like marinated salmon,
fillet of reindeer and beef stroganoff. The setting is rather grand,
in a 19th-century Czarist nobleman's home with marble floors and
stone walls. *Open noon-midnight. Closed Sun in winter. Public
parking.* AMERICAN EXPRESS *Diners, Mastercard, Visa.*

THE APARTMENT SERVICE
Tel in UK: (0181) 748 4207   Fax: (0181) 748 3972
The Apartment Service will find you the right apartment
worldwide to suit your needs, whether you are on a short or
long-term stay. A 96-page colour catalogue is free on request.
All budgets are catered for.

Helsinki   **Amadeus**

Tel (0) 62 66 76   Fax (0) 63 60 64   **R**

Sofiankatu 4 00170 Helsinki
Seats 99   Meal for 2 approx FIM800

Inside this two-storey 18th-century hall, the owner-chef cooks to a
high standard, mixing international dishes with more traditional
Finnish fare. The usual reindeer and fish dishes are served as well
as elk, venison, wild duck and pheasant. Game can come with
vegetables in a terrine and a nut sauce on the side; salted fillet
of venison with a *sauerkraut* mousse is unusual, as is home-smoked
wild duck with a mandarin sauce. There is an unusually
comprehensive wine list, with 350 different bins and several
excellent Bordeaux house wines. *Open 11-midnight (Sat from 5pm).
Closed L Sat (all Sat in Jul), all Sun. Public parking.* AMERICAN EXPRESS
Diners, Mastercard, Visa.

Helsinki   **Bellevue**

Tel (0) 17 95 60   Fax (0) 63 69 85   **R**

Rahapajankatu 3 00160 Helsinki
Seats 100   Meal for 2 approx FIM400

Down a quiet old street in the centre of the city, this 19th-century
building has been the scene of some great Russian feasts. It is the
oldest Russian restaurant in Helsinki, dating back to 1917 and has
built up a good reputation. Lamb dumplings in a consommé with
mushroom sauce, Baltic herrings and fried salmon with a cold
smoked reindeer sauce are some popular dishes. The speciality
is fillet of beef *Novgorod* (with *sauerkraut*, barley cooked
in consommé, carrots, parsnips, sour cream and garlic butter). The
chicken kiev here is filled only with butter. The 25 wines are
international, with a Hungarian house red and white. *D 5-
midnight. Closed Jul.* AMERICAN EXPRESS *Diners, Mastercard, Visa.*

Helsinki — **Havis Amanda**

Tel (0) 66 68 82   Fax (0) 63 14 35   R

Unioninkatu 23 00170 Helsinki

Seats 85   Meal for 2 approx FIM500

Finnish coldwater fish dishes are the speciality of this place right
by the market square in the centre of Helsinki. Grilled salmon
with creamed morels, also an assortment of fish roes, and cold
pickled Baltic herrings are all on the menu. But for those hoping
to get away from ubiquitous fish dishes, sautéed grouse cooked
in a creamy game sauce is on offer. Wines are traditionally French
with a few other European choices. *Open noon–midnight. Closed
Sun. Public parking.* AMERICAN EXPRESS *Diners, Mastercard, Visa.*

★

Helsinki — **Hesperia**

Tel (0) 431 01   Fax (0) 431 09 95   H

Mannerheimintie 50 00260 Helsinki

Rooms 360   Double room from FIM1120

A scenic stroll away from Töölö Bay, the main shopping streets
and the main sights: the Congress Hall, National Museum and the
brand-new Opera House. The hotel itself opened in the early 70s
and has played host to many stars, plus innumerable international
business meetings, some of whose delegates arrive on the roof-top
helipad. The rooms are light, airy and well equipped, with
modern bathrooms. From cold plunge-pools to saunas and
an indoor swimming pool, there are also plenty of ways
to unwind, including the obligatory Scandinavian massage.
*Cable/satellite TV/safe. Theatre-style conference facilities for up to 450.
Swimming pool, cold plunge, gym, golf-simulator, saunas, solarium,
massage. Closed 24 Dec–1 Jan. Private garage.* AMERICAN EXPRESS *Diners,
Mastercard, Visa.*

Helsinki — **Kabuki**

Tel (0) 694 94 46   Fax (0) 888 67 60   R

Lapinlahdenkatu 12 00180 Helsinki

Seats 36   Meal for 2 approx FIM350

The chef-owner, Mr Takayama, prepares perhaps the only sushi
available in Finland, as well as other traditional Japanese dishes.
Each table has a small grill in the middle and guests can watch the
chef cooking their fish. Tuna is a particular house speciality, served
as sashimi as well as sushi. Tofu soup, fried squid with ginger, raw
squid with horseradish sauce, raw trout and sliced grilled fillets
of beef with vegetables are also popular dishes. Traditional sakes
are served along with French and Australian wines. *L 11.30-2
D 5-11 (open 2-11 Sun). Closed Sat. Public parking.* AMERICAN EXPRESS
Diners, Visa.

> To dial overseas from the UK, 010 will change to 00
> on 16th April 1995.

Helsinki   Lehtovaara

Tel (0) 44 08 33   Fax (0) 49 34 08   **R**

Mechelininkatu 39 00250 Helsinki
Seats 120   Meal for 2 approx FIM600

The restaurant moved from Viipuri to Töölö Bay, five minutes
from the centre of Helsinki, 50 years ago. It serves an international
and Finnish menu, with starters like roe served with blini or
garlic soup, followed by such dishes as fried pike-perch in a shrimp
sauce and fillet of reindeer in a mustard butter sauce. The lunch
menu changes every day with a buffet laid out for those who
would like to help themselves to a simpler meal. The selection
of beef dishes is very popular. French, Spanish and New World
wines. *Open 11am-1am Mon-Fri, 1pm-1am Sat, 1pm-2am Sun.
Diners, Mastercard, Visa.*

Helsinki   Lord Hotel

Tel (0) 680 16 80   Fax (0) 680 13 15   **H**

Lönnrotinkatu 29 00180 Helsinki
Rooms 48   Double room from FIM540

Tranquil and scenic, the Lord Hotel sits by the harbour, minutes
away from a flea market and park. It was formerly an early
Jugendstil castle, and the rooms have still retained that dramatic,
romantic feel, despite being renovated in the late 80s. Now, they
are well equipped with modern furniture. The arched-cellar
restaurant serves international à la carte dishes. *Room service.
Cable/satellite TV. Conference facilities for up to 200. Squash courts,
gym, saunas. Closed 24-26 Dec. Private garage.* AMERICAN EXPRESS®
Mastercard.

Helsinki   Palace

Tel (0) 13 45 61   Fax (0) 65 47 86   **H**

Eteläranta 10 00130 Helsinki
Rooms 50   Double room from FIM970

Built back in the 50s for the Olympic Games, this hotel has
recently been renovated. The rooms now have cable and satellite
TV and safes, as well as elegant modern furniture. It is quite
an unusual set-up; the first eight floors of the building are offices
and the hotel starts on the ninth floor; there are three saunas.
Theatre-style conference facilities for up to 200. AMERICAN EXPRESS® *Diners,
Mastercard, Visa.*

Helsinki   Ramada Presidentti

Tel (0) 69 11   Fax (0) 694 78 86   **H**

Eteläinen Rautatiekatu 4 00100 Helsinki
Rooms 495   Double room from FIM920

The Ramada has been run by a co-operative since 1980 and many
of the staff have been here from the start. The eight-floor hotel
is right in the city centre, but is not noisy. The rooms, all recently
renovated, are modern, simply decorated and well equipped, and
there's also a swimming pool and three saunas. Conference
facilities are extensive and can seat 400 people theatre-style. They
have an international rules casino – the state owns the casino and

gives all your money away to charity. *Cable/satellite TV. Secretarial/translation services on request. Private parking.* AMERICAN EXPRESS® *Diners, Mastercard, Visa.*

Helsinki   Rivoli (Kala and Cheri)

Tel (0) 64 34 55   Fax (0) 64 77 80   **R**

Albertinkatu 38 00180 Helsinki

Seats 120   Meal for 2 approx FIM350

The female chef cooks traditional food with a fish menu in the summer: salmon soup, fish roe and blinis and scampi in a Pernod cream sauce. Other dishes include *chateaubriand* with herb potatoes, pike-perch in an onion and cream sauce and grilled slightly salted salmon with creamed chanterelles. Save some room for the delicious brown bread ice cream with fresh berries, or candied caramel pudding. *Open 11am-midnight (Sat & Sun from 6pm). Closed Sat & Sun (Jun & Jul) 24-26 Dec, 1-4 Apr, National Holidays. Public parking.* AMERICAN EXPRESS® *Diners, Mastercard, Visa.*

Helsinki   SAS Royal Hotel

Tel (0) 695 80   Fax (0) 69 58 71 00   **HR**

Runberginkatu 2 00100 Helsinki

Rooms 72   Double room from FIM460

One of the newer SAS International Hotels, this establishment, only 20km from the airport and 500m from the main railway station, was built in the early 90s. The hotel is ideally situated between the park, the beach and the centre of town. Like most Helsinki hotels, it has the obligatory sauna as well as a gym. The business centre can cater for every working need. The rooms are classically furnished, decorated in Oriental, Italian or Scandinavian styles and some are even specially designed for guests with allergies. *Theatre-style conference facilities for up to 300. Private garage.* AMERICAN EXPRESS® *Diners, Mastercard, Visa.*

Restaurant Johan Ludvig

Seats 66   Meal for 2 approx FIM650

Most of the dishes are traditionally Finnish, or leaning towards more international cuisine, with a charcoal grill stacked with the choice of the day such as entrecote, lamb and reindeer. The grilled fillet of reindeer is served with a pepper sauce, while roasted rack of lamb is served with a light thyme sauce. Some Finnish fish dishes on offer are gravlax with a dill mustard sauce, cold smoked salmon with scrambled eggs. Desserts are pretty universally recognisable: home-baked apple pie with vanilla ice cream and cheesecake. A German house wine is served along with an international choice. *L 11.30-2.30 D 6-11. Closed Sun, Good Fri-Easter Mon, 21 Jul-8 Aug, 21 Dec-5 Jan.*

> Opening times are often liable to change at short notice,
> so it's always best to book.

Helsinki   **Sipuli**

Tel (0) 17 99 29   Fax (0) 63 06 62   **R**

Kanavaranta 3 00160 Helsinki

Seats 140   Meal for 2 approx FIM600

One of Helsinki's most traditional settings for archetypal
traditional cooking with tartare of cold smoked salmon and roe,
marinated beef and apple-fennel compote, grilled Arctic char
(salmon-trout) with spinach and spring onion sauce. Fish is the
food to eat in these Northern climes, but game dishes are also
deliciously prepared, so try the noisettes of reindeer in a rich game
sauce. Desserts are lighter: fragrant rosehip mousse with a fresh
cheese sauce or mint and chocolate mousse. *D 6-midnight. Public
parking.* AMERICAN EXPRESS *Diners, Mastercard, Visa.*

Helsinki   **Hotel Strand Intercontinental**

Tel (0) 39 35 1   Fax (0) 39 35 25 5   **HR**

John Stenbergin Ranta 4 00530 Helsinki

Rooms 200   Double room from FIM1290

The hotel is on Siltasaari, the former island turned peninsula, right
by the waterfront, beside the old city centre with great views over
the harbour and up to the Gulf of Finland. The rooms are
equipped with every facility one would expect in an international
hotel and there are jacuzzis in the suites. The birch bedheads are
an elegant touch too, as is the Lapland marble and Finnish stone
that lines the reception rooms. *Cable/satellite/fax. Theatre-style
conference facilities for up to 250. Closed 23-27 Dec, 13-17 Apr.
Private garage.* AMERICAN EXPRESS *Diners, Mastercard, Visa.*

Restaurant Pamir

Seats 65   Meal for 2 approx FIM700

The food here is very popular and very traditional, ranging from
grouse salad with sweet turnip purée to smoked fillet of reindeer
with a cheese sauce, or reindeer calf's liver braised in onions and
white wine and grilled fresh fillet of perch served with seasonal
vegetables. Other fish specialities are served seasonally: fish roe,
crayfish and lobster. There are some 250 wine listings,
representing all the major wine-growing regions. *D 6-midnight.
Closed Sat & Sun, 8 Jul-8 Aug. Private parking.*

Helsinki   **Svenska Klubben**

Tel (0) 135 4706   Fax (0) 135 4896   **R**

Maurinkatu 6 00170 Helsinki

Seats 50   Meal for 2 approx FIM500

Most of the indigenous food eaten in Finland comes from the
forests or lakes: reindeer, fish and game are served here, in season,
and are well worth trying. Otherwise, typically Scandinavian fare
is on offer, like marinated fillet of beef in a mustard sauce, baked
salmon with a morel sauce, pike-perch with a horseradish sauce.
Open noon-midnight. Closed Sun, mid Jun-mid Aug. AMERICAN EXPRESS
Diners, Mastercard, Visa.

Helsinki   **Torni Hotel**

Tel (0) 13 11 31   Fax (0) 13 13 61   **HR**

Yrjönkatu 26 00100 Helsinki
Rooms 155   Double room from FIM790

Part of a large Finnish chain this 30s hotel is called the 'Tower'
and is the tallest building in Helsinki – you can see five cities from
the top. A new wing was built in the 80s in German *Jugendstil* and
looks very like a castle. The elegant glass-roofed reception hall
seats 40. There are no real conference facilities. Finland is one
of the few countries to have special hotel rooms for asthmatics and
those with allergies and there are four of them here. *Cable/satellite
TV. Saunas. Closed 23 Dec-5 Jan. Public parking.* AMERICAN EXPRESS
Diners, Mastercard, Visa.

Restaurant Ritarisali
Seats 80   Meal for 2 approx FIM450

Ritarisali means knights' chamber, where guests feast on Finnish
delicacies and French cuisine, while listening to Hungarian
musicians. Clams and scallops are cooked with gorgonzola, and
there's also a salad of smoked duck, as well as sweetbreads and
noisettes of beef au gratin with goat's cheese. The menu is well
balanced between game, meat and fish. The game season is from
the beginning of October and brings hare, venison and reindeer.
L 11.30-2.30 D 6-midnight. Closed Sat, Sun, mid Jun-mid Aug.

Helsinki   **Vaakuna**

Tel (0) 13 11 81   Fax (0) 13 11 82 34   **H**

Asema-aukio 2 00100 Helsinki
Rooms 288   Double room from FIM880

Sharing the building with a popular department store, City Sokof,
the hotel only occupies the fifth to eighth floors. But despite being
in the centre and only 80m from the main railway station, it is
very quiet. The rooms are well equipped and decorated in an
American minimalist style. But in spite of its size, the hotel has
no extensive conference nor any sports facilities. *Cable/satellite TV.
Theatre-style conference facilities for up to 50. Secretarial/translation
services on request.* AMERICAN EXPRESS *Diners, Mastercard, Visa.*

Tampere

Tampere   **Arctia Rosendahl Hotel**

| Tel (31) 244 11 11   Fax (31) 223 33 75 | **HR** |

Pyynikintie 13 33230 Tampere
Rooms 213   Double room from FIM580

15 minutes out of the centre of the city, this 70s hotel, which
is attractively surrounded by a national park and lake, has always
been conference-orientated; quite surprising, considering that they
do not offer any secretarial or translation services. But the 20
different conference rooms they do have are fully equipped. The
bedrooms are modern, simple and functional. *Satellite/cable TV.
Theatre-style conference facilities for up to 700. Squash courts,
swimming pool, 3 tennis courts, indoor golf.* AMERICAN EXPRESS *Diners,
Mastercard, Visa.*

Cantina Rosa
Seats 75   Meal for 2 approx FIM300

The Finnish menu gives little more than a nod towards
international cuisine. Smoked trout tartare comes on rye bread,
an assortment of pickled local fish is accompanied by mayonnaise
and dill potatoes and peppered roast fillet of beef is served cold
with a mushroom and onion salad. Typically Finnish desserts
round off the meal. *Open noon-midnight.*

Tampere   **Ravintola Henrik's**

| Tel (31) 21 21 91   Fax (31) 21 21 192 | **R** |

Satamakatu 7 33200 Tampere
Seats 98   Meal for 2 approx FIM320

Ever since he opened his own restaurant Timo Anitila has striven
to serve European dishes made with Finnish ingredients. He has
succeeded to a large extent, with dishes like warmed sweetbreads
with marinated asparagus, braised salmon and perch with
a crayfish sauce. Other house specialities are more Finnish:
reindeer ravioli and breast of chicken glazed with hazelnuts.
Wines are a little sparse, with only seven to choose from, but
remember, this is Finland with all its authoritarian drinking laws.
L 11-3 D 5-12. Closed Sun, 4-24 July. Private parking.
AMERICAN EXPRESS *Diners, Mastercard, Visa.*

Tampere   **Ravintola Tiiliholvi**

| Tel (31) 212 12 20   Fax (31) 212 12 19 | **R** |

Kauppakatu 10 33210 Tampere
Seats 160   Meal for 2 approx FIM300

Merga Orkosalo has been running this kitchen for the last ten
years in the old Tampere University student halls of residence,
which were built in *Jugendstil*. The menu has an interesting
mixture of local and French cooking; for example, starters like
reindeer mousse on rye bread toast and main courses like fillet
of mutton *au gratin*, chicken in pastry with blue cheese, sautéed
snow grouse and fried perch with lemon butter. The house
speciality makes an interesting choice for the brave-hearted –
herring ice cream. The European wines offered are mainly
French. *L 11-3 D 5-12. Private parking.* AMERICAN EXPRESS *Diners,
Mastercard, Visa.*

Finland Index

Recommended by

EGON RONAY'S GUIDES

1995

YOUR GUARANTEE
OF
QUALITY AND INDEPENDENCE

- Establishment inspections are anonymous

- Inspections are undertaken by qualified
  Egon Ronay's Guides inspectors

- The Guides are completely independent
  in their editorial selection

- The Guides do not accept advertising,
  hospitality or payment from listed
  establishments

Hotels & Restaurants	Pubs & Inns
Europe	Just a Bite
Family Hotels & Restaurants	Paris
Oriental Restaurants	Ireland
New Zealand & South Pacific	Australia

Egon Ronay's Guides are available from all good bookshops or can be
ordered from Leading Guides, 35 Tadema Road, London SW10 0PZ
Tel: 071-352 2485 / 352 0019   Fax: 071-376 5071

France

Currency: French Franc   **Exchange Rate:** £1 = approx Fr 8

International dialling code: 010 33
(Paris + 1)

Passports/Visas: No visa required by British passport holders.

British Consulate in Paris Tel: 1-42 66 38 10   Fax: 1-40 76 02 87

TRANSPORT
Airports:
Roissy Charles de Gaulle Tel: 1-48 62 12 12;
Orly Tel: 1-49 75 52 52; Le Bourget Tel: 48 62 12 12,
Lyon-Satolas Tel: 72 22 72 21; Marseilles-Provence Tel: 42 78 21 00;
Nice-Cote d'Azur Tel: 93 21 30 30; Strasbourg International tel: 88 64
67 67.
Rail:
SNCF Paris Tel: 1-45 65 60 60. French Railways Ltd, 179 Piccadilly,
London W1 Tel: 0171 493 9731.
Car hire:
Contact UK international branches for information - Avis Tel: 0181-848
8733 / Budget Tel: 0800 181181 / EuroDollar Tel: 0895 233300 / Hertz
Tel: 0181-679 1799/1777.
Speed limits: 130km/h on toll motorways, 110km/h on dual carriages/
motorways without tolls, 90km/h on other roads, 50km/h in towns.

Banks open: 9am-noon, 2-4pm weekdays. Closed either Sat or Mon, and
early the day before a National Holiday.

Shops open: 9/10am-6.30/7pm Mon-Sat. Many closed all day or half day
Mon.

National Holidays: New Year's Day, Easter Sun & Mon, 1, 8 & 25
May, 4 & 5 Jun, 14 Jul, 15 Aug, 1 & 11 Nov, Christmas Day.

Tourist Offices:
French Tourist Board in London - Tel: 0891-244 123
in France –
Paris Tel: 1-49 52 53 54 / Bordeaux Tel: 56 44 28 41 / Lille Tel: 20 30
51 00
Lyons Tel: 78 42 25 75 / Nice Tel: 93 87 07 07 / Reims Tel: 26 47 25
69
Strasbourg Tel: 88 52 28 22 / Toulouse Tel: 61 11 02 22/61 / Cannes
Tel: 93 99 19 77

American Express Travel Service Offices:
Paris - AETS
  11 Rue Scribe
  75009
  Tel: 1-47 77 70 07/47 77 79 79 #

Paris

Paris   **L'Ambroisie**

`Tel (1) 42 78 51 45`   **R**

9 Pl des Vosges 75004 Paris
Seats 35   Meal for 2 approx Fr1600

Tucked away amongst the tiny streets of the Marais district, this
beautiful 17th-century square is a delightful discovery, and the
same can be said for Bernard Pacaud's restaurant which is set back
under the arcaded buildings surrounding the square. The
restaurant's interior reflects the 17th-century atmosphere with
a hanging tapestry, Thonet chairs, stone floors and rich wood.
In these elegant surroundings, excellent and beautifully-crafted
dishes are served. Bernard is admired for the fact that he never
leaves his kitchen to visit the dining room in order
to acknowledge his clients' praise. Instead he leaves that to his   ★
charming wife Danielle. The menu is changed according to the
season. In the autumn, for example, he suggests duck foie gras
terrine served with a compote of fresh figs as a starter, followed
by *poularde de Bresse aux truffes de la Mère Brazier*, or pastry cases
of langoustine tails with a slightly curried sauce, and a dark
chocolate tart with vanilla ice cream to finish. On wines,
sommelier Pierre Le Moullac is on hand to offer his expert advice.
Book well in advance. No set menu. *L 12-1.30 D 8-9.30. Closed
Sun, Mon, 2 wks Feb & 3 wks Aug. Mastercard, Visa.*

THE APARTMENT SERVICE
Tel in UK: (0181) 748 4207   Fax: (0181) 748 3972
The Apartment Service will find you the right apartment
worldwide to suit your needs, whether you are on a short or
long-term stay. A 96-page colour catalogue is free on request.
All budgets are catered for.

Paris   **Amphyclès**

`Tel (1) 40 68 01 01   Fax (1) 40 68 91 88`   **R**

78 Ave des Ternes 75017 Paris
Seats 42   Meal for 2 approx Fr1400

Philippe Groult's cooking is a marvellous mixture of traditional
and modern, inventive and often light, with many dishes featuring
subtle use of herbs and spices. Much of the menu involves
intriguing combinations: lobster roasted with mushrooms and
served with a macaroni of foie gras, a liquor of melon and port
with brochettes of zander and smoked eel, crisps of sweetbreads
and courgette flowers with langoustines, rack of veal cooked
en cocotte with a fondue of new potatoes and salsify. There are
also some more familiar favourites (ox cheek with confit   ★
of carrots is a speciality), plus fine cheeses and superb desserts – try
the *pyramide au chocolat amer* or *banane flambée*. Two fixed-price
menus are available for everyone at a table – 'menu des nos
terroirs' and 'menu crustacés aux saveurs printanières'. Private
room 5/25. Set L 260F. Also menu dégustation L&D Fr580/Fr780.
L 12-2.30 D 7-10.30. Closed L Sat, all Sun. AMERICAN EXPRESS *Diners,
Mastercard, Visa.*

Paris   Apicius

Tel (1) 43 80 19 66   Fax (1) 44 40 09 57   **R**

122 Ave de Villiers 75017 Paris
Seats 60   Meal for 2 approx Fr1300

Jean-Pierre Vigato's cooking is firmly grounded in the classics, but
many of his superb dishes have a contemporary ring. *Terrine glacé
de concombres au raifort et caviar* and a speciality dish of escalopes
of duck foie gras sautéed in a sweet-sour sauce with confit of black
radishes are examples of his modern thinking, while at the other
end of the scale are simpler dishes such as roast turbot with new
potatoes and bacon. Desserts based on chocolate are definitely
worth leaving space for. Wide-ranging French wine list. The
restaurant itself is divided into three areas by eye-catching
bouquets and floral sculptures. Valet parking. *Menu dégustation*:
Fr520. *L 12.30-2 D 7.30-10.15. Closed Sat, Sun & Aug.*
AMERICAN EXPRESS *Diners, Mastercard, Visa.*

★

Paris   L'Arpège

Tel 45 51 47 33   Fax 44 18 98 39   **R**

84 Rue de Varenne 75007 Paris
Seats 45   Meal for 2 approx Fr1700

L'Arpège is among Paris's very best. Decor is strikingly
minimalist, there are only two works of art on display, a sculpture
of a burst cello and a portrait of the chef's grandmother. The chef
in question is Alain Passard. Now in his late 30s, he has spent time
with the likes of Boyer at Rheims and Senderens of *Lucas Carton.*
On offer is haute cuisine of the highest order. Therefore, his set
lunch of 390F for five courses represents remarkable value. This
could begin with a chaud-froid of eggs followed by asparagus
mousseline, then a choice of either sole with sorrel or Oriental-
style lamb. Afterwards a plate of regional cheeses and, to finish,
strawberries flavoured with hibiscus. The gastronomic menu
comprises six courses priced at a mighty Fr890 per person with
a two-person minimum. It is a remarkable composition of very
recherché creations including calf's sweetbreads with liquorice,
rack of lamb with walnuts and asparagus, and perhaps most
intriguing of all, a dessert comprising a cooked tomato filled with
twelve distinct "flavours" and topped with ice cream. Set menus:
L Fr390, L & D Fr890. *L 12-2.30 D 7.30-10.30. Closed L Sun, all
Sat.* AMERICAN EXPRESS *Diners, Mastercard, Visa.*

★

Opening times are often liable to change at short notice,
so it's always best to book.

Paris   A Sousceyrac

Tel (1) 43 71 65 30   Fax (1) 40 09 79 75   **R**

35 Rue Faidherbe 75011 Paris
Seats 60   Meal for 2 approx Fr700

One of the culinary delights of the little town of Sousceyrac in the
Lot region of France is its cassoulet. This dish therefore features
as one of the South-Western specialities served in this typical
1920s-30s bistro with its tiled floors, wood panelling and diplomas
on the walls. Others are their home-made foie gras (goose
or duck), hare à la royale (in season) and coquilles St Jacques with
sorrel, which you might follow with an apple feuilleté with
armagnac or crème brulée maison. 260 bins on the wine list. Set
menu: L & D Fr175. *L 12-2 D 7.30-10. Closed L Sat, all Sun
& Aug.* AMERICAN EXPRESS *Diners, Mastercard, Visa.*

Paris   Le Bellecour

Tel (1) 45 55 68 38   **R**

22 Rue Surcouf 75007 Paris
Seats 80   Meal for 2 approx Fr860

South of the Quai d'Orsay and close to the Esplanade des Invalides,
Le Bellecour is a restaurant renowned for its Lyonnais specialities
such as *salade de clapotons* (lamb's trotters), *quenelles de brochet*, and
Bresse chicken in vinegar with a gratin of macaroni. These feature
on a carte of well-thought-out modern dishes such as lobster
risotto with morel mushrooms in a cream sauce, roast lamb with
sesame seeds, and veal fillet with lime confit. Gerald Goutagny's
desserts are a particular forte with an amazing selection from hot
charlotte soufflé and millefeuille of summer fruits to caramelised
apple tart, a trio of crème brulées and a cherry blancmange with
sweet almond milk sorbet. Set menus from Fr160. *L 12.30-2.30
D 7.30-10.30. Closed Sat, Sun & Aug.* AMERICAN EXPRESS *Diners,
Mastercard, Visa.*

Paris   Benoit

Tel (1) 42 72 25 76   **R**

20 Rue Saint-Martin 75004 Paris
Seats 70   Meal for 2 approx Fr900

There are two dining rooms in this elegant Parisian bistro with its
old parquet floors, red velvet banquettes, white table linen, plants,
pretty glass and silver cutlery. The classic old dishes of France are
to be found here, most of which need a lengthy cooking time:
cassoulet maison, boudin noir, knuckle of veal *provençale,* casseroled   ★
duck (for 2) or the very traditional *boeuf mode.* The wine list
is uniquely French and nothing is available by the glass. No set
menu. *L 12-2 D 8-10. Closed Sat, Sun & 1st 3 wks Aug.
No credit cards.*

Paris   **Bistrot d'à Coté**

Tel (1) 43 54 59 10   Fax (1) 43 29 02 08   R

16 Bd St-Germain 75005 Paris
Seats 65   Meal for 2 approx Fr450

One of four popular offshoots of Michel Rostang's brilliant
restaurant in the 17th arrondissement. This one retains the
handsome panelling and mirrors of its previous incarnation and
offers a menu of updated rustic, traditional dishes – eight or so at
each course. Specialities include brochettes of mussels with a
mushroom salad, veal kidneys with a compotée of pig's trotters
and a splendid hot chocolate soufflé. Two courses cost Fr135, three
Fr178.
The other Bistrots d'à Coté are at 16 Ave de Villiers 75017 Paris
Tel 47 63 25 61, 10 Rue Gustave Flaubert 75017 Paris Tel 42 67
05 81 and 4 Rue Boutard at Neuilly 9220 Tel 47 45 34 55. *L 12-2
D 7-11. Closed L Sat (all Sat Aug), all Sun.* AMERICAN EXPRESS
Mastercard, Visa.

Paris   **Bistrot du Dome**

Tel (1) 48 04 88 44   Fax (1) 48 04 00 59   R

2 Rue de la Bastille 75004 Paris
Seats 80   Meal for 2 approx Fr450

An offshoot of the renowned Brasserie Le Dome (see entry) and
a sister restaurant to the Montparnasse Bistrot (14th arr), with the
same effective decor mix of rag-painted walls, fish tiles and plastic
grapes as table lights and on the vine overhead, and the same à la
carte ideas on the blackboard menu. The menu is all fish, the
cooking skilful and relatively unembellished: an excellent dish
of pepper stuffed with brandade lapped by a thick tomato sauce,
fillet of St Pierre with aubergine purée, *tartare de saumon, friture
d'éperlans,* grilled sardines, skate salad, *St Jacques provençale,* rascasse
with olive oil potato purée, *bourride, solettes meunière,* whole bream
buttery-braised with new potatoes and cloves of garlic in their
skins. St Nectaire farmhouse cheese, or simple sweets like dark
chocolate tart, pineapple or gratin of pears round off a good,
reasonably priced meal. All the wines (no Beaujolais) are Fr98 per
bottle, Fr20 by the glass. *L 12.15-2.30 D 7.30-11.30.* AMERICAN EXPRESS
Mastercard, Visa.   ★

Paris   **Bistrot du Dome**

Tel (1) 43 35 32 00   R

1 Rue Delambre 75014 Paris
Seats 60 (plus terrace 16)   Meal for 2 approx Fr450

Very near the famous Brasserie Le Dome, the Bistro is solely fish-
orientated. The menu is renewed daily according to availability
and written on slate boards which are passed around the tables. All
is simply cooked – open with a tuna and salmon tartare or pan-
fried shrimps, move on to roasted John Dory with herbs or skate
with a vinaigrette sauce (hot) and finish with *pommes miettes* (apple
crumble). All wines are Fr98 per bottle. No set menu. *L 12.15-
14.30. Closed Sun and Mon in Aug only.* AMERICAN EXPRESS *Mastercard,
Visa.*   ★

Paris La Bourdonnais

Tel (1) 47 05 45 42   Fax (1) 45 55 75 54   **H R**

111 Ave de la Bourdonnais 75007 Paris
Rooms 60   Double room from Fr610

Turn-of-the-century building offering comfortable
accommodation in traditional Parisian style (there are now also
three suites). AMERICAN EXPRESS® *Diners, Mastercard, Visa.*

La Cantine des Gourmets

Seats 60   Meal for 2 approx Fr1000

Next door to the hotel at no 113, the restaurant (Tel 47 05 47 96
Fax 45 51 09 29) is among the most cheerful, most popular and
best in town. Provence is the provenance of Philippe Bardau's
cooking, and his background with Outhier and Maximin means
that fine fresh country flavours are very much to the fore. Typical
dishes on an autumn menu could be salad of pigeon, almonds and
broad beans, sole meunière with pommes charlotte à la moelle,
crayfish with a baby squid risotto, rabbit with rosemary and black
olives, and a choco-caramel dome with glace nougatine. Strong
showing of Bordeaux wines. Set menus L Fr180/Fr220
D Fr280/Fr380. *L 12-2.30 D 8-11. Closed Dec 25.*

Paris Brasserie Lipp

Tel (1) 45 48 53 91   Fax (1) 45 44 33 20   **R**

151 Bd Saint-Germain 75006 Paris
Seats 150   Meal for 2 approx Fr560

Perhaps the capital's most famous brasserie, founded in 1880
by Léonard Lipp. It now has a 20s decor of ceramics, mirrors and
painted ceiling (it's classed as a historic monument). It was, and is,
the haunt of the famous, from Malraux to Madonna, from
Hemingway to Harrison Ford. Throughout its long opening hours
it serves a classic brasserie menu, and listed as specialities are
cervelas rémoulade, Bismarck herrings, grilled stuffed pig's trotters,
and choucroute with pork knuckle. The choice is extensive and
each day there are additional dishes such as poached haddock
beurre blanc, navarin of lamb and Provençal stuffed vegetables.
No set menu. *Meals 10am-1am.* AMERICAN EXPRESS® *Diners, Mastercard,
Visa.*

Paris Le Bristol

Tel (1) 42 66 91 45   **H R**

112 Rue du Faubourg St Honoré 75008 Paris
Rooms 195   Double room from Fr2950

One of the most expensive but also most luxurious and exclusive
of Paris hotels. Refined day rooms blend genuine antiques with
pine reproduction pieces and tapestry wall hangings. A peaceful
garden is an unexpected pleasure in a city-centre hotel, as are views
across the rooftops of Paris from the swimming pool. A recent
addition to the amenities is a fully-equipped gymnasium. Most
rooms and suites are decorated and furnished in traditional style
but a few, in a wing that was formerly a Carmelite convent, are
more modern in style. Well-drilled staff provide impeccable
service. Good business facilities with fax sockets in all rooms,
secretarial and translation services (8am-10pm), a direct link to the

Bourse and a number of conference rooms, the largest seating 180.
Valel parking. AMERICAN EXPRESS *Diners, Mastercard, Visa.*

Restaurant
Seats 60   Meal for 2 approx Fr1500

The walls are wood-panelled from floor to ceiling in this beautiful
circular dining room. Part of the ceiling is glassed over and
paintings depicting the four seasons look down on small round
tables with Louis XV armchairs. Bouquets of flowers, chandeliers
and a large Flemish tapisserie also take the eye. If you're visiting
in winter, chef Emile Tabourdiau offers a wide choice of seasonal
produce such as open ravioli of lobster with leek and tomato,
followed by roasted bass with a fennel sauce, and a dark chocolate
and pistachio dessert with a coconut and rum sauce to finish.
Excellent wine list. Set menus: L Fr360, L & D Fr450, Fr620.
L 12-2.30 D 7-10.30.

Paris   **La Butte Chaillot**

| Tel (1) 47 27 88 88   Fax (1) 47 04 85 70 | **R** |

112 Ave Kléber 75116 Paris
Seats 90   Meal for 2 approx Fr600

On the ground floor and basement of a luxurious modern
development, this Guy Savoy restaurant is very much a place
of the moment, especially for business lunches and social evenings.
Decorative features include iron girders and columns and
turquoise for seats, matching the shirts of the coolly efficient
waiters. Cooking is innovative without being *too* adventurous, and
the menus feature seasonal, regional themes. Summer brought   ★
a Mediterranean angle with gazpacho, *marbré* of mozzarella,
tomatoes and basil, *marmite* of red mullet with pistou and a gratin
of aubergines, *magret* of duck with honey and cassis, *fondant*
of coffee and mascarpone cream. Choose à la carte or the Fr210
menu which offers two choices from the carte for each course.
L 12-2.30 D 7-12. AMERICAN EXPRESS *Mastercard, Visa.*

Paris   **Carré des Feuillants**

| Tel (1) 42 86 82 82   Fax (1) 42 86 07 01 | **R** |

14 Rue de Castiglione 75001 Paris
Seats 70   Meal for 2 approx Fr1100

Charming restaurant in an arcade off the Rue de Rivoli with three
elegant bourgeois-style dining rooms and a glass-covered
courtyard. Alain Dutournier's accomplished cooking is firmly
based in his native Gascony with a strong awareness of the seasons,
as in the six-course no-choice "Ideas of the Season" menu which,
for an extra Fr180, comes with glasses of four different wines
chosen to complement the various courses; this menu is only
available if taken by the whole table. Typical dishes from the main
carte might be terrine of duck foie gras; roast mullet stuffed with
its liver and puréed oyster with balsamic vinaigrette and potatoes   ★
mashed with bone marrow; knuckle of veal *en cocotte* with
aubergines; and amongst the desserts (most of which need to be
ordered at the beginning of the meal) millefeuille of rhubarb,
raspberries with pistachio sabayon and strawberry soup. A large
and impressive wine list has some 1,200 bins. Set menu: Fr560.
L 12-2 D 7.30-10.30. Closed L Sat, all Sun & Aug. AMERICAN EXPRESS
Diners, Mastercard, Visa.

Paris   **Chez Georges**

Tel (1) 42 60 07 11   R

1 Rue du Mail 75002 Paris
Seats 60   Meal for 2 approx Fr520

Serving simple food with fine wine has been a family tradition for
five generations, currently upheld by Bernard Brouillet at this
archetypal brasserie – crisply-clothed tables squeezed together
against banquettes down each side of a long room with mirrored
walls – near the Place des Victoires. On one side of the menu
(handwritten but nostalgically reproduced in pink and mauve
on an ancient Roneo machine) are listed the likes of *jambon persillé*,
rillettes of goose (which comes in an earthenware pot from which
you help yourself, along with a large jar of gherkins), grilled
turbot with béarnaise sauce, and grilled lamb cutlets with haricots
verts. On the other side is printed a wine list that is full of famous
names including all the first-growth clarets, and burgundies such
as Richebourg, La Tache (both from Romanée Conti) and
Echezeaux. Some dozen wines are available by the glass – if you're
strong-willed that is, as the bottles are left on the table and you
pay for what you drink. *L 12-2 D 7-9.30. Closed Sun, 1st 2 wks
Aug, Public Holidays.* AMERICAN EXPRESS *Mastercard, Visa.*

Paris   **Concorde Lafayette**

Tel (1) 40 68 50 68   Fax (1) 40 68 50 43   HR

3 Pl Général Koenig 75017 Paris
Rooms 970   Double room from Fr1420

The top six of the 33 floors of this building are called 'Le Top
Club', where 157 executive bedrooms (supplement) have butler
service and use of a business support centre as well as a health club
located in the basement of the hotel (not part of the establishment).
It has its own check-in area and private lounge. The hotel is part
of the Palais des Congrès, where exhibitions, conventions,
congresses, trade fairs and concerts are held and eighty shops plus
four cinemas are located. The conference room, divisible into
smaller sections, has a capacity of 4000. The business centre is fully
equipped and staffed, with translation and secretarial services
available. The view from the standardised, comfortable and well-
equipped bedrooms across Paris is exceptional. It can be even more
appreciated from the panoramic bar 'Plein Ciel' on the 33rd floor.
AMERICAN EXPRESS *Diners, Mastercard, Visa.*

Etoile d'Or
Tel (1) 40 68 51 28
Seats 60   Meal for 2 approx Fr1000

On the first floor of the hotel is a modern, comfortable restaurant
with lightwood panelled walls and ceiling and claret-coloured
carpet and chairs. Diners are serenaded by a harpist in the evenings
whilst enjoying Jean-Claude Lhonneur's classic but inventive
cuisine: salami of eel and mullet in a salad; lobster cromesquis
en rémoulade; Challans duckling with orange-scented tagliatelle;
hot chocolate soufflé. Set menu: 250F. *L 12-2 D 7-10.30. Closed
Sat, Sun, Aug & Bank Holidays.*

Paris   La Coupole

Tel (1) 43 20 14 20   Fax (1) 43 35 46 14   **R**

102 Bd de Montparnasse 75014 Paris

Seats 450   Meal for 2 approx Fr440

Listed as a historic monument, this famous, vast and air-conditioned brasserie opens at 7.30am for breakfast and takes last orders at 2am (lunch from noon). Completely renovated a few years ago by the new owners, it is still as popular as when it first opened in 1927. Frequented over the years by writers, poets and artists living in the Montparnasse area, it has changed little and remains a popular venue with the media. Reservations are only taken up to 8.30pm, so should there be a wait for a table, order a drink at the bar to the left of the entrance and watch the comings and goings to pass the time. The daily-changing mainly fish menu offers salmon and crab terrine with lobster sauce or a *dariole* of courgettes with a tomato coulis, followed by a house speciality, *choucroute paysanne*, or pan-fried wild mushrooms à la bordelaise or goose cassoulet, with the *dessert du jour* to finish. Fish and shellfish are delivered daily. Terrace. Set menus: L (until 3pm) Fr85/Fr109 D (only after 10pm) Fr109. *Open 7.30am-2am (lunch served from noon).* AMERICAN EXPRESS *Diners, Mastercard, Visa.*

Paris   Hotel de Crillon

Tel (1) 44 71 15 00   Fax (1) 44 71 15 02   **HR**

10 Place de la Concorde 75008 Paris

Rooms 163   Double room from Fr3500

Each capital has its favourite and most reputable *palace*. The Hotel de Crillon, owned by the Taittinger family, maintains the tradition of quality that built the hotel's reputation. The central hall made of Siena and Portor marble has intimate proportions, an open fire and private desks for checking in and out. A history of customers is kept, retaining personal preferences and tastes. From the central hall, a few steps lead to the *grand salon d'honneur* looking out on to the patio used as a summer restaurant and *salon de thé* with harp music. Facing the Place de la Concorde, on the southern side of the *salon d'honneur*, is Les Ambassadeurs restaurant. Different in style and feel, the hotel's second bar and the restaurant l'Obélisque have low ceilings and a clubby atmosphere of panelled walls. The hotel's first floor is dedicated to conferences and receptions with a series of linked historic rooms: *salon Marie-Antoinette* with its delightful terrace, *salon des Aigles* and *salon des Batailles* all look out on to the famous obelisk. The salons, carefully decorated, have been solemnly restored to their former glory. Air-conditioned and quiet, the bedrooms are traditional in decor. Many are tastefully decorated by Sonia Rykiel. Bedrooms are particularly roomy, equipped with modern comforts of cabled television, mini-bar and 24hr room service. Most of the beautiful marble bathrooms have separate showers and bath. Small flats on the top floor have private terraces and breathtaking views of the capital's roofs. Fax machines are available in the bedrooms if needed, there are several conference rooms, and secretarial services are available on request. AMERICAN EXPRESS *Diners, Mastercard, Visa.*   *See over*

Les Ambassadeurs
Tel (1) 44 71 16 16
Seats 60   Meal for 2 approx Fr1500

The grandiose surroundings have ideal proportions, making the
dining room comfortable and enjoyable rather than intimidating,
and this remarkable setting, Christian Constant can express his
talent without reserve. The seasonally changing menu is precisely
executed, and instead of the traditional miniature amuse-bouche
systematically offered in this category of restaurant, a refreshing
chilled *soupe de cocos* (white beans) with miniature diced truffle
makes a perfect introduction to the meal. Look out for dishes such
as *foie gras de canard poelé au pain d'épices, marrons concassés
et topinambours mijotés* (pan-fried foie gras with a light crust
of sweet ginger-bread served with chestnuts and braised Jerusalem
artichokes), *filet de rouget, os et branche de céleri-rave à la moelle, sauce
civet* (red mullet served in a delicate red wine sauce, garnished
with celeriac stuffed with a mix of celery leaves and marrow),
*jarret de porcelet caramelisé aux aromates, fine choucroute de navets
à l'aigre-doux* (caramelised piglet hock served with sweet and sour
pickled turnips). Talent reaches its zenith with desserts like the
extraordinary *truffe glacée à la fleur de thym frais, ganache au chocolat
"Manjari" fondue*, when a spoonful of thyme-scented ice cream –
like inhaling a bouquet of fresh thyme – is the perfect answer
to the intoxicating richness of the chocolate sauce. Complementing
all this, the service, never stiff, is a joy of attention and kindness.
Half bottles under Fr100 are scarce on the exceptional but pricy
wine list. Set L Fr330. *L 12-12.30 D 7-9.30.*

★

L'Obélisque
Seats 50   **Meal for 2 approx Fr750**

Separate entrance on Rue Boissy d'Anglas. The elegant wood-
panelled dining room with touches of red velvet and Lalique
chandeliers is extremely busy at lunchtime. Supervised
by Christian Constant, the attractive menu offers *fines tartes de St
Jacques, fondue d'endives à l'orange amère* (scallops with bitter
orange-flavoured chicory), *dos de cabillaud, herbes en salade, haricots
frais au pistou* (cod served with a herb salad and pesto beans),
estouffade de marcassin aux petits oignons et marrons (a stew of young
wild boar, pearl onions and chestnuts) and *tarte tatin aux poires
et glace pistache*. Full meals are not a requirement in this informal
restaurant. For wine-lovers the menu *Les Coordonnées* associates,
for Fr250, basil-flavoured fresh pasta with a glass of Chateau
Mouton-Rothschild Pauillac 1984, or classic foie gras with
Chateau d'Yquem Lur-Saluces Sauternes 1981. *L 12-2.30 D 7-
10.30. Closed Aug.*

Paris   **Le Dome**

Tel (1) 43 35 25 81   Fax (1) 42 79 01 19   R

108 Bd de Montparnasse 75014 Paris
Seats 130   Meal for 2 approx Fr700

Bouillabaisse, oysters and lobster remain among the traditional
specialities at this most durable of Montparnasse institutions, but
Franck Graux's menu also moves with the times. Carpaccio
of tuna fish with aubergine purée, Saint-Pierre sautéed with
potatoes and courgette 'spaghetti', and *sole de l'Ile de Yeu à la*

meunière show the contemporary side. Fruit is put to excellent use in many desserts, including baked figs, apple tart and a gratin of red fruits. *L 12-3 D 7-12.30. Open for coffee and snacks from 8am. Closed Mon, also Sun in Aug.* ▨▨▨▨▨ *Diners, Mastercard, Visa.*

Paris	**Drouant**	

Tel (1) 42 65 15 16   Fax (1) 49 24 02 15   **R**

18 Pl Gaillon 75002 Paris

Seats 70   Meal for 2 approx Fr1200

A short stroll from the Place de l'Opéra with a restaurant as well as a café, Drouant is distinguished by its elegant art deco styling. It's under the same ownership as the *Jules Verne*, on the second storey of the Eiffel Tower, and the latter's one-time head chef now cooks here. Its location close to the Paris Bourse means that lunchtimes are invariably busy with diners from the business community. Louis Grondard's cooking is of extremely well-thought-out dishes prepared in a style that's decidedly modern but retaining a clear classical pedigree. The carte features a short section of old favourites such as a soup of shellfish and saffron or Challans duck with pepper and paprika. Typical offerings otherwise could be duck foie gras with peppercorns and sea salt, veal sweetbread fritters with gribiche sauce, roast turbot with parsley and pumpkin, pigeon with coriander and orange zest and Pauillac lamb roasted under a herb crust. A speciality is a charlotte of langoustines with aubergines. Desserts include such delicacies as a triple chocolate charlotte with ginger cream or a fruit savarin flavoured with Grand Marnier. *L 12-2.30 D 7-10.30. Closed D 25 Dec, 1 Jan.* ▨▨▨▨▨ *Diners, Mastercard, Visa.* 🐂

Paris	**Duquesnoy**	

Tel (1) 47 05 96 78   Fax (1) 44 18 90 57   **R**

6 Ave Bosquet 75007 Paris

Seats 45   Meal for 2 approx Fr1100

Jean-Paul Duquesnoy prepares haute cuisine dishes for a smart, civilised clientele in his handsomely decorated, wood-panelled restaurant just South of Pont d'Alma. His skill, finesse and light touch are evident throughout exceptionally enticing menus: *soupe crémeuse de girolles au cerfeuil et grosses langoustines,* crab-stuffed courgette flowers, *rouelles d'abats de la "Saint Cochon",* beef with truffles in a Cahors wine sauce with quenelles of bone marrow and ethereal pommes soufflées, a spectacular dessert of four different chocolate creations. Choosing is a delightful, but difficult task, and Jean-Paul will do it for you if you (and all at your table) order the *menu dégustation* of four specialities served in small portions. The Fr250 lunchtime menu provides great value for money. Classic wines accompany the classic food. Françoise Duquesnoy is a charming and knowledgable hostess. *L 12-2 D 8-10. Closed L Sat, all Sun, 1st 2 wks Aug, 25 Dec, 1 Jan.* ▨▨▨▨▨ *Mastercard, Visa.*

★

Paris   Gallopin

Tel (1) 42 36 45 38   Fax (1) 42 36 10 32   **R**

40 Rue Notre Dame des Victoires 75002 Paris
Seats 120 (+ 30 outdoor)   Meal for 2 approx Fr460

Little changed in looks since it opened in 1876, this is one of the
capital's most durable institutions. The wood is all mahogany,
with brass, glass and moulded ceilings completing the traditional
picture. M. Wafrez, here since 1980, presents a menu that's also
very much in the classical French tradition, based on *cuisine
du marché* and featuring familiar favourites like *oeuf en geleé*,
omelettes, sole meunière, grilled pig's trotters, andouillettes and
steaks. Good food is accompanied by a well-chosen selection
of wines at affordable prices (you're welcome at any time to sit
at the mahogany bar counter and enjoy a drink). Set menu:
D Fr150. *L 11.30-3 D 7.30-11.30. Closed Sat, Sun.* AMERICAN EXPRESS
Diners, Mastercard, Visa.

Paris   George V

Tel (1) 47 23 54 00   Fax (1) 47 20 40 00   **H R**

31 Ave George V 75008 Paris
Rooms 260   Double room from Fr2800

Named after an English king, designed by an American (in the
late 1920s) and run by the international Forte group, the George
V is nevertheless the one Parisian hotel that most people will have
heard of. Grand, high-ceilinged public rooms boast antique
furniture, 17th-century tapestries, objets d'art and even a Renoir
plus lots of fresh flowers, all helping to create an atmosphere
of elegance and luxury. Whether staying in one of the many
sumptuous suites or in an individually designed bedroom one can
expect the same high standards of service. Numerous private
function rooms include the wood-panelled Louis XIII salon with
its massive stone fireplace and the Chantilly room with cool
stylised classical murals. Business travellers can have fax machines
installed in their bedrooms; secretarial and translation services are
available on request, and conference facilities can cater for up to
600. AMERICAN EXPRESS *Diners, Mastercard, Visa.*

Les Princes Restaurant
Seats 60   Meal for 2 approx Fr900

Chandeliers above widely spaced tables with elegant place settings
and a huge floral centrepiece – this is a truly grand hotel dining
room with a suitably expansive menu. The main carte
is supplemented by a limited choice fixed-price menu and,
in season, a special game menu. Latest specialities include pan-fried
langoustines, St Pierre and crab in a light green onion sauce, and
miniature pompoms of fowl, truffles and foie gras with
an asparagus salad. If you want to go the whole hog try the no-
choice tasting menu that consists of eight suitably small-sized
courses. A large terrace can seat up to 70 and when in use the
dining room itself is not. Set menus Fr240/Fr450. *L 12-2.30
D 7-10.30.*

Paris   **Gérard Besson**

Tel (1) 42 33 14 74   Fax (1) 42 33 85 71   **R**

5 Rue Coq-Héron 75001 Paris

Seats 45   Meal for 2 approx Fr1100

Well-spaced tables with immaculate settings, old paintings and
silver carafes in display cases are all part of the elegant scenery, but
it's Gérard Besson's superb cooking which takes centre stage at this
outstanding restaurant in the old Les Halles area. With Garin,
Chapel and Jamin among his mentors, Besson has the soundest
of classical bases from which to make some exciting and
innovative excursions. Truffles and mushrooms are great
favourites, appearing in such dishes as scrambled egg with truffles
and duck terrine with marinated mushrooms. Game is another
seasonal speciality, and lobsters from Erquy Bay are prepared *à la
nage* or baked in the shell. Desserts such as raspberry sponge cake
are no less irresistible, and the wine cellar is just about as classy
as the kitchen. Set menus: L Fr260 D from Fr650. *L 12-2.30
D 7.15-10.30. Closed L Sat, all Sun & 3 wks Jul.* AMERICAN EXPRESS
Diners, Mastercard, Visa.

★

Paris   **Grand Hotel Inter-Continental**

Tel (1) 40 07 32 32   Fax (1) 42 66 12 51   **HR**

2 Rue Scribe 75009 Paris

Rooms 514   Double room from Fr2500

On the corner of Place de l'Opéra and facing the opera house itself,
this luxurious and tastefully decorated hotel dating back to the
Napoleon III era has twenty-five spacious suites among its 500+
rooms. The hotel's central reception room, the Cour d'Honneur,
is a marble-floored glass-domed lounge. Take your breakfast in the
Brasserie du Café de la Paix, which runs along two sides of the
building. Conference rooms (max 700). Fax machines available in
bedrooms, secretarial and translation services on request.
AMERICAN EXPRESS *Diners, Mastercard, Visa.*

Restaurant Opéra
Tel (1) 40 07 30 10
5 Pl de l'Opéra 75009 Paris

Seats 75   Meal for 2 approx Fr1000

The Grand Hotel Inter-Continental is home to this very grand
gastronomic restaurant. It also has its own entrance on the Place
de l'Opéra – an elegant restaurant decorated in blue and gold, with
original gold leaf mouldings, and famous painted ceiling murals
of stylised cherubim and clouds. With the advent of a new chef
significant changes can be expected to both the carte and set
menus. Comprehensive wine list. Set menus: L and D Fr285,
Fr450, Fr385. *L 12-3 D 7-11. Closed Sat, Sun & Aug.*

See over for 2nd restaurant

Brasserie du Café de la Paix
Tel (1) 40 07 30 20
12 Bd des Capucines 75009 Paris
Seats 220   Meal for 2 approx Fr350

Taking up two sides of the hotel, one on the boulevard and the
other on the Place de l'Opéra, this famous brasserie has been
a popular meeting place for 130 years. With its 19th-century fresco
paintings on the ceiling and wall panels and stylised winter garden
decor, the inside area serves traditional French cuisine while the
glass-roofed pavement terrace is an ideal spot for cocktails, coffee,
simple meals and elite people-watching! Set menu: Fr135. *Meals
12-1.15am.* 🐄

Paris   **Le Grand Véfour**

Tel (1) 42 96 56 27   Fax (1) 42 86 80 71   R

17 Rue de Beaujolais 75001 Paris
Seats 60   Meal for 2 approx Fr1350

A historic restaurant that can trace its origins back to a café
opened in 1784 in one wing of the then new Palais Royal. With
its richly ornate original interior recently restored by new owners,
Taittinger, and with Guy Martin now getting to grips with the
kitchen, the fortunes of Grand Véfour are again on an upward
path. Salmon mousse with fennel salad, ravioli of foie gras with
truffle cream, sausage of veal sweetbread and rice with haricot
beans, gourmet 'cottage pie' made with oxtail and truffles, and best   ★
end of lamb with aubergine and confit show the style. A 'Menu
Plaisir' at Fr750, served only to the whole table, brings the chef's
chosen menu for the day – ideal if you find it difficult to choose.
There is also a relatively good-value set lunch, with a choice
of about six dishes at each stage, at Fr305. Air-conditioned. Valet
parking. *L 12.30-2.15 D 7.30-10.15. Closed Sat, Sun & Aug.*
AMERICAN EXPRESS® *Diners, Mastercard, Visa.*

Paris   **Guy Savoy**

Tel (1) 43 80 40 61   Fax (1) 46 22 43 09   R

18 Rue Troyon 75017 Paris
Seats 100   Meal for 2 approx Fr1500

When a restaurant can afford a glossy brochure and provide valet
parking and/or chauffeured limousines, it's usually a sign that
you're about to dine somewhere rather special, as is the case here.
Close to the Arc de Triomphe, Guy Savoy's air-conditioned
restaurant is one of *the* gastronomic temples in a city that's not
short of good tables! It's an intimate restaurant with columned
lightwood screens sectioning off areas, with pastel colours, quite
bold wallpaper, exquisite china and table settings, plants and fresh
flowers all combining to create a sophisticated atmosphere. Since
opening in 1986, Guy Savoy has become one of the top chefs   ★
in Paris – his secret of success can perhaps be put down to his
refreshingly simple style and just cooking for sheer pleasure,
though there's probably an element of profit in between. English
translations hardly do justice to the dishes here, but you could start
with a warm turbot salad and artichoke vinaigrette or a light soup
of lentils and langoustines, followed by baby turbot roasted whole
with steamed vegetables or pigeon served in two parts, poached
and grilled. Sea bass grilled in its skin with a lightly spiced sauce

is a new speciality. Also relatively new is a *menu dégustation* at Fr750. Cheeses come in prime condition, and the desserts (grapefruit terrine with a tea sauce, vanilla millefeuille in a red fruit coulis, flaky rhubarb tart with a blackberry sauce) end the meal on a high note. Unusually for a French restaurant, there's a good selection of wines from other areas, with Italy, Spain and California making a respectable show. Some own label house wines. Private rooms 6/35. *L 12-2.30 D 7.30-11. Closed Sun.* AMERICAN EXPRESS *Mastercard, Visa.*

Paris	Hilton	
Tel (1) 42 73 92 00 Fax (1) 47 83 62 66		**H**

18 Ave de Suffren 75015 Paris

Rooms 456   Double room from Fr1850

Only a few yards from the Eiffel Tower, the Paris Hilton overlooks the Palais de Chaillot and Trocadero Gardens. All rooms are equipped with air-conditioning, cable TV (18 channels) in stereo with remote control, radio, mini-bar and direct-dial telephone. The Toit de Paris on the 10th (rooftop) floor has a panoramic view of Paris and is a good spot for de luxe seminars. Up to 800 can be accommodated theatre-style in the conference and banqueting area, where the business centre is located. AMERICAN EXPRESS *Diners, Mastercard, Visa.* 🐂

Paris	Holiday Inn République	
Tel (1) 43 55 44 34 · Fax (1) 47 00 32 34		**HR**

10 Pl de la République 75011 Paris

Rooms 318   Double room from Fr1380

Both the standard and luxurious categories of air-conditioned bedrooms at this large hotel are well equipped. The building, which dates back to 1850, is now a listed historic monument and the original attractive courtyard is popular for sitting out in or for hiring for private functions. Nine conference rooms (max 400 people). AMERICAN EXPRESS *Diners, Mastercard, Visa.*

La Belle Epoque

Seats 200   Meal for 2 approx Fr700

Renovated a few years ago but retaining the decor of the era, the Belle Epoque restaurant no longer offers set menus but a buffet priced at Fr175 (Fr195 on Friday and Saturday nights for a Buffet Océan) in addition to the 'carte'. The choice may include fillet of sea brill in a provençal sauce and pan-fried duck breast with fresh vegetables, followed by a caramel and Cointreau mousse with candied orange peel. Wines from Australia and Spain as well as France. *L 12-2.30 D 7.30-10.30. Closed L Sat, all Sun, Aug & Bank Holidays.* 🐂

Meal prices for 2 are based on à la carte menus.
When set menus are available, prices will often be lower.

Paris   **Hotel Inter-Continental**

Tel (1) 44 77 11 11   Fax (1) 44 77 14 60   **HR**

3 Rue Castiglione 75001 Paris
Room 450   Double room from Fr2500

Situated off Place Vendome and facing the landscaped Tuilieries
Gardens, this extremely elegant hotel is a listed historic
monument. Of the 450 air-conditioned rooms, 70 are spacious
suites, and all offer the highest standards of luxurious
accommodation. 12 function rooms (max 1000) – two with
elaborately mouldings and painted ceilings, chandeliers and
columns. Fax machines available in bedrooms; secretarial and
translation services. AMERICAN EXPRESS *Diners, Mastercard, Visa.*

Terrasse Fleurie
Tel (1) 44 77 10 44
Seats 40 (**+**90 outdoor)   Meal for 2 approx Fr1000

Passing through the lobby of the Hotel Inter-Continental, this
pleasant restaurant comes into view through the columns that
surround the central courtyard. In summer the Fr250 set lunch
is replaced by a Fr350 buffet out in the courtyard itself around
which the hotel is constructed. The interior has a 'winter garden'
decor with a marble floor, large windows and fixed conservatory
blinds across the glass ceiling. Chef Raoul Gaiga serves French
nouvelle cuisine with dishes such as clam and crab salad with
a vegetable tartare or a *friture* of red mullet and baby sole with
a julienne of deep-fried leeks as starters, followed by breast
of duckling with stuffed turnips or young turbot roasted with
sweet garlic (for two). Set menus: L Fr250 (Fr350 in summer)
DFr450. *L 12-2.30 D 7-10. Closed 25 Dec-1 Jan.* 🐂

Paris   **Jacques Cagna**

Tel (1) 43 26 49 39   Fax (1) 43 54 54 48   **R**

14 Rue des Grands-Augustins 75006 Paris
Seats 60   Meal for 2 approx Fr1200

Jacques Cagna is a well-known name within French gastronomic
circles which recognise, support and appreciate good restaurants.
Situated in the St Germàin area near the Seine, his first-floor
restaurant, housed in a fine old building with a heavy oak-beamed
ceiling, light oak panelling and Flemish paintings, has a refined
atmosphere, which contrasts perhaps with the energetic *cuisine*
emanating from the kitchens. The modern but classically based
à la carte menu changes four times a year, though some specialities
reappear and the Fr260 fixed-price (four courses) *déjeuner* has
seasonal dishes. Try the *petits escargots frais des Charentes en surprise*,
followed by a classic poached turbot with sauce hollandaise,
sometimes served with green ravioli and glazed onions. Main
courses might offer a Challans duck with a Bourgogne red wine
sauce with lemon and orange zest, and a *cote de veau de lait
de Corrèze au gingembre et citron vert.* Super sweets include a trio
of *sablés* (strawberries, raspberries and wild strawberries) or a large
plate of assorted chocolate desserts. Splendid coffee and excellent
service under the direction of Jacques' sister Anny, who lovingly
looks after the exceptional wine list. Private room for 10.

Set meals: L Fr260 and Fr480 D Fr480. *L 12-2 D 7.30-10.30.*
Closed L Sat, 1st 3 weeks Aug, Christmas to New Year.
AMERICAN EXPRESS *Diners, Mastercard, Visa.* 🐂

Paris   **Jules Verne**

| Tel (1) 45 55 61 44   Fax (1) 47 05 29 41 | R |

2ème Etage Tour Eiffel 75007 Paris
Seats 100   Meal for 2 approx Fr1400

A private lift transports guests up to the second level of the Eiffel
Tower to this unique setting. The interior decor purposefully
doesn't detract from what's outside – everything is black and grey,
even the paintings! Chef Alain Reix specialises in country cooking
(*cuisine du terroir*) with an emphasis on fish: little loaves of bread
filled with crab and a shrimp sauce, followed by fillet of bass with
truffles or pigeon tournedos with a honey-scented sauce, and finish
with a white chocolate 'beehive' filled with dark chocolate mousse.
Reservations should be made 6-7 weeks in advance. Set menus:
L Fr290 (Mon-Fri), D Fr660. *L 12.15-2.30 D 7.30-10.30.*
AMERICAN EXPRESS *Diners, Mastercard, Visa.*

Paris   **Kléber Palace**

| Tel (1) 44 05 75 00   Fax (1) 44 05 74 74 | H |

81 Ave Kléber 75016 Paris
Rooms 83   Double room from Fr1300

A prestigious, ultra-modern *résidence hotelière* inaugurated
in October 1993. Bedrooms (no suites) vary in size and a little
in their appointments, but all have kitchenettes (sometimes just
a sink and hob in a cabinet) which provide the possibility of life
without the hotel's considerable facilities; these include a bright
breakfast room and a full-scale restaurant. The hotel is built round
an atrium in which a jungle of plants grows. All bedrooms
overlook either this or the street, and the latter also get a look
at greenery, in this case bamboo plants in a dramatic vertical
greenhouse clinging to the facade. Bedroom furniture is simple,
stylish and practical, and some inside rooms have terraces with
wooden outdoor furniture. All rooms have individual air-
conditioning, fax points and marble bathrooms. Day rooms
include a long, long lounge beyond the always-manned reception
desk, a bar with a crescent counter and fitness centre in the
basement with mini-gym, sauna, turkish bath, solarium and
a jacuzzi the size of a small swimming pool. Room service can
provide snacks at any time. Parking Fr60 per day. AMERICAN EXPRESS
Diners, Mastercard, Visa.

Opening times are often liable to change at short notice,
so it's always best to book.

Paris   **Lasserre**

Tel (1) 43 59 53 43   Fax (1) 45 63 72 23   **R**
17 Ave Franklin D Roosevelt 75008 Paris
Seats 100   Meal for 2 approx Fr1500

Arriving in Paris between the wars, at the age of 12, from humble
origins in Bayonne, René Lasserre created one of the most notable
restaurants in town, one that generates intense loyalty from both
customers – regulars have their own Club de la Casserole – and
staff, whose former members have their own organization "Les
Anciens de Lasserre" which includes such now famous chefs
as Gérard Boyer, Guy Savoy and Marc Haeberlin among its
number. Attention to detail is the hallmark of all aspects of both
service and decor, the latter including silver table decorations,
specially commissioned chandeliers and the famous sliding roof
(itself a work of art with stylised figures painted against a blue sky
background) that retracts on summer evenings to magical effect.
The menu is not so much traditional or old-fashioned as timeless
with specialities including a warm salad of sweetbreads and
langoustines, clams roasted in their shells with hazelnuts, sole
soufflé with a salpicon of shellfish, "Le Ragout '74", escalope of foie
gras with grapes, duck with orange "Lasserre" (kept on the menu
by popular demand), and, another immovable fixture this, the
mesclagne Landais Mère Irma named after, and based on a dish of,
René's mother involving a rich chicken "dumpling" concealing
slices of foie gras in a sauce with morel mushrooms and truffle
garnish. The vast cellar of over 200,000 bottles is a veritable
treasure-house of famous names and rare vintages. Upstairs in the
dining room the decanting of old red wines is a serious business
too, involving a wonderful collection of antique cut-glass silver-
necked pitchers. *L 12.30-2.30 D 7.30-10.30. Closed L Mon, all Sun.*
AMERICAN EXPRESS *Mastercard, Visa.*

Paris   **Laurent**

Tel (1) 42 25 00 39   Fax (1) 45 62 45 21   **R**
41 Ave Gabriel 75008 Paris
Seats 100 (+ 100 outdoor)   Meal for 2 approx Fr1800

A former hunting lodge dating back to Louis XIV and now
a beautifully furnished and exquisite setting for Philippe Braun's
cooking. There's a splendid terrace for al fresco dining in the
summer. The menu, devised by Robuchon with whom Braun
trained is a carefully executed and studied working of modern
cooking. Textures and flavours are juxtaposed with great finesse
ensuring a level of sophistication and harmony that complements
the fine decor. Hors d'oeuvre include fresh crab meat with
avocado, langoustines with basil and duck liver paté with black
beans. For fish there is pan-fried lobster with potatoes and
rosemary and spider crab in aniseed jelly with a cream fennel
sauce. Wonderful sweets range from the classic crepes Suzette
to crumble aux fruits de saison and made-to-order ices and sorbets.
Set menu Fr380. *L 12.30-3. D 7.30-11. Closed L Sat, all Sun, Bank
Holidays.* AMERICAN EXPRESS *Diners, Mastercard, Visa.*

Paris   Ledoyen

Tel (1) 47 42 35 98   Fax (1) 47 42 55 01   **R**

Carré des Champs-Elysées 75008 Paris
Seats 50   Meal for 2 approx Fr1200

Patronised by Robespierre, painted by Tissot, written about
by Maupassant – Ledoyen's claim to be the "most legendary
gastronomic address in Paris" is no idle boast. Opened in 1792 (as
Chez Doyen) the setting, in a pavilion near the Petit Palais in the
Jardin des Champs Elysées, is incomparable, with the most elegant
first-floor dining room looking out over the gardens. Restaurants
are all about food, however, and the hotel group which now
owns Ledoyen have lured husband and wife team Jean-Paul and
Ghislaine Arabian (the former as ebullient manager, the latter
to take charge of the kitchen) from their highly acclaimed
restaurant in Lille to reinvigorate the cuisine here. Deceptively
simple dishes concentrate on taste and flavour rather than
spectacular presentation: scallops in a fluffy liquor flavoured with
beer (something of a signature ingredient – it also appears as a
flavouring for the eel in aspic, turbot is roasted in it and it crops
up again in a hot sabayon served with the chicory parfait for
dessert); ravioli of lobster and girolle mushrooms. Game in season
might include a terrine of hare with rhubarb chutney, and
noisettes of venison flavoured with juniper berries and served with
figs cooked in red wine. Prices are not totally astronomic and one
can even find a Fr50 half bottle of Cotes de Blaye rubbing
shoulders with Ch Petrus on the wine list. Set menu Fr480. On the
ground floor, and also under the supervision of Ghislaine Arabian
(although she is very much 'at the stove' of the gastronomic
restaurant above), is Le Cercle Ledoyen (also open on Saturday,
Tel 47 42 76 02 for reservations) where all the main dishes are
priced at Fr100. *L 12-2 D 7-10. Closed Sat, Sun, August.*
AMERICAN EXPRESS *Diners, Mastercard, Visa.*

Paris   Lucas Carton

Tel (1) 42 65 22 90   Fax (1) 42 65 06 23   **R**

9 Place de la Madeleine 75008 Paris
Seats 100   Meal for 2 approx Fr2600

This temple of French gastronomy is actually Japanese-owned now
although Alain Senderens remains in charge of the kitchen and
it is his genius that comes up with such creations as his famous
raviolis de pétrouches (baby scallops) *aux courgettes*. The carte
is unique in giving the option of a glass of wine individually
chosen to complement each and every dish, including the puds – a
truly wonderful idea. A glass of '86 Jurançon with the cabbage-
wrapped foie gras, for example, a grand chablis with a dish
of langoustines, ginger and fried oysters; Pomerol with the wild
duck and the Ch Latour '87 with the noisettes of lamb. Desserts
are all prepared individually to order so it is necessary to make
your selection along with the starter and main dish, unless leaving
all decisions to the kitchen by going for the no-choice 'Menu
Lucas Carton' – served only to the whole table. Set menu Fr1100.
*L 12-2.30 D 8-10.30. Closed L Sat, all Sun, 23 Dec-3 Jan, 1st 3 wks
Aug. Mastercard, Visa.*

Paris   Hotel Lutétia

Tel (1) 49 54 46 46   Fax (1) 49 54 46 00   **HR**

45 Bd Raspail 75006 Paris
Rooms 280   Double room from Fr1100

One of the grandest and most famous of the Left Bank hotels,
opened in 1910 and renovated in magnificent Art Deco style
in 1983, under the direction of Sonia Rykiel. Day rooms are
splendid in their size and appointments – marble, gilt, velvet,
Lalique, Taki's sculptures, glass screens from the 30s – and the Bar
Lutèce, looking down on the vast reception area has long been
a favourite meeting place of the smart set. A pianist plays in the
evening, jazz trios make frequent appearances and the barman and
his assistant are stars in the world of mixing and inventing
cocktails. There are no less than 12 conference rooms, the largest
seating 450 theatre-style. The bedrooms, elegantly done out
in grey, purple and gold, have the style of the 30s (ornate period
furnishings, octagonal bedheads, mahogany wardrobes, bathrooms
in light marble and black faïence), and the amenities of today,
including 17-channel TVs, air-conditioning, sound-proofing and,
for rooms overlooking the street, double glazing. AMERICAN EXPRESS
Diners, Mastercard, Visa.

Le Paris
Seats 35   Meal for 2 approx Fr1200

Philippe Renard is one of the chefs of the moment in Paris, and
in the hotel's small and refined first restaurant diners can enjoy the
full range of his considerable talents which combine classical skills
(he's a disciple of Escoffier) with a real sense of creativity. The
major menu (Fr495 with wine) offers alternatives at each stage:
among recent specialities are turbot cooked with Guérande salt
and Breton seaweed, braised knuckle of veal with mushrooms and
thick pasta ribbons, and crunchy triangles of liquorice with
a rhubarb and strawberry compote. Set menus: L Fr250 and Fr350
D Fr350 and Fr495. *L 12-2 D 7.30-10.30 Closed Sat, Sun & Aug.*
Brasserie Lutétia, the hotel's second restaurant, is open from
7am to midnight, first for breakfast (till noon) then with a menu
of grand brasserie classics including *fruits de mer,* crispy salmon
with salad and cream dressing, *andouillette de Troyes* and *crème
brulée à la vanille.* A la carte or prix-fixe menus at Fr95 and Fr160.

Paris   Méridien Montparnasse

Tel (1) 44 36 44 36   Fax (1) 44 36 49 00   **HR**

19 Rue Cdt-Mouchotte 75014 Paris
Rooms 953   Double from Fr900

Being one of the few skyscraper buildings (25 floors) in the centre
of Paris, the view from the top floors is exceptional. Located in the
heart of Montparnasse and close to the railway station, home
to the TGV Atlantique high-speed rail link, guests here are
perfectly placed for a stay in Paris, whether on business or pleasure,
in comfortable, well-equipped bedrooms. 10 conference rooms
(max 2000). AMERICAN EXPRESS *Diners, Mastercard, Visa.*

Montparnasse 25
Tel (1) 44 36 44 25   Fax (1) 44 36 49 03
Seats 70   Meal for 2 approx Fr700

The decor emphasises the mid-1920s – photos of stars of the stage
and screen of the period hang on the walls next to reproductions
of Modigliani paintings. This is an elegant restaurant where tables
are well spaced and service is discreetly efficient. The cuisine
is 'classical French' with dishes such as langoustines with a warm
vinaigrette with herbs and potato salad, followed by roast saddle
of pork or sole with Cantonese spices and a mousseline sauce.
Desserts may include a passion fruit soufflé or a hot pear strudel
with a caramel ice cream. California, Italy and Spain are
represented on the wine list, as well as France. Set menus:
L Fr230F, D Fr290, Fr380. *L 12-2.30 D 7.30-10.30. Closed Sat,
Sun, Aug & 25 Dec – 1 Jan.* 🐄

Justine
Tel (1) 44 36 44 00
Seats 280   Meal for 2 approx Fr500

On the hotel's first floor overlooking a 100-square-metre terrace
of garden with trees, plants, shrubs and flowers, this brasserie
resembles an enclosed verandah. It opens for breakfast at 7am and
the buffet menu (Fr195) operates from midday. Alternative dishes
to the buffet are *rascasse au gratin, sauce hachée à l'olive noire* or *trois
mignons aux trois sauces.* On Sundays, the 'Bébé Brunch' menu
(adults Fr220, children 4-12 Fr110, under 4s free) is especially
geared towards families. The interior reflects the terrace garden
theme with a pastel green and pink decor. Guests at tables by the
large windows enjoy a view of the greenery. Open 7-10.30 for
breakfast and noon-11pm. *L (buffet) 12-2.30 D 7-11.*

Paris   **Meurice**   **HR**
Tel (1) 44 58 10 10   Fax (1) 44 58 10 17
228 Rue de Rivoli 75001 Paris
Rooms 180   Double room from Fr2500

Dating from the time when Prefect Haussmann was replanning
Paris, the Meurice, with its location overlooking the Tuileries
Gardens, quickly established itself as a favourite of the Imperial
Court. More recently it has become a haunt of the literati with the
jury of a new literary prize 'Le Jury Du Prix Novembre' making
their home here. Following the hotel's acquisition by the Ciga
group in 1988 considerable refurbishment has returned the sparkle
to the stunning Salon Pompadour with its elaborate gilt
decoration, and other public rooms and restored the hotel's
position amongst the best in Paris. Antique furniture, fresh
flowers, original paintings and the occasional marble fireplace are
among the elements that bring individuality and luxury to both
the bedrooms and the 37 suites. Bathrooms are marble and
standards of service high. Conference facilities for up to 250
theatre-style. AMERICAN EXPRESS *Diners, Mastercard, Visa.*

Le Meurice
Seats 50   Meal for 2 approx Fr1000

Marc Marchand's menu changes with the seasons in this
exquisitely appointed restaurant, but on Wednesdays you might
get all four seasons at once, as Vivaldi is often included in the
musical 'saveurs lyriques' evenings. Salad of pasta and shellfish with
olive oil; *parmentier* of snails with an almond and parsley-infused
jus; delicate pastry of tomato, sardine, mozzarella and black olives;
turbot roasted whole with salted butter; rascasse with confit
tomatoes and basil; guinea fowl with a spicy coating and *faux-filet*
grilled and served with nutmeg-seasoned spinach are typical
choices. Palette of caramel tastes with a gently spiced sauce is a
speciality dessert. Set menus: L Fr300 D (inclusive of wine) Fr380.
L 12.15-2.30 D 7.30-11.

Paris   **Michel Rostang**

Tel (1) 47 63 40 77   Fax (1) 47 63 82 75   **R**

20 Rue Rennequin 75017 Paris
Seats 65   Meal for 2 approx Fr1500

The man himself is not always in situ – there's an empire
to oversee, as far afield as New York and the Antibes. The
restaurant, north of Place des Ternes, is at the angle of Rue
Gustave-Flaubert; it's strikingly and boldly decorated, almost
Oriental, with a cream and red ceiling, deep red lacquered
woodwork and matching walls, carpets and chairs, complemented
by beautiful flower arrangements. Mirrors abound, as do staff, all
very professional, who glide effortlessly around the room. As in
many Parisian restaurants, fixed-price menus (lunch Fr298, dinner
Fr520) offer the best value, with several dishes taken from the
carte. Here, for instance, both *poelée de homard en anchoïade, salade
de pointes d'asperges et artichauts violets à l'huile de homard* and *terrine
de langoustines "mi-crue mi-cuite" en demi-gelée de crustacés* appear
on the *menu dégustation* (Fr720 per person for six courses with
a suggestion that the entire table chooses the same menu). Also
worth trying are the braised sole in a red wine jus with girolles,
and roast squab pigeon with blackcurrants, baby turnips and
cracked pepper. There's a fine selection of mature and goat's
cheeses, super desserts such as Rostang's own favourite hot bitter
chocolate tart, and delightful petits fours to accompany excellent
coffee. The wine list carries some 600 bins, mostly French. Private
rooms 8/20. *L 12-2 D 8-10.15. Closed Sat (but open D Sep-Jun), all
Sun and first three weeks Aug.* AMERICAN EXPRESS *Mastercard, Visa.*

Paris   **Miravile**

Tel (1) 42 74 72 22   Fax (1) 42 74 67 55   **R**

72 Quai de l'Hotel de Ville 75004 Paris
Seats 70   Meal for 2 approx Fr650

Next to the Seine, Gilles Epié's restaurant features an elegantly
stylish turn-of-the-century decor which evokes the spirit
of Provence and Italy. Polished marble floors and beautiful trompe
l'oeil murals create a beautiful setting in which to enjoy some
outstanding and moderately priced food. The menu is relatively
short and fixed-price (Fr220) with a few main course supplements.
Innovation is much to the fore making for both exciting and

satisfying eating. The flavours of the Mediterranean region are evident in a cold lobster minestrone and roast tuna with bacon and matured parmesan. The restaurant's signature dishes include caramelised foie gras beignets with port sauce. Other notable dishes are skate wing with marinated peppers, sea bream with olive oil and clams, and baked pigeon with grilled duck liver paté in hazelnut oil. Superb sweets include a macaroon with fresh figs, a sablé of apple and quince and a warm chocolate mousse. *L 12.30-2.30 D 7.30-10.30. Closed L Sat, all Sun & Aug.* AMERICAN EXPRESS *Mastercard, Visa.*

Paris   Nikko de Paris

Tel (1) 40 58 20 00   Fax (1) 45 75 42 35   **HR**

61 Quai de Grenelle 75015 Paris
Rooms 779   Double room from Fr1630

On the banks of the Seine between the Eiffel Tower and Mirabeau Bridge, the Nikko is a tall (31 floors), strikingly modern Japanese-owned hotel. Public areas are bright, cool, smart and spacious. La Seine Bar shows a more classic side with well-upholstered light wood furniture, splendid Japanese murals and a nightly pianist. The majority of the bedrooms offer good views and are modern in style and design, each with cable TV and mini-bar among the up-to-date facilities provided. Executive rooms are on the top floors. Fax machines and PCs on request. 17 conference rooms, the largest with room for 900 theatre-style. *Indoor swimming pool, gym, sauna.* AMERICAN EXPRESS *Diners, Mastercard, Visa.*

Les Célébrités
Tel 40 58 21 29
Seats 70   Meal for 2 approx Fr600

A table by the window looking out over the Seine must be the best location to sit in this spacious, modern restaurant. Hare terrine *à l'ancienne* or oyster soup with a mussel and asparagus sauce are two of the starter suggestions on the gastronomic menus and grilled John Dory with onions and fennel or fillet of beef *marchand de vin* as main courses. Open for breakfast 7am-9.30am. Set menus: L and D Fr280, Fr370. *L 12-2.30 D 7-10. Closed Aug.* AMERICAN EXPRESS *Diners, Mastercard, Visa.* 🐄

Benkay
Seats 120   Meal for 2 approx Fr800

The decor may be contemporary but essentially this is a traditional Japanese restaurant offering a variety of set meals as well as a short but comprehensive carte. Lunchtime is best for lower priced set menus: L from Fr110, D from Fr280. *L 12-2 D 7-11.*

The Golden Eurostar [★] denotes our pick of the restaurants. Cooking is the major consideration, but other factors are also taken into account, including ambience, comfort and service.

Paris   L'Oulette

`Tel (1) 40 02 02 12   Fax (1) 40 02 02 13`   **R**

15 Pl Lachambeaudie 75012 Paris
Seats 45 (+ 30 outdoor)   Meal for 2 approx Fr650

A modern restaurant, square in shape, with a wood block floor
and picture windows opening on to the terrace. Bold fabric on the
chairs and banquette seating contrast with the pale yellow
tablecloths, plants, central flower arrangements, small earthenware
table pots with dried flowers, English china, and Villeroy & Boch
loos! The back wall has a shelf displaying copper cooking pans
and jars of home-made preserves, pickles and fruit. Mostly
regional cooking, as in the *menu du marché* (Fr160) and *menu
de saison* (Fr230) which includes an excellent French country   ★
wine: try the warm *tartine de moelle au foie gras, confit de canard
grillé, cabécou de Rocamadour* (goat's cheese), and *tourtière aux
pommes et aux mendiants* – an apple, almond and prune filo pastry
concoction baked in the oven. Choice of 12 arabica coffees served
with *madeleines* and mini-chocolate marquises. *L 12-2.15 D 8-
10.15. Closed L Sat, all Sun.* AMERICAN EXPRESS *Mastercard, Visa.*

Paris   Au Pactole

`Tel (1) 46 33 31 31   Fax (1) 46 33 07 60`   **R**

44 Bd St-Germain 75005 Paris
Seats 45   Meal for 2 approx Fr700

Designed to resemble a rather smart private dining room –
pictures, shelves of books, crystal chandeliers – Roland Magre's
increasingly appreciated restaurant has enormous charm as well
as fine food. The cuisine is classically-based but interpreted with
Roland's own inventiveness: *raviolis d'escargots à la crème d'ail*,
fricassée of lobster with girolles mushrooms, stuffed pig's trotter,
escalope of salmon in a pesto sauce, *tarte au chocolat, crème brulée
aux parfums des iles*. In addition to the à la carte there's a set five-
course *menu gourmand* (Fr279) and a limited-choice business lunch
(Fr149). There's a public car park across the street. *L 12-2.30
D 7.30-10.45. Closed L Sat, 24, 25 Dec and 1 May.* AMERICAN EXPRESS
Mastercard, Visa. 🐂

Paris   Paolo Petrini

`Tel (1) 42 60 56 22   Fax (1) 42 36 55 50`   **R**

9 Rue d'Argenteuil 75001 Paris
Seats 30   Meal for 2 approx Fr650

Paolo Petrini is doing wonders for the reputation of Italian
cooking at his tiny restaurant in a side street just off the Palais
Royal. The decor is modern Italian, of the sort that looks simple
but does not come cheap, and reflects Paolo's own contemporary
approach to mainly north Italian dishes, particularly those of his
native Tuscany. Courgette and ricotta ravioli with sage butter
sauce; leg of rabbit *en cocotte* with celery, lardons and green olives;
langoustines with ceps and fresh white haricot beans; desserts like
semifreddo di Torrone (iced nougat with dark chocolate sauce) and
zuccotto al'Alkerms (gateau of almonds, nuts, chocolate and
Alkerms liqueur). Home-baked Tuscan *schiacciata* bread topped
with olive oil, rosemary and rock salt arrives with the menu and

unless you're keen to visit the dentist don't forget to dunk the little biscuit that comes with the coffee. Short list of good Italian wines. *L 12-2.30 D 8-11. Closed L Sat, all Sun, Aug. Mastercard, Visa.*

Paris   **Le Parc Victor Hugo**

Tel (1) 44 05 66 66   Fax (1) 44 05 66 00   **HR**

55 Ave Raymond Poincaré 75116 Paris
Rooms 120   Double room from Fr2200

Nina Campbell masterminded the renovation of this handsome hotel, which tries to combine British refinement with French hospitality. It comprises five buildings set around an interior courtyard garden (not quite a park!) set with trees and flowers, a feature which emphasises the country-house style. Among the day rooms are a cosy bar, a library with tartan upholstery and two conference rooms, the larger seating 400 theatre-style. Bedrooms combine the Campbell style with all the expected up-to-date facilities, including fax/computer points, two telephones, electronic safes and Bang & Olufsen cable TVs. 24hr room service. Guests at the Parc now have the choice of two restaurants on the premises, both under the aegis of master-chef Joël Robuchon. AMERICAN EXPRESS *Diners, Mastercard, Visa.*

Joël Robuchon
Tel (1) 47 27 12 27
59 Ave Raymond Poincaré
Seats 45   Meal for 2 approx Fr2000

Acknowledged as one of *the* greatest chefs in the world, Robuchon, previously at Rue de Longchamp, has moved his restaurant round the corner to this early 20th-century building. The ground-floor dining room has original panelling, period furniture, fine paintings and objets d'art, and there's a private room (seats 12) on the first floor. You will have to book well in advance to get a table here, because even at these prices there is no shortage of customers eager to sample the master's cooking. He describes his style as *moderne*, others seem to think it's classical, almost *bourgeoise*, though does it matter? What is beyond argument is the quality of the dishes. Three of his specialities are *gelée de caviar à la creme de chou-fleur, tarte friande de truffes aux oignons et lard fumé* (December-March), and *lièvre à la royale du Senateur-Couteaux* (October-December). Other dishes might include thyme-scented scallops, red mullet served with grilled potatoes and basil, spicy pan-fried chunks of lobster, baby lamb in herbs and cubes of sweetbreads arranged around a risotto with summer truffles and parmesan shavings. Before a dessert like *feuillantine* of wild strawberries with a honey sauce there might be a marvellous plate of cheeses in tip-top condition, and to end, excellent espresso coffee with *mignardises*. Service is, of course, extremely professional, the wine list expensive, give or take a few country wines. Fixed-price menus Fr890-Fr1100. *L 12.15-2.15 D 7.30-10.15. Closed Sat, Sun, 4 wks Jul/Aug. Mastercard, Visa.*   *See over for 2nd restaurant*

★

Le Relais du Parc
Tel (1) 44 05 66 10

Seats 80   Meal for 2 approx Fr520

Before moving his top restaurant (see above) here, Joël Robuchon
set the 16th alight with this less formal spot. Two rooms running
conservatory-style by the side of the leafy courtyard are decorated
in a colonial style that includes old photographs of safaris. Red
wood is used for the bar, the tables and the chairs, whose grey-
and-white striped upholstery takes up the colour scheme of the
tiled floor. Managers are smartly and soberly suited, and the
waiters wear distinctive silk waistcoats. Gilles Renault's menu
is notable for its immediate straightforward appeal, and among the
popular dishes are a salad of leaves and vegetables with a lively
oriental dressing, marinated herring in a herby salad and haunch
of veal cooked with lemon and served with tagliatelle. Duck and
pigeon are spit-roasted to succulent perfection (the latter served
with broad beans and bacon) and duck also appears in a
comforting *hachis parmentier* – a duck version of shepherd's pie!
Desserts are generally equally approachable: fresh fruit salad,
vanilla cream and chocolate pots, sorbets, excellent hot fruit tarts.
A touch of Robuchon style at very un-Robuchon prices. A la carte
only. Be sure to book – this is one of the hot spots of the moment.
L 12-2.30 D 7.30-10.30. AMERICAN EXPRESS *Diners, Mastercard, Visa.*

Paris   Pavillon de la Reine

Tel (1) 42 77 96 40   Fax (1) 42 77 63 06   **H**

28 Pl des Vosges 75003 Paris
Rooms 55   Double room from Fr1500

Set back from one of the finest and most beautiful squares (built
in the 17th century) in Paris, the entrance to this hotel is an
attractive hall with massive exposed beams and stone-tiled floor
strewn with antiques. The panelled lounge has a fine old fireplace
and leather armchairs. Tastefully decorated bedrooms vary in size
and colour, and some overlook the flowered courtyard. Choice
of continental (Fr90) or full (Fr130) breakfast. No restaurant.
Private parking. AMERICAN EXPRESS *Diners, Mastercard, Visa.*

Paris   Le Petit Colombier

Tel (1) 43 80 28 54   Fax (1) 44 40 04 29   **R**

42 Rue des Acacias 75017 Paris
Seats 80   Meal for 2 approx Fr950

Bernard Fournier's provincial-style auberge has remained for 60
years a bastion of classic French cooking. Amid the woodwork
and the flowers and the copper ornaments an appreciative clientele
tucks into terrine of foie gras with brioche, confit de canard and
rib of beef with bone marrow and two sauces. Pigeon roasted in a
salt crust with truffle juice is a speciality along with a kebab
of eggs with fresh truffles. Equally appreciated are dishes such
as roast turbot with fresh pasta and woodland mushrooms
or casserole of suckling calf with cèps and girolle mushrooms.
There's a great cellar, with bottles selected from all round the
world. The Fr200 four course *menu carte* offers remarkable value
for money. Set D: Fr350. *L 12.15-2.30 D 7.30-10.30. Closed
L Sun, all Sat.* AMERICAN EXPRESS *Mastercard, Visa.*

Paris   Au Petit Marguery

`Tel (1) 43 31 58 59`   **R**

9 Bd du Port-Royal 75013 Paris
Seats 80 (+ 20 terrace)   Meal for 2 approx Fr600

The three Cousin brothers, Michel, Jacques and Alain, create
a very friendly ambience at this genuine Parisian bistro. Michel
and Jacques spend most of their time in the kitchen, occasionally
coming out to greet customers or join in the conversation. Alain
makes sure all runs smoothly in the two dining rooms with their
ancient tiled floors and aged pink walls covered with mirrors. The
brothers specialise in game, offal, fresh fish and regional dishes
such as a purée of partridge with juniper berries or pan-fried wild
mushrooms with garlic, followed by a charlotte of coquilles
St Jacques, plaice and courgettes or a noisette of deer *à la romaine,*
and a Grand Marnier soufflé or dark chocolate cake to finish. Set
menus only: L Fr160, L & D Fr200 (*menu carte*), Fr320, Fr450
(game menu in season). *L 12-2.15 D 7.30-10.30. Closed Sun, Mon,
Aug & 24 Dec-2 Jan.* AMERICAN EXPRESS *Diners, Mastercard, Visa.*

Paris   Pile ou Face

`Tel (1) 42 33 64 33   Fax (1) 42 36 61 09`   **R**

52 bis rue Notre-Dame-des-Victoires 75002 Paris
Seats 40   Meal for 2 approx Fr850

Heads you win, tails you can't lose at this warm, cosy restaurant
on two floors with burgundy red walls and a small bar/greeting
area near the entrance. The choice in question is between the
regular carte – ravioli of snails with herbs; pike mousse with
pistachio; salmon and ginger – and a special menu using the
produce from their own farm in Normandy, rabbits (confit of the
leg with sweet garlic purée, terrine with thyme and rosemary),
chicken (en croute with herbs), eggs (scrambled with wild
mushroom purée), and ducks plus foie gras. Lunch is a fixed-price
affair of four courses (including cheese) of dishes taken from the
evening menus with about half a dozen choices at each stage. Set
menu: L Fr235. *L 12-2 D 8-10. Closed Sat, Sun, Aug, Bank
Holidays.*

Paris   Plaza Athénée

`Tel (1) 47 23 78 33   Fax (1) 47 20 20 70`   **HR**

25 Ave Montaigne 75008 Paris
Rooms 250   Double room from Fr3010

Surrounded by the great haute-couture houses, the Plaza has its
own inimitable sense of style and has long been a haunt of the
famous – and sometimes infamous; Mata Hari was arrested in the
hotel's darkwood and leather English bar. Other public areas
include a large circular lobby, vaulted Galerie de Gobelins with
pairs of columns down each side, and a verdant courtyard garden
with fountains and red umbrellas that match the awnings of the
balustraded bedroom windows that overlook it. Bedrooms
in Louis XV, Louis XVI or Regency style are elegant and
comfortable, with air-conditioning and ultra-modern bathrooms.
Services include 24-hour room service, hairdressing salon, perfume
boutique and theatre desk. Four conference rooms, the largest
seating 100 theatre-style. Forte. AMERICAN EXPRESS *Diners, Mastercard,
Visa.*

See over

Le Régence

Seats 110 (**+** 80 outdoor)   Meal for 2 approx Fr1050

An elegant dining rom with fluted pilasters supporting
an elaborate gilded frieze, and widely spaced tables displaying
silver place settings. The menu is very much Grand Hotel in both
style – separate sections for grills, fish etc – and content; the
starters include oysters, caviar, smoked salmon and foie gras.
Amongst the more interesting dishes are a lobster soufflé, curried
monkfish with shellfish, green noodles and sweet peppers, and
breast of chicken simmered with lemon and peppermint. From
a good varied choice of desserts this would be just the place
to enjoy the spectacle that is crepe Suzette flambée. *L 12-2.30
D 7.30-10.* 🐂

Relais Plaza

Seats 120   Meal for 2 approx Fr650

Informal, all-day eaterie with 1930s' decor and entrance direct
from the street as well as from within the hotel. It's breakfast till
11am after which the full menu runs through until the early
hours. With something to suit all appetites the choice ranges from
club sandwiches and croque monsieur, via pasta, salads and egg
dishes to lamb curry, sole meunière and grills. Set menu Fr285.
Meals 8am-1.30am.

Paris   **Le Pré Catelan**

`Tel (1) 45 24 55 58   Fax (1) 45 24 43 25`   **R**

Route de Suresnes, Bois de Boulogne 75016 Paris
Seats 80 (+80 outside)   Meal for 2 approx Fr1400

A magic spot in the Bois de Boulogne, and perhaps the most
beautiful restaurant in all Paris, superbly restored to its 18th
century elegance by Christian Benais. The dining rooms are
magnificent, and in summer terraces make the most of the
marvellous setting. Chef-director Roland Durand describes his
cooking as 'neo-classic with rustic tendencies and light touches
of the orient'. Specialities include *risotto noir de langoustines
au basilic Thaï, les cuisses de lapin à la brioche* with a *ragout
de légumes aux artichauts, saucisse de Couenne et jeunes légumes
au parfum de truffe noire*, mushrooms and game in their seasons and
tarte au chocolat avec sorbet cacao. A remarkable wine list covering
all the French classic kicks off with over 40 champagnes. Set
L from Fr270 (Fr330 with wine) set D Fr400 and Fr690. *L 12-
2.30 D 7.30-10.30. Closed D Sun, all Mon, last 2 wks Feb.*
AMERICAN EXPRESS *Diners, Mastercard, Visa.*   ★

Paris   **Le Récamier**

`Tel (1) 45 48 86 58   Fax (1) 42 22 84 76`   **R**

4 Rue Récamier 75007 Paris
Seats 80   Meal for 2 approx Fr1000

A really splendid place for late spring and summer when the
restaurant's open-air terrace comes into its own. Extending into
a delightful, pedestrianised street awash with flowers long-
established, the restaurant majors on classics from the Burgundy
region as in beef bourguignon with fresh noodles and *jambon
persillé.* Modern influences also appear as in an escalope of tuna
with pesto or fillets of red mullet with basil and mashed potato.

Gratin dauphinois is a favourite accompaniment, appearing with
the likes of rack of lamb, Auvergne-style calf's liver and various
steaks. The wine list is phenomenal – particularly strong
on bordeaux and champagne. *L 12-2.30 D 7.45-10.30. Closed Sun.*
AMERICAN EXPRESS *Diners, Mastercard, Visa.*

Paris	Résidence Maxim's de Paris

Tel (1) 45 61 96 33   Fax (1) 42 89 06 07   **H**

42 Ave Gabriel 75008 Paris

Rooms 30   Double room from Fr2250

Pierre Cardin's name is synonymous with haute couture and when
he acquired this grand building a few years ago he set about
indulging all his design skills and fantasies. The result has been
to create some of the most refined and elegant bedrooms and suites
to be found anywhere, though the hotel brochure hardly does
them justice. Individually furnished, they vary greatly, ranging
in style from those with an ultra-modern, cool, late 20th-century
decor to some with exquisite original Art Deco furniture and
others with genuine 18th-century pieces. All except four standard
bedrooms are suites but even the former are spacious and all have
almost the full alphabet of amenities, from air-conditioning
to video players. Bathrooms feature highly polished fossil stones
together with stunning murals. Hallways too are extraordinary,
with their beautiful antiques and fine paintings. Standards
of service are exemplary and there is valet parking. A hotel
of outstanding quality and merit, with prices to match. Small
conferences – up to 65 theatre-style. AMERICAN EXPRESS *Diners,
Mastercard, Visa.*

Paris	Ritz

Tel (1) 43 16 30 30   **HR**

15 Pl Vendome 75001 Paris

Rooms 187   Double room from Fr2970

Since being opened by César Ritz in 1898, this hotel, and his
name, have become a synonym for opulence and luxury. Still
in private hands, and unconnected with other hotels bearing the
name, the Ritz continues to live up to its own legend. Day rooms
in the 18th-century former private residence retain their authentic
period atmosphere but today are joined by facilities such as the
Ritz Health Club with its hi-tech fitness centre and romanesque
pool and the Ritz Club for dancing until the small hours; for the
less energetic high tea is served in the Vendome garden to the
sound of a harp. Recently re-opened is the Hemingway Bar, with
books and letters of the great man and other literary giants, and
cocktails shaken by an Englishman. Antique-furnished bedrooms
include nearly 50 full suites, some especially luxurious named after
the Duke of Windsor, Coco Chanel, Scott Fitzgerald and the like.
Air-conditioning and all the usual up-to-date amenities combine
with the sort of service that runs to a 24hr valet – all in all
making you feel well and truly pampered. Five conference rooms,
the largest seating 120 theatre-style. Own parking. AMERICAN EXPRESS
Diners, Mastercard, Visa.

L'Espadon

Seats 60   Meal for 2 approx Fr1500

In Guy Legay they have one of the most experienced head chefs
in the business but there is nothing old guard about a carte which
includes the likes of foie gras with glazed green walnuts, red
mullet in a vegetable minestrone flavoured with saffron and a basil
aioli, whole turbot roasted with fresh peppery mint accompanied
by a purée of fresh peas and broad beans and a light veal sauce, and
sweetbreads and capers with pasta and lemon sauce, while the
balsamic ice cream that comes with a cassolette of red berries
is positively avant garde. Plenty of more familiar dishes too such
as lobster bisque with cognac, rack of lamb with mint and parsley
and the hot soufflé of your choice to finish – dishes more befitting
the legendary Escoffier, once in charge of the Ritz stoves. The
Fr360 fixed-price menu comes with a short list of suggested wines
at less than Fr200 a bottle (which is quite useful as the main list
goes on for ever) and, at night only, there is a tasting menu for
Fr580 (only served to whole parties). The restaurant has recently
moved into a grand Second Empire style room with a trompe
l'oeil sky ceiling in the Vendome wing of the hotel opening on to
a garden with fountains. *L 12-3 D 7-11.*

Paris   **Hotel Scribe**

Tel (1) 44 71 24 24   Fax (1) 42 65 39 97   **HR**

1 Rue Scribe 75009 Paris

Rooms 217   Double room from Fr2200

A major corner site, formerly the Jockey Club, whose Napoleon
III façade today conceals a busy cosmopolitan hotel.
Refurbishment over recent years has extended from the spacious
lobby with its Baccarat crystal chandeliers and the luxurious,
softly-lit cocktail bar to the bedrooms. Things like air-
conditioning, double-glazing (for streetside rooms) and endless
TV channels provide the modern comforts for rooms that are
mostly furnished in Louis Philippe or Louis XVI style, although
some rooms are in 'English' style and there are some suites,
featuring mezzanine bedroom floors, that are more contemporary
in concept. Two conference rooms, the larger seating 100 theatre-
style. Fax can be installed in the bedrooms. AMERICAN EXPRESS *Diners,
Mastercard, Visa.*

Les Muses

Tel 44 71 24 26

Seats 40   Meal for 2 approx Fr700

Guests at this sophisticated restaurant sit at round tables in sombre
surroundings of wood panelling, black lacquer, mirrors and
bouquets of flowers. The cooking is traditionally French but
modern in its execution. Begin with an oxtail compote and foie
gras with flat parsley, followed by a panaché of roasted fish served
with young leeks and preserved tomatoes, then perhaps mango
tatin with cinnamon ice cream to finish. Set menu: L and D Fr190
and Fr250. *L 12-2.30 D 7.30-10.30. Closed Sat, Sun, Aug & Bank
Holidays.*

Paris   Taillevent

Tel (1) 45 61 12 90   Fax (1) 42 25 95 18   R

15 Rue Lammenais 75008 Paris
Seats 120   Meal for 2 approx Fr1350

Excellence sustained over many years is the achievement of this
most civilised and refined of restaurants presided over by the
urbane second-generation owner Jean-Claude Vrinat. Wood-
panelled walls and discreet, polished service help to create
an almost club-like atmosphere relished by the good and the great
of the capital's establishment. Philippe Legendre is now firmly
established in the kitchen and continues in the tradition of his
predecessor Claude Deligne (who was head chef here for 30 years)
of acknowledging modern trends but only gradually and from
a solidly classical base. Specialities include a moreish *boudin*   ★
de homard Breton à la nage, poulette de Bresse en cocotte and a *moelleux
au chocolat et à thym* that shares the dessert section of the menu
with such wonderfully old-fashioned sounding puds as *riz
à l'impératrice* and *blanc-manger à l'ancienne* (a world away from the
blancmange of children's tea parties). The legendary wine list
is supported by their own wine shop, one of the best in Paris,
in the nearby rue du Faubourg Saint-Honoré. *L 12-1.30 D 7.30-
10. Closed Sat, Sun, 3 wks Aug.* AMERICAN EXPRESS *Diners, Mastercard,
Visa.*

Paris   Terminus Nord

Tel (1) 42 85 05 15   Fax (1) 40 16 13 98   R

23 Rue Dunkerque 75010 Paris
Seats 200+   Meal for 2 approx Fr450

A railway journey to or from the channel ports is all that brings
most visitors to this part of Paris, but this classic, rambling 1925
brasserie is very well worth a visit. A vast bank of shellfish is on
eye-catching display all year round, and is the subject of a separate
menu. Other specialities include asparagus in its brief season,
choucroute and steaks, and the daily specials such as veal Marengo,
navarin of lamb or salmon with sorrel are always in demand.
Serious service from well-drilled, smartly attired waiters and
waitresses. Set menus Fr109 and Fr185 (+ children's menu). Also
open for breakfast, teas and coffees. Pavement terrace. *Meals 11am-
12.30am.* AMERICAN EXPRESS *Diners, Mastercard, Visa.*

Meal prices for 2 are based on à la carte menus.
When set menus are available, prices will often be lower.

Paris   La Timonerie

Tel (1) 43 25 44 42   **R**

35 Quai de la Tournelle 75005 Paris

Seats 22   Meal for 2 approx Fr800

The walls of Philippe de Givenchy's charming little restaurant are
lined with natural wood and decorated with old etchings. Having
worked with Chibois and Senderens, his cuisine is very refined
and personalised. At lunchtime, his four-course *carte menu* (210F)
offers six choices at each course. In the evening, the *carte du soir*
comes into operation and for one of his starters he uses an old
country recipe from the Poitou area, *petatou Poitevin*, a goat's
cheese and potato tart served with a chive sauce. Main courses
might be pig's cheek or grilled tuna served with a pipérade and
Serrano ham, to be followed by a cold gratin of red fruits or a hot
apricot tart with almonds (both to be ordered at beginning
of meal). Parking is permitted on the quai after 7.30pm. *L 12-2.30
D 7.30-10.30. Closed L Mon, all Sun. Mastercard, Visa.*

Paris   La Tour d'Argent

Tel (1) 43 54 23 31   Fax (1) 44 07 12 04   **R**

15 Quai de la Tournelle 75005 Paris

Seats 110   Meal for 2 approx Fr2000

Almost a historic monument, this is the restaurant that once-in-a-
lifetime visitors to Paris head for – if their pockets are deep
enough. Even their speciality dish, a duck *à la presse* with cherries,
has been on the menu for over 100 years and comes with
a numbered certificate; they are currently up to around 800,000.
Start saving now and you could be the millionth. There are now
some lighter dishes on an essentially traditional carte that competes
with luxurious surroundings, spectacular views of the Seine and   ★
Notre Dame from the coveted window tables and a fabulous
cellar which also contains a museum of wine. If the prices are
beyond your reach (there *is* a more manageable set lunch menu
at Fr375) head for their shop opposite, *Comptoirs de la Tour
d'Argent*, where souvenirs bearing the restaurant's logo are sold –
tinned foie gras, tableware, silk ties and the like. *L 12-2.30 D 8-
10.30. Closed Mon.* AMERICAN EXPRESS *Diners, Mastercard, Visa.*

Paris   Le Train Bleu

Tel (1) 43 43 09 06   Fax (1) 43 43 97 96   **R**

Gare de Lyon 75012 Paris

Seats 200   Meal for 2 approx Fr550

Classified as a historic monument in 1972, the buffet of the Gare
de Lyon (Le Train Bleu) is like no other. Named after a legendary
sumptuous Paris-Cote d'Azur express train of the 20s,
it appropriately represents the luxury of the era. A gastronomic
restaurant, it consists of two rooms, the Golden Room with its
golden stuccos and the larger Main Room. In 1900, thirty artists,
some of them famous, were commissioned to paint scenes
depicting the most beautiful spots in France crossed by the Paris-
Lyon-Marseille rail network. These forty-one paintings cover the
ornate ceilings and walls. The ceiling and arches are divided into
squares that are emphasised by massive raised mouldings on which

the paintings rest. Heavy purple velvet hangings, warm colours, bronze and opaline-shaped glass lights, brown leather seats and mahogany furniture complete the picture. The kitchen offers traditional French cuisine with *'spécialités foréziennes'* (from an area near Lyon/St Etienne) such as hot Lyon sausage with potatoes or light mousse of brill with wild mushrooms, followed by grilled andouillette with apple and potato plus peppered steak flamed with cognac and accompanied by one of 150,000 bottles kept in stock. If you have actually come to catch a train, there's a 260F 'rapid menu' (inclusive of wine). Set menus: L and D Mon-Fri 195F. *L 12-2.30 D 7-10.* AMERICAN EXPRESS *Diners, Mastercard, Visa.*

Paris	**Hotel Vernet**	

Tel (1) 47 23 43 10 Fax (1) 44 31 85 69	**HR**

25 Rue Vernet 75008 Paris
Rooms 57   Double room from Fr1850

Built at the turn of the century and completely refurbished in 1989, the Vernet combines period style with modern comforts. Antique-furnished bedrooms and suites are all air-conditioned and the splendid marble bathrooms all have jacuzzi tubs. Day rooms include an elegant lounge with panelled walls where afternoon tea and cocktail hour are accompanied by the piano. Guests have use of the health and beauty centre of the nearby Royal Monceau Hotel. 24hr room service (cold food only after 11pm). *L 12-2 D 7-10.* AMERICAN EXPRESS *Diners, Mastercard, Visa.*

Les Elysées du Vernet
Seats 40 (+ 15 outdoor)   Meal for 2 approx Fr1000

The magnificent, glass-roofed Belle Epoque dining room provides a really splendid setting for some fine cooking with a sunny Mediterranean slant: *petits farcis provençaux servis frais avec un jus de tomate crue; filets de rougets de roche poelés aux olives; canette mi-sauvage rotie au poivre, compotée de patate douce et raisins, figues poelées à l'infusion de thé.* Farmhouse cheeses, unmissable desserts and a comprehensive French wine list. Set L Fr300 Set D Fr450. *Closed Sat, Sun, Aug.*

Paris	**La Villa Maillot**	

Tel (1) 45 01 25 22 Fax (1) 45 00 60 61	**H**

143 Ave de Malakoff 75016 Paris
Rooms 42   Double room from Fr1500

Ideally situated for visitors, whether on business or pleasure bent, a five minute walk from the Arc de Triomphe and the Champs-Elysées, this is an elegant and quiet 'art-deco' style hotel of much charm. Behind the white facade (illuminated at night) the public areas are quite striking, from the marble-floored foyer and pastel-coloured lounge with sofas aplenty to the boldly decorated bar and garden conservatory restaurant, the setting for an inviting buffet breakfast. Comfortable and restful bedrooms in soft colours, with 'Queen-size' beds and floor-length curtains, are soundproofed and air-conditioned and offer satellite TV, mini-bar, kitchenette and trouser press. Modern bathrooms, in rose-coloured marble, provide excellent hotel-monogrammed toiletries. There are three suites, named after Picasso, Chagall and Modigliani. *Garage (6 cars), garden.* AMERICAN EXPRESS *Diners, Mastercard, Visa.*

Paris   **Vivarois**

| Tel (1) 45 04 04 31   Fax (1) 45 03 09 84 | R |

192 Ave Victor Hugo 75016 Paris
Seats 50   Meal for 2 approx Fr1200

Chef-patron Claude Peyrot has been in situ for over 25 years, and
is acknowledged as being one of the finest in the city, together
with some of the more recognisable names that generally attract
most of the media's attention. If the interior of the restaurant
is nothing to enthuse over, his classical cooking certainly is,
though opinions are divided whether you can actually attribute
a style to his cuisine. The menu has changed little over the years,
though every day perhaps half a dozen dishes appear that may
never figure in his repertoire again, such as *ris de veau aux girolles,
compotée de légumes; sole farcie; galette de pommes de terre truffée
et foie gras.* In addition, there's a three-course *menu déjeuner* (Fr345)
alongside the à la carte, featuring many dishes that will require
translation and explanation since they are often idiosyncratically
described, for instance *ravioli Rastellini, bar antiboise* and *plaisir
d'agneau.* For afters try the more explicable *tarte fine au chocolat.*
Claude's wife Jacqueline charmingly marshals the staff, who are
unobtrusively professional and efficient, greatly enhancing the
enjoyment of a meal here. *L 12-2 D 8-9.45. Closed Sat, Sun
& August.* AMERICAN EXPRESS *Diners, Mastercard, Visa.*

Around Paris

Versailles   **Trianon Palace**

| Tel (1) 30 84 38 00   Fax (1) 39 49 00 77 | HR |

1 Boulevard de la Reine 78000 Versailles
Rooms 98   Double room from Fr1600

Ten miles from the city, on the edge of the royal park and a short
walk from the Palace of Versailles, the Trianon, set in seven acres
with hundred-year-old trees and grazing sheep, sits in palatial
splendour. Steeped in history, especially around the two World
Wars, many illustrious figures have walked through the marble-
laid corridors and slept in the high-ceilinged, elegant bedrooms
with antique furniture and heavy drape curtains. All are
luxuriously and extremely well equipped with the latest hi-tech
facilities for fax and computer connections or for broadcasting
video transmissions worldwide. Ideal for conferences – there's
an international conference centre in the *Trianon Hotel* (97
antique-style bedrooms), reached via a landscaped walkway,
consisting of six conference rooms, boardrooms, press centre, and
broadcasting control room, not to mention the lounge, bar and
brasserie. A Japanese restaurant with private rooms is due to open
soon. *24hr room service. Satellite/cable TV (38 channels!). Theatre-
style conference facilities for up to 360. Business
centre/secretarial/translation services. Leisure centre. Tennis. Bicycles.
Ample parking.* AMERICAN EXPRESS *Diners, Mastercard, Visa.*

Les Trois Marches
Tel (1) 39 50 13 21
Seats 60   Meal for 2 approx Fr1500

Chef Gérard Vié can even offer guests a healthy and balanced
dietetic cuisine, based on a nutritionist's programme of 1300
calories, yet with all the necessary proteins, minerals and vitamins.
But, thankfully perhaps, there are plenty of other more enticing
menus to choose from offering such dishes as *cote de veau rotie
au jus truffé* (roast veal cutlet with a light truffle jus), *pavé de thon
grillé, vinaigrette aux truffes* (grilled tuna steak with a truffle
vinaigrette), *ragout de homard à l'orange*, oysters topped with foie
gras, or a mixed herb salad with Banyuls vinegar. For the most
part, dishes are light and not for those with a hearty appetite, quite
meagre portions almost in *nouvelle* style. Well over a thousand
binbins on the wine list, but no house wines. *Closed Sun, Mon,
Aug.*

Aix-en-Provence

Aix-en-Provence	**Les Bacchanales**	
Tel 42 27 21 06		**R**

10 Rue de la Couronne 13001 Aix-en-Provence

Seats 50   Meal for 2 approx Fr500

This traditional restaurant right in the centre of Aix has been serving lunch and dinner for over 100 years. Jean-Marc Taillefer, who used to cook in the kitchens at the *Petit Nice Passédat* in Marseilles, has kept the dishes simple and traditional, with several set menus, a *menu gourmand* and an à la carte menu: veal sweetbread and courgette flan, duck liver paté served with an avocado and cream sauce and salmon lasagne served with aubergines preserved in aniseed. Like all good Provençal restaurants, local apéritifs are given pride of place and proudly served in the *comptoir* before visitors go on into the stone-floored, wood-panelled dining room. *L 12-2 D 7.45-11. Closed L Sat, Sun & Mon Jun-Aug, L Thur & all Wed Sep-Jun.* AMERICAN EXPRESS *Diners, Mastercard, Visa.*

Around Aix-en-Provence

Meyreuil	**Auberge Provençale**	
Tel 42 58 68 54 Fax 42 58 68 05		**R**

Le Canet de Meyreuil 13590 Meyreuil

Seats 50   Meal for 2 approx Fr600

Blending innocuously in among a sparse scattering of wooden-beamed homes that could hardly be called a village (8km from Aix itself), this Provençal restaurant sticks staunchly to regional cooking and local ingredients. In the kitchen, Monsieur Astouric lavishes local herbs, olive oil and lavender on his cooking, with his specialities *panaché de poisson, sa giclée huile d'olive* (an assortment of grilled local fish served in a pool of olive oil) and *pigeon roti aux gousses d'ail et jus de nos garrigues* (pigeon roasted with cloves of garlic and served in a light herb sauce). Local specialities are also served for dessert: try the crispy almond pancakes with a lavender glaze. The accent is definitely on regional wines such as Cote de Provence. *L 12-2 D 8-10. Closed D Tues, all Wed, 2 weeks Feb. Private car park.* AMERICAN EXPRESS *Diners, Mastercard, Visa.*

Les Baux-de-Provence

Les Baux-de-Provence	La Cabro d'Or

Tel 90 54 33 21 Fax 90 54 45 98	**H**

La Cabro d'Or 13520 Les Baux-de-Provence

Rooms 22   Double room from Fr575

This hotel, built in the 60s on the site of some old riding stables
130km from Avignon, is owned by the same family as *Oustau
de Baumanière*. Guests can survey the extensive grounds around the
building while they breakfast on their own terrace (in the case
of 12 rooms – those without can use the communal terraces). The
rooms are well equipped, with invaluable air-conditioning. Many
of their guests come from their restaurant, or to eat the chef's
house specialities in the Oustau mode but at half the price! *Satellite
TV. Theatre-style conference facilities for up to 100.
Secretarial/translation/fax services on request. Outdoor swimming pool,
2 tennis courts, golf, riding. Closed 17 Nov-20 Dec. Private parking.*
AMERICAN EXPRESS *Diners, Mastercard, Visa.*

Les Baux-de-Provence	Oustau de Baumanière

Tel 90 54 33 07 Fax 90 54 40 46	**H R**

13520 Les Baux-de-Provence

Rooms 24   Double room from Fr1000

A 500-year old *mas* and its annexes, beautifully surrounded
by trees, rocks and vines, offers luxurious and charming rustic
accommodation (canopy beds, beams, fireplaces, and period
furniture). Tennis, horse riding and golf nearby. *Conference
facilities. Swimming pool. Closed mid Jan-1 Mar, Wed (Mar only).
Ample parking.* AMERICAN EXPRESS *Diners, Mastercard, Visa.*

Restaurant

Seats 100   Meal for 2 approx Fr1700

Created by the legendary Raymond Thuilier, the restaurant used
to be one of the 16th-century outbuildings attached to the Chateau
des Baux, 100m up the road, and it still retains most of the
original features, like the impressive vaulted ceiling, stone walls
and wood panelling, offset by colourful tablecloths designed
by the owners. Carrying on his grandfather's proud tradition, chef-
patron Jean-André Charial and his team have adopted a strong
Mediterranean/Southern style of cooking, which, added to the
Provençal ingredients readily available, gives subtle and inventive
flavours: *ravioli de truffes aux poireaux, filets de rouget au basilic,
gigot d'agneau en croute,* or *queues de langoustines aux épices*
(langoustine tails with spices and aubergine purée). Sea bass
in pastry is served with a cream-based sauce with tomatoes and
other vegetables, which come direct from their own gardens,
while scallops are served in almond butter. Not to be missed are
desserts such as *millefeuille de chocolat aux fruits,* crepes and soufflés.
Massive wine list, including a wine (Chateau de Romarin) from
their 50-acre vineyard nearby. *L 12-2.30 D 7.30-9.30. Closed (from
Nov-Mar) L Thu, all Wed.*

Les Baux-de-Provence   **La Riboto de Taven**

Tel 90 54 34 23   Fax 90 54 38 88   **R**

Les Baux-de-Provence 13520

Seats 40   Meal for 2 approx Fr900

Jean-Pierre Novi's parents started this restaurant in an 18th-
century Provençal farm and he has been cooking here since he was
tall enough to reach the table. Situated right on the edge of a cliff
face in the centre of Les Baux village (65km from Aix), the two
available rooms are actually built into the rock itself and simply
furnished in Provençal style. The cooking is as unusual as the
setting, with lively interpretations of traditional regional dishes.
Two dishes with a difference are *lasagne de homard* dressed up in
a delicious coral sauce and *selle d'agneau sur un fondant de légumes*
(saddle of lamb, lightly cooked and served with thinly sliced
potatoes cooked with onions, white wine and lamb stock). Try
one of their bottles of Coteaux d'Aix en Provence, an *appellation*
shortly to disappear off the regional wine map. *L 12-2 D 7.30-10.*
Closed D Tue (Oct-Jun), all Wed, 5 Jan-mid Mar. Private parking.
AMERICAN EXPRESS *Diners, Mastercard, Visa.*

Bordeaux

Bordeaux   **Burdigala**

Tel 56 90 16 16   Fax 56 93 15 06   **H**

115 Rue Georges Bonnac 33000 Bordeaux
Rooms 83   Double room from Fr800

Built six years ago in a modern part of Bordeaux, near Mérignac
Airport, this small hotel is informally run: the manager also does
concierge and reception duties. 15 suites were added in 1992,
designed in colonial style, with wooden furniture and rich,
chintzy curtains. *Theatre-style conference facilities for up to 100.
Private parking.* AMERICAN EXPRESS *Diners, Mastercard, Visa.*

Bordeaux   **Le Chapon Fin**

Tel 56 79 10 10   Fax 56 79 09 10   **R**

5 Rue Montesquieu 33000 Bordeaux
Seats 50   Meal for 2 approx Fr900

Le patron Francis Garcia and his wife have been running this
restaurant for 15 years with a large team of kitchen staff. And
being Spanish, he has a definite penchant for seafood and his
personal specialities include a summer *gaspacho de homard* (lobster
gazpacho) and *gratin d'huitres* (oyster gratin). His Spanish
influences pervade other dishes like *ravioles de langoustines au citron
vert* (small prawn-filled ravioli with a lime sauce) and *aiguillettes
de caneton au foie gras avec sauce miel et citron* (minced breast
of duck cooked as cutlets with foie gras served with a sweet honey
and lemon sauce). The place is one of Bordeaux's oldest dining
room; carved out of rock, it is like an intimate grotto. *L 12.30-2
D 8-10. Closed Sun, also Mon in Jul & Aug. Public parking.*
AMERICAN EXPRESS *Diners, Visa.*

Bordeaux   **Jean Ramet**

Tel 56 44 12 51   Fax 56 22 19 80   **R**

7/8 Place Jean Jaurès 33000 Bordeaux
Seats 35   Meal for 2 approx Fr500

Jean Ramet developed his culinary strengths in the kitchens of the
Troisgros brothers, and has not looked back since he opened this
very successful restaurant south of the Esplanade des Quinconces,
on the west bank of the Garonne, 13 years ago. He chose an 18th-
century house for his gastronomic delights, keeping the original
wood panelling and stone work. Here he has continued to add his
own innovative light touch to traditional French cooking.
Le feuilleté d'huitres au caviar (a light millefeuille, filled with oysters
and caviar) and *le panaché de poissons aux épices* (an assorted platter
of fish cooked with mixed spices) are two examples of his
unexpected touches. The raw ingredients used are all fresh and
simple, like lobster, but the end creation is always unusual:
le gaspacho de homard à la vanille (lobster gazpacho with a swirl
of vanilla sauce). Savour the whole experience with one of their
good Bordeaux wines. *L 12.15-2 D 7.45-10. Public parking.*
AMERICAN EXPRESS *Mastercard, Visa.*

Bordeaux   Hotel de Normandie

`Tel 56 52 16 80   Fax 56 51 68 91`   **H**

7 Cours du Trente Juillet 33000 Bordeaux
Rooms 100   Double room from Fr500

A 300-year-old family-run hotel with well-decorated, double-
glazed bedrooms, but unfortunately no restaurant or conference
facilities (though secretarial and translation services can
be arranged). The bar is open 24 hours a day and serves light
brasserie snacks. However, situated as it is in a square in the centre
of Bordeaux, there are plenty of restaurants to choose from and
squash, golf, and swimming nearby. *Satellite TV. Private parking.*
AMERICAN EXPRESS *Diners, Mastercard, Visa.*

Bordeaux   Le Pavillon des Boulevards

`Tel 56 81 51 02   Fax 56 51 14 56`   **R**

120 Rue Croix de Seguey 33000 Bordeaux
Seats 45   Meal for 2 approx Fr900

Inside this typically Bordelaise house, the owner-chef takes
traditional ingredients, such as foie gras or lobster, and
experiments with new, creative combinations. His *foie gras
de canard aux épices douces, marmelade de pommes* (lightly spiced
duck liver paté served with an apple compote) is the most popular
dish. His lobster dish is again just a little different: *poelée de homard
bardée de choux au vin de sauternes* (fried lobster with cabbage
tossed in Sauternes). Look out for the *Petit Paradis* wine list with
some distinguished old bottles of Chateau Latour and Chateau
Mouton Rothschild. *L 12-1.45 D 8-10.15. Closed L Sat, all Sun,
2-9 Jan, 14-20 Aug.* AMERICAN EXPRESS *Diners, Visa.*

Bordeaux   Le Rouzic

`Tel 56 44 39 11   Fax 56 40 55 10`   **R**

34 Cours du Chapeau Rouge 33000 Bordeaux
Seats 45   Meal for 2 approx Fr360

For the last 20 years, Michel Gautier has been in firmly charge
of the kitchen, while Madame (affectionately called Zizi) has
controlled, the extensive Bordeaux wine cellar. His regional
cooking has some interesting combinations: *lamproie* (lamprey)
à la bordelaise and *rognon de veau à la graine de moutarde* (kidneys
cooked in a mustard seed sauce). He maintains a healthy balance
of beef, fish and duck on his *menu sans surprise*, while the more à la
carte *menu surprise*, re-interprets local dishes. The 300-year-old
building is quite a setting for serious *dégustation* with dark brown
mirrors, a gold and black painted ceiling and a tiger skin hanging
on the wall. *L 12-2 D 7-10. Closed L Sat, all Sun. Private car park.*
AMERICAN EXPRESS *Diners, Visa.*

Cannes

Cannes   **Carlton Inter-Continental**

Tel 93 68 91 68   Fax 93 38 20 90   **HR**

58 Boulevard La Croisette 06400 Cannes
Rooms 349   Double room from Fr1750

The Carlton today is still *the* place to stay and be seen in Cannes.
Its location at the centre of La Croisette and its likeness to a huge
wedding cake, with the famous cupolas, ensures that its very
presence dominates the seafront. Its rooms and apartments have all
recently been refurbished in elegant style to match the wonderful
high ceilings of most of the rooms, which are all fully air-
conditioned. Furnishings match the elegance in all rooms but the
suites in particular have some lovely antique furniture in addition.
The best rooms and suites are situated on the front of the building
overlooking the sea, and the higher up the better the views.
Bathrooms have been refitted in marble with elegant fittings, the
bigger rooms, again generally on the front elevation, have
enormous bathrooms with additionally double basins and separate
shower. Towels are luxurious and plentiful and valeting facilities
for guests are first class and provided as fast as one could hope for
in any hotel, you even have a choice offered as to how you like
your shirts starched and folded (or hung!). Among the public
rooms the entrance lobby is particularly impressive with its
double-height ceiling and marble floors and columns. Adjacent to
this are the listed banqueting rooms with wonderful gilded
ceilings and ornate mirrors. The Café Carlton and Piano Bar are
situated at the far end of the lounge and open on to the famous
Carlton Terrace which overlooks La Croisette. There is also a
small lobby Caviar Bar called le Petit Bar which is near the main
reception area. On the penthouse seventh floor is the Carlton
Casino Club with its Casino Restaurant and terrace overlooking
the sea and also La Belle Otéro, and terrace overlooking the old
port. A piano bar and the Club Otéro night club with its small
dance floor are actually situated within one of the famous cupolas.
Additionally there are a number of boutiques within a small
arcade and the hotel has its own garage for 100 cars at the rear of
the building. AMERICAN EXPRESS *Diners, Mastercard, Visa.*

La Belle Otéro
Tel 93 68 00 33   Fax 93 39 09 06
Seats 80   Meal for 2 approx Fr1000

Eat in this early 20th-century, classical-style restaurant near the top
of the hotel during the film festival and the atmosphere buzzes
with hype and Hollywood, but for the rest of the year it has a
calm, elegant charm all of its own. Most of chef Chauveau's
cooking is, not surprisingly, Mediterranean with a liberal use of
olive oil and plenty of fresh fish and shellfish; however, his
eclectic sauces and interesting presentation add a great deal to the
traditional Southern raw materials. *Meunière* of local rock mullet
is garnished with thyme and served with a chanterelle, potato and
garlic galette and grilled violet artichokes, while his grilled lobster
is served in a light lobster, coral and tarragon sauce with a fine
celery and truffle purée. *L 12-2 D 7.30-11. Open Tue-Sat mid Sept-*
mid June; D only every day in summer, otherwise L & D Tues-Sat.
Closed L in summer, all Sun & Mon mid Sep-mid Jun, 1 Nov-13
Nov, 13 Jun-3 Jul. Private parking. AMERICAN EXPRESS *Diners,*
Mastercard, Visa.

Cannes   **Hotel Martinez**

Tel 92 98 73 00   Fax 93 39 67 82   **HR**

73 Boulevard la Croisette 06400 Cannes
Rooms 430   Double room from Fr1540

Built in the 20s, when Cannes' Croisette attracted starlets and
paparazzi like bees to a honeypot, it has played host to celebrities
and would-bes ever since. The Concorde Hotel group now own
it and have recently renovated the older, more traditional wing
(with 144 rooms) and 286 more modern rooms. Price quoted is
for a standard room without a view. The art deco entrance, which
looks over the waterfront, and the old Waring and Gillow
English furniture undoubtedly add glamour, but the real
attractions here are the excellent amenities: theatre-style
conference facilities for up to 750 people, a swimming pool,
private beach and tennis courts. *24hr room service. Satellite TV/fax.
Secretarial/translation/valet services on request. Private/valet parking.*
AMERICAN EXPRESS *Mastercard, Visa.*

La Palme d'Or
Seats 80   Meal for 2 approx Fr1400

The restaurant and menu owe much to the individuality of the
chef, Christian Willer: customers can even ask for a table for five
in the kitchen. His menu has been strongly influenced by his love
of Mediterranean cooking and its heavy emphasis on fish and
creative use of vegetables: *salade de rouget* (red mullet served in a
chilled salad), *langouste rose de mediterranée* (pink Mediterranean
crayfish salad) and *loup de mer bouché aux petits légumes* (sea bass
served in a vol-au-vent with fresh mixed vegetables). The
dégustation at 550Fr offers the best value. *L 12-2 D 7.30-10.30.
Closed Mon, Tue.*

Around Cannes

Auribeau-sur-Siagne   **Auberge de la Vignette Haute**

Tel 93 42 20 01   Fax 93 42 31 16   **HR**

370 Route du Village 06810 Auribeau-sur-Siagne
Rooms 12   Double room from Fr900

Right on the edge of the *Massif Central* range of mountains, this
17th-century farmhouse is only 15km from Cannes and 30km
from Nice International Airport. The surrounding countryside is,
however, largely deserted and incredibly peaceful. When first
converted it was just a restaurant, but in the 80s started taking
guests as well. In 1986, a fire swept through the hotel and
restaurant, leaving little more than a pile of charred remains.
However, over the subsequent two years the hotel and restaurant
were restored. The rooms are rustically elegant, with terracotta
floors, wood-panelled walls and country-style antique furniture.
The rooms are reasonably well equipped (but only have French
channels on television), with jacuzzis in the bathroom. Two *salons*
can be used for meetings for up to 40 people. *Private parking.*
AMERICAN EXPRESS *Mastercard, Visa.*

Restaurant
Seats 130   Meal for 2 approx Fr700

Alain Ducane, the Belgian chef, has worked with Roger Vergé
and owes a great deal to his gastronomic techniques and creations.
There is just one menu, and he chooses a starter for you; but you
are free to select a main course and dessert. Fish is a big speciality,
whether it is the catch of the day braised in a Chablis sauce,
or grilled salmon served with virgin olive oil. A bottle of *Le
Domaine de St Baillon* comes free along with the à la carte menu
and any additional bottle of wine you choose off the main wine
list comes at a much lower price than normal. *L 12-2.30 D 8-
10.30. Closed early Nov-early Dec.*

Juan-les-Pins   Juana

Tel 93 61 08 70   Fax 93 61 73 60   **HR**

Avenue Gallice la Pinède 06160 Juan-les-Pins
Rooms 51   Double room from Fr1800

The third family generation to manage this hotel since the 30s
have kept the original feel with art deco furniture in the lobby
and bedrooms. However, it is not just flamboyant showbiz stars
who stay here; Jaguar launched their XJ convertible here and
many other companies take advantage of the conference centre
next door to the hotel; they also have a small meeting room (for
up to 20). Floating in the heated outdoor swimming pool, tucked
away in a secluded grove of pine trees leading down to the sea,
is an excellent way to unwind. *24hr room service. Cable TV/fax.
Closed end Oct-Easter. Mastercard, Visa.*

Restaurant La Terrasse
Seats 80   Meal for 2 approx Fr1400

The garden terrace is right on the water, with only a few pine
groves between the diners and and the beach. Both the terrace and
restaurant have only been here since the late 70s, when it was
opened for hotel guests only. Now most of their customers come
here specifically to eat; however, the set menu is only for
residents. The cooking sticks to traditional regional dishes with
a comprehensive choice of seafood: a house speciality is *cannelloni
de suppions et palourdes à l'encre de seiche, jus de coquillages aux feuilles
de basilic* (baby squid and clams in cannelloni with cuttlefish ink
and a shellfish and basil sauce). *L 12-2 D 7.30-10 (to 10.30
in summer). Closed Wed (except Jul/Aug).*

The Golden Eurostar [★] denotes our pick of the
restaurants. Cooking is the major consideration, but
other factors are also taken into account, including
ambience, comfort and service.

Mougins   **Le Moulin de Mougins**

Tel 93 75 78 24   Fax 93 90 18 55   **RR**

Quartier Notre Dame de Vie 06250 Mougins
Seats 60   Meal for 2 approx Fr1800

Only 6km out of Cannes in the depths of the countryside,
surrounded by palms and mimosa, lies Roger and Denise Vergé's
restaurant with rooms set in a 16th-century olive oil mill, still
retaining the original wood and stone, the dining rooms housing
a very impressive contemporary art collection including paintings
and sculptures by César, Arman, Venet, Felon and Farhi (all
friends of *le patron*!). Vergé continues to create dishes
of unparalleled gastronomic excellence, making this a small
culinary corner of world renown, and he has also introduced
a cookery school and shop, selling amongst other things of course
his own books. He still works in the kitchen with Serge Chollet,
his right-hand man for 20 years, producing dishes that are finely
and meticulously prepared – a labour of love rarely seen
or experienced inside, or for that matter, outside France. Menus
are seasonal (*déjeuner* is a very reasonable Fr295, the other fixed-
price ones somewhat more expensive at Fr585 or Fr700) offering
such delights as: *consommé double au parfum de morille et son oeuf cuit
en vapeur de truffe noire de Vaucluse* (double-straining the
consommé leaves it with a subtle flavour of morels and it is served
with a truffle-scented egg), *blanc de loup de ligne en matignon*   ★
de légumes, truffée cuit à la feuille, courte sauce au vin de Madère (fillet
of local bass wrapped in cabbage and spinach leaves and served
with a Madeira sauce), *fricassée de homard breton au poivre rose
et crème de Sauternes* (with a spicy pink pepper and Sauternes cream
sauce), or one of the house specialities *traditionnel poupeton de fleur
de courgette à la truffe noir et champignons de bois* (courgette flowers
with black truffles served with a wild woodland mushroom
sauce). Marvellous Savoie farmhouse cheeses come from *Maitre
Ceneri* and sensational desserts include a bitter chocolate mousse
with a coffee bean sauce to a huge plate of assorted mini-desserts.
Some non-French wines appear on an extensive list that has lots
of local Provence and Rhone offerings nestling alongside the
grands crus. Five very comfortable bedrooms are often hard
to book, since they are quite reasonably priced at around Fr900 for
a double. If this place is beyond your budget, try Vergé's less
expensive restaurant, *L'Amandier*, at the top of the village. *L 12-
2.30 D 7.30-10.30. Closed L Thur, all Mon (but open D Mon 15
Jul-31 Aug), 5 Feb-9 Mar. Ample parking.* AMERICAN EXPRESS *Diners,
Mastercard, Visa.*

Nice   **Négresco**

Tel 93 88 39 51   Fax 93 88 35 68

HR

37 Promenade des Anglais 06000 Nice
Rooms 150   Double room from F1250

Like César Ritz, Henri Négresco came to France to seek his
fortune, and ended up building his own palatial hotel in Belle
Epoque-style on the waterfront of Nice's most famous boardwalk,
with its own private beach. The interior is still filled with
valuable artefacts acquired when the building was designed: 17th-
century tapestries, a late 19th-century Baccarat crystal chandelier
commissioned by the Tsar of Russia (listed as a historic monument,
with a similar example hanging in Moscow's Kremlin) and stained
glass by Gustav Eiffel. The Salon Louis XIV has paintings that are
part of a series in the Palace of Versailles and the same style
of ceiling and fireplaces. The bedrooms are also filled with
extraordinary pieces of period furniture, and are constantly being
renovated, refurbished and redecorated to a high standard, offering
every conceivable luxury. A special hotel, with special rates often
available, such as honeymoon and 'prestige' packages. The room
rate listed is for a more modest room without a view. *24hr room
service. Cable/satellite TV/fax. Theatre-style conference facilities for
up to 2500. Secretarial/translation services on request. Own
garage/valet parking.* AMERICAN EXPRESS *Diners, Mastercard, Visa.*

Restaurant Chantecler
Seats 80   Meal for 2 approx F1000

Chef Dominique Le Stanc naturally leans towards Mediterranean
cooking here – lots of olive oil, black olives, sun-dried tomatoes,
artichokes and fresh herbs. Alongside the à la carte menu, there are
several fixed-price menus (all written in English too): *menu
Dégustation* (served only to an entire table), *menu Chantecler, menu
de la Mer*, and the 3-course *Fr200 menu Plaisir*, which is only
served at lunch; for an extra Fr50 you get wine and coffee. Red
mullet is a popular dish, served with warm potato and chive salad
topped with caviar, and one of the house specialities is open ravioli
filled with asparagus tips, artichokes, langoustines and thyme-
flavoured extra virgin olive oil. Other dishes showing the style
of cooking are squid risotto with tomatoes and basil, or roast fillet
of sea bass, marinated in olive oil and star anise, and served with
sautéed local asparagus, tomatoes and chervil. Non-fish aficionados
might go for the suckling lamb roasted with herbs and
accompanied by stuffed vegetables, or pigeon roasted with cumin,
garnished with Swiss chard. Delicious desserts include a warm
chocolate tart with almond-flavoured cream, or layers of liquorice-
flavoured meringue with whipped cream and a raspberry sorbet.
Many *grands crus* and Provençal wines on the list. The sumptuous
wood panelling you see in the dining room was created in 1751
for the state room at the Chateau de Chaintre near Macon. *L12-
2.30 D 7.30-10.30. Closed mid Nov-mid Dec.*

★

To dial overseas from the UK, 010 will change to 00
on 16th April 1995.

Nice   **Palais Maeterlinck**

Tel 92 00 72 00   Fax 92 04 18 10   **HR**

30 Boulevard Maurice Maeterlinck 06300 Nice
Rooms 28   Double room from Fr1500

Most of this hotel, which looks out over its private beach and
large garden, was built at the turn of the century, the rest, more
recently, in the 1980s; but the hotel itself only opened four years
ago, when the whole of the former private club was redecorated.
Individual Provençe-style rooms are comfortable and well
equipped. There are two conference rooms, which they can equip
if necessary. *Satellite TV/fax. Theatre-style conference facilities for
up to 25. Secretarial/translation services on request. Closed 1 Nov-1
Mar. Private parking.* AMERICAN EXPRESS *Diners, Mastercard, Visa.*

Restaurant
Seats 100   Meal for 2 approx Fr600

Traditional French regional cooking is served in two large dining
rooms, one with rich red carpets and sombre wooden panelling,
the other in an enclosed veranda with a marble floor, overlooking
the sea. The menus range from the business lunch at Fr90 to the
Fr370 *dégustation*; all the menus feature plenty of seafood dishes.
*Filets de sole aux pates fraiches, sauce de morilles farcies, escalope de foie
gras chaud* (fillets of sole served on a bed of fresh pasta with
a morel mushroom sauce and an escalope of foie gras); another
typical dish is *turbot aux écailles de courgettes farci avec une mousse
de homard, sauce fine* (turbot wrapped in ribbons of courgette and
stuffed with a lobster mousse). *L 12-2.30 D 8-10. Closed D Sun,
1 Nov-1 Mar.*

Lille

Lille   A l'Huitrière

Tel 20 55 43 41   Fax 20 55 23 01   R

3 Rue des Chats Bossus 59800 Lille
Seats 80   Meal for 2 approx Fr700

Three generations ago, this was a fish shop which sold oysters and
snails, with a small room in the back where customers came
to taste the produce. The *dégustation* was so popular it expanded
into an informal fish restaurant, where the chef comes out and
discusses dishes with diners. Sitting in old oak rooms surrounded
by Breton-style mosaics, you can choose from a menu heavily
weighted towards shellfish, with traditional old house specialities:
huitres chaudes avec mousse d'échalote (warmed oysters with a light
shallot mousse) and *coquilles Saint Jacques à la Bercy* (only from
Oct to Mar, served in a reduced white wine, cream and shallot
sauce). *Saumon sauvage croustillant au concombre et à l'ail* and
fricassée de filets de sole et de homard, au coulis de homard are just two
more of the tempting dishes. The large cellars are well stocked
with white Loire wines and champagnes. *L 12-2.30 D 7-10.*
Closed D Sun and National Holidays, Aug. Private room for 12/14.
AMERICAN EXPRESS *Diners, Mastercard, Visa.*

Around Lille

Verlinghem   Chateau Blanc

Tel 20 40 71 02   Fax 20 40 99 40   RR

20 Route de Lambersart 59237
Seats 80   Meal for 2 approx Fr700

This old textile merchant's house, set in impressive grounds a ten-
minute drive from the centre of Lille, looks like a *chateau ancien*,
with its tall chimneys and Italianate porch. Attached to the house
is a little chapel with a stained-glass window depicting the twelve
children the textile merchant fathered. Inside, the dining room
and reception rooms are stylishly decorated, with fine fireplaces,
natural wood floors and crystal chandeliers. Owned by Brigitte
and Stéphane Lecocq, it only opened just over two years ago, and
unlike perhaps most chefs in the area, Stéphane likes to bring
oriental influences into his cooking style, as in *emincé de saumon cru
en marinade de neuf parfums* (marinated in light spices and fruit
juices), *ravioli de St-Jacques au curcumin* (ravioli of scallops), or *duo
de canard au caramel d'épices*. More traditional dishes also appear:
pavé de pieds de cochon et son jus de foie gras (pig's trotters with foie
gras), or *piccatas de veau forestière* (fillets of veal with a mushroom
sauce). For a dessert try the apple tart with a *Wambrechies* (local
sweet liqueur) syllabub or a classic chocolate tart with vanilla ice
cream. In addition to the carte, there are three set menus to choose
from, ranging between Fr160 and Fr300. Brigitte looks after the
French-only wine list, and she will happily recommend a suitable
accompaniment. Four very comfortable bedrooms (doubles
at Fr700) for restaurant diners to sleep off their excesses. *L 12-1.30
D 7.30-9.30. Closed D Sun, all Mon, 2 weeks Aug. Ample parking.
Mastercard, Visa.*

Lyons

Lyons	L'Alexandrin

Tel 72 61 15 69 Fax 78 62 75 57	R

83 Rue Moncey 69003 Lyons
Seats 40   Meal for 2 approx Fr500

Spices are a feature of Alain Alexanian's cooking, something
he thinks he subconsciously inherited from his mother and
grandmother. His style therefore is quite unique; he is perhaps
better known for for his regional fish specialities, often not
available elsewhere, such as *féra rotie coté peau sur ragout de pois
gourmands, sauce marinière au verjus* or *goujonettes de rascasse
en beignet au beurre de romarin et tombée d'epinard à la moëlle.* Cod
and char also feature regularly, while *blinis au caviar* stuffed with
aubergine and accompanied by a smoked salmon mousse or calf's
sweetbreads served with citrus fruits and spiced green peppers are
also considered house specialities. You can even get a dish
of famous Lyons tripe here, served with a paprika sauce. They
pride themselves on never repeating the same dish on either the
two fixed-price or à la carte menus, which change every two
months or so and are also written in English and German.
Outstanding cooking, moderately priced regional wines to the
fore. Friendly service from Véronique Alexanian (she speaks
excellent English) and her smiling all-ladies team. *L 12-1.30
D 7.30-9.30. Closed Sun, Mon, 2 weeks Aug, 24 Dec-2 Jan. Public
parking.* AMERICAN EXPRESS *Mastercard, Visa.*

★

Lyons	Auberge de L'Ile

Tel 78 83 99 49 Fax 78 47 80 46	R

Quartier St Rambert Ile Barbe 69009 Lyons
Rooms 55   Meal for 2 approx Fr600

Hidden away on a tiny residential island in the centre of Lyons,
the restaurant, formerly a 17th-century monastery, has kept its
atmosphere of austerity with bare stone floors and simple wooden
beams. It has been serving traditional French food to locals for 26
years and is still the only restaurant on the island. There are four
set menus to choose from, ranging from Fr130 to Fr295, with
plenty of fresh fish served in mildly spicy sauces. The good Cote
du Rhone house wine can add to making this a very reasonably
priced meal. *L 12-2 D 7.15-10. Closed D Sun, all Mon, 2 weeks
Feb, 2 weeks Aug. Private parking.* AMERICAN EXPRESS *Diners, Mastercard,
Visa.*

Lyons	Bourillot

Tel 78 37 38 64 Fax 78 38 20 35	R

8 Place des Célestins 69002 Lyons
Seats 35   Meal for 2 approx Fr800

Local Lyonnais styles inspire the cooking and the place. The
building was constructed out of old bricks from the Célestins
convent and the wine cellars are the convent's original ones.
Inside, the two dining rooms are simple, with wooden floors. The
owner-chef, Monsieur Bourillot, concentrates his efforts on re-
interpreting local dishes like *rouget à la purée de poivrons au jus
de romarin* (red mullet served on a purée of peppers with

a rosemary sauce) and *quenelles de brochet* (pike dumplings in a lobster sauce). His old grandmother's recipe has been a long-standing favourite: *volaille de Bresse 'Marie' et pommes aux truffes* is local Bresse fowl served with potatoes cooked in thick cream and truffles. Naturally, most of the wines are French, but there are some Spanish and Californian bottles. *L 12-2 D 7.30-10. Closed L Mon, all Sun, Jul. Public parking.* AMERICAN EXPRESS *Diners, Mastercard, Visa.*

Lyons   Cour des Loges

Tel 78 42 75 75   Fax 72 40 93 61   **H**

6 Rue du Boeuf 69005 Vieux Lyons
Rooms 63   Double room from Fr980

A collection of 14th-century Jesuit buildings was modernised back in 1987 and converted into a hotel. The beamed bedrooms, with parquet floors and bright, modern furniture, attract young artistes to stay; and the classical evening concerts have become so popular that they are now a regular feature. A large Renaissance glass-covered courtyard leads through to a small garden and an indoor swimming pool. *24hr room service. Video. Theatre-style conference facilities for up to 200. Private parking.* AMERICAN EXPRESS *Diners, Mastercard, Visa.*

Lyons   Fédora

Tel 78 69 46 26   Fax 72 73 38 80   **R**

249 Rue Marcelle Merieux 69007 Lyons
Seats 55   Meal for 2 approx Fr650

The Breton chef-patron of this art deco-style restaurant still concentrates on cooking dishes originating from his home region; and many of those are fish or shellfish recipes. *De l'orge et du blé flambés au vieux malt et filet de sardine à peine grillotté* (malt and wheat boiled and then flambéed in malt whisky and served with a lightly grilled fillet of sardine) is a most unusual dish; lobster comes in a salad with squid, topped with caramelised pears sprinkled with pepper. One of his many good bottles of burgundy perfectly complements the fish-orientated menu. In the summer, the garden comes alive with buzzing birds and bright flowers. *L 12-2 D 7.45-9.45. Closed L Sat, all Sun, 22 Dec-4 Jan, 1 week mid Aug. Public parking.* AMERICAN EXPRESS *Diners, Mastercard, Visa.*

The Golden Eurostar [★] denotes our pick of the restaurants. Cooking is the major consideration, but other factors are also taken into account, including ambience, comfort and service.

Lyons **Le Gourmandin**

Tel 78 52 02 52   Fax 78 52 33 05   **R**

14 Place Jules Ferry 69006 Lyons
Seats 100   Meal for 2 approx Fr500

Coffee and croissants used to be the main culinary delights
on offer here, but then it was just the buffet in the railway station.
Now, even though it is still part of the station, the restaurant
offers a more sophisticated repertoire of regional cooking. The
chef moves round the country with the season: at the time
of going to press the menu was full of Southern French fish dishes
cooked with fresh fruits and vegetables. When *La Chasse* starts,
the menu is dominated by game dishes served in rich sauces.
A winter speciality is *loup au fenouil farci croquant à l'oseille* (sea bass
served with half a fennel bulb stuffed with fish or vegetable
mousse with crisp-fried sorrel leaves on the side). *L 12-1.45 D 8-
9.45. Closed L Sat, all Sun. Private parking.* AMERICAN EXPRESS *Diners,
Visa.*

Lyons **Léon de Lyon**

Tel 78 28 11 33   Fax 78 39 89 05   **R**

1 Rue Pléney 69001 Lyons
Seats 80   Meal for 2 approx Fr1100

Present chef-patron Jean-Paul Lacombe continues the tradition
of Lyonnaise cuisine here, having spent his entire life growing
up in the family restaurant and working alongside his father since
his early teens. He now owns six other restaurants (one is the
cheaper *Bistrot de Lyon*). This is, however, still his main
gastronomic venture, situated in the old quarter known as *Place des
Terreaux* near the *St Nizier* church between the Rhone and Saone
rivers. With his wife Fabienne, who looks after front-of-house,
and a dedicated team that includes a dozen in the kitchen, they run
an almost old-fashioned restaurant – in the nicest sense – with
leather seating, panelling and stained-glass windows, an impressive
collection of paintings and pictures, and objets d'art – note the
copper cooking pots and pans, and porcelain models of chefs. The
Fr490 *menu dinette* probably gives you the best flavour of cooking
here, perhaps a *ballotine de poularde de Bresse, tarte fine et croustillante
à la provençale, langoustines roties* with girolles and straw potatoes,
pavé de foie de veau de lait, cuit entier, petits farcis, the latter
a summer dish of calf's liver with stuffed vegetables, climaxing
with the cheeseboard, and a crispy caramel dessert with
raspberries, a few strawberries, a sorbet and a coulis. Other
specialities include a winter pheasant soup with kidney beans,
potato stuffed with pig's trotter and foie gras, and sweet sugared
praline desserts *St Genix* (the village where almonds come from).
Lobster-lovers can have an entire menu based on the *breton* beast,
from cold soup to stuffed ravioli. Several bottles around the Fr150
mark on the wine list, where alongside the local(ish) Beaujolais
and Cotes du Rhone, clarets are in prominence. *L 12-2 D 7.30-10.
Closed Sun. Valet parking.* AMERICAN EXPRESS *Mastercard, Visa.*

★

Lyons   **La Mère Brazier**

Tel 78 28 15 49   Fax 78 28 63 63   **R**

12 Rue Royale 69001 Lyons
Seats 100   Meal for 2 approx Fr600

Owner Jacotte Brazier's great-grandmother opened this restaurant
back in 1921 in an 18th-century merchant's house; and her great-
granddaughter still runs it and also gives a helping hand in the
kitchen. Three menus are served: the Fr290 set, traditional Fr370
with all her grandmother's original recipes and the à la carte. Two
dishes that have survived the generations are typically Lyonnais:
quenelles de brochet 'Mère Brazier' (pike quenelles topped with
a béchamel sauce) and *volaille de Bresse au demi-deuil* (Bresse
chicken with truffles stuffed under the skin). Ingredients are very
fresh and dishes mainly regional. The wine list is heavily weighted
towards burgundy and Bordeaux. *L 12-2 D 7.30-10. Closed L Sat,
all Sun, Aug. Public parking.* AMERICAN EXPRESS *Diners, Mastercard, Visa.*

Lyons   **Nandron**

Tel 78 42 10 26   Fax 78 37 69 88   **R**

26 Quai Jean Moulin 69002 Lyons
Seats 50   Meal for 2 approx Fr500

Not long after the end of the Second World War, Monsieur and
Madame Nandron opened this restaurant on the banks of the
Rhone right in the centre of Lyons, and they are still running it.
Monsieur cooks typically Lyonnais dishes that have hardly
changed over the last 40 years. His excellent specialities, *quenelle
de brochet à la Nantua* (pike quenelles with a cream and tomato
sauce) and *rognon de veau en cocotte au thym* (calf's kidney and
thyme casserole) are worth trying; so is the home-town dish,
terrine tiède de champignons de bois (a warm woodland mushroom
terrine). The Fr350 and Fr450 set menus change only seasonally,
but the cheaper Fr200 one varies all the time. *L 12-2 D 7.30-10.
Closed Sat, Aug. Private parking.* AMERICAN EXPRESS *Diners, Mastercard,
Visa.*

Meal prices for 2 are based on à la carte menus.
When set menus are available, prices will often be lower.

Lyons   **Paul Bocuse**

Tel 72 27 85 85   Fax 78 27 95 97   **R**

Pont de Collonges au Mont d'Or 69660 Lyons
Seats 120   Meal for 2 approx Fr1400

You really cannot miss this somewhat garish restaurant, a 1920s
building painted bright green and orange with scarlet shutters,
with a *rue des Grands Chefs*, a gallery of trompe l'oeil paintings
by Lyons artists. The restaurant is situated on the Collonges bridge
about three miles out of town; Collonges, incidentally, is twinned
with Illhaeusern, site of another temple of gastronomy. Though
Paul (third generation of Bocuse ownership) himself perhaps
spends less time here – he's constantly travelling and looking after
other business ventures – than in the past, the remarkable
consistency that has been built up every day (the restaurant never
closes) continues in the capable hands of head chef Roger Jaloux
and second-in-command Christian Bouvarel, both *meilleurs ouvriers
de France* in their own right. Dishes such as *volaille de Bresse rotie
à la broche* (Bresse chicken roasted on a spit over an open fire in the
restaurant), *poularde de Bresse en vessie* (chicken cooked in a pig's
bladder), and *carré d'agneau roti à la fleur de thym* (rack of lamb
roasted with thyme) are just a few specialities. Other local   ★
influences can be seen in *soupe aux truffes noires V.G.E.*(a black
truffle soup with a pastry crust created for President Valéry
Giscard d'Estaing at the Elysée Palace in 1975), *quenelles de brochet
lyonnaise*, with a *sauce Nantua, loup en croute à la mousse de homard*
with a *sauce choron* (a *béarnaise* sauce blended with tomato juice),
lièvre à la royale (a classic hare dish available only in the hunting
season) and all manner of fowl/birds in puff pastry. There are
several fixed-price menus ranging from lunch at Fr290 to a not
inconsiderable Fr710 for six courses. Children under 12 can have
three courses for a bargain Fr90. Simpler dishes such as pumpkin
soup and coq au vin also feature in Bocuse's recipe books. There
are few non-French wines on the list; sommelier Yann Eon, with
his remarkable bristling moustache, will give you all the necessary
advice, steering you, no doubt, towards the Paul Bocuse
Beaujolais! *L 12-2 D 7-10. Public parking.* AMERICAN EXPRESS *Diners,
Mastercard, Visa.*

Lyons   **Pierre Orsi**

Tel 78 89 57 68   Fax 72 44 93 34   **R**

3 Place Kléber 69006 Lyons
Seats 90   Meal for 2 approx Fr1000

Having trained with Paul Bocuse and then at *Maxim's* in Paris,
Orsi brought a wealth of culinary experience to his Lyonnais
restaurant, which opened in 1975. He has continued to expand and
develop his menu and repertoire. Southern Mediterranean ideas
filter through his dishes: *ravioli de foie gras de canard au jus de porto*
(ravioli filled with foie gras and served with a rich port sauce) and
rouget mediterranéen à l'huile d'olive vierge (red mullet cooked
in virgin olive oil). There are also plenty of good meat dishes. For
a cheaper meal try his other restaurant in Lyons, *le Cazenove* (75
Rue Boileau). *L 12-3.30 D 8-10. Closed Sun in summer. Public
parking.* AMERICAN EXPRESS *Mastercard, Visa.*

Lyons   **Tour Rose**

Tel 78 37 25 90   Fax 78 42 26 02   **HR**

22 Rue du Boeuf 69005 Lyons
Rooms 12   Double room from Fr950

Each of the 12 suites in the hotel is unique in that it has been
individually and stylishly decorated by a different Lyonnais silk
manufacturer and the finished suite bears the decorator's name.
Rich rugs, restoration art and high beamed ceilings grace all the
suites, from the restoration rooms to the textile designers' salons.
The 15th- to 17th-century hotel buildings are as stunningly
irregular as the rooms: painted in rich burnt siennas and ochres,
they rise up like Roman buildings around a long, narrow
courtyard. The place is very informal and in the evenings an arty
crowd of guests start in the bar and soon proceed to the restaurant.
Conference facilities for up to 50. Private parking. AMERICAN EXPRESS
Diners, Mastercard, Visa.

Restaurant
Seats 70   Meal for 2 approx Fr1000

Monsieur Chavent came from Paul Bocuse to start up this
restaurant seven years ago. Since then, he has determinedly set out
to develop his own style and has added a nouvelle cuisine style
to the traditional French dishes. *Pot au feu de pigeon en feuille
de chou à l'infusion de feuilles de citronnier* (pigeon wrapped in a
cabbage leaf and casseroled with onions, leeks, carrots and turnip
and served with a sauce made from an infusion of lemon leaves);
oeufs pochés aux oursins et betteraves frites (poached eggs in a sea
urchin sauce served with fried beetroots). All the dishes are
imaginative, constantly changing to adapt to new fresh products.
The house specialities are particularly interesting: *cote de veau
de lait panée aux morilles, vrai jus gras, pois gourmands* (veal cutlet
in breadcrumbs fried with morels and served with peas) and *fonds
d'artichauts au foie gras, langoustines roties, fondue d'échalotes
au cerfeuil et vinaigre balsamique* (artichoke hearts and foie gras with
roasted langoustines and a shallot, chervil and balsamic vinegar
fondue). Some of their wines have been specially chosen for the
restaurant with some grands crus from the Juliénas and Morgon
vineyards. *L 12.30-2.30 D 7.30-10.30. Closed Sun.*

Lyons   **Villa Florentine**

Tel 72 56 56 66   Fax 72 40 90 56   **H**

25 Monté Saint Barthelemy 69005 Lyons
Rooms 19   Double room from Fr1200

Poverty-stricken girls used to be sent to this old orphanage back
in the 1600s, but 25 years ago all the buildings were converted
into a new hotel by the *Groupe Lyonnais.* The original chapel
is now the reception. The rooms have obviously been modernised,
but the old parquet floors and sombre, heavy furniture have been
retained. Two of the rooms have their own private terraces.
Despite being right in the heart of the old part of Lyons, the hotel
is peaceful, surrounded by gardens with an outdoor swimming
pool. *24hr room service. Fax. Conference facilities for up to 25.
Translation services on request. Permanent secretary. Private parking.*
AMERICAN EXPRESS *Diners, Mastercard, Visa.*

Around Lyons

Caluire eut Cuire   Auberge de Fond-Rose

Tel 78 29 34 61   Fax 72 00 28 67   **R**

23 Quai Georges Clémenceau 69300 Caluire eut Cuire
Seats 100   Meal for 2 approx Fr1200

A wonderful setting (15 minutes out of Lyons) for *une grande
bouffe*: old trees circle the house and gardens stretch out around
it with a mini-aviary in the corner. In the summer the tables are
dotted around the patio and in winter diners warm themselves
by the old fireplaces. The three set menus and the *dégustation* all
take full advantage of the fruits and fish in season: red mullet
is marinated in bitter oranges and basil. A regular house speciality
is *homard grillé aux deux sauces* (grilled lobster half served in lobster
sauce and half in a white butter sauce). In the winter, lamb and
game can be roasted on a spit over the fire (must request
in advance). Every French region is well represented on the wine
list. *L 12-2 D 7.30-9.30. Closed D Sun, all Mon (but open Mon Oct-
May). Private parking.* AMERICAN EXPRESS *Diners, Mastercard, Visa.*

Dardilly-le-Haut   Le Panorama

Tel 78 47 40 19   Fax 78 43 20 31   **R**

Place Général Brosset 69570 Dardilly-le-Haut
Seats 90   Meal for 2 approx Fr600

Dardilly is a tiny village ten minutes north of Lyons, which has
the main Paris-Lyons motorway cutting straight through it. The
set and à la carte menus have plenty of fish like red mullet and
bass to choose from and there is also a lobster-only menu: lobster
salad comes with green beans with a trickle of virgin olive oil,
while grilled lobster in a shallot, chervil, white wine and tarragon
sauce is served as a main course. This place has always made great
patés, so look out for them on the menu. The set menus start
at Fr190 – excellent value. *L 12-2 D 7.30-10. Closed D Sun, all
Mon. Public parking.* AMERICAN EXPRESS *Diners, Visa.*

Mionnay   Alain Chapel

Tel 78 91 82 02   Fax 78 91 82 37   **RR**

1 Route Nationale 01390 Mionnay
Seats 50   Meal for 2 approx Fr2000

The restaurant, still bearing the name of the great master chef,
who sadly died in 1989, is as good as ever. Alain's wife Suzanne
is continuing the reputation built up over the years with the help
of some old lieutenants, notably chef Philippe Jousse, who
returned from Japan (where there's another *Alain Chapel*
restaurant) and maitre d' Hervé Duronzier. The cooking style has
hardly changed and still produces superbly executed dishes
featuring fine sauces. Three of the many house specialities to look   ★
out for are *crème de primeurs à l'estragon, en gelée de crustacés*
(savoury jellies being something of a Jousse favourite), *bouillon
de champignons de printemps comme cappuccino, des écrevisses
au cerfeuil* (spring mushroom bouillon whisked up with a blend
of crayfish and chervil), and *salade de homard, de gorges
de pigeonneaux au pourpier et truffes noires* (lobster salad served with
baby pigeon breast, purslane and black truffles). The Fr450 (Fr550

with an additional first course) *'une idée de menu'* is a good bet,
offering dishes such as langoustines and large ravioli of fromage
frais infused with coriander; roast loin of lamb, served with
a warm artichoke salad and new season shallots in olive oil;
farmhouse cheeses; almond strudel with roast figs. Push the boat
out further and you can spend Fr780 a head on a seasonal fixed-
price menu (min two persons). The restaurant, situated in an 18th-
century former posting house at Mionnay some 20km from
Lyons, comprises three delightful dining rooms and also has
fourteen luxurious bedrooms. *L 12-1 D 7-9. Closed L Tue, all
Mon, Jan. Private parking.* AMERICAN EXPRESS *Diners, Mastercard, Visa.*

Montrond-les-Bains   Hostellerie La Poularde

Tel 77 54 40 06   Fax 77 54 53 14   **HR**

2 Route de Saint-Etienne 42210 Montrond-les-Bains
Rooms 14   Double room from Fr500

Once an 18th-century coaching inn, the original charm and style
have been restored by the Etéocle-Randoing family. The
comfortable bedrooms, mostly with antique furniture and
paintings by local artists, are decorated with fresh flowers daily;
the duplex apartments, overlooking an internal courtyard garden,
are more modern in style. Superb breakfasts start the day in style.
Despite its somewhat sleepy location, the village (only 8km from
St Etienne airport) tends to come alive with tourists visiting the
natural spa and seawater therapy centre. *Theatre-style conference
facilities for up to 40. Closed Mon, 2-15 Jan. Private garage.*
AMERICAN EXPRESS *Diners, Mastercard, Visa.*

Restaurant

Chef Gilles Etéocle's fixed-price menus, alongside the à la carte,
certainly demonstrate his interesting and innovative style
of cooking to good effect. The emphasis is on quality, with plenty
of choice within every course. The menus are perhaps weighted
more towards fish/shellfish dishes, with the delicious desserts
something of a lottery and not normally described on the menus.
Among his non-fish specialities are *pigeonneau du Forez braisé dans
sa gelée de cuisson, compotée d'oignons rouges aux épices* (baby Forez
pigeon, braised in its own juices, with a compote of red onions and
spices), *chausson aux truffes noires de St Donat, escalope de foie gras
chaud poelée* (a puff pastry case filled with black truffles and served
with a slice of warm foie gras), *choisi d'agneau de lait roti à la fleur
de thym, son épigramme au seigle* (choice cut of baby lamb roasted
with thyme and accompanied by its "epigrams" rolled in rye-bread
crumbs). Those with a penchant for fish may opt for the warm
lobster salad served with foie gras and Norwegian salmon, *blanc
de turbot au four, beurre ambré, lardons en coque et céleri confit* (roasted
fillet of turbot, served with melted brown butter, lardons and
a celery confit), or just grilled catch of the day with a sauce
of your choice. The wine cellar has been built up over the years
and contains many superb vintages. *L from 12, D from 7.30. Closed
L Tue, all Mon.*

La Mulatière   **Roger Roucou 'Mère Guy'**

Tel 78 50 11 36   Fax 78 51 99 47   **R**

35 Quai Jean-Jacques Rousseau 69350 La Mulatière
Seats 150   Meal for 2 approx Fr600

Roger Roucou and his daughter are in the process of building
a hotel, which will make this restaurant (founded in 1759) an all
the more appealing place to stop, near the banks of the Saone, for a
meal. The menu is classical, suiting the interior, which is filled
with Louis XV furniture. Most of his ingredients come fresh from
the different regions: *foie gras* from Quercy, *volaille de Bresse* and
other poultry and meat. The three set menus run every lunch and
dinner starting at Fr200. *L 12-2 D 7-9. Closed D Sun, all Mon,
Aug. Private parking.* AMERICAN EXPRESS *Diners, Visa.*

Neyron-le-Haut   **Le Saint Didier**

Tel 78 55 28 72   Fax 78 55 01 55   **R**

7 rue de l'Eglise 01700 Neyron-le-Haut
Seats 25   Meal for 2 approx Fr800

This 19th-century farmhouse in the tiny hamlet of Neyron opened
as a restaurant 12 years ago and has been extended to fit in a brand
new kitchen. Despite the glittering new workplace, the cooking
remains loyal to its Lyonnais roots: *nage de grenouilles désossées à la
Rousette* (boned frogs' legs cooked in local wine and served in an
aromatic *bouillon*), *caille rotie en crapaudine beurre de foie sur
paillasson* (roasted quail served with a piquant mushroom, mustard
and tarragon vinegar sauce and quail liver paté on toast). These
local delicacies are served up in a room very like a sitting room,
with a general clutter of bookcases, pictures and ornaments. The
wine list has a healthy selection of rosés. *L 12-1.15 D 7.30-8.45.
Closed D Sun, all Mon, 3 weeks Aug. Private parking. Visa.*

Rilleux-la-Pape   **Larivoire**

Tel 78 88 50 92   Fax 78 88 35 22   **R**

Chemin des Iles 39140 Rilleux-la-Pape
Seats 80   Meal for 2 approx Fr600

The chef has an impressive pedigree: the *Savoy* in London,
Drouant and *Maxim's* in Paris. And here, in this restaurant
overlooking the Rhone, he has created his own seasonal menu
with dishes like *pressé de tourteau en millefeuilles aux légumes fines
gelées* (Breton crab in a millefeuille layered with spinach and
asparagus) and *fricassée de volaille de Bresse au vinaigre de vieux vin*
(Bresse chicken fricasseed in vintage wine vinegar). Game, fish and
shellfish all appear in their season. *L 12-2 D 7-10. Closed D Mon,
all Tue, 14-25 Feb. Private parking.* AMERICAN EXPRESS *Diners, Visa.*

St Etienne   **Pierre Gagnaire**

Tel 77 42 30 90   Fax 77 42 30 15   **R**

7 Rue de la Richelandière 42100 St Etienne
Seats 80   Meal for 2 approx Fr1800

A pharmacist built this house in the 30s and Gagnaire designed the
inside in art deco style in keeping with the era. His cooking
continues to chart a path all of its own, with adventurous
interpretations of traditional dishes using a variety of exciting

ingredients: try *filet de sole et céteaux de petits bateaux pochés dans un beurre fondu à la badiane, une bouillabaisse serrée* (fillet of sole and tiny flat fish poached in melted butter and star anise and served with a Mediterranean fish soup), or *corail roti aux cristes marines, une étuvée de blettes et escargots petits gris au basilic à feuille de meurisier* (lobster corals roasted with seaweed and served with chard, small snails and a type of basil with leaves like those of a wild cherry tree). His pigeon dish is also unique: the pigeon is not drawn until a few hours before cooking and is served with a mushroom, mustard, tarragon vinegar and grilled cardamon seed sauce. For Fr780, there is a choice of two menus: a meat, game and fish menu, or the special lobster-only menu. A bottle from every wine-growing region in France can be found in the cellar. *L 12-2 D 8-10. Closed D Sun, 3 weeks Aug. Private garage.* AMERICAN EXPRESS *Mastercard, Visa.*

Vienne   La Pyramide

Tel 74 53 01 96   Fax 74 85 69 73   **RR**

14 Boulevard Fernand Point 38200 Vienne
Seats 70   Meal for 2 approx Fr900

The great Fernand Point, acknowledged as the master of French cuisine and inspiration for many of today's great French chefs, started this restaurant in 1923, naming it after the Roman monument next to the building, said to mark the start of chariot races. The Roman theme is much in evidence as their primary motif in the decor with romanesque columns inside and big urns and jars on the terrace, where there are some twenty tables for al fresco eating in the summer months. Ownership remained in the hands of the Point family until 1989, since when Patrick Henriroux has been chef-patron. A great deal of his cooking is typically Lyonnais, but his style, by his own admission, also has Mediterranean influences with its liberal use of aromatic herbs and accompaniments such as sun-dried tomatoes and basil as in *ballotine de pigeonneau farci d'herbes des jardins, un jus corse à la livèche* (baby pigeon stuffed with garden herbs, casseroled and served with a Corsican wild celery *jus*), *grosse tomate d'Ampuis confite à l'huile d'olives et aux aromates, un sauté minute d'agneau de l'Adret à la marjolaine* (large tomato pickled in olive oil and aromatic herbs, served with lightly cooked lamb with marjoram). Point's speciality *turbot au champagne* remains on the menu with the ingredients still a closely guarded secret, while a Lyonnais dish might be *poulette de Bresse 'Jean Verne' farcie aux herbes sous la peau et aux abattis dans le coffre, une poelée de chayotte au thym frais* (stuffed with giblets and herbs under the skin served with a marrow and fresh thyme purée). Jean Verne, incidentally, is probably the most famous breeder of poultry in the country. For dessert, try the house speciality *piano au chocolat, praliné, amandes et noisettes, sauce café grillé.* Huge wine cellar, almost 2,000 bins on the list heavily featuring two great wines of the region: Condrieu and Cote Rotie – sommelier Jean-Claude Ruet will advise. 25 bedrooms including four suites (from around Fr880 for two) overlook the garden. Excellent breakfasts are served in the conservatory. *L 12-1.30 D 7.30-9.30. Closed L Thur, all Wed, Feb. Ample parking. Conferences for up to 30.* AMERICAN EXPRESS *Diners, Mastercard, Visa.*

Marseilles

Marseilles   **Le Petit Nice Passédat**

Tel 91 59 25 92   Fax 91 59 28 08   **HR**

Anse dè Maldormé Corniche J.F. Kennedy 13007 Marseilles
Rooms 18   Double room from Fr1200

This white colonial-style building sits on a peninsula, right on the
water's edge, with superb views. It is glamour itself, with its palm-
and plant-lined swimming pool and colonnaded balconies glowing
in the rich sunsets over the sea. The rooms are equally stylish,
ranging from stark simplicity to elaborate suites covered with rich
brocade. All the rooms are air-conditioned, with personal safes
provided, and were recently re-designed by Klein. There are
no reception rooms, but the hotel does offer secretarial and
translation services if arranged in advance. *24hr room service.
Outdoor swimming pool/solarium/water sports. Private parking.*
AMERICAN EXPRESS *Mastercard, Visa.*

Restaurant
Seats 60   Meal for 2 approx Fr2000

Back in 1917, the Passédat family built this wood-panelled, stone-
floored restaurant, which is situated right on the harbour. Now,
the third generation Passédat son, Gérald, is in the kitchen, having
had an extensive training all over the world, as well as in France,
at the prestigious *Paul Bocuse* establishment. Sauces have always
been his forte and have not become any less imaginative with
time: roast Bresse pigeon comes in a grain mustard and Oriental
spice sauce and sea bass is served in his grandmother's sauce
(a closely guarded and delicious secret). Another innovative touch
is his fillet of Normandy beef, which comes with beetroot ravioli.
The menu changes with the seasons. *L 12-2 D 8-10. Closed (Oct-
Mar) L Sat, all Sun.*

Around Marseilles

Carry-le-Rouet   **L'Escale**

Tel 42 45 00 47   Fax 42 44 72 69   **R**

Promenade du Port 13620 Carry-le-Rouet
Seats 70   Meal for 2 approx Fr1000

Situated in a picturesque fishing village overlooking the harbour,
seafood is the obvious choice here and most definitely chef Gérard
Clor's speciality. A wonderful Provençal restaurant, with a terrace,
colourfully decorated with murals and art deco paintings.
Fishermen bring him sea bass, lobsters, prawns and clams literally
still wriggling in the nets, which in turn become dishes such
as *casserole de poissons "cote bleue"*, a fish stew from the Cote Bleue,
the section of the Cote d'Azur between Marseilles and
Montpellier, *tartare de loup en liaison d'huitres fines, cassoulet
de palourdes aux épinards* (a bean-based casserole of clams with
spinach, a dish originally from the Languedoc region), and a classic   ★
bouillabaisse. However, if fish does not appeal, there are some
good lamb and duckling dishes to choose from. The menu changes
every month, reflecting the different fish available. Many local
wines feature on the list: Cassis, Bandol and Coteaux d'Aix
en Provence. The light, crisp rosé wines complement the style
of food ideally, a traditional style with new and interesting
approaches both in cooking and presentation, a touch of *cuisine
moderne* perhaps. *L 12-2 D 8-9. Closed D Sun, all Mon (except
D July and Aug), Nov-Feb.* AMERICAN EXPRESS *Visa.*

Reims

Reims	Boyer "Les Crayères"	
Tel 26 82 80 80 Fax 26 82 65 52		**HR**

64 Boulevard Henry-Vasnier 51100 Reims
Rooms 19   Double room from Fr1000

In a 17-acre English-style park in the centre of town, Gérard and
Elyane Boyer spent two years converting this old turn-of-the-
century chateau into a charming hotel of great style and comfort.
Elegant and luxurious bedrooms (3 suites are situated in a pavilion
in the grounds) are decorated in a variety of period styles with
high standards of service to match. *Conference facilities. Tennis.
Closed 23 Dec-13 Jan.* AMERICAN EXPRESS® *Diners, Mastercard, Visa.*

Restaurant
Seats 100   Meal for 2 approx Fr1600

The chateau, commissioned by Madame Pommery, and once the
home of the Prince of Polignac, has an English bar, three dining
rooms, two of them wood-panelled, all with an impressive array
of original 16th, 17th and 18th-century paintings, as well as a lot
of contemporary works by local artists. There are also some
stunning early 16th-century tapestries and in one of the dining
rooms note the wooden carving of St John the Evangelist. The
location is certainly a fitting venue for Boyer's lavish gastronomic
cooking, prepared with a religious zeal and devotion to detail, seen
in dishes such as *bar roti sur sa peau, des poireaux légèrement
croquants, sauce au Bouzy rouge et à la moëlle* (fillet of bass roasted
in its skin, with lightly crunchy leeks in red wine and bone
marrow sauce), or *deux grenadins de veau au lait, crème à l'ail doux,
polenta et 'brick' de risotto aux cèpes* (small triangular slices cut from
a fillet of veal, larded with bacon and braised with white wine,
onions, carrots and stock, served with a mild garlic cream sauce
with polenta porridge and a finely blended mushroom risotto).
Other dishes that demonstrate Boyer's style are pig's trotter stuffed
with foie gras and ceps, accompanied by a stir-fry of vegetables,
and locally-caught langoustines, lightly roasted, and served in a
coral sauce with a garnish of baby vegetables. Every six weeks the
menu is changed right down to the last dessert (*croustillants
d'agrumes caramélisés, sauce à l'orange, sorbet au cacao*). If you're
going for the full *dégustation menu*, try one of their excellent
champagnes – there are some 200 to choose from! *L 12-2.30
D 7.30-10.30. Closed as above, L Tue, all Mon.*

★

Reims	Le Chardonnay	
Tel 26 06 08 60 Fax 26 05 81 56		**R**

184 Avenue d'Epernay 51100 Reims
Seats 70   Meal for 2 approx Fr790

Purpose-built in the 30s, this place is still as traditional as it has
always been, with a well-spaced dining room and local art on the
walls. In the kitchen, haute cuisine meets traditional regional
cooking, with splendid results. The chef, Monsieur Lange, worked
with Gérard Boyer before coming here and closely follows his
culinary largesse: *millefeuilles de veau au homard* (layered with veal
and lobster), *escalope de sandre au Bouzy* (escalope of pike-perch
with Bouzy champagne). The business lunch, *dégustation* and

champagne menu – the latter is for two people and naturally,
includes a bottle of bubbly – all change seasonally. For dessert,
don't try to resist the warm chocolate soufflé. *L 12-2.30 D 7.30-
10. Closed L Sat, D Sun. Private parking.* AMERICAN EXPRESS *Diners,
Mastercard, Visa.*

Reims   Le Florence

Tel 26 47 12 70   Fax 26 40 07 09   **R**

43 Boulevard Foch 51100 Reims
Seats 50   Meal for 2 approx Fr600

Hearty helpings of imaginative cuisine are served here
by Monsieur Maillot, the chef, who has been running this place
with his wife for the last 17 years. Meaty house specialities like
pot-au-feu de foie gras à la crème d'ail doux (pot-au-feu with foie gras
and a mild garlic and cream sauce) and *selle d'agneau cuite sous
sa croute d'herbes, échalotes et gratin de céleri* (saddle of lamb roasted
with herbs and shallots with gratinated celery) come with the
fresh fish of the day. However, be prepared, as even the fish dishes
are substantial: *croustillant de saumon cuit, l'andouille fermière
et pommes de terre* (crispy pastry cases filled with salmon and home-
made sausages and served with potatoes). For determined diners,
the steaming hot bitter chocolate tart is the most delicious dessert.
240 different regional wines make up an impressive list with some
popular and reasonably-priced champagnes. *L 12-2 D 7.15-9.30.
Closed Sun, 1-7 Aug, 1 week Feb school holidays. Public parking.*
AMERICAN EXPRESS *Diners, Visa.*

Reims   Hotel Reims

Tel 26 40 01 08   Fax 26 40 34 13   **HR**

37 Boulevard Paul Doumer 51100 Reims
Rooms 80   Double room from Fr440

Choice Hotels had only just taken this place over at the time
of going to press and have ambitious plans to renovate the rooms
and expand the conference facilities that may, or may not, come
to fruition. At the moment, the rooms are a little sparse, with
plain white carpets and curtains – very modern (the hotel was
only built in 1990). The location is, however, a plus point: only
five minutes from the cathedral, backing on to the banks of the
canal, it is central but quiet. *Theatre-style conference facilities for
up to 100. Secretarial/translation/fax services on request. Private garage.*
AMERICAN EXPRESS *Diners, Mastercard, Visa.*

Restaurant Orphée
Seats 60   Meal for 2 approx Fr450

The local chef serves an abundance of seafood and game in season,
while the rest of the menu also changes seasonally. Fillet of salmon,
roasted then fried with mushrooms and served with different
sauces, and a fricassee of mullet and small grey snails from
Champagne with a vegetable and garlic sauce are his particular
penchants; accompanied by regional wines from the well-stocked
cellar. *L 12-2 D 7-10. Closed L Sat, all Sun.*

Around Reims

Champigny sur Vesle   **La Garenne**

Tel 26 08 26 62   Fax 26 84 24 13   **R**

Route de Soissons 51370 Champigny sur Vesle
Seats 70   Meal for 2 approx Fr500

About 5km out of town north west on the N31, this tiny village
is just two minutes off the main A4 autoroute. Previously it was
the restaurant/café of the old race track, but since chef/patron
Laurent Laplaige (he used to work with Boyer) took over, the
cooking has moved up a gear to produce some splendid haute
cuisine. He enjoys cooking with fish (*marmite de homard, turbot
et St Jacques* is a clear strong broth of lobster, turbot and scallops),
and other specialities include stuffed Landes pigeon, a salad
of warm foie gras, and red fruits with crème patissière.
Champagne is obviously well represented on the vast wine list
(some 12,000 bottles in the cellar) and there's a good selection
of half bottles. Very much a rustic decor with prominent
stonework and beams in the restaurant, with some nice country
landscape paintings. *L 12-2 D 7.30-10. Closed D Sun, all Mon,
1 week early Feb. 1st 3 weeks Aug, Ample parking.* AMERICAN EXPRESS
Diners, Mastercard, Visa.

The Golden Eurostar [★] denotes our pick of the
restaurants. Cooking is the major consideration, but
other factors are also taken into account, including
ambience, comfort and service.

Strasbourg

Strasbourg   Hotel Baumann

Tel 88 32 42 14   Fax 88 23 03 92   **HR**

16 Place de la Cathédrale 67000 Strasbourg

Rooms 9   Double room from F580

The hotel came after the restaurant and was opened only four years ago. The old building is in a superb location, looking out over the square at the cathedral and only 15 minutes walk from the railway station and 20 minutes drive from the airport. Only four of the rooms are doubles, but they all have marble bathrooms, televisions and mini-bars. Room service is not strictly offered, but meals from the restaurant can be brought up to the rooms. *Conference facilities for up to 150. Public parking.* AMERICAN EXPRESS® *Diners, Mastercard, Visa.*

Restaurant Maison Kammerzell

Seats 200   Meal for 2 approx F500

Inside this listed building, with its 12 salons all decorated with frescoes and panelled with dark wood, the chef cooks an eclectic menu with a definite regional accent. Try *brochette océane au beurre de concombre* (a mixture of sea fish grilled on a skewer served with a cucumber butter), or *supreme de pintade aux légumes croquantes, crème de brocolis* (guinea fowl breast served with fresh, crunchy vegetables and a broccoli cream sauce). The two set menus offer good value and start at Fr190. Only French wines are served. Baumann, who cooked for Pope John-Paul when he visited Strasbourg, still oversees all the cooking. *L 12-3 D 7-12. Closed 24 Dec.*

To dial overseas from the UK, 010 will change to 00 on 16th April 1995.

Strasbourg   Buerehiesel

Tel 88 61 62 24   Fax 88 61 32 00 ·   **R**

4 Parc de l'Orangerie 67000 Strasbourg
Seats 80   Meal for 2 approx Fr1300

This 17th-century Alsatian wooden house was actually taken apart
and reconstructed on its present site in an old park opposite the
Conseil de l'Europe, ten minutes from the city centre. A glass-
roofed conservatory, made with natural wood, has been added
to the charming and snug dining rooms, where you'll be warmly
welcomed by chef/patron Antoine and Viviane Westermann, who
have just celebrated 25 years here. Cooking excellent traditional
French dishes with a nod to the region's culinary heritage in his
own inimitable way, he changes the menu seasonally: *anguille rotie
à la coriandre fraiche, poireaux et pommes de terre fondantes* (eel
roasted with fresh coriander, leeks and butter potatoes), *matelote
de poissons d'eau douce en raviole au Riesling* (braised assortment
of freshwater fish – including eel, again – in ravioli with a Riesling
sauce), and a particular favourite, *pigeon d'Alsace roti en cocotte aux
oignons et à l'ail nouveau, fricassée de petits pois frais* (Alsace pigeon
roasted in an earthenware pot with onions and fresh garlic and
served with a fricassee of fresh peas). During the game season you
must try the splendid *persillé de chevreuil au foie gras de canard*
(marbled venison with duck liver paté). For a dessert look
no further than apricot crepes with almond ice cream or a
millefeuille of raspberries with vanilla ice cream. Two *dégustation*
menus, available for an entire table only, are priced between Fr550
and Fr590. *L 12-2.30 D 7-9.30. Closed all Tue (but open for L Apr-
Oct), all Wed, 2 weeks school holidays Feb/Mar, 2 weeks mid-Aug,
2 weeks Christmas/New Year. Ample parking.* AMERICAN EXPRESS *Diners,
Mastercard, Visa.*

★

Strasbourg   Hotel Cathédrale

Tel 88 22 12 12   Fax 88 23 28 00   **H**

12 Place de la Cathédrale 67000 Strasbourg
Rooms 35   Double room from Fr340

This early-20th-century house is in a pedestrian-only square (only
20 minutes from the airport and ten minutes from the railway
station), sometimes quiet and sometimes more boisterous (but they
do have double-glazing). The rooms have good facilities and have
been tastefully renovated with Cerusi wooden furniture and thick
double curtains. *24hr room service. Satellite TV. Theatre-style
conference facilities for up to 100. Secretarial/translation services
on request. Private parking.* AMERICAN EXPRESS *Diners, Mastercard, Visa.*

Strasbourg   Le Crocodile

Tel 88 32 13 02   Fax 88 75 72 01   **R**

10 Rue de l'Outre 67000 Strasbourg
Seats 80   Meal for 2 approx Fr1000

Rumour has it that the crocodile hanging outside the restaurant
was brought home from the famous Egyptian campaign on the
Nile by Captain Ackermann, the aide-de-camp of General Kléber
(the restaurant is only 100m from the town square named after
him, and close to the Cathedral). Originally an old farmhouse, the

restaurant has a very much *maison bourgeoise* look inside with mellow wood panelling and lovely original canvases dotted about, including a painting depicting a Strasbourg fete, an allusion to the Alsatian cooking you'll encounter here, though there's an eclectic spread on the menu. After a classical training in a number of top restaurants around France, Emile Jung, with his wife Monique, set up here over twenty years ago, since when the restaurant has grown in stature. There are various menus to choose from, perhaps the *déjeuner Club Crocodile* at a bargain Fr390 including an aperitif and selected wines, with such dishes as *terrine de rouget barbet et sole au jeune fenouil et tomate confite, pied et oreille de porc truffés en crépinette, chou nouveau et pommes darphin, nougat glacé à la bergamote et poire Williams.* Jung believes that to best bring out the flavours of raw ingredients one must cook with the wine suited to them: thus a fillet of beef is casseroled with vegetables, potatoes and Riesling, while foie gras d'oie is accompanied by a Gewurztraminer aspic. Wine goes into the lamb consommé served with small ravioli stuffed with fresh basil, and a silky Volnay burgundy enters the sauce accompanying beef served with a potato cake. Several hot desserts, such as a cherry strudel, need to be ordered in advance. The fabulous wine list is one of the main features of the restaurant and is recognised as having the finest selection of wines from the Alsace region in the world, not to mention some rare vintage *crus.* No private car park – park nearby at Place Kléber. *L 12-2.30 D 7-9. Closed Sun, Mon, last 3 weeks Jul, 10 days Christmas/New Year.* AMERICAN EXPRESS *Diners, Mastercard, Visa.*

Strasbourg   Julien

| Tel 88 36 01 54   Fax 88 35 40 14 | R |

22 Quai des Bateliers 67000 Strasbourg
Seats 35   Meal for 2 approx Fr850

On the quays, five minutes from the Cathedral square, this 17th-century building stands opposite the Chateau des Rohan. Inside, the dining room is decorated with lamps and other pieces of original art deco, with reproduction paintings on the walls. The cooking is traditionally Alsatian, and tends to be lighter in the summer, using plenty of fish and herbs, and the rest of the year more filling, with more robust vegetable and meat dishes. Good old-fashioned recipes, like thick cutlets of veal roasted in almond butter and Guérande salt and fried goose liver paté encased in a crispy pastry and served with crunchy *sauerkraut* and a rhubarb-based sauce are plentiful. The set menu is excellent value at Fr340. *L 12-2 D 7-10. Closed Sun, Mon, 7-31 Aug, 25 Dec-1 Jan. Public car park. Mastercard, Visa.*

To dial overseas from the UK, 010 will change to 00
on 16th April 1995.

Around Strasbourg

Illhaeusern   **Auberge de l'Ill**

Tel 89 71 83 23   Fax 89 71 82 83   RR

68970 Illhaeusern Strasbourg
Seats 100   Meal for 2 approx Fr1600

60km from Strasbourg, the restaurant has been in the Haeberlin family's hands since it was built at the end of the 19th century. Originally a farmhouse with a small restaurant attached to it, the building was reconstructed after the war, having been virtually razed to the ground. In an idyllic garden setting with the grounds sloping down to the banks of the river Ill, the dining room is filled with silver and crystal ornaments, antique tables, chairs and rugs on the floor. In the kitchen, Haeberlin father (Paul) and son (Marc) create an imaginative modern French menu featuring, among others, plenty of interesting fish dishes: *filet d'esturgeon roti sur un lit de chou et choucroute 'misala' à la crème de caviar* (fillet of roasted sturgeon (from the Gironde) served on a bed of crisp cabbage and sauerkraut with potatoes and a cream and caviar sauce), *lotte de ligne rotie à l'ail aux lardons accompagnée d'un risotto d'épautre* (roasted monkfish with garlic and lardons and accompanied by a wheat risotto), or the house speciality *saumon soufflé 'Auberge de l'Ill'* (salmon surrounded by a fish mousse and encased in a soufflé). If your fancy is for something non-fishy, try the *salade de tripes panées au foie d'oie et aux fèves, cotelette de pigeonneau aux choux et aux truffes,* or their version of roast beef and Yorkshire pudding rather enchantingly titled *filet de boeuf 'Black Angus' et la petite chartreuse de queue de boeuf à la moëlle* (oxtail and bone marrow), *Yorkshire pudding.* Cheese-lovers should order a plate of local Munster at the start of the meal – it is served in a variety of ways both hot and cold, while those with a sweeter tooth may well plump for the gingerbread charlotte with a Sauternes sabayon. The huge cellar has Rieslings, Gewurztraminers and Sylvaners by the bucketful featuring all the best growers (Théo Faller, Trimbach, Léon Beyer, Lorentz, Hugel etc). The family also owns the *Hotel des Berges* in the garden (11 rooms, including two suites and a fisherman's cottage, double room from Fr1350, Tel 89 71 87 87, Fax 89 71 87 88). *L 12-2 D 7-9. Closed D Mon, all Tue, Feb. Ample parking.* AMERICAN EXPRESS *Diners, Mastercard, Visa.*

Toulouse

Toulouse	**Brasserie Beaux Arts**

Tel 61 21 12 12   Fax 61 21 14 80   **R**

1 Quai de la Daurade 31000 Toulouse
Seats 140   Meal for 2 approx Fr300

The Flo group turned this cosy café into a vast, clattering
restaurant ten years ago. The chef, Monsieur Morichon, came
from one of their other successes, *La Coupole* in Paris. The cooking
is traditionally Mediterranean, with succulent seafood and plenty
of fresh fish being the order of the day. Among the specialities:
filet de julienne, sauce Noilly and *coquilles Saint-Jacques, crème
de safran*. The set lunch menu (Fr99) is great value and the set
dinner (Fr141) is quite a steal too! *L 12-3.30 D 7-1. Public parking.*
AMERICAN EXPRESS *Diners, Mastercard, Visa.*

Toulouse	**Les Jardins de l'Opéra**

Tel & Fax 61 23 07 76   **R**

1 Place du Capitole 31000 Toulouse
Seats 80   Meal for 2 approx Fr1000

Sheltered from the sunshine in this cool, uncovered courtyard,
diners sip aperitifs surrounded by the Hotel de l'Opéra, off
Toulouse's main square. Afterwards, they move inside for
Dominique Toulousy's prize-winning cooking. His dishes are
as refined as the setting, with plenty of fresh fish on offer: *poisson
du marché aux haricots blancs* (fresh market fish with white beans).
Other typically gastronomic French dishes like *ravioli de foie gras
frais au jus de truffes* (ravioli stuffed with foie gras served with
a light truffle sauce) and *poelée de homard frais aux cèpes et artichauts
violets, jus vinaigre au soja* (stir-fry of fresh lobster with ceps and
violet artichokes, light vinaigrette and soya sauce). *L 12-2 D 8-10.
Closed Sun, National Holidays. Public parking.* AMERICAN EXPRESS *Diners,
Mastercard, Visa.*

Toulouse	**Mermoz**

Tel 61 63 04 04   Fax 61 63 15 64   **H**

50 Rue Matabiau 31000 Toulouse
Rooms 53   Double room from Fr450

Peeping out of the bedroom window on to the courtyard below,
it is hard to believe that the hotel is right in the centre of the city.
Six years ago, the Ponsot family bought this 19th-century
building, renovating it into a tasteful hotel. The rooms are all well
equipped, with bright, light colours and marble bathrooms.
There's no restaurant, but dishes are whisked up in the kitchen for
room service. *Satellite TV. Theatre-style conference facilities for up to
40. Secretarial/translation services on request. Private parking.*
AMERICAN EXPRESS *Diners, Mastercard, Visa.*

Toulouse   **Les Ombrages**

Tel 61 07 61 28   Fax 61 06 42 26   **R**

48 bis Route St Simon 31100 Toulouse

Seats 60   Meal for 2 approx Fr600

This restaurant is splendidly suburban, with salmon and peach
walls, and is a gentle 10km from the city centre. Monsieur Zagot,
the chef-manager, like many others in his profession, loves
cooking with fresh fish and the three set and à la carte menus are
clearly biased in favour of dishes like fillet of sole cooked
in champagne, fillet of pike-perch in a light sorrel sauce and ragout
of spring lobster. Meat and fowl dishes are simple and traditional:
baby pigeon is roasted with cloves of fresh garlic. *L 12-2 D 8-
10.30. Closed Mon. Private parking.* AMERICAN EXPRESS *Diners,
Mastercard, Visa.*

Around Toulouse

Vigoulet-Auzil   **Auberge de Tournebride**

Tel 61 73 34 49   Fax 62 19 11 06   **R**

31320 Vigoulet-Auzil

Seats 60   Meal for 2 approx Fr500

This old country house, in an even older country village ten
minutes south of Toulouse, was turned into a relaxed bistro before
becoming a fully-fledged restaurant. The chef, extraordinarily,
is English, a nationality not usually popular in a traditional French
kitchen. He has, however, managed to make his special mark,
notably with a plethora of fish dishes, which he loves. Cold
platters of langoustines, salmon tartare and smoked salmon are
served together, along with puff pastry cases filled with monkfish.
His cooking may not be distinctively Mediterranean, but neither
does it bear any trace of his English culinary heritage (which no
doubt pleases the locals!). *L 12.30-2 D 7.30-10. Closed D Sun, all
Mon, 1st 2 weeks Aug. Private parking. Mastercard, Visa.*

Tours

Tours   Charles Barrier

Tel 47 54 20 39   Fax 47 41 80 95

R

101 Avenue de la Tranchée 37100 Tours

Seats 45   Meal for 2 approx Fr1000

Chef/patron Charles Barrier and his wife Nicole have been in situ
for fifty years, yes 50, at this stylish air-conditioned restaurant,
which has its own flowery patio overlooking lush green lawns.
His style of cooking has changed little during this time, sticking
very much to *cuisine traditionelle* with many different regional
specialities with a nod towards fish dishes – pike-perch (*sandre*)
cooked in its skin with a beurre blanc, or sole simply filleted and
cooked in butter. He has neither lost his enthusiasm nor taken his
hands off the reins in the kitchen, where he leads a small team
of some half dozen. Whether you choose from the fixed-price
menus or à la carte (the menus change four times a year
in accordance with the seasons), look out for dishes such as *foie gras*   ★
*frais des Landes en terrine, homard breton à la bonne femme, canette
de Challans au suc d'ananas, miel et pommes de reinettes, pied de cochon
farci aux ris d'agneau et aux truffes, pommes purée.* Home-smoked
salmon with blinis and chive cream is a favourite as is *pigeon
de pays en vessie, sauce fleurette*, pigeon cooked in a pig's bladder
to retain the juices and served with a whipped cream sauce. The
Loire valley is well represented on the French-only wine list,
which also has a decent Bordeaux showing. *L 12-2 D 7-10. Closed
D Sun. Private parking. Mastercard, Visa.*

Tours   Jean Bardet

Tel 47 41 41 11   Fax 47 51 68 72

HR

57 Rue Groison 37100 Tours

Rooms 21   Double room from Fr850

Sophie and Charentes-born Jean Bardet's magnificent white
Touraine stone and colonnaded 19th-century house is set in its
own grounds on the banks of the Loire. Primarily an elegant
restaurant, itself an extension of the original Napoleon III house
to which a dining conservatory has also been added, the bedrooms,
some benefiting from veranda balconies (the perfect spot for
breakfast), are equally lovely. Charmingly designed by Sophie
in light combinations of flowery quilts and pale curtains with
antiques, decent paintings and splendid marble bathrooms, they
are in either *style anglais*, Louis XV or Louis XVI. Impressively
parked outside the house are a Rolls-Royce and an old Citroën,
both available as hotel limousines. *24hr room service. Conference
facilities for up to 40. Secretarial/translation services on request.
Outdoor swimming pool.* AMERICAN EXPRESS *Mastercard, Visa.*
See over for restaurant entry

Restaurant

Seats 80   Meal for 2 approx Fr1500

The herb and kitchen garden (there always seems to be a chef
outside plucking vegetables) plays an important role for the
flamboyant cigar connoisseur Bardet, who produces his own
interpretations of traditional French cooking with a variety
of menus to choose from. Perhaps the *menu dégustation* (for
an entire table and priced at Fr590 per person or Fr720 if you
wish to substitute one of the dishes with lobster), where you are
likely to encounter dishes such as *millefeuille de foie gras*, alternate
layers of thinly sliced apples, warmed foie gras and little cubes
of turnips; oysters in a light watercress sauce, followed by equally
appetising main courses, say, wild duck with a chanterelle cream
sauce with endives and chestnuts set in aspic or farm guinea fowl
with shiitake mushrooms. Foie gras appears in several guises here,
a speciality being *foie gras de canard confit dans sa graisse*, but also
not to be missed are the fillets of red mullet with aubergines
served with a basil vinaigrette, and whole grilled lobster with   ★
a simple brown butter accompaniment (for two). Leave room for
sensational desserts, for example *craquant aux framboises* or *fraises*,
crispy apricot tart with a hint of lavender, or a choice of sorbets
(passion fruit, China tea and apricot – again!). Daily home-baked
bread, good farmhouse cheeses and two more bonuses – a carefully
compiled wine list (with some lesser known Loire wines) which
perfectly complements the style of food, and being able to eat out
on the terrace in summer or at tables scattered around the grounds
in shady places. Each table is decorated with a different gourd
or marrow. Inside, the tables are prettily decorated with dark
cerise tablecloths, pale yellow overlays and large white flower
arrangements. Relax in one of the lounges with their decorative
ceilings after your meal and choose one of the many Havana
cigars, cabinet-kept in perfect condition. *L 12-2 D 7-10. Closed
D Sun, all Mon (but open D Mon Apr-Nov).*

Tours   **La Roche Le Roy**

Tel 47 27 22 00   Fax 47 28 08 39   R

55 Route de Sainte Avertin 37200 Tours
Seats 50   Meal for 2 approx Fr700

The restaurant is a converted 17th-century chateau with Louis
XV furniture blending with the heavy, ornate curtains and old
paintings, a traditional setting for chef Alain Couturier's classic
cuisine with a hint of *nouvelle*. The family have been here some
seven years, and helpfully Alain's wife is English, so translating
menus presents no problems. Frogs' legs, snails, foie gras, fresh
asparagus in season, lobster and pigeon are favourite dishes, with
Loire perch roasted in spices and butter served as a house
speciality. Exceptional bread, ice creams and petits fours, all made
on the premises. Only France gets a look-in on the wine list, with
Loire wines obviously to the fore. *L 12-2 D 7.30-9.30. Closed
L Sat, all Sun, 1 week Feb, 1-24 Aug. Private parking.* AMERICAN EXPRESS
Mastercard, Visa.

Around Tours/Loire Valley

Onzain   Domaine des Hauts de Loire

Tel 54 20 72 57   Fax 54 20 77 32   **HR**

Route de Harbault 41150 Onzain-en-Touraine

Rooms 35   Double room from Fr650

Originally a hunting lodge built in 1860 and surrounded by many
acres of secluded parkland and two lakes, this ivy-clad hotel with
white shutters is a restful spot with a relaxed setting. The wood-
panelled reception is as welcoming as the long-serving staff, and
the lounge is furnished with 19th-century antiques, antique brass
pots with wonderful floral displays and rich blue curtains. A spiral
staircase leads to charming and well-maintained bedrooms with
painted beams and oak bathrooms; some of the best rooms are
in the annexe. *Satellite TV. Theatre-style conference facilities up to 60
(only out of season). Secretarial/translation/fax services on request.
Tennis. Swimming pool. Fishing. Closed Dec-March. Private parking.*
AMERICAN EXPRESS *Diners, Mastercard, Visa.*

Restaurant

Seats 70   Fr1200

Candlelight dining in a pretty restaurant where chef Rémy Giraud
only uses top-quality ingredients for his fixed-price menus or à
la carte. Add Fr70 to the Fr480 *menu dégustation* (for an entire
table only) and you will also receive regional wines
to complement the dishes. Look out for specialities such as *salade
d'anguille croustillante* with a shallot vinaigrette, '*pigeonneau
du Vendomois' au jus de presse, darphin aux oignons et foie gras chaud,
boeuf poché au vin de Montlouis* (a Loire wine next to Vouvray),
and *glace cardamone à la confiture de fraises*. Both fish and game also
feature heavily on the menus, perhaps *noisettes de lapin aux noisettes*
(really!), *pousses d'épinards et cuisses de grenouilles, or caille de chèvre
au concombre parfumé au basilic*. The *sandre* here is simply roasted
with a sorrel jus, tuna fish gets the Mediterranean treatment with
tomatoes, olives and herbs, and mullet is served with a vinaigrette
ratatouille and a purée of new-season garlic. Desserts include
wonderful wild strawberries with a hint of lavender. *L 12.30-2
D 7.30-9. Closed L Tues, all Mon.*

Rochecorbon   Les Hautes Roches

Tel 47 52 88 88   Fax 47 52 81 30   **H**

86 Quai de la Loire 37210 Rochecorbon

Rooms 11   Double room from Fr995

Back in the 11th century, a monastery was built in the cliff; and
today the hotel still has eight of its rooms set in the rock, with
excellent views over the Loire flowing near the hotel. It has been
open only for five years, and they have plans to extend it by
a further three rooms. The sunny, large-windowed rooms in the
main house have neat wooden furniture and dark chintzy covers;
whereas the barer rough-walled cave rooms have four-poster beds
and minimalist modern bathrooms. *Conference facilities for up to
25. Secretarial services. Closed 30 Jan-5 Mar. Private parking.*
AMERICAN EXPRESS *Mastercard, Visa.*

Elsewhere in France

Bracieux	**Bernard Robin**	

Tel 54 46 41 22　Fax 54 46 03 69	**R**

1 Avenue de Chambord 41250 Bracieux
Seats 60　　　　　　　　　　　Meal for 2 approx Fr1000

Bernard Robin and his wife have run this restaurant in a 19th-
century post house for the last 20 years. All this time he has stuck
to traditional local dishes, using mostly regional produce:
asparagus, mushrooms and snails. When the hunting season starts,
he concentrates on game dishes, which are extremely popular with
locals who come to this sleepy village place, with its warm
wooden tables and soft salmon-coloured walls. Specialities change
regularly with choices like *salade de pigeon et homard, filet de bar
avec des oeufs en neige et du caviar* (fillet of bass served with savoury
meringue topped with caviar) and *queue de boeuf en hachis
parmentier* (a cottage-type pie filled with braised and sliced oxtail
mixed with a demi-glace sauce). *L 12-1.45 D 7.30-9. Closed
D Tues, all Wed, end Dec-mid Jan (but open all week Jul & Aug).
Public parking.* AMERICANEXPRESS *Mastercard, Visa.*

Chagny	**Lameloise**	

Tel 85 87 08 85　Fax 85 87 03 57	**RR**

36 Place d'Armes 71150 Chagny
Seats 80　　　　　　　　　　　Meal for 2 approx Fr700

An elegant 15th-century rustic restaurant with rooms (17
charming and spacious bedrooms) situated on the town square in a
village in the heart of Burgundy. It has been in the family for
three generations and is now run by chef/patron Jacques Lameloise
and his wife Nicole. The food is traditionally French with some
notable Lyonnais influences, specialising in game and fish: a lobster
salad, for instance, is served with a lemon cream sauce, or you can
have it stir-fried with puréed potatoes and a shellfish sauce. Turbot
is roasted with a citrus fruit purée and served with creamed
potatoes and chives, while roast lamb has its sauce delicately
flavoured with black olives. Other specialities include a classic
ravioli of snails served in a garlic-infused bouillon, and pigeon
either roasted and served with a butter truffle sauce and fried
leeks, or cooked *en vessie* and served with fresh pasta and foie gras.
End with a delicious dessert such as *griottines croustillantes sur une
marmelade d'oranges et leur sorbet au chocolat noir.* The Fr580 7-
course *menu dégustation* served in slightly smaller portions has
choices in both the starter and main course, as well as in between:
palate-cleansers of either a red wine *granité* or cold melon soup.
A large and impressive wine list has an emphasis on local
Burgundies. *L 12-2.30 D 7.30-9.30. Closed L Thur, all Wed, 21
Dec-26 Jan (rooms also closed Wed, 1 May). Garage.* AMERICANEXPRESS
Mastercard, Visa.

★

Eugénie-les-Bains   **Les Prés d'Eugénie**

Tel 58 05 06 07   Fax 58 51 13 59   **HR**

40320 Eugénie-les-Bains
Rooms 43   Double room from Fr1250

Tucked away in a little spa village in Gascony, this is a spacious,
palatial, colonial house, built for Napoleon III's wife Eugénie, and
surrounded by extensive scented gardens and trees. Over the years
it has become a magnet for those seeking healthy food and a rest
in Christine Guérard's individually designed rooms of impeccable
taste, which are large, yet intimate, bright and luxurious. 35 are
in the original house, the rest in the converted 18th-century
Couvent des Herbes that opens out on to the herb garden. Fantastic
leisure facilities include an outdoor heated swimming pool, spa
and hot springs, sauna, beauty salon, and tennis. *24hr room service.*
Conference facilities. Ample parking. AMERICAN EXPRESS *Diners,*
Mastercard, Visa. Closed Dec-late Feb.

Restaurant Michel Guérard
Seats 80   Meal for 2 approx Fr1200

Synonymous with healthy eating and *cuisine minceur*, Michel
continues to bring new meaning to the artistic and aesthetic
presentation of food. Here you really can eat like a king and lose
weight into the bargain, since dishes are perfectly balanced from
a calorific and health point of view. Fixed-price menus from
Fr390 to Fr630, or à la carte, feature truffles, wild mushrooms and
lots of vegetables, the emphasis always on the freshest products.
Lobster, for instance, is cooked how you want it: *demi-homard*
selon votre bon plaisir, grillé et fumé à la cheminée (grilled and
smoked over hot coals), *au gratin* or *de l'Abbé Pistre au bouillon*
d'aromates (cooked in a bouillon of aromatic herbs, attributed to a
cleric of that name). Other choices might be *soupe fraiche de tomates*
farcies (served hot or cold), a stir-fry of diced beef, fresh herbs and   ★
marinated potatoes, a warm tart of duck and quail with foie gras
and Madeira sauce and sensational desserts, a particular forte
of Guérard, who started his career as a pastry chef: *la peche blanche*
de Gascogne et la glace verveine du jardin (verbena) or *le dessert du roi*
'tout en chocolat', a hot chocolate soufflé, chocolate sorbet and
chocolate pot. Service in the chic and relaxing dining room
is beyond reproach, the wine list classically French, strongest
in Bordeaux with quite hefty prices, but try perhaps the *Baron*
de Bachen, a well-respected wine from Guérard's own vineyard
a few miles down the road. 1989, we are assured, is an excellent
vintage! *L 12.30-2.30 D 7.30-10.30. Closed L Thu, all Wed (except*
in summer) and as above.

Opening times are often liable to change at short notice,
so it's always best to book.

Grenade sur l'Adour   **Pain Adour et Fantaisie**

Tel 58 45 18 80   Fax 58 45 16 57   **R**

7 Place des Tilleuls 40270 Grenade sur l'Adour
Seats 70   Meal for 2 approx Fr600

The chef-owner and his apprentice chef concentrate on a regional
French menu where *foie gras frais de canard*, salmon and tiger
prawns are regular dishes. Early evening, take one of their many
Bordeaux wines, or an apéritif on to the terrace overlooking the
river. Inside, the 17th-century private house, which was converted
to a restaurant in the 80s, has kept the rosewood panelling and old
fireplaces. *L 12-2 D 8-10.30. Closed D Sun, all Mon (Jul & Aug
closed L Mon only). Private parking.* AMERICAN EXPRESS *Diners,
Mastercard, Visa.*

Joigny   **La Cote Saint Jacques**

Tel 86 62 09 70   Fax 86 91 49 70   **HR**

14 Faubourg de Paris 89304 Joigny
Rooms 29   Double room from Fr800

From modest beginnings forty years ago Michel and Jacqueline
Lorain have created a remarkable hotel and restaurant complex
on the river Yonne, an hour-and-a-half's drive from Paris. The old
building, with comfortable rooms and the restaurant, is on the
main road but by entering a 'secret' tunnel, strikingly decorated
with Roman artefacts, you can reach the modern attractive
building that houses the luxurious rooms overlooking the river.
They all have marble bathrooms and many have terraces. Below
are a heated indoor swimming pool, a sauna and an attractive
garden. On the river is anchored a small yacht which belongs
to the hotel and is available for parties and river cruises.
A helicopter landing pad and a large outdoor pool are on the river
bank opposite. *Ample parking and garage, tennis.* AMERICAN EXPRESS
Diners, Mastercard, Visa.

Restaurant
Seats 80   Meal for 2 approx Fr1600

While Michel Lorain retains overall responsibility, his son Jean-
Michel is in day-to-day charge of the cuisine of this very fine
restaurant, one of the best in France. Madame Jacqueline Lorain
is the wine-buyer and creator of the fine and well-composed wine
list, as well as a gracious hostess in the three elegant dining rooms.
Her daughter and the in-laws are also active in reception and
restaurant management, so this is a real family business. The menu
is a mixture of traditional and new creations. At a recent meal
we tried one of the two tasting menus comprising several dishes
in small portions. This enabled us to try five different dishes
followed by a cheese tray and a couple of sweets. A starter
to remember was *huitres bretonnes en petite terrine océane* – a very
delicate and most unusual terrine of oysters from Brittany
wrapped in jelly made from the oyster juice. We followed this
with *bar légèrement fumé, sauce au caviar* – lightly smoked sea bass
in a cream and caviar sauce. Keeping to products of the sea next
came *langoustines en nage de coquillages émulsionnée à la coriandre
fraiche et pates noires à l'encre de seiche* which sounds quite
a mouthful – and it was. The langoustines were in a shellfish and

coriander sauce on top of a small portion of squid ink pasta. Delicious! Another speciality is pan-fried duck foie gras with potatoes fried in olive oil. A more robust meat dish and with a change of style is *osso buco* with a truffle risotto. Desserts are works of art in their composition and range from passion fruit soufflé to millefeuille with crispy apple to numerous hot and cold fruit dishes. Service is friendly and fast, and the espresso and petits fours put the seal on a truly memorable meal. *L 12-1.30 D 7.30-9.30.*

Pont-de-l'Isère	**Michel Chabran**	
Tel 75 84 60 09 Fax 75 84 59 65	°	**RR**

Avenue du 45ème parallèle 26600 Pont-de-l'Isère
Seats 100   Meal for 2 approx Fr1000

In 1935 Michel Chabran's grandfather opened a small roadside village bistro in this 19th-century building, some ten miles from Valence on the N7, and over the years it has gradually expanded into today's half-rustic, half-modern restaurant (with 12 comfortable rooms for overnight diners from Fr400 per double), which Michel and Rose-Marie took over in 1973. Exposed stonework and original wood are used to good effect in the light and airy dining room, with a large fireplace, decent pictures and lots of flower arrangements (from the patio garden perhaps?). Candle-lit at night, it's a romantic and quiet setting in which to enjoy Chabran's artistry, based on local ingredients whenever possible: Bresse poultry, Charolais beef, Remuzat lamb, plenty of fresh asparagus, truffles, cheeses (*St Marcellin*, best between April and September), garlic etc. The traditionally French menu offers some classic combinations: sautéed scallops with spinach and oysters, fillets of red mullet with a smoky red wine reduction and *beurre blanc* with anchovy, medallions of lamb simply roasted with garlic and served with a Provençal vegetable tart, or thin slices of Charolais beef with an old Hermitage wine sauce. End with a large plate of assorted chocolate desserts or the roasted local apricots served with crunchy cookies and an apricot sorbet. One of the finest selections of Rhone wines around – try perhaps Jean-Louis Chave's Hermitage, St Jospeh or *vin de paille*, a sweet wine made from grapes dried on straw mats. *L 12-2.30 D 8-10. Ample parking.* AMERICAN EXPRESS® *Diners, Mastercard, Visa.*

★

> The Golden Eurostar [★] denotes our pick of the restaurants. Cooking is the major consideration, but other factors are also taken into account, including ambience, comfort and service.

Puymirol　　l'Aubergade

Tel 53 95 31 46　Fax 53 95 33 80　　　　　　　　　**RR**

52 Rue Royale 47270 Puymirol
Seats 60　　　　　　　　　　　Meal for 2 approx Fr900

Also known as *Les Loges de l'Aubergade* since there are ten exquisite
bedrooms starting at Fr750 for a double. And, what bedrooms!
Most of the furniture and fittings come from Italy,
complementing the bare walls of this 13th-century white-stoned
medieval country house, originally built for *les Comtes
de Toulouse*. Maryse Trama was instrumental in the large
bedrooms' design, while her self-taught Havana cigar-loving chef-
patron husband Michel cooks both creatively and triumphantly.
During the week there's a set-price 'business' lunch at a very
reasonable Fr160; other set menus *du marché* and *gourmand* are
priced at Fr280 and 490 respectively, and there's also a carte.
Ingredients are always the freshest in the market with plenty
of herbs and spices added, as in a 'mushroom' of chopped　　　　　★
vegetables flavoured with cumin and herbs, lobster lasagne with
truffle stock, warm foie gras hamburger served with ceps, ending
with warm chocolate cake accompanied by a sour fruit (usually
cherries) or the delightfully named *cristalline de pomme verte*.
Decent wine list with plenty of Bordeaux, Cotes de Duras from
the Dordogne, and Buzet – drink *cuvée* Michel Trama, his
personal selection. In fine weather you can eat outside under white
parasols, inside under heavy oak beams. *L 12-2 D 7.30-9.30.
Conferences up to 50. Plunge pool. Garage for hotel guests, ample
parking next door. Closed Mon (out of season), 2 weeks Feb/Mar
(school holidays).* AMERICAN EXPRESS *Diners, Mastercard, Visa.*

Roanne   **Troisgros**

Tel 77 71 66 97   Fax 77 70 39 77

Place Jean Troisgros 42300 Roanne
Rooms 20   Double room from Fr700

Guests often stay here accidentally – well, not really; they eat and
drink well in the restaurant, and stay to eat and drink some more,
knowing they can retire to the unashamed luxury of one of the
bedrooms overlooking either the garden or the station square
(named in memory of Jean Troisgros, owner Pierre's brother).
In the centre of Roanne, around 100km from Lyons, the hotel has
two wings, the old one completely renovated with the bedrooms
now very modern and well equipped, and the new wing also
luxuriously decorated in contemporary style. The hotel does not
aim to cater for conferences, but there is a fax at reception and
a meeting room for up to 30. Note the hotel is closed two nights
a week – Tuesday and Wednesday. *24hr room service. Cable TV.
Secretarial/translation services on request. Closed Tue, Wed, 3 weeks
Feb/Mar, 1st 2 weeks Aug. Ample parking.* AMERICAN EXPRESS *Diners,
Visa.*

Restaurant
Seats 100   Meal for 2 approx Fr1200

The dynasty began in 1930 when grandfather Troisgros opened
a small café, which in turn became a respected restaurant,
expanding in the early 70s when Jean and Pierre introduced their
own ideas that eventually blossomed into what most of us
associate with *nouvelle cuisine*. The restaurant's interior has recently
been modernised, but customers come here specially to eat, and are
far more interested in the gastronomic delights created in the
kitchen than the decor! With Pierre's son Michel now at the helm
in the kitchen, the cooking continues to be well executed and
inventive, constantly re-interpreting traditional French dishes:
chapelure de cuisses de grenouilles à la rapée de raifort (frogs' legs fried
in egg and breadcrumbs and served with a piquant horseradish
sauce) and *tete de veau à la tomate serrée* (calf's head served with
a thick tomato sauce). Two set menus (Fr500/640) are offered
along with a 'spontaneous' menu, which aims to produce whatever
customers desire. Several dishes have been passed down the
Troisgros generations, like *saumon à l'oseille* (pan-fried escalope
of salmon served in a sorrel sauce) and *chateau au Fleurie à la moëlle*
(poached fillet of local Charolais, arguably the world's greatest
beef, with a sublime Fleurie-based sauce with bone marrow.
Desserts are no less enticing: a lime and acacia honey soufflé,
or raspberry *norvégienne*, a sort of baked Alaska, while the hand-
made goat's cheese comes with its own glass of Sancerre – of
course, it's worth exploring the cellar with its huge selection, the
red Cote Roannaise being the local house wine. *L 12-2 D 7.30-
9.30. Closed D Tue, all Wed and as above.*

★

Romorantin

Grand Hotel du Lion d'Or

Tel 54 76 00 28   Fax 54 88 24 87   **HR**

69 Rue Georges Clemenceau 41200 Romorantin-Lanthenay
Rooms 16   Double room from Fr800

A deep sense of history pervades this magnificent house, originally
built by a relative of François I in the 16th century, and remaining
in the same family's hands up until the Revolution. Set in the
centre of town, surrounded by picturesque countryside, it became
a coaching inn towards the end of the 18th century; now
it belongs to the Barrat family and their son-in-law, chef Didier
Clément. The have been here for over thirty years, and have
converted it into an elegant country inn with really luxurious
bedrooms, most of which overlook a quiet courtyard garden filled
with trees, plants, herbs, bleach-white tables and chairs, and white
parasols – the perfect spot in fine weather for an apéritif before
your meal. Antiques abound – note the 18th-century bedheads –
in the beautifully furnished bedrooms and suites (the latter air-
conditioned and with a separate shower in the granite and
terracotta-tiled bathrooms). *Conference facilities for up to 40.
Secretarial/translation/fax services on request. Charge for private
parking. Closed Jan–mid Feb.* AMERICAN EXPRESS *Diners, Mastercard, Visa.*

Restaurant
Seats 50 (**+** 45 outside)   Meal for 2 approx Fr1000

A huge Dutch brass chandelier dominates the wood-panelled
dining room that has antique mirrors and good watercolours
on the walls. The exciting menus (two fixed-price at Fr400/600)
can change from one day to the next, concentrating as they do on
fresh seasonal produce in dishes such as foie gras in chilled bouillon
with vegetables, *cuisses de grenouilles à la Rocambole, langoustines
roties à la poudre fine d'épices douces, pigeon farci entre chair et peau
de foies blonds épicés,* and *macarons tendres glacés à la fleur d'oranger
et au miel.* In summer try the strawberries glazed in red wine with
iced milk. Autumn game provides popular dishes too, perhaps
roast partridge with foie gras and a fondu of chicory, or roe deer
noisettes served with a clementine sauce. There's a remarkable
wine list with a comprehensive selection of Loire wines (very
carefully selected by the whole family and the sommelier who
regularly meet and discuss revisions, additions and deletions).
Outstanding representation of red Chinon and Bourgueil, or white
Sancerre and Vouvray. *L 12-2 D 7.30-9.30.*

St-Jean-Pied-de-Port

Les Pyrénées

Tel 59 37 01 01   Fax 59 37 18 97   **RR**

19 Place du Général de Gaulle 64220 St-Jean-Pied-de-Port
Seat 90   Meal for 2 approx Fr600

Situated in the heart of a Pyrenean village, some 60km from
Biarritz, with cobblestone streets and pink sandstone buildings,
Anne-Marie and Firmin Arrambide's restaurant, built in 1728, was
once the post house where stage coaches would stop en route
to Spain. The restaurant has two terraces, one overlooking the
main street where you can watch the local Basques coming and
going, the other, with a heated outdoor swimming pool, looking
onto the lovely garden that slopes down to the river Adour.
There are twenty comfortable bedrooms, though they don't enjoy
the fabulous mountain views, with a double room starting

at Fr550. The dining room is classically decorated in light peach colours with antique furniture, the cooking, by self-taught Firmin, (well actually he learnt from his grandmother and father), is traditionally Pays Basque with his own original touches. The raw ingredients are mostly local: the *cèpes*, the lobster, the fresh salmon that he catches in the river, the game (hare, wood pigeon, woodcock) which he personally shoots in season, and the Spanish cod from over the border. House specialities abound: *petits poivrons farcis à la morue* (baby peppers with a salt cod stuffing), *soupe aux écrevisses* (freshwater crayfish soup), *terrine chaude de cèpes aux herbes* (a warm terrine of freshly picked ceps and herbs), *ris d'agneau/veau poelé aux poivrons et aux cèpes* (sweetbreads with peppers and ceps), and *filet de merlu de ligne poelé en vinaigrette de chipirons* (fillet of hake served with a vinaigrette and baby squid-infused vinaigrette), or simply grilled salmon with a warm béarnaise. For a dessert look no further than the *grande assiette de desserts au chocolat* or a terrine of fresh fruits served with an almond mousse. There are several set menus to choose from, starting at Fr220, up to the *grand menu* at Fr480. You'll find a page of Spanish wines on the wine list, which includes the local red and white Irouléguy made by the neighbouring Brana family, and *petit Bordeaux réserve de la maison* (house wine) personally selected by Arrambide. *L 12.15-2 D 7.45-9.15. Closed D Mon (Nov-Mar), Tue (except Bank Hols and in summer), 5-28 Jan, 20 Nov-22 Dec. Garage.* AMERICAN EXPRESS *Mastercard, Visa.*

Saint-Père-sous-Vézelay	L'Espérance	
Tel 86 33 20 45 Fax 86 33 26 15		**RR**
89450 Saint-Père-sous-Vézelay		
Seats 80	Meal for 2 approx Fr1400	

A native of this sleepy little village, Marc Meneau converted the family grocery shop into today's restaurant some twenty-five years ago. With his charming wife Françoise, they have created something very special: a stylish restaurant with two glassed-in dining rooms overlooking the delightful garden, and lovely bedrooms: there are forty to choose from, either in the main house, at the *Pré des Marguerites* (with terraces) or more rustically decorated suites in the converted mill. Wherever you sleep, it's worth waking up to the excellent breakfasts. Room prices for two start at around Fr650. Meneau is a fine chef, influenced by some great gurus of the past (Humbert, Bénard and Guillot), following their eclectic approach to cooking. His menus, and there are several ranging from Fr330 to Fr780 fixed-price or à la carte, change constantly, reflecting what's available from the markets, but it's safe to say that every dish is well prepared and well presented with wonderful flavours and smells. No long and fancy menu descriptions here, but just a simple down-to-earth approach to what you'll be served: *poulette de Bresse aux champignons, rougets aux citrons confits* (mullet with pickled lemon), *tete de porc rotie à la broche* (spit-roasted pig's head), *turbotin poché au lait, sauce hollandaise*, or *navets confits au Beaumes de Venise au foie gras* (preserved turnips and foie gras simmered in Beaumes de Venise). Regular customers love his his foie gras and truffle cromesquis, while bananas served with passion fruit and peppery ice cream end a meal in style. Enormous cellar, huge wine list featuring either red or white Vézelay burgundies from his own vineyard. *L 12-2 D 7.30-10. Closed L Wed, all Tues, Feb. Ample parking. Swimming pool.* AMERICAN EXPRESS *Diners, Mastercard, Visa.*

Saulieu   Bernard Loiseau La Cote d'Or

Tel 80 64 07 66   Fax 80 64 08 92   **RR**

2 Rue d'Argentine 21210 Saulieu

Seats   Meal for two approx Fr1600

Situated half way between Paris and Lyons in the Burgundy
region, the restaurant retains old beams and fine wood panelling.
There are some good 18th-century paintings, and service, led
by Dominique Loiseau, is exemplary. Bernard Loiseau is a high-
profile, media-conscious chef whose popularity and publicity
ensure that the three attractive dining rooms overlooking the
English garden are usually well filled with the food-conscious
French and tourists from afar looking for a different cuisine. And
different it is. Loiseau is one of the leading proponents of a light
non-cream cuisine and his sauces are the subject of a story
attributed to the famous chef Paul Bocuse. Looking at the waters
of the River Saone flowing past his restaurant he said "there   ★
my friends you see the sauce of Bernard Loiseau". A good way
to sample the Loiseau cooking style is the tasting menu of four
courses served in half portions plus cheese and three sweets
at Fr780. Another interesting and lighter menu consists of four
vegetable dishes, cheese and dessert. At lunchtime on weekdays
there is also a good-value Fr290 menu. Some seafood dishes worth
noting are *langoustines à la poelée d'artichauts au coriandre et au coulis
de tomates* and *bar roti entier au fenouil*. A real taste sensation
is *homard Breton roti à cru à la sauce corail*. Meat-eaters could try
blanc de volaille et le foie gras chaud de canard au jus de truffes.
L 12.30-2.30 D 7.30-10. AMERICAN EXPRESS *Diners, Mastercard, Visa.*

Rooms

Double room from Fr980

As far back as 1803 Napoleon Bonaparte discovered that the
village of Saulieu provided a good resting place for the night and
in modern times the Cote d'Or has become famous as a
comfortable inn with great cooking. When Bernard Loiseau
became the owner in 1982 he started a period of expansion which
is still continuing. There are now luxurious double rooms and
suites with private terraces overlooking the attractive and peaceful
garden. Five new rooms are under construction. The breakfast
is advertised as "the best in the world". It is indeed very good.

Valence   Le Pic

Tel 75 44 15 32   Fax 75 40 96 03   **RR**

285 Avenue Victor Hugo 26000 Valence

Seats 100   Meal for 2 approx Fr1500

Five minutes outside Valence, the Pic family have been
restaurateurs (hoteliers as well, since there are five very
comfortable bedrooms) for four generations, serving their classic
and contemporary cuisine in a wood-panelled, beamed dining
room with culinary and landscape paintings scattered around.
An added attraction is the courtyard that's a most agreeable spot   ★
for alfresco eating. Since the death of Jacques Pic (note that one
or two dishes are attributed to his name) in 1992, his son Alain has
taken over in the kitchen, still keeping on some old favourites
such as *filet de loup au caviar* (sea bass served with caviar) and *strate
de boeuf et foie de canard à l'Hermitage* (layers of thinly sliced beef

and foie gras cooked in the local Rhone valley red wine). As there's a particular emphasis on fish on the menus (there are four of them and an à la carte: a business lunch menu at Fr280, and others ranging from Fr520 to Fr890). Your choice might be a langoustine salad with olive oil and truffles or a plate of assorted grilled fish, their identities changing according to what's available. An iced orange soufflé is the perfect finale. There's a wonderful selection of Rhone wines, including Condrieu, Cote-Rotie, St-Joseph, Hermitage, Cornas and Chateauneuf-du-Pape with great growers like Jaboulet, Chapoutier and Guigal to the fore. The house Cotes-du-Rhone Pic is a bargain at Fr80. *L 12-2 D 8-9.30. Closed D Sun, all Wed, 1st 2 weeks Aug. Ample parking.* AMERICAN EXPRESS *Diners, Mastercard, Visa.*

Vonnas	Georges Blanc	
Tel 74 50 00 10 Fax 74 50 08 80		**HR**

Place du Marché 01540 Vonnas
Rooms 38   Double room from Fr1100

Jacqueline and Georges Blanc are the third generation of the family at this informal hotel, built in 1872 on the banks of the river Veyle. The hotel, actually named *"la Mère Blanc"*, is just an hour's drive from Lyons and only a little longer from Geneva, and despite being in the centre of the village, is situated in its own grounds with a heated swimming pool, tennis and helipad. Bedrooms were refurbished very recently with new carpets and fabrics, yet retain the antique furniture collected over many years. The majority of the bedrooms (27), several with balconies, including suites and two apartments, are situated in the main house, with a further eleven (cheaper, at Fr700) in a new building across the road, accessible via a covered bridge. There, you will also find *La Boutique Gourmande*, which exclusively sells Blanc's charcuterie, wines from his own vineyard and gourmet food. For large receptions and cocktail parties, Blanc will open up his nearby chateau. *Theatre-style conference facilities for up to 100. Secretarial/translation/fax services on request. Closed 2 Jan-10 Feb. Own garage.* AMERICAN EXPRESS *Diners, Mastercard, Visa.*

Restaurant
Seats 100   Meal for 2 approx Fr2000

With a classical and traditional training, Monsieur Blanc's influences come from a long line of family restaurateurs including his grandmother, with many of her recipes handed down. He remains loyal to them, but has added his own interpretation and perhaps more modern techniques. The several set menus and à la carte are seasonal; for instance there's an extensive game menu during *la saison de la chasse,* and one of the house specialities *St Jacques roties aux cèpes* only available from October to April. His *poularde de Bresse aux gousses d'ail et foie gras* (Bresse capon stuffed with cloves of garlic and foie gras) is a classic, indeed the commercial success of Bresse poultry is probably down to him! Other favourites are *crepe parmentière* (potato pancake) *au saumon et caviar, turbot à la compote d'aubergines et au caviar,* and *cuisses de grenouilles* – frogs' legs stewed with mushrooms. For a dessert, try the honey and nougat roasted pears with a bitter chocolate sauce, while cheese-lovers will appreciate many local goat varieties. Exquisite petits fours, own-label champagne and wines on an extensive list, and caring service under Jacqueline's direction. *L 12.30-2 D 7.30-9.30. Closed Wed, Thur (open D Thur 15 Jun-15 Sep).*

Scotch Beef Club Members: France

PARIS
PARIS 75001: Le Grand Louvre
PARIS 75001: Hotel Intercontinental
PARIS 75001: Hotel Meurice
PARIS 75001: Hotel St James & Albany
PARIS 75002: Drouant
PARIS 75005: Au Pactole
PARIS 75006: Jacques Cagna
PARIS 75006: Le Jules Verne
PARIS 75006: Hotel Lutetia
PARIS 75008: La Couronne
PARIS 75008: Hotel George V
PARIS 75008: Ledoyen
PARIS 75008: Hotel Plaza Athénée
PARIS 75009: Café de la Paix
PARIS 75009: Le Pub Saint-Lazare
PARIS 75009: Hotel Scribe
PARIS 75009: La Taverne Kronenbourg
PARIS 75011: Hotel Holiday Inn
PARIS 75014: Ciel de Paris
PARIS 75014: Hotel Méridien Montparnasse
PARIS 75015: Hotel Adagio
PARIS 75015: Hotel Hilton
PARIS 75015: Hotel Nikko
PARIS 75015: Le Relais de Sèvres
PARIS 75016: La Petite Tour
PARIS 75017: Hotel Concorde Lafayette
PARIS 75017: Michel Rostang
PARIS 75017: Parisbas
PARIS 75018: Beauvilliers

SEINE ET MARNE
COUBERT: à l'Escargot d'Or
LOUAN VILLEGRUIS FONTAINE: Le Restaurant

YVELINES
MAISONS-LAFITTE: Le Tastevin
VERSAILLES: La Fontaine Trianon Palace
VERSAILLES: Le Potager du Roi

ESSONNE
EVRY: Académie Accor

HAUTS-DE-SEINE
LA DEFENSE: Hotel Sofitel

VAL DE MARNE
ORLY: Maxim's

VAL D'OISE
ROISSY-EN-FRANCE: La Dime
ROISSY-EN-FRANCE: Maxim's
ROISSY-EN-FRANCE: Hotel Sofitel

ALSACE
COLMAR: Schillinger

AQUITAINE
BIARRITZ: Hotel du Palais
BORDEAUX: Baud et Millet
BORDEAUX: Hotel Chateau Chartrons
BORDEAUX: Sofitel Aquitania
CREON: Hostellerie Chateau Camiac
MONTIGNAX LASCAUX: Chateau de Puy Robert

BOURGOGNE
CUISEAUX: Hotel du Nord
TOURNUS: Le Rempart

FRANCHE-COMTE
CUBRY: Le Maugre

LANGUEDOC-ROUSSILLON
PERPIGNAN: Brasserie Vauban

LIMOUSIN
VARETZ: Chateau de Castel Novel

MIDI-PYRENEES
CASTERA VERDUZAN: Le Florida
SAINT-FELIX: Auberge du Poids Public
TARBES: L'Aragon

France Index

Recommended by

EGON RONAY'S GUIDES

1995

YOUR GUARANTEE
OF
QUALITY AND INDEPENDENCE

- Establishment inspections are anonymous

- Inspections are undertaken by qualified
  Egon Ronay's Guides inspectors

- The Guides are completely independent
  in their editorial selection

- The Guides do not accept advertising,
  hospitality or payment from listed
  establishments

Hotels & Restaurants	Pubs & Inns
Europe	Just a Bite
Family Hotels & Restaurants	Paris
Oriental Restaurants	Ireland
New Zealand & South Pacific	Australia

Egon Ronay's Guides are available from all good bookshops or can be
ordered from Leading Guides, 35 Tadema Road, London SW10 0PZ
Tel: 071-352 2485 / 352 0019 Fax: 071-376 5071

Germany

Currency: Deutschmark   **Exchange Rate:** £1 = approx DM 2.5

International dialling code: 010 49
(Berlin + 30 Bonn + 228 Cologne + 221 Dresden + 351 Düsseldorf + 211
Frankfurt-am-Main + 69 Hamburg + 40 Hanover + 511 Munich + 89
Stuttgart + 711)

Passports/Visas: No visa required by British passport holders.

British Embassy in Bonn Tel: 228-234601 Fax: 228-234070/237058

TRANSPORT
Airports:
Berlin-Tegel Tel: 30-41011 / Berlin-Tempelhof Tel: 30-69510 /
Düsseldorf Tel: 211-4210
Frankfurt-am-Main Tel: 69-691844 / Hamburg Tel: 40-50750 /
Hannover Tel: 511-9770 / Munich Tel: 89-97500 / Stuttgart Tel: 711-9480
Railway Stations: Berlin Zoo Tel: 30-297 61131 / Berlin
Hauptbahnhof 30-297 22256; Central train information Tel: 30-19419
Car hire:
Contact UK international branches for information - Avis Tel: 0181-848 8733 / Budget Tel: 0800 181181 / EuroDollar Tel: 0895 233300 /
Hertz Tel: 0181-679 1799/1777.
Speed limits: 100 km/h on trunk roads, no limit on motorways unless
indicated (generally in urban areas), km/h as indicated in towns.

Banks open: 8.30am-1pm, 2.30-4pm Mon-Fri (Thur to 5.30pm).

Shops open: 9am-6.30pm Mon-Fri (some shops to 8.30pm Thur), to
2pm Sat. Closed Sun.

National Holidays: New Year's Day, 6 Jan, Good Friday, Easter
Monday, 1 May, 25 May, 5 Jun, 15 Jun, 15 Aug, 3 Oct, 31 Oct, 1 Nov,
22 Nov, Christmas Day & Boxing Day.

Tourist Offices:
German National Tourist Office in London - Tel: 0171-493 0080
In Germany -
Berlin Tel: 30-21234 / Cologne Tel: 2-213345 / Hamburg Tel: 40-300510 / Frankfurt Tel: 69-21238800 / Munich Tel: 89-2390 /
Stuttgart Tel: 7-1122280

American Express Travel Service Office:
Berlin - AETS
    Uhlandstr 173
    D-10719
    Tel: 30-884588/0 #

Berlin

Berlin   Alt Luxemburg

Tel (30) 323 87 30 **R**

Windscheidstrasse 31 10627 Berlin
Seats 35   Meal for 2 approx DM300

Unification has put this restaurant right at the centre of the new
map of Berlin. The area, Charlottenburg, has altered since the
political changes as the government encourages people to live
there with the lure of cheap housing, turning it into a bohemian
enclave. But inside the restaurant, it is still old-fashioned, with
lamps hanging from the ceiling and wooden-panelled and
mirrored walls. Like many German restaurants, they have been
heavily influenced by French cuisine, applying many of the
techniques to their own dishes. Ravioli are stuffed with calf's
sweetbreads and baby leeks and topped with a citronella sauce;
fillets of bass are sautéed in olive oil served with marinated green
vegetables and fillet of beef is served with a piquant pine nut sauce
and small potato dumplings. *D only 7-11. Closed Sun, Mon.*
AMERICAN EXPRESS *Diners, Visa.*

★

Berlin   Restaurant Anselmo

Tel (30) 323 30 94   Fax (30) 324 62 28 **R**

Damaschkestrasse 17 10711 Berlin
Seats 84   Meal for 2 approx DM200

In a quiet corner of the city, the Bufacchi family have been
running their Italian restaurant for the last 21 years. They serve
plenty of light fish, seafood and meat dishes. Their house speciality
is baked fish dishes like sea bream with rosemary, with sliced
tomatoes and plenty of garlic. Most of the wines served are Italian.
During the day, the modern tables are filled with businessmen but
at night the oil lamps are turned on and Italian songs are sung.
Open noon-midnight. Closed 23-28 Dec. Private garage. AMERICAN EXPRESS
Mastercard.

Berlin   Art Hotel Sorat

Tel (30) 88 44 70   Fax (30) 88 44 77 00 **H**

Joachimstaler Strasse 29 10719 Berlin
Rooms 75   Double room from DM270

A pilot project for a new chain of hotels, Sorat, planning
to expand and develop around Europe, this place is ultra-modern
and bang in the centre of the city, close to the railway station,
Europa shopping centre and zoological gardens. Interior designers
have had a field-day with gold-coloured corrugated iron ceilings
and the waves of the River Danube designed on the walls. Philippe
Starck has designed the chrome and wooden furniture, so perhaps
you should expect elegance over comfort! The rooms have cable
TV and are full of mirrors and original paintings by Wolf Vostell.
Despite its ambitious intentions, this hotel does not have
a restaurant or conference facilities. *Private garage.* AMERICAN EXPRESS
Diners, Mastercard, Visa.

Berlin   **Bamberger Reiter**

Tel (30) 218 42 82   **R**

Regensburgerstrasse 7 10777 Berlin
Seats 40   Meal for 2 approx DM145

Close to avenues of big touristy hotels in Schönberg, this
restaurant is down a quiet side street in the centre of Berlin. The
influences on this family-run kitchen stretch from the Austrian
homelands to regional Italian and German. Langoustines are served
in a risotto, pike-perch is served with pesto noodles and pigeon
crépinettes (flat French sausages) are accompanied by a truffle purée.
Finish this light meal with a subtle elderflower sorbet. The family
have opened a bistro inside the restaurant, which is cheaper
(DM40) and offers a simpler version of the same menu. The wines
range from DM40 to 4000, with a proud array of Austrian
bottles. *D only 6-1. Closed Sun, Mon, 1-21 Jan. No parking.*
AMERICAN EXPRESS® *Diners, Visa.*

★

THE APARTMENT SERVICE
Tel in UK: (0181) 748 4207   Fax: (0181) 748 3972
The Apartment Service will find you the right apartment
worldwide to suit your needs, whether you are on a short or
long-term stay. A 96-page colour catalogue is free on request.
All budgets are catered for.

Berlin   **Bristol Hotel Kempinski**

Tel (30) 88 43 40   Fax (30) 883 60 75   **HR**

Kurfürstendamm 27 10719 Berlin
Rooms 315   Double room from DM380

One of the main venues in Berlin, for either conferences, state
visits, galas, or just social whirls, this 50s hotel is right in the city
centre, 20 minutes by car to Tegel Airport. The bedrooms are
classical, stylish, air-conditioned and double-glazed, the main
feature being impressive marble baths. For fitness freaks, there are
plenty of weights to lift, sun beds to bronze on and a large indoor
pool to exercise in. *Theatre-style conference facilities for up to 450.
Indoor swimming pool, sauna, solarium, steam bath, gym. Private
parking.* AMERICAN EXPRESS® *Diners, Mastercard, Visa.*

Restaurant
Seats 70   Meal for 2 approx DM180

The international menu has an eclectic combination of dishes from
liver with mashed potatoes and onions to a roulade of salmon and
pike-perch with a light mint sauce and a terrine of goose liver
served on raisin toast with a Waldorf salad. Fresh lobster, pigeon
and duck dishes are worth looking out for in season. Game is
another seasonal speciality with saddle of venison accompanied by
a warm cranberry sauce, mushrooms in cream and suet dumplings.
Wines are international, but from a limited selection try the dry
house Riesling. *L 12-3 D 6-12. Closed Aug.*

Berlin   Ephraim-Palais

| Tel (30) 242 51 08   Fax (30) 32 19 29 2 | **R** |

Spreeufer 1 10178 Berlin

Seats 50   Meal for 2 approx DM100

As in London, many museums throughout Europe now offer very
good food in their restaurants. This one in the famous Ephraim-
Palais Museum built in the 18th century is no exception. The
cooking, by an Alsace-trained chef, is French with some lively
interpretations of quite classical cuisine. The choice changes
constantly on two set menus (starting from DM54). A fricassee
of sole fillets is presented on a bed of salad, calf's liver is cooked
in a rich port sauce and served with baby vegetables and
medallions of monkfish are served in a leek sauce with creamed
potatoes. The cheeses are interesting and tempting. The excellent
and exclusive list of French and Italian wines comes as another
pleasant surprise. *Open 11.30am-midnight.* AMERICAN EXPRESS *Diners,
Mastercard, Visa*

Berlin   Fortshaus Paulsborn

| Tel (30) 813 80 10   Fax (30) 814 11 56 | **R** |

Hüttenweg 90 14193 Berlin

Seats 110   Meal for 2 approx DM180

Game used to be brought back from the hunts in the surrounding
Grunewald forest (just outside Berlin) and hung up from the
rafters, ready to be made into venison pie. Now, it is a rather
more sophiscated French restaurant, with just a few regional dishes
and the obligatory game menu in the autumn. Starters are
traditionally French with roasted veal sweetbreads served on a
crisp leaf salad and smoked Icelandic salmon cooked in a light
cream sauce; breast of duck and baked salmon are among the
main dishes. Some unusual desserts come as a surprise: blueberry
terrine is served dripping in a honey cream sauce. *Open 11-11.
Closed Mon. Private parking.* AMERICAN EXPRESS *Diners, Mastercard, Visa.*

Berlin   Frühsammes Gasthaus

| Tel (30) 803 80 23   Fax (30) 803 77 36 | **R** |

Matahornstrasse 101 14129 Berlin

Seats 45   Meal for 2 approx DM100

The Frühsammer family own this one villa restaurant, and also
have a 120-hectare farm, where they breed their own animals for
the kitchen. Accordingly, there is a plethora of dishes for serious
carnivores: ragout of oxtail served with red wine and shallots,
beef bourguignon with mashed potatoes and carrots and offal
served with herbs and tomatoes. The menu is hearty rather than
refined, with only a few dishes, such as fillet of cod in mustard
sauce and gravlax with potato fritters, appealing to the more
delicate palate. *D 6-10.30. Private parking.* AMERICAN EXPRESS
Mastercard, Visa.

Berlin   Grand Hotel Esplanade

Tel (30) 25 47 80   Fax (30) 265 11 71   **H**

Lützowufer 15 10785 Berlin
Rooms 402   Double room from DM430

Modern and large are the two words which immediately come
to mind; but there is more to this place than that. It is right
opposite the *Tiergarten*, the largest inner-city park, and the central
railway station is only 2km away. The decor inside is one step
beyond modern with Corbusier and Bauhaus-style suites and
bedrooms, double-glazed and equipped with cable TV and faxes.
There are also seven fully-equipped conference rooms. *24hr room
service. Theatre-style conference facilities for up to 450. Private garage.*
AMERICAN EXPRESS *Diners, Mastercard, Visa.*

Berlin   Grand Slam

Tel (30) 825 38 10   Fax (30) 826 63 00   **R**

Gottfried von Crammweg 47-55 14193 Berlin
Seats 50   Meal for 2 approx DM250

A tennis complex is an unlikely place to build a restaurant, but six
years ago this place opened in one of the most prestigious sports
clubs in Germany, only ten minutes walk from the city centre.
The owner-chef applies French techniques to local, seasonal
ingredients. Quail is served in a celery and truffle sauce, fried pike-
perch is dressed with chanterelles and red mullet comes with
barley risotto. For the really famished, there is the extra long
Grand Slam set menu for DM350 served with a Grand Slam
cocktail of peach liqueur and champagne. *D 6.30-10. Closed 1-14
Jan, 1-21 Aug. Public parking.* AMERICAN EXPRESS *Diners, Mastercard,
Visa.*

Berlin   Hemingway's

Tel (30) 825 45 71   Fax (30) 89 00 62 70   **R**

Hagen Strasse 18 14193 Berlin
Seats   Meal for 2 approx DM250

In this old villa in a residential area of the city, three rooms are
decorated the way the owner-chef, Grosse Segerath, imagines
Hemingway lived, with mirrors around the walls and a colonial-
style bar. The menus, despite professing to be international, lean
heavily towards Mediterranean French cuisine with five course
courses (starting at DM85) to choose from. All the classics are
there: sweetbreads, seafood salad, fish consommé, medallions
of monkfish, and fillets of sea bass. There is a wide selection of fish,
which makes a refreshing change in a country of dedicated meat-
eaters. *D 6-11.30. Public parking. Mastercard, Visa.*

> Opening times are often liable to change at short notice,
> so it's always best to book.

Berlin   Inter-Continental Berlin

Tel (30) 260 20   Fax (30) 260 28 07 60   **H**

Budapester Strasse 2-6 10787 Berlin
Rooms 511   Double room from DM345

Minutes from the famous Gedächtnis Kirche and
Kurfürstendamm Square, this Inter-Continental is vast and formal,
with 13 floors of rooms and theatre-style conference facilities for
up to 1250 people. Not surprisingly, the rooms, renovated
in 1993, are well equipped, with functional modern furniture. The
concierge has been here for 35 years and can guide anyone
through the maze of Berlin. Lastly, the main railway station
is only seven minutes stroll away and the airport 20 minutes
by car. *24hr room service. Cable/satellite TV/fax. Conference facilities.
Business centre (secretarial/translation services). Private parking.*
AMERICAN EXPRESS *Diners, Mastercard, Visa.*

Berlin   Maritim Grand Hotel

Tel (30) 232 70   Fax (30) 23 27 33 62   **HR**

Friedrichstrasse 158-164 10117 Berlin
Rooms 349   Double room from DM480

An early-80s purpose-built hotel, it offers every possible facility
in the centre of a city aiming to attract new business and
conference loads of businessmen. For those wishing to relax, there
are a swimming pool, three saunas, a gym and a beauty salon. The
rooms overlook the new unified centre of Berlin and have every
facility from a fax to videos and satellite TV. At the time of going
to press they were in the process of renovating 52 rooms in the
Linden wing. Two rooms have been adapted for disabled guests.
*24hr room service. Theatre-style conference facilites for up to 180.
Secretarial/translation services. Sports facilities. Private/valet parking.*
AMERICAN EXPRESS *Diners, Mastercard, Visa.*

Restaurant Le Grand Silhouette

Seats 90   Meal for 2 approx DM170

The chef, Rolf Schmidt, is a well-known gastronomic figure
in Berlin, and he also has a restaurant of his own. The menu
is flamboyantly modern German, with stuffed quail's breast served
with goose liver and Muscat jelly, lobster lasagne with a chive,
asparagus and gorgonzola sauce and saddle of Schorfheide venison
which comes with bread dumplings glazed with goat's cheese. The
home-made mango mousse is another treat in store for diners. The
wine list is, as one would expect, comprehensive, with a burgundy
house red and Riesling house white. *D 6-1. Closed Sun, Mon, Aug.*

Berlin   Maxwell

Tel (30) 854 47 37   Fax (30) 854 47 37   **R**

Helmstädterstrasse 9 10717 Berlin
Seats 12   Meal for 2 approx DM150

The owners, three musicians from Bremen in the North
of Germany, are very easy-going and have decorated a 90-year-old
building like a home, with the two small, cosy dining rooms
being the living rooms. Despite this being a tiny restaurant, the
extensive menu changes every day, with a good variety of modern
and traditional German dishes. Confit of duck is served in a cherry

sauce with gnocchi and marinated saddle of lamb with artichokes and tomatoes; while the traditional house speciality is spit-roasts, like *tafelspitz* (spit-roasted beef gratinated with horseradish and served with vegetables and bacon dumplings). The desserts owe more to *nouvelle cuisine*, with white chocolate soufflé with an orange mint sauce and strawberry bavarois with fresh dates. *D 7-12. Private parking.* AMERICAN EXPRESS *Mastercard.*

Berlin   **Opernpalais-Königin Luise**

Tel (30) 20 26 83   Fax (30) 200 44 38   **R**

Unter den Linden 5 10117 Berlin
Seats 80   Meal for 2 approx DM160

The Opernpalais now contains a plethora of cafés and restaurants in a newly renovated complex. The original Palais was built in 1733, and was the Court for the King and his family until the end of World War I and later an exhibition room for the Schinkel Museum. Many of the restaurants are good; the Operncafé is worth a visit, simply for the choice of 50 different home-made pastries and cakes, but this particular restaurant still leads the culinary way off the Unter den Linden boulevard into the Palais. The menu is imaginative, with plenty of modern German dishes: fillet of pike-perch is coated with red lentils and served with a garlic cream and potatoes, marinated salmon is filled with courgettes and served on a horseradish sauce and breast of Barbary duck is prepared in a vegetable aspic and served with fresh blinis. Many more appetising dishes appear on the à la carte menu, including some unusual desserts: an oatmeal cream is accompanied by an assortment of red berries and a sorrel parfait. A healthy selection of French and German wines is on offer. *D 5.30-12. Closed Sun, Mon, 1st 3 weeks Aug. Public parking.* AMERICAN EXPRESS *Mastercard, Visa.*

Berlin   **Palace Hotel**

Tel (30) 250 20   Fax (30) 26 26 577   **H**

Im Europa-Center Budapester Strasse 10789 Berlin
Rooms 321   Double room from DM330

The renovations to this 60s hotel have certainly brought it up to date, with modern, glossy furniture and fittings throughout, plus good facilities in the bedrooms. The hotel is only 500m from the railway station, right inside the *Europa-Center* (a large shopping mall) and has access to the *Therman im Europa-Center* where there are indoor and outdoor swimming pools, a gym and a sauna. *Cable TV. Theatre-style conference facilities for up to 450. Secretarial/translation services on request.* AMERICAN EXPRESS *Diners, Mastercard, Visa.*

To dial overseas from the UK, 010 will change to 00
on 16th April 1995.

Berlin   **Ponte Vecchio**

`Tel (30) 342 19 99`   **R**

Spielhagenstrasse 3 10585 Berlin
Seats 45   Meal for 2 approx DM140

Down a quiet residential street in the centre of Berlin, this
restaurant has been cooking authentic Tuscan food for eight years,
with a chef who graduated from Italian catering school. The menu
is as cosy and comfortable as the Italian furniture and simple
tablecloths, which makes it feel like a small country trattoria.
Starters range from rabbit on a bed of green salad to a light
minestrone soup. Main courses are equally traditional: sole
poached in white wine then baked on a bed of spinach and lamb
baked in olive oil and herbs. The mascarpone mousse is a must for
all lovers of that rich Italian cheese. The house wines are good
Chiantis. *D 6.30-11. Closed Tue, 1 month Jul/Aug (school holidays),
1-6 Jan. Public parking. Diners.*

Berlin   **Radisson Plaza Hotel Berlin**

`Tel (30) 238 28   Fax (30) 23 82 75 90`   **H**

Karl-Liebknechtstrasse 5 10178 Berlin
Rooms 500   Double room from DM274

The Radisson chain spreads right across East and West Europe
now, all modern hotels fully equipped with conference and sports
facilities. This hotel is no exception, with ten conference rooms
and a swimming pool, gym and sauna. The rooms are equally
well equipped, having cable TV and faxes, and some of them even
boast French four-poster beds and two-seater sofas. The hotel
is only 10 minutes walk from Friedrichstrasse Railway Station.
*24hr room service. Häagen-Dazs café. Theatre-style conference facilities
for up to 600. Secretarial/translation services. Sports facilities. Private
parking.* AMERICAN EXPRESS *Diners, Mastercard, Visa.*

Berlin   **Hotel Riehmers Hofgarten**

`Tel (30) 78 10 11   Fax (30) 78 66 059`   **H**

Yorckstrasse 83 10965 Berlin
Rooms 21   Double room from DM240

Quiet and cosy, tucked away in a courtyard off a pedestrian-only
street, yet just five minutes from Tempelhof Railway Station. Run
by a family, the place is full of plants and has a small, homely
breakfast room with marble tables and leather chairs. The rooms
have cable TV and private safes and are decorated in muted
colours and filled with wooden furniture. *Secretarial/translation
services on request. Private parking.* AMERICAN EXPRESS *Diners, Mastercard,
Visa.*

Berlin   **Rockendorf's Restaurant**

`Tel (30) 402 30 99   Fax (30) 402 27 42`   **R**

Düsterhauptstrasse 13469 Berlin
Seats 50   Meal for 2 approx DM110

Deep in the suburbs of Berlin, Rockendorf has made quite a name
for himself and has managed to lure the city's foodie connoisseurs   ★
out into their cars to see him in his *Jugendstil* (German art
nouveau) villa with walls decorated by young local artists. The

reason for all this attention is because he still continues
to modernise regional German cooking, adding his own
imaginative flair to the dishes. Wild salmon and crayfish tails are
cooked in tarragon and served on a bed of spinach leaves, turbot
is served on a bed of minestrone and a roasted rack of venison
comes with noodles and a cauliflower salad. The wines are
international, with a Mosel house white. Some people here eat
as many as nine courses (DM222), so come prepared to be tempted
and also with a very empty stomach. *L 12-2 D 7-9.30. Closed mid
Jul-mid Aug, 22 Dec-6 Jan, National holidays. Private parking.*
AMERICAN EXPRESS *Diners, Mastercard, Visa.*

Berlin   Savoy Hotel

Tel (30) 31 10 30   Fax (30) 31 10 33 33   HR

Fasanenstrasse 9-10 10623 Berlin
Rooms 125   Double room from DM254

This 1930s building used to be the British Embassy and was
converted into a hotel in 1987. Since then, the Savoy has attracted
film stars and high-powered political figures and the paparazzi that
inevitably follow them. The hotel is in the city centre, only 500m
from the zoological gardens, and within walking distance of the
main shopping streets and banking district. The rooms have been
modernised, with cable TV installed, but only the sixth floor has
air-conditioning. *Private safes. Theatre-style conference facilities for
up to 80. Secretarial/translation services. Sauna/gym. Private parking.*
AMERICAN EXPRESS *Diners, Mastercard, Visa.*

Restaurant Belle Epoque
Seats 69   Meal for 2 approx DM160

The menus here are long with a wide choice of meat, fish and
poultry, and even run to a separate asparagus list: baked with ham
and roquefort, or served with smoked salmon or, more
traditionally, just with hollandaise sauce. The rest of the cooking
is also devoted to modern German food. Lentils and red and green
peppers are served in a soup with merguez sausages; guinea fowl
consommé comes with marrow dumplings and slices of truffle,
and crayfish ravioli are served with a saffron sauce and
a mushroom risotto and avocado and cherry tomato salad.
Desserts, however, are more traditional with the popular *konditorei*
classic cheesecake with blueberry sauce. Wines are notably
German, with a few well-chosen French and Italian choices. *L 12-
3.30 D 6-12.*

Berlin   Trio

Tel (30) 321 77 82   R

Klausenerplatz 14 14059 Berlin
Seats 24   Meal for 2 approx DM176

This modern place, with its post-modern black and white
furniture and young artists' works on the walls, is in a quiet
suburb of Berlin. Surprisingly, it serves a very traditional French
menu with goose liver, consommé, salmon, lamb and venison
dishes. They also serve red snapper (quite unusual for the North)
cooked with basil and served with ratatouille. Treat yourself and
try the dessert *dégustation.* The wine list is international, with some
good Californian bottles on offer. *D only 7-11.30. Closed Wed,
Thur. Public parking. No credit cards.*

Cologne

Cologne   **Antik Hotel Bristol**

Tel (221) 12 01 95   Fax (221) 13 14 95　　　　　　　　**H**

Kaiser-Wilhelm-Ring 48 50672 Cologne
Rooms 44　　　　　　　　　　Double room from DM195

Ornate carved four-posters and canopied Louis XV beds fill the
rooms along with antique chandeliers, chairs and pictures. The
Hummel family have been collecting this eclectic assortment
of objets d'art for the last 30 years and is clearly their great passion.
But understandably, modernisation has fallen a little behind;
facilities are adequate, with satellite TV in the bedrooms, but
no mini-bar and there is no restaurant. *Conference facilities for up to
50. Closed 24 Dec-2 Jan. Private parking.* AMERICAN EXPRESS *Diners,
Mastercard, Visa.*

Cologne   **Die Bastei**

Tel (221) 12 28 25   Fax (221) 139 01 87　　　　　　　　**R**

Konrad Adenauer Ufer 80 50668 Cologne
Seats 180　　　　　　　　　　Meal for 2 approx DM192

Part of the old city walls, this octagonal watch tower looks out
over the Rhine. Tourists tramp around the tower on their
sightseeing circuit, but the most splendid sight is the restaurant,
with its shimmering chandeliers and slabbed-stone walls. The chef,
Jochen Blatzheim, cooks mostly fish and game (in season), with
local dishes like home-marinated salmon served with potato cakes,
baby turbot baked in a Riesling sauce and scampi in port sauce.
A four-course lunch is a reasonable DM53 a head and well worth
indulging in. *L 12-3 D 7-12. Closed L Sat. Private parking.*
AMERICAN EXPRESS *Diners, Mastercard, Visa.*

Cologne   **Börsen-Restaurant Maitre**

Tel (221) 13 30 21   Fax (221) 13 30 40　　　　　　　　**R**

Unter-Sachsenhausen 10-26 50667 Cologne
Seats 60　　　　　　　　　　Meal for 2 approx DM220

In the Stock Exchange building, this French restaurant serves
traditional food, using regional German raw ingredients. Home-
made goose liver terrine, *bouillabaisse* and fillet of salmon in a
black pepper sauce are all regular dishes on the menu but the
house speciality is fillet of veal served in a creamy white wine
sauce. The wine list stays safely within the boundaries of French
Chablis and German Rieslings. *L 12-2 D 6-9.30. Closed Sun. Public
parking.* AMERICAN EXPRESS *Diners, Mastercard, Visa.*

Cologne   **Excelsior Hotel Ernst**

Tel (221) 27 01   Fax (221) 13 51 50　　　　　　　　**HR**

Trankgasse 1-5 50667 Cologne
Rooms 440　　　　　　　　　　Double room from DM440

The Swiss Kracht family have been running this exquisite 19th-
century hotel, right in the centre of Cologne opposite the Gothic
cathedral, for over 100 years. Only 300m from the main railway
station, the location is great and they have a continuous
programme of modernisation. All the rooms now have CNN and
mini-bars and marble bathrooms; a steambath, whirlpool, gym

and massage facilities were being installed as we went to press; and they can now cater for up to 200 people for a theatre-style conference. *Conference facilities. Secretarial/translation services. Health facilities. Hairdresser. Public parking.* AMERICAN EXPRESS *Diners, Mastercard, Visa.*

Hanse Stube

Seats 80   Meal for 2 approx DM180

This imaginative, international menu truly departs from the heavy German restrictions of traditional regional cooking, with starters like a light tomato carpaccio served with tempura of prawns and light main courses such as poached turbot and crayfish served with a *bouillabaisse* sauce. For dessert, try the perfect blend of lemon and honey parfait with caramel strudel. Open bottles are served as house wines from the international, but heavily French and German-biased wine list. *L 12-2.30 D 6-11.*

Ambiance am Dom
Tel (221) 139 19 12

Seats 30   Meal for 2 approx DM210

Though situated in the hotel, this restaurant is privately owned. The food goes well beyond the imaginative bounds of most hotels. Classic French food is delightfully presented, with wild salmon slices served with a light balsamic vinaigrette, or cannelloni filled with lobster and served with a lobster sauce. The daily changes to the menu add plenty of interest. Many concert connoisseurs eat two courses, go to hear the Philharmonic Orchestra round the corner, then come back for their dessert. *L 12-3 D 6-1. Closed Sat, Sun, National Holidays.*

Cologne	**Köln Renaissance Hotel**	**H**

Tel (221) 203 40   Fax (221) 203 47 77

Magnusstrasse 20 50672 Cologne

Rooms 236   Double room from DM275

Part of the Ramada chain, this hotel is centrally located only minutes from the cathedral and 1km from the central railway station. It is a very modern building that looks like a university and offers a wealth of facilities: indoor swimming pool, sauna, solarium and steam room, plus cable TV and in-house movie channels in the rooms. The conference facilities, as one would imagine, are excellent, with ten theatre-style rooms for up to 350 people. *Cable TV. Conference facilities. Business centre (secretarial/translation services). Sports facilities. Private parking.* AMERICAN EXPRESS *Diners, Mastercard, Visa.*

> Meal prices for 2 are based on à la carte menus.
> When set menus are available, prices will often be lower.

Cologne   Rino Casati

Tel (221) 72 11 08   Fax (221) 72 80 97   **R**

Ebertplatz 3-5 50668 Cologne
Seats 70   Meal for 2 approx DM130

Creative Italian cooking has been coming out of this modern
kitchen for the last 27 years, offering some of the best Italian food
in Germany. Nothing fundamental has changed: the home-made
goose liver terrine, carpaccio and fillet of veal in truffle sauce are
as delicious as ever. However, a few more tasty pasta dishes have
been added to their already extensive list: home-made fettucine   ★
is served with a truffle sauce and home-made black noodles come
in a rich lobster sauce. An impressive list of Italian regional wines
is boosted by some strong French offerings and excellent
champagnes. *L 12-2.30 D 6-11.30. Public parking.* AMERICAN EXPRESS
Diners, Mastercard, Visa.

Cologne   Savoy

Tel (221) 162 30   Fax (221) 162 32 00   **H**

Turinerstrasse 9 50668 Cologne
Rooms 100   Double room from DM225

Despite its name this is a family-run hotel, traditional and quiet.
It is right in the centre of the city, within easy reach of the main
railway station. The rooms are classically, but newly decorated,
and cable TV is installed. The hotel has conference facilities, with
six theatre-style rooms for up to 120 people, but no restaurant
or room service. *Conference facilities. Secretarial/translation services
on request. Sauna/steam room. Closed 23 Dec-2 Jan. Private parking.*
AMERICAN EXPRESS *Diners, Mastercard, Visa.*

Cologne   Hotel im Wasserturm

Tel (221) 200 80   Fax (221) 200 88 88   **H**

Kaygasse 2 50676 Cologne
Rooms 90   Double room from DM590

A very unusual hotel has been created in a 120-year-old water
tower, with the interior design as fabulously individual
as Anouska Hempel's *Blakes Hotel* in London. Clearly one pays for
such extravagant luxury, not to mention the collectable modern
art on the walls. But sitting in a suite decorated by the chic French
designer, Andrée Putman is an experience not to be missed. The
130-strong staff provide an incredibly high guest/staff ratio.
Tucked away in a park, the hotel is near the old city centre and
only 2km from the main railway station. *24hr room service.
Cable/satellite TV. Theatre-style conference facilities for up to 350.
Sauna, solarium, massage. Private garage.* AMERICAN EXPRESS *Diners,
Mastercard, Visa.*

Cologne   Weinhaus im Walfisch

Tel (221) 257 78 79   Fax (221) 258 08 61   **R**

Salzgasse 13 50667 Cologne
Seats 90   Meal for 2 approx DM200

Renovated before the war, this 17th-century building stands right
in the middle of the old part of town. The chef, who has worked
his way up in the kitchen, cooks a mixture of modern German

dishes and more traditional French cuisine. Fillet of sole is served with a citron mousse and new potatoes, veal is sautéed and served on a bed of courgettes in a morel and cream sauce. The restaurant itself is very elegant, with furniture over 300 years old and an impressive collection of oil paintings hanging from the heavy wood panelling. *L 12-2 D (Sat only) 6-11. Closed L Sat, all Sun, 23 Dec-5 Jan. Private parking. Visa.*

Around Cologne

Cologne-Müngersdorf	**Landhaus Kuckuck**

Tel (221) 49 23 23 Fax (221) 497 28 47	**R**

Olympiaweg 2 50933 Cologne-Müngersdorf

Seats 60   Meal for 2 approx DM200

In the middle of the Stadtwald park, in the city centre, this restaurant is a tranquil and romantic retreat for a dinner for two, especially in the summer when the large terrace is open for diners. It is well worth coming here just for the modern German cooking by the chef who has been with the owner since he opened the restaurant five years ago. A consommé of pigeon is served with semolina dumplings and pearls of vegetables; vegetable ravioli with a purée of tomatoes and green rye risotto; and roasted prawns on a purée of yellow peppers with rice dumplings. Lamb is a particular house speciality: home-smoked fillets are served with a terrine of goat's cheese and a vegetarian salad. Comprehensive selection of French and German wines. *L 12-2 D 6-9. Closed during the Carnival (10 days Feb). Private parking.* AMERICAN EXPRESS *Diners, Mastercard, Visa.*

Dresden

Dresden   **Dresden Hilton**

Tel (351) 484 10   Fax (351) 484 17 00   **H**

An der Frauenkirche 5 01067 Dresden
Rooms 330   Double room from DM345

Right in the city centre, near the River Elbe, this Hilton offers the
usual gamut of internationally-recognised facilities, with an indoor
swimming pool, jacuzzi and sauna and theatre-style conference
facilities for up to 400. The rooms are well equipped, with four
rooms adapted for the disabled and 12 apartments. *Satellite
TV/fax. Conference facilities. Secretarial/translation services on request.
Private parking.* AMERICAN EXPRESS *Diners, Mastercard, Visa.*

Dresden   **Maritim Hotel Bellevue**

Tel (351) 566 20   Fax (351) 559 97   **H**

Grosse Meissner Strasse 15 01097 Dresden
Rooms 340   Double room from DM399

Converted in 1985 into a modern business hotel, this 17th-century
merchant's house has retained plenty of its old charm, though
many of the rooms are in the new extension. The location
is equally appealing: right on the banks of the River Elbe in a
large, leafy park. The railway station is a 500m-walk away, while
the airport is 10km from here. *Theatre-style conference facilities for
up to 350. Indoor swimming pool, sauna and solarium.* AMERICAN EXPRESS
Diners, Mastercard, Visa.

Dresden   **Ringhotel Residenz Alt Dresden**

Tel (351) 428 10   Fax (351) 428 19 88   **H**

Mobschatzer Strasse 29 01147 Dresden
Rooms 215   Double room from DM185

Six kilometres from the city, this purpose-built hotel opened
in 1993. The rooms are functional, but a little small and plainly
decorated. Downstairs, velour chairs are clustered round mock-
wooden tables, with a shiny chrome bar. The restaurant offers
a mixture of international and traditional German cooking.
*No room service. Satellite TV/fax. Theatre-style conference facilities for
up to 120. Secretarial/translation services. Sauna, steam bath, gym,
solarium.* AMERICAN EXPRESS *Diners, Mastercard, Visa.*

Dresden   **Hotel Villa Emma**

Tel (351) 37 48 10   Fax (351) 374 81 18   **H**

Stechgrundstrasse 2 01324 Dresden
Rooms 21   Double room from DM310

This *Jugendstil* hotel is privately owned and opened only a year
ago, putting the emphasis on charm and cluttered cosiness above
functionality. Not surprisingly, it attracts the Dresden film and
publishing crowd, who hold an annual ball here. The rooms are
airy and light with balconies and satellite TV. The only other
particular facilities are the saunas. Situated in a suburb of Dresden,
Weisse Hirsche, some 5km from the city centre; the main railway
station is 15 minutes away and the airport 20 minutes by car.
Satellite TV/fax. Private parking. AMERICAN EXPRESS *Diners, Mastercard,
Visa*

Dusseldorf

Dusseldorf	**Breidenbacher Hof**

Tel (211) 130 30   Fax (211) 130 38 30   `H`

Heinrich-Heine allee 36 40213 Dusseldorf

Rooms 132   Double room from DM490

One of Germany's first luxury hotels, it was built in 1806 and
took six years to complete. The majority of their guests are
regulars, who are lured back to this superb location (right behind
the Königsallee, with the largest number of designer shops in the
world, according to Karl Largerfeld, and five minutes from the
main railway station), by the elegant, high-ceilinged rooms with
marble bathrooms, all fully equipped. Antiques, art and sculptures
decorate the reception, while grand tapestries and chandeliers hang
in the conference rooms. The decor may be traditional-chic, but
the service and facilities are welcomingly modern. *24hr room
service. Cable/satellite TV/air-con/fax. Theatre-style conference facilities
for up to 60. Beauty salon. Private garage. Mastercard, Visa.*

Dusseldorf	**Düsseldorf Renaissance-Hotel**

Tel (211) 621 60   Fax (211) 621 66 66   `H`

Nördlicherzubringer 6 40470 Dusseldorf

Rooms 245   Double room from DM260

Part of the Ramada chain of hotels, this place looks and feels like
an international hotel; its six floors were built in the early 80s,
with a swimming pool on the sixth floor looking over the whole
of Dusseldorf, saunas, steam rooms and a gym. The rooms are very
large, with comfortable, heavy furniture. *Translation services
on request. Theatre-style conference facilities for up to 520. Fully-
equipped business centre.* AMERICAN EXPRESS® *Diners, Mastercard, Visa.*

Dusseldorf	**Esplanade Hotel**

Tel (211) 37 50 10   Fax (211) 37 40 32   `H`

Fürstenplatz 17 40215 Dusseldorf

Rooms 81   Double room from DM180

Close to a small park in the centre of Dusseldorf, the area around
this family-run hotel is quiet and leafy and yet only 2km away
from the main railway station. The 60s building is well equipped,
with a swimming pool, sauna and solarium and cable and satellite
TV and faxes in all the rooms. Modern English blue-marble
bathrooms blend in with the white decor and mahogany furniture
in the bedrooms. There are also two theatre-style conference
rooms for up to 55 people. *24hr room service. Conference facilities.
Secretarial/translation services on request. Sports facilities. Private
parking.* AMERICAN EXPRESS® *Diners, Mastercard, Visa.*

> To dial overseas from the UK, 010 will change to 00
> on 16th April 1995.

Dusseldorf   Hummer Stübchen

Tel (211) 59 44 02   Fax (211) 597 97 59   **R**

Bonifatiusstrasse 35 40547 Dusseldorf
Seats 35   Meal for 2 approx DM400

Since the mid-80s, Sybille and Peter Nöthel have been running
this modern German restaurant, on the outskirts of the city near
the Rhine, with some success. Nöthel learnt his culinary skills
in various German and Austrian establishments and has adapted
his more traditional experience to produce a highly interesting
menu. Plenty of grilled fish and lobster are served: grilled lobster   ★
with sugar peas and nutmeg butter, roasted pike-perch presented
on a bed of fresh spinach, chanterelles and noodles. Desserts are
equally adventurous: coconut soufflé sitting in an iced raspberry
sauce. The wine list is extensive. *D only 6-10. Closed Sun, Mon.
Private parking.* AMERICAN EXPRESS *Diners, Mastercard, Visa.*

Dusseldorf   Im Schiffchen

Tel (211) 40 10 50   Fax (211) 40 36 67   **R**

Kaiserwerther Markt 9 40489 Dusseldorf
Seats 50   Meal for 2 approx DM164

In a building dating from 1733, the restaurant lies to the north
of the town, right on the Rhine. Since the late 70s onwards, it has
been run by Jean-Claude Bourgeuil, an ardent enthusiast
of modern French cooking who has also gradually applied his skill
and knowledge to German cooking; his eclectic but satisfying
menu is the result. Baby Breton lobster is steamed with camomile
blossoms, fillet of beef is served in a rich burgundy jus and   ★
charlotte of asparagus is served on a truffle cream. Desserts are
equally well executed – try passion fruit crepes. The wine list
is truly cosmopolitan, but heavily weighted towards the major
French wine-growing regions. *D only 7-9.30. Closed Sun, Mon.
Valet parking.* AMERICAN EXPRESS *Visa, Mastercard, Diners.*

Dusseldorf   Majestic

Tel (211) 36 70 30   Fax (211) 367 03 99   **H**

Cantadorstrasse 4 40211 Dusseldorf
Rooms 52   Double room from DM265

Facilities in the bedrooms of this new privately-owned hotel are
good, with cable and satellite TV and faxes. It is also very central,
only five minutes walk from the main railway station. *24hr room
service. Theatre-style conference facilities for up to 30. Closed 23 Dec-1
Jan. Private garage.* AMERICAN EXPRESS *Diners, Mastercard, Visa.*

Dusseldorf   Rema Hotel Savoy

Tel (211) 36 03 36   Fax (211) 35 66 42   **H**

Oststrasse 128 40210 Dusseldorf
Rooms 123   Double room from DM240

A French hotelier bought the franchise in May 1994 and has just
started renovating this early 19th-century hotel in the centre
of Dusseldorf, not far from the main park. Inside, most of the
furniture, carpets and curtains are *Jugendstil* (German art nouveau),
with arresting marble floors and mirrors. Conference facilities are

adequate and the sports facilities (swimming pool, gym and sauna) good. Unusually, there is no restaurant and room service only stretches to the odd cup of tea and plate of sandwiches. *Cable TV. Theatre-style conference facilities for up to 90. Private parking.* AMERICAN EXPRESS® *Diners, Mastercard, Visa.*

Dusseldorf Savini

| Tel (211) 39 39 31 Fax (211) 39 17 19 | R |

Stromstrasse 47 40221 Dusseldorf
Seats 100   Meal for 2 approx DM120

This Italian restaurant is right by the harbour, with newly-renovated art deco interior. Inside, the light coming from the Murano glass lamps is deep red and dark green, a truly Italian setting. The menu is also Italian, but with innovative touches: Milanese minestrone is served with calf's sweetbreads, ravioli are stuffed with wild salmon and served in a pesto sauce and risotto is prepared with fresh chanterelles. Finish with the richly delicious marscarpone cream, served with fresh fruit and warm cherry sauce. The menu changes every day. Wines are Italian to the bottle. *Open 12-11. Private parking.* AMERICAN EXPRESS® *Mastercard.*

Dusseldorf La Scala

| Tel (211) 32 68 32 Fax (221) 32 83 37 | R |

Königsallee 14 40212 Dusseldorf
Seats 60   Meal for 2 approx DM180

On one of the busiest streets in the business district of Dusseldorf, this restaurant has been a going concern for the last 80 years, though the current owner took over only eight years ago. The religiously home-made food is typically Italian, with dishes like carpaccio served in truffle oil, a salad of breast of duck with fresh basil, *crepes* stuffed with artichokes and *tortellini* with tomato and fresh basil. The wood-panelled dining room has a relaxed but discreet atmosphere. *L 12-2.30 D 6.30-11. Closed Sun, 22 Dec-5 Jan. Public parking.* AMERICAN EXPRESS® *Diners, Mastercard.*

Dusseldorf Victorian

| Tel (211) 32 02 22 Fax (211) 13 10 13 | R |

Königstrasse 3a 40212 Dusseldorf
Seats 35   Meal for 2 approx DM450

Günther Scherrer opened this place in the centre of Dusseldorf ten years ago, after his successful run at Dusseldorf Hilton's restaurant. His winning formula has not changed, merely developed, with a more refined modern French menu. A terrine of turbot is served with a sea trout and fennel salad, a tomato consommé comes with basil ravioli delicately on the side and grilled ham is served in a rich burgundy sauce with cauliflower and dauphinoise potatoes. A large selection of French cheeses rounds off the menu. *L 12-3 D 7-12. Closed Sun, National Holidays. Public parking.* AMERICAN EXPRESS® *Diners, Mastercard, Visa.*

Dusseldorf   Villa Viktoria

Tel (211) 46 90 00   Fax (211) 469 06 01   **H**

Blumenthalstrasse 12 40476 Dusseldorf
Rooms 40   Double room from DM280

This turn-of-the-century orphanage is part of a small chain
of private hotels, all run in an informal, friendly way. The well-
equipped rooms are decorated like an elegant English home, with
Laura Ashley quilts and covers, and chintzy furniture. Outside,
there is a large garden, complete with a duck pond and ducks. The
hotel is right in the centre, 10 minutes drive away from the main
railway station. *24hr room service. Cable/satellite TV/fax/safe.
Conference facilities for up to 20. Secretarial/translation services. Closed
24 & 25 Dec. Private parking.* AMERICAN EXPRESS *Diners, Mastercard,
Visa.*

Dusseldorf   Weinhaus Tante Anna

Tel (211) 13 11 63   Fax (211) 13 29 74   **R**

Andreasstrasse 2 40213 Dusseldorf
Seats 120   Meal for 2 approx DM200

A 16th-century Jesuit chapel, now on a pedestrian-only walkway
in the old city, has been converted into a regional and French
restaurant. A gratin of snails is served in a garlic butter, along with
more traditional North German dishes like white herrings served
in a beer sauce. The menu is very balanced, with a healthy
selection of fish, meat and chicken dishes from medallions of veal
to roasted fillets of pike-perch. They also always have interesting
vegetarian option like courgette and tomato soufflé served with
rice, fresh basil and grated truffles. Most of the wines are German,
with 220 different bins. *D 6-12. Closed Sun (except during fairs).
Public parking.* AMERICAN EXPRESS *Diners, Mastercard, Visa.*

Around Dusseldorf

Essen   Sheraton Essen Hotel

Tel (201) 100 70   Fax (201) 100 77 77   **HR**

Huyssenallee 55 45128 Essen
Rooms 205   Double room from DM360

In a quiet park on the outskirts of the city the hotel was built
in the early 80s. It offers a wide range of sports facilities, from
an indoor swimming pool to a sauna, solarium and gym. Because
of the wide range of conference facilities (up to 150 theatre style),
it is popular with businessmen, especially as it is only 30km from
Dusseldorf Airport. The rooms are well equipped, with CNN and
an in-house video channel. Two of the six floors were renovated
in 1991. *Conference facilities. Secretarial/translation services. Indoor
swimming pool, gym, sauna, solarium.* AMERICAN EXPRESS *Diners,
Mastercard, Visa.*

Restaurant am Park
Seats 150   Meal for 2 approx DM200

The house speciality is prime beef carved on a silver platter, but
other dishes are equally appealing: fresh goat's cheese is served
with a tamarillo vinaigrette and herb baguette and fried fillet of St
Pierre is served with a Noilly Prat sauce. Wines range from
Australian to German. *L 12-3 D 6-12.*

Meerbusch Büderich   **Landhaus Mönchenwerth**

Tel (2132) 779 31   Fax (2132) 718 99   R

Niederlörickerstrasse 56 40667 Meerbusch-Büderich

Seats 60   Meal for 2 approx DM220

This family restaurant, in a 17th-century monastery 50km from
Dusseldorf, has been passed from father to son and so has the
menu, a happy mix of Italian and French dishes. Everything is
seasonal, with plenty of seafood, from lobster to herrings and
turbot. There are also some typical regional German dishes, like
Dusseldorf-style boiled breast of beef with a *bouillon* of vegetables
and a purée of celery. The location is superb: the terrace, which
is surrounded by gardens, looks out over the Rhine. *L 12-2.30
D 6.30-9.30. Closed Sat. Private parking.* AMERICAN EXPRESS *Mastercard,
Visa.*

Frankfurt on Main

Frankfurt on Main   **Arabella Grand Hotel**

Tel (69) 298 10   Fax (69) 298 18 10   **H**

Konrad Adenauer Strasse 7 60313 Frankfurt on Main
Rooms 378   Double room from DM415

The Arabella German chain opened this hotel five years ago,
having had hotels around Munich for over 20 years. It is a facility
fanatic's paradise, with 13 high-tec conference rooms, a swimming
pool, sauna and gym, plus all the mod cons in the bedrooms. The
place is modern and comfortable with a plethora of restaurants.
*24hr room service. Satellite/cable TV/fax. Theatre-style conference
facilities for up to 500. Secretarial/translation services. Sports facilities.
Private parking.* AMERICANEXPRESS *Diners, Mastercard, Visa.*

Frankfurt on Main   **Bistrorant Die Leiter**

Tel (69) 29 21 21   Fax (69) 29 16 45   **R**

Kaiserhofstrasse 11 60313 Frankfurt on Main
Seats 40   Meal for 2 approx DM172

A place to see, and to be seen: right opposite Yves Saint Laurent
in a chic shopping street, this brasserie is the meeting place for
businessmen, artists and actors, attracted by the chic black and
white decor and reliably good food. The Mediterranean menu
sticks to the tried and tested path with such dishes as salmon
carpaccio, Caesar salad, grilled lobster and roasted guinea fowl,
with no particular house specialities. *Open noon-1am. Closed Sun,
National Holidays. Private parking.* AMERICANEXPRESS *Diners, Mastercard,
Visa.*

Frankfurt on Main   **5 Continents**

Tel (69) 69 053 901   Fax (69) 47 30   **R**

Abflughalle B Frankfurt Airport 53901 Frankfurt on Main
Seats 35   Meal for 2 approx DM170

Airport restaurants on the Continent are often very good, and this
is one of them. The French regional cooking, with oysters in a red
wine and shallot sauce, roast pike-perch in tarragon sauce and roast
duck breast on a warm lentil salad, is imaginative and fresh. The
menu changes seasonally but the warm chocolate cake topped
with vanilla sauce and served with a rum and raisin ice cream is a
must throughout the year. *Open 12-9pm. Private parking.*

Frankfurt on Main   **Die Gans**

Tel (69) 61 50 75   Fax (69) 61 50 75   **R**

Schweizerstrasse 76 60594 Frankfurt on Main
Seats 30   Meal for 2 approx DM160

This hotch-potch of German, French and international cooking
in a trendy shopping street has become quite popular. Vegetable
stew is served with fusilli, chicken curry comes with bananas, rice
and mangetout and more traditionally, roast goose is served with
potato dumplings and red cabbage. Every day, three fish specials
are recommended to guests. 80 wines on an international list. *D 6-
1. Closed Sun (except during trade fairs), 22 Dec-2 Jan.* AMERICANEXPRESS
Diners, Mastercard, Visa.

Frankfurt on Main   Hessischer Hof

Tel (69) 754 00   Fax (69) 754 09 24   **H**

Friedrich-Ebert-Anlage 40 60325 Frankfurt on Main
Rooms 117   Double room from DM400

A fairground and all its fanfare comes regularly to the site
opposite this traditional hotel but thankfully all the windows are
double-glazed. The rooms are traditional but some of their
appointments are quite unexpected, notably exercise machines.
The conference facilities are excellent, with 11 theatre-style rooms
seating up to 600 people. *24hr room service. Satellite TV. Conference
facilities. Secretarial/translation services on request. Private parking.*
AMERICAN EXPRESS *Diners, Mastercard, Visa.*

Frankfurt on Main   Tse Yang

Tel (69) 23 25 41   Fax (69) 23 78 25   **R**

Kaiserstrasse 67 60329 Frankfurt on Main
Seats 170   Meal for 2 approx DM100

Part of a small chain of excellent Chinese restaurants (quite rare
in Germany, though there are plenty of Indonesian
establishments). Most of the dishes are Cantonese, with wonton
soup, crispy duck in spicy sauce, veal and broccoli in oyster sauce
and sweet and sour pork. The house speciality is a bird's nest
of egg noodles with fried seafood. *Open noon-11pm. Closed 24 &
25 Dec. Private parking.* AMERICAN EXPRESS *Mastercard, Visa.*

Frankfurt on Main   Villa Leonhardi

Tel (69) 74 25 35   Fax (69) 74 04 76   **R**

Zeppelinallee 18 60325 Frankfurt on Main
Seats 60   Meal for 2 approx DM160

Local authorities built this mock 19th-century house, a replica
of Count Von Leonhardi's residence in the centre of the
Palmengarten, 2km from the city centre. The terrace outside is a
great place for a meal. The menu, which changes every six weeks
or so, is a mixture of German, French and more international
dishes, from a fricassee of filleted sole served with asparagus and
oysters, to venison with noodles and a mushroom sauce and baby
pigeon *en croute* served with truffles. Wide-ranging wine list.
L 12-2 D 7-10. Closed Sat, Sun, 23 Dec-10 Jan. Private parking.
AMERICAN EXPRESS *Diners, Mastercard, Visa.*

Frankfurt on Main   Weinhaus Brückenkeller

Tel (69) 28 42 38   Fax (69) 29 60 68   **R**

Schützenstrasse 6 60311 Frankfurt on Main
Seats 200   Meal for 2 approx DM300

Deep in this 16th-century cellar, the chef has been cooking
a modern German menu for several years now, with quite a few
traditional meat dishes, like roast beef served in a red wine sauce,
roast pork and beef Wellington with a port gravy. The menu
changes every day, but not radically. The most dramatic feature
here is the collective languages spoken by the staff, including
Chinese, Japanese and Zulu. *D 6.30-11. Closed Sun, 24 Dec-2 Jan.
Private parking.* AMERICAN EXPRESS *Diners, Mastercard, Visa.*

Frankfurt on Main   **Westend**

| Tel (69) 74 67 02   Fax (69) 74 53 96 | **H** |

Westendstrasse 15 60325 Frankfurt on Main

Rooms 20   Double room from DM180

Grandfather clocks, heavy tallboys, quilt-covered mahogany beds
and fine, frilly white curtains all add to the feeling that this hotel
is a private home, buried deep in the English countryside. But,
in the middle of discreet embassy-land, five minutes walk from the
main railway station, it has become the elegant retreat
of romantic, high-profile couples. Businessmen also stay here, but
with no conference facilities its appeal is limited. 24 hour room
service is offered but there is no restaurant and the only thing one
can eat in the pretty walled garden is breakfast. The rooms are
well equipped, with cable TV and fax facilities. *Closed 23 Dec-2
Jan. Private parking.* AMERICAN EXPRESS *Diners, Mastercard, Visa.*

Around Frankfurt on Main

Dreieich-Götzenhain   **Gutsschänke Neuhof**

| Tel (6102) 300 00   Fax (6102) 30 00 55 | **R** |

Hofgut Neuhof 63303 Dreieich-Götzenhain

Seats 200   Meal for 2 approx DM180

Eighteen kilometres from Frankfurt in the middle of country
meadows, this restaurant was opened by the Schumacher family
back in the 40s, serving an international menu of grilled pike-
perch, smoked salmon, calf's liver, grilled lamb chops and
chateaubriand. The apricot dumplings are one of the few truly
German dishes in sight. *L 12-2.30 D 6-10. Private parking.*
AMERICAN EXPRESS *Diners, Mastercard.*

Frankfurt-Niederrad   **Weidemann**

| Tel (69) 67 59 96   Fax (69) 67 39 20 | **R** |

Kelsterbacherstrasse 66 60528 Frankfurt-Niederrad

Seats 60   Meal for 2 approx DM160

Under the wide arms of old chestnut trees, 10km from the centre
of the city, this elegant restaurant, with its glistening crystal and
crisp, white tablecloths, offers a light French menu. Crab terrine,
cod carpaccio and salmon lasagne are all popular dishes. Wines are
French and German, with whatever is open as the house wine.
L 12-3 D (Sat only) 6-10.30. Closed L Sat, all Sun. Private parking.
AMERICAN EXPRESS *Diners, Mastercard, Visa.*

Kronberg   **Schloss Hotel**

| Tel (6173) 701 01   Fax (6173) 70 12 67 | **HR** |

Hainstrasse 25 61476 Kronberg

Rooms 58   Double room from DM465

A few miles north-west of Frankfurt this hotel is a popular retreat
from the hubbub of the financial centre. Guests can play a round
of golf, or a game of tennis, and golfing and gourmet weekends
are organised, including champagne English afternoon teas. For
those keen to do the tourist round, they organise a 'castles tour',
which starts at one hotel and ends up at another. The eldest
daughter of Queen Victoria built this house as a monument to her

husband and it is still filled with unusual objects dating back
to her time. The rooms are equipped with marble bathrooms,
wooden furniture and cable TV. Conferences and banquets can
be organised here, but only for up to 60 people. *Conference
facilities. Secretarial/translation services on request. Indoor swimming
pools/golf/tennis courts/gym. Private parking.* AMERICAN EXPRESS®

Restaurant
Seats 40   Meal for 2 approx DM300

Guests here enjoy an international menu prepared by Günther
Ledermüller. Carpaccio of rabbit is served with fresh chanterelles;
truffle strudel nestles on a leek fondue; pike-perch with lobster
roulade on savoy cabbage. Desserts are also refreshingly different
from the normal, run-of-the-mill German offerings: warm
marzipan cake comes with a smooth almond sauce. Some excellent
Bordeaux are served along with German house wines. *L 12-2
D 6.30-10.*

Mannheim   Da Gianni
Tel (621) 203 26   **R**

R7 34 68161 Mannheim
Seats 40   Meal for 2 approx DM290

The chef's culinary pedigree includes a spell under the expert hand
of Heinz Winkler at *Tantris*, in Munich. Here, however, in
civilised, elegant surroundings, the menu is devotedly Italian, with
plenty of Mediterranean dishes: seafood salad, sea bass cooked
in salt and olive oil served with marinated vegetables, lasagne
layered with salmon and mushrooms and roasted pigeon served
in a black olive sauce. *L 12-2 D 6.30-9.30. Closed Mon, 14-31 Jul.
Private parking.* AMERICAN EXPRESS® *Mastercard.*

Hamburg

Hamburg   Abtei

Tel (40) 44 95 95   Fax (40) 44 98 20   **H**

Abteistrasse 14 20149 Hamburg
Rooms 11   Double room from DM300

A turn-of-the-century villa in the most unlikely place: down
a quiet suburban street with a neat front and back garden. With
only 11 rooms, it is informal and friendly, with all the cosy
comfort of one's own home. The rooms, however, do have the
usual mod cons, like cable TV and mini-bars. This is not the place
for long sessions in the boardroom, as the clubroom only seats 15
and is dominated by a much-used snooker table. AMERICAN EXPRESS
Diners, Mastercard, Visa.

Hamburg   Anna & Sebastiano

Tel (40) 422 25 95   Fax (40) 420 80 08   **R**

Lehmweg 30 20251 Hamburg
Seats 48   Meal for 2 approx DM300

Anna Sgroi, the chef-owner, trained with Gualtiero Marchesi
outside Milan, before returning to Germany to open one of the
few modern Italian restaurants in a residential district of the city.
Inside, she has one contemporary Milanese-style dining room,
while the other is filled with rustic Tuscan furniture. Her cooking
owes a lot to these two influences: a Tuscan salad of warmed
lobster and white beans is a highlight, along with plenty   ★
of different risottos and rarer dishes like baby goat baked in the
oven. All the wines are Italian, with some strong contenders from
Tuscany and Piedmont. *D only 7-10. Closed Sun, Mon, 3 weeks
summer (school holidays), 4 weeks from 23 Dec.* AMERICAN EXPRESS *Diners,
Mastercard, Visa.*

Hamburg   L'Auberge Française

Tel (40) 410 25 32   Fax (40) 410 58 57   **R**

Rutschbahn 34 20146 Hamburg
Seats 45   Meal for 2 approx DM220

For 24 years now, this has been an extremely popular restaurant
devoted to all things French; it is run and owned by a Frenchman,
with a totally French team. Monkfish is cooked in saffron and
garlic; calf's kidneys come with a mustard sauce and a fillet of beef
is served in a red wine and shallot sauce. Try the *crepe normande*,
which is filled with apples and calvados and served with vanilla
ice cream. The wines are French too, with red Bordeaux and
white sauvignon house wines. One last reason for recommending
this restaurant, is its excellent location, right in the centre of the
old city. *L 12-2.30 D 6.30-10.30. Closed Sat, Sun (Jul-Aug), 23
Dec-4 Jan. Private parking.* AMERICAN EXPRESS *Diners, Mastercard, Visa.*

Hamburg   Le Canard

Tel (40) 880 50 57   Fax (40) 47 24 13   **R**

Elbchausee 139 22763 Hamburg

Seats 50   Meal for 2 approx DM250

The Viehausers have been running this restaurant for the last six
years; Herr Viehauser cooks Northern German food, which
is heavily influenced by more aesthetic French cuisine. Iced
vichyssoise topped with caviar, marinated lobster with chanterelles
and turbot baked in spinach leaves and served with a red wine
sauce are all deliciously fresh and well presented. The wine list has
a vast choice of 800 German wines, with some *grands crus* among
them. The restaurant looks out over the River Elbe and beyond
to the port, which makes a refreshing change from being in a busy
city street. *L 12-2.30 D 7-11. Closed Sun. Private parking.*
AMERICAN EXPRESS *Diners, Mastercard, Visa.*

Hamburg   Elysee Hotel

Tel (40) 41 41 20   Fax (40) 41 41 27 23   **H**

Rothenbaumchausse 10 20148 Hamburg

Rooms 305   Double room from DM310

This 80s building is right by the Dammtor International Railway
Station. Glossy marble floors and a sophisticated lighting system
grace the reception area, and there is a library with mahogany
furniture and plenty of books and newspapers. The rooms are
triple-glazed, with air-conditioning and private safes. All are
brightly and simply decorated. *24hr room service. Cable TV.*
Theatre-style conference facilities for up to 600. Secretarial/translation
services. Private garage. AMERICAN EXPRESS *Diners, Mastercard, Visa.*

Hamburg   Garden Hotels Pöseldorf

Tel (40) 41 40 40   Fax (40) 414 04 20   **H**

Magdalenenstrasse 60 20148 Hamburg

Rooms 60   Double room from DM280

Just out of the centre of Hamburg in the Harvestelunde district
(15 minutes from the airport and 10 minutes from the main
railway station), this hotel has wide and varied appeal. All the
bedrooms have cable and satellite TV, private safes and
CD players and boast modern, stylish furniture while retaining the
charm of the original early 20th-century *Patrichia* houses. They
have a conservatory, where up to ten people can gather for
an informal meeting, but no other more structured conference
facilities. It is also important to note that it is a *hotel garni* (bed and
breakfast) so there is no restaurant and room service (available
round the clock) is limited to drinks and sandwiches. *Private*
parking for 6 cars. AMERICAN EXPRESS *Diners, Mastercard, Visa.*

Opening times are often liable to change at short notice,
so it's always best to book.

Hamburg   **Landhaus Scherrer**

| Tel (40) 880 13 25   Fax (40) 880 62 60 | R |

Elbchaussee 130 22763 Hamburg

Seats 40   Meal for 2 approx DM336

The Scherrens have been running this restaurant between
Elbchaussee and the fashionable quarter of Hamburg, Blankenese,
since the 70s. However, their menu has changed with the times,
and is now lighter and more modern. They have definitely
adapted to the new trend towards more fish and less of the
traditional heavy meat and game dishes that once dominated
German menus, especially in the north of the country. Medallions
of lobster come in a pesto and onion sauce and are served with
home-made gnocchi and salmon carpaccio is served with creme
fraiche and caviar. Traditional game dishes are lightened, with
more interesting ingredients: venison has a cherry, cassis and
juniper berry sauce and is accompanied by savoy cabbage and
chanterelles. Their house speciality, of which they are justifiably
proud, is crispy whole duck carved at the table and served with
a light black pepper sauce. Look out for the interesting rustic
regional dishes as well, with lentils served in the most amazing
ways. *L 12-2.30 D 6.30-10.30. Closed Sun. Private parking.*
AMERICAN EXPRESS *Diners, Mastercard, Visa.*

★

Hamburg   **Tafelhaus**

| Tel (40) 89 27 60   Fax (40) 899 33 24 | R |

Holstenkamp 71 22525 Hamburg

Seats 55   Meal for 2 approx DM180

In the industrial heartland of Hamburg, this area is filled with
bustling businessmen and thundering traffic during the day, but is
quiet at night. The entrance can be difficult to find: down a small
lane and through the front garden, but it is well worth
discovering this restaurant serving modern German dishes. Roast
breast of pigeon is served on a bed of red cabbage, a ragout
of turbot and lobster is served with green beans and a roasted rack
of lamb comes with a fragrant rosemary jus and leek cakes. More
than most German restaurants, this place also has some great
desserts: a rich, but fitting finish to the meal must be the warmed
chocolate tart with Cointreau ice cream. *L 12-2 D 7-9. Closed Sun,
Mon, 17 Jul-8 Aug. Private parking. No credit cards.*

Hanover

Hanover   **Gastwirtschaft Fritz Wichmann**

Tel (511) 83 16 71   Fax (511) 837 98 11   **R**

Hildesheimerstrasse 230 30519 Hanover
Seats 100   Meal for 2 approx DM170

In a 19th-century farmhouse south of the city centre, the owner-chef combines regional French recipes with more traditional German restaurants. Like many of the newer Northern German restaurants, this place has introduced a lot of lighter fish dishes on the menu, moving away from the traditional heavy platters of meat and game. Irish salmon is served in a chanterelle and truffle sauce, turbot is cooked in a champagne sauce. Their very popular speciality is roast duck served in a red cabbage and orange sauce. Desserts are traditionally German: fresh cheese dumplings and an assortment of sorbets. *L 12-3 D 6-11. Private parking.* AMERICAN EXPRESS *Mastercard, Visa.*

Hanover   **Kastens Hotel Luisenhof**

Tel (511) 304 40   Fax (511) 304 48 07   **H**

Luisenstrasse 1-3 30159 Hanover
Rooms 160   Double room from DM248

1856 saw the opening of this hotel as Hanover's answer to European luxurious living. Since then, it has attracted politicians, Presidents and businessmen from all over the world. The original hotel is filled with baroque-style antique furniture, while the extension is decorated with *Jugendstil* (German art nouveau) pieces. All the rooms have basic facilities, with nothing startlingly new or modern. But apart from the grand building, steeped in history and surrounded by a quiet courtyard, the other attraction of this place is its convenient location: opposite the main railway station. *24hr room service. Theatre-style conference facilities for up to 160. Private parking.* AMERICAN EXPRESS *Diners, Mastercard, Visa.*

Hanover   **Landhaus Ammann**

Tel (511) 83 08 18   Fax (511) 843 77 49   **HR**

Hildesheimerstrasse 185 30173 Hanover
Rooms 16   Double room from DM290

It feels and looks like a country hotel, surrounded by the Eilenriede forest, with large baroque gardens and a sunny summer terrace; however, it is only 10 minutes by car from the main railway station. The two-storey house was built as a hotel ten years ago and the rooms are simply decorated with old-fashioned chairs, sofas and standard lamps. The facilities are basic, but they do have several large rooms downstairs with a conference capacity of 120. *Conference facilities. Private parking.* AMERICAN EXPRESS *Diners, Mastercard, Visa.*

Restaurant
Seats 45   Meal for 2 approx DM300

If you are staying at this haven of calm, it is worth spending an evening here to sample the excellent cooking as well. There are two menus to choose from, featuring light modern German dishes like a terrine of sole and salmon served with a caviar sauce. The house speciality is grilled langoustines served with lemon on a bed of home-made noodles. *L 12-2 D 7-10.*

★

Hanover — Schweizerhof

Tel (511) 349 50   Fax (511) 349 51 23   **HR**

Hinüberstrasse 6 30175 Hanover

Rooms 200 Double room from DM325

This privately-run 80s hotel in the city centre has modern rooms
with good basic facilities. 90 of the rooms are decorated
in modern art deco style, while the lobby is lined with marble and
warmed by open fireplaces. They have conference facilities for
up to 450 people in six seminar rooms. *Cable/satellite TV. Private
parking.* AMERICAN EXPRESS® *Diners, Mastercard, Visa.*

Restaurant Schu's

Tel 511 349 52 52

Seats 50 Meal for 2 approx DM170

This art deco-cum-rococo-style restaurant is a very good reason
for staying in the hotel. The chef constantly experiments with his
ever-evolving Mediterranean menu. In keeping with this, the
house speciality is the catch of the day in a light white butter sauce
served on a bed of mixed salad. Other dishes are equally
refreshing: risotto is served with morels and sweetbreads, fine
French Marennes oysters on a gratin of cabbage and poached fillet
of beef with a pesto sauce and gratinated vegetables. Desserts are
wickedly delicious: white chocolate and mint parfait with mango
sauce. New World and European wines. *D 6-11.30. Closed Aug.*

Hanover — Titus Restaurant

Tel (511) 83 55 24   Fax (511) 838 65 38   **R**

Wiehbergstrasse 98 30519 Hanover

Seats 36 Meal for 2 approx DM120

Recently taken over by former partner Dieter Grubert, the
kitchen still owes a lot to previous owner Joachim Stern's
innovative techniques and fresh modern German recipes. The
menu changes every day adapting to the freshest products
available in the market. Dishes like chanterelles tossed in fresh
noodles and herbs, and turbot baked in a champagne sauce are
house specialities. The light French cheese soufflé served with fresh
rhubarb must be tried. *L 12-2 D 6-10. Closed Sun, Mon. Private
parking.* AMERICAN EXPRESS® *Diners, Mastercard, Visa.*

Hanover — Treff-Hotel Britannia Hanover

Tel (511) 878 20   Fax (511) 863 466   **H**

Karlsruherstrasse 26 30880 Laatzen

Rooms 100 Double room from DM235

Right next to the main railway station in the centre of the city,
this modern, typically German hotel is part of the international
chain of Treff hotels. The rooms are plain and functional with
mahogany furniture and modern amenities including satellite
TV and faxes. Sports facilities are excellent, with four tennis courts
and a state-of-the-art gym and sauna. *24hr room service. Theatre-
style conference facilities for up to 250. Secretarial/translation services
on request. Private parking.* AMERICAN EXPRESS® *Diners, Mastercard, Visa.*

Around Hanover

Garbsen   Landhaus am See

Tel (5131) 468 60   Fax (5131) 46 86 66   **H**

Seeweg 27 30827 Garbsen

Rooms 36   Double room from DM180

Even though the Löhmann family only opened this hotel two
years ago, on the *Berenbostelersee* (Berenbosteler Lake) right in the
middle of the park, it already has the well-worn feel of an old
North German country house. In the main 75-year-old building,
the rooms have old wooden furniture, while the rooms in the new
wing are modern. *24hr room service. Cable TV. Conference facilities.
Secretarial/translation services on request. Sauna.* AMERICAN EXPRESS
Diners, Mastercard, Visa.

Ronnenberg-Benthe   Benther Berg

Tel (5108) 640 60   Fax (5108) 64 06 50   **H**

Vogelsangstrasse 18 30952 Ronnenberg-Benthe

Rooms 67   Double room from DM180

It is hardly surprising that so many artists come to this small,
friendly hotel on the edge a large national park; it is a tranquil
retreat from city life encircled by large gardens and a sizeable
forest stretching for miles beyond that. Ten years ago, a new
extension was added and inside they have installed modern
furniture, rather than the older wooden beds and wardrobes in the
original house. But all the rooms are quite plainly decorated with
basic facilities: a television, radio and telephone. *Theatre-style
conference facilities for up to 60. Swimming pool/sauna. Private
parking.* AMERICAN EXPRESS *Diners, Mastercard, Visa.*

Munich

Munich   Aubergine

Tel (89) 59 81 71   Fax (89) 550 43 53   R

Maximiliansplatz 5 80333 Munich
Seats 50   Meal for 2 approx DM300

It has been acknowledged that Austrian-born chef-patron Eckart
Witzigmann runs one of the best restaurants in Germany ever
since its opening in 1978. The restaurant, formerly the *Regina
Palace Hotel* built in the 30s, is coolly luxurious, the cooking
probably best described as modern French-influenced German,
both inspirational and imaginative, based on top quality
ingredients. The six-course tasting menu (DM198) demonstrates
his talents to the full in dishes such as calf's head salad with root
vegetables, pumpkin and dill soup, sautéed lobster with Jerusalem
artichokes, leeks and onions, turbot on a bed of *Provençal*   ★
vegetables, medallions of venison prepared in the classic *St Hubert*
style, and, for a memorable finish, fresh figs served with
elderberries. Alongside this menu are wines suggested
to complement the dishes. From the à la carte menu you could
choose roasted goose liver with a salad of haricot beans, halibut
with a purée of potatoes and white truffles (the truffles are charged
extra by the gram!), and curd cheese dumplings with *Zwetschgen*
(black plums) and vanilla ice cream. *L 12-3 D 7-midnight. Closed
L Mon, all Sun.* AMERICAN EXPRESS *Diners, Mastercard, Visa.*

Munich   Bayerischer Hof

Tel (89) 212 00   Fax (89) 212 09 06   HR

Promenadeplatz 2-6 80333 Munich
Rooms 428   Double room from DM240

With its 19th-century portals as much of a landmark for tourists
as the Opera House, this family-owned hotel has attracted the rich
and the famous since its opening in 1841. Well over a century
later, the Palais Montgolas, adjacent to the hotel, was acquired and
is now the site for the conference and banqueting rooms. The
rooms are sumptuous, stylish and lavish and have been totally
renovated since the days when the hotel could accommodate up to
1000 guests then the largest in Europe (1924). Even now, it is one
of the smartest places in town, and still vast with Travel Vic's, a
Polynesian restaurant, a nightclub and a lively bar. *Room service.
Cable TV. Theatre-style conference facilities for up to 1500.
Secretarial/translation services on request. Terrace, swimming pool,
sauna, massage.* AMERICAN EXPRESS *Diners, Mastercard, Visa.*

Garden Restaurant
Seats 150   Meal for 2 approx DM180

Newly opened with a fresh lick of paint, this place with its winter
gardens and summer terrace serves a modern German menu,
featuring plenty of fish dishes. Fillet of sole is served in a butter
cream sauce and salmon soufflé comes with mashed potatoes.
Regional wines are particularly well represented on the eclectic
wine list, stretching from excellent Cote du Rhone to a strong
showing of burgundies. *L 12-3 D 6-11. Private parking.* 🐂

Munich	**Boettner**

| Tel (89) 22 12 10   Fax (89) 22 21 10 | **R** |

Theatinerstrasse 8 80333 Munich

Seats 30   Meal for 2 approx DM240

One of Munich's oldest restaurants, this family-run place opened
its doors in 1905, serving regional German cooking. These days,
however, the menu has become more eclectic, boasting a wide
range of seafood. Particular house specialities are Dutch Imperial
oysters, local mushrooms, black and white truffles and venison
(served only in season). Beluga caviar is served on blinis, and also
garnishes carpaccio. Other dishes have been inspired by traditional
Italian cooking, like steamed fillets of sole served with truffled
noodles. Lobster is served in every conceivable way: steamed,
grilled, boiled, in a stew with morels and potatoes or cold in a
salad. *Open 11.30am-10pm.* AMERICAN EXPRESS *Diners, Mastercard, Visa.*

Munich	**Drei Löwen**

| Tel (89) 55 10 40   Fax (89) 55 10 49 05 | **H** |

Schillerstrasse 8 80336 Munich

Rooms 130   Double room from DM230

Despite being right next to the main railway station, this is a
tranquil spot, since most of the bedrooms look down on to
an inner courtyard and the rest of the rooms are double-glazed.
They are all decorated in traditional German style, with chintzy
furnishings and solid wooden furniture, and have satellite TV.
Most of the staff have been here over 20 years and maintain
a friendly, cosy atmosphere. However, this is very much a business
hotel, with few tourists. *Satellite TV. Theatre-style conference
facilities for up to 40. Private parking.* AMERICAN EXPRESS *Diners,
Mastercard, Visa.*

Munich	**Le Gourmet**

| Tel (89) 212 09 58   Fax (89) 212 09 79 | **R** |

Hartmannstrasse 8 80333 Munich

Seats 35   Meal for 2 approx DM200

Otto Koch continues to keep the gastronomic torch blazing with
new ideas and fresh ingredients in his aptly named and justly
renowned 20-year-old restaurant in the city centre. The menu,
as one would expect, changes constantly with the seasons, but
dishes to look out for are roasted quail baked on potatoes, sea bass
wrapped in spinach and pastry and cooked in champagne, and
roasted saddle of lamb served with black olives and polenta. *L 12-
2.30 D 7-11. Closed Sun, Mon. No parking.* AMERICAN EXPRESS *Diners,
Mastercard, Visa.*

Meal prices for 2 are based on à la carte menus.
When set menus are available, prices will often be lower.

Munich   Halali

Tel (89) 28 59 09   Fax (89) 28 27 86   **R**

Schönfeldstrasse 22 80539 Munich

Seats 60   Meal for 2 approx DM280

Down a quiet street between the city centre and the heart
of Munich's caféland, Schwabing, this restaurant (the name means
Tally Ho), is stacked with hunting trophies, which diners spend
hours scrutinising. In fact, everything here is traditional, from the
meat-laden menu to Wagner playing discreetly in the background.
As one might expect, game is a big speciality during the hunting
season, with dishes like venison served in a cherry and port sauce.
The meat is very carefully prepared, with all the fat removed and
the meat lightly cooked. Other dishes are more international:
ravioli stuffed with mushrooms and breast of duck, salmon and
asparagus cooked in pastry, and a strudel of scampi and turbot.
L 12-3 D (Sat only) 6-10. Closed Sun, 1-14 Aug. Private parking.
AMERICAN EXPRESS *Mastercard.*

Munich   Das Kleine Restaurant im Gasthof Böswirth

Tel (89) 864 41 63   Fax (89) 86 43 85   **R**

Waidachanger 9 81249 Munich

Seats 25   Meal for 2 approx DM250

Werner Böswirth, the owner and head chef, has created
an international menu based on German cooking. Much of the
produce comes from the local market, providing plenty of choice
for diners. His desserts stretch beyond the usual German culinary
bounds with a delicious sesame mousse with fresh mango and
rosemary ice cream with a raspberry compote. The restaurant
is five minutes outside Munich in a quiet country street. *D only*
6.30-9. Closed Mon, Sun, 7-31 Jan. AMERICAN EXPRESS *Mastercard.*

Munich   Marriott Hotel

Tel (89) 36 00 20   Fax (89) 36 00 22 00   **H**

Berliner Strasse 93 80805 Munich

Rooms 348   Double room from DM225

This traditional business hotel is right on the edge of the city
by the English Garden. Like other Marriotts, it has a good range
of sports facilities, from a swimming pool to gym, sauna and
solarium; there are even bikes for rent for those seriously keen
to keep fit and see the city. The rooms are air-conditioned, with
satellite and cable TV, with an in-house movie channel; some
have special facilities for the disabled and others are non-smoking
rooms. *24hr room service. Theatre-style conference facilites for up to*
480. Public parking. AMERICAN EXPRESS *Diners, Mastercard, Visa.* 🐂

Munich   Palace

Tel (89) 470 50 91   Fax (89) 470 50·90   **H**

Trogerstrasse 21 81675 Munich

Rooms 71   Double room from DM320

It is an art to combine modernity with traditional elegance, and
the owner, Klaus Lieboldt, has done just that in this hotel that
he built during the late 80s. The new building is filled with Louis
XVI furniture and old oil paintings collected by him, while

in contrast the white and beige linen-clad sofas are the very latest designs. The suites are particularly spectacular, with graceful spiral staircases leading up to the bedrooms, giving a great feeling of space, unusual in a hotel setting. The facilities are good, the central location excellent and the garden a secluded retreat in a busy city. *24hr room service. Cable TV/fax/computer. Theatre-style conference facilities for up to 42. Secretarial/translation services on request. Sauna/gym. Private parking.* AMERICAN EXPRESS *Diners, Mastercard, Visa.*

Munich   **Park Hilton**

| Tel (89) 384 50   Fax (89) 384 518 45 | **HR** |

Am Tucherpark 7 80538 Munich
Rooms 477   Double room from DM360

This 70s Hilton, ten minutes from the main railway station and right by the English Garden, is a 14-floor tower. Every imaginable facility is available and expertly organised events range from G7 meetings to the launch of Witney Houston's new album. Recent DM40million renovations, guarantee modern, comfortable rooms; some feature handsome old pieces of furniture. *Cable/satellite TV/fax. Theatre-style conference facilities for up to 1500. Secretarial/translation services. Swimming pool, sauna, gym, beach club. Private parking.* AMERICAN EXPRESS *Diners, Mastercard, Visa.*

Restaurant   Hilton Grill
Seats 100   Meal for 2 approx DM300

The menu has a number of French specialities, with plenty of grilled fish and seafood dishes, like grilled char with saffron vegetables in vinegar. A long list of the different set menus start at DM51.50, with dishes like salmon carpaccio with a dill jelly and roasted sweetbreads served with cucumbers and capers on a bed of noodles. Wines are international. Other catering outlets here include a Chinese restaurant (Tse-Yang) and one featuring vegetarian dishes. *L 12-2.30. D 7-10.30. Closed L Sat.* AMERICAN EXPRESS *Diners, Mastercard, Visa.* 🐂

Munich   **Platzl**

| Tel (89) 23 70 30   Fax (89) 23 70 38 00 | **H** |

Sparkassenstrasse 10 80331 Munich
Rooms 167   Double room from DM274

The original family-run hotel was knocked down in the early 80s and the present one was built on the same site. It is right in the centre of the historically older part of the city, near the main railway station. The new building has saunas, jacuzzis, steam baths and a gym. Rooms are traditional in their furnishings, but more up-to-date in their amenities: cable TV in all rooms, fax in just five. *No room service. Theatre-style conference facilities for up to 120. Private parking.* AMERICAN EXPRESS *Diners, Mastercard, Visa.*

To dial overseas from the UK, 010 will change to 00
on 16th April 1995.

Munich   Hotel Preysing-Keller

Tel (89) 48 10 15   Fax (89) 447 09 98   **HR**

Innere Wiener Strasse 6 81667 Munich
Rooms 71   Double room from DM298

Friendly Anneliese Würbser owns and runs this 70s hotel, next
to the English Garden and *Deutsches Museum*. For a smallish hotel,
it is surprisingly well equipped, with satellite TV in the bedrooms
and a swimming pool, whirlpool, sauna, solarium and gym. The
rooms boast mahogany furniture, fresh flowers and fruit, while
the rest of the hotel is invitingly decorated with plants and small
trees. *Theatre-style conference facilities for up to 50. Closed 23 Dec-
7 Jan. Private garage.* AMERICAN EXPRESS *Diners, Visa.*

Restaurant
Seats 70   Meal for 2 approx DM178

30,000 bottles sit in the 300-year-old, vaulted-wine cellar, deep
down under the hotel. Despite appearing to be a typical German
cellar restaurant, the atmosphere is as refined as the menu. Roasted
sweetbreads are served on a bed of summer salad; fillets of salmon-
trout are presented with a vegetable and horseradish purée;
medallions of venison are served with a chanterelle and cream
sauce. The chef, Gottfried Lenz, changes the menu two or three
times a week, sticking to light combinations of fresh market
produce. *D only 6-1. Closed Sun, National Holidays, 23 Dec-7 Jan.
Private parking.*

★

Munich   Ratskeller

Tel (89) 22 03 13   Fax (89) 22 91 95   **R**

Marienplatz 8 80331 Munich
Seats 400   Meal for 2 approx DM180

In a splendid culinary setting, deep in the 19th-century cellars
of the former town hall, this cavernous restaurant has served
traditional *Bayerisch* (Bavarian) cooking since 1868, with a few
more international dishes now on the menu. Smoked trout, potato
soup, sauerkraut and suckling pig with potato dumplings are the
hearty regional staples, along with roasted knuckle of veal served
with a mushroom sauce, savoy cabbage and bread dumplings.
Even if the heavy German platters do not appeal, the place has
many other attractions, including 19th-century frescoes on the
intersecting vaults, old carved wooden panelling and antique pew-
like benches. *Open 10am-midnight. Closed 24 Dec. Private parking.*
AMERICAN EXPRESS *Diners, Mastercard, Visa.*

Munich   Splendid

Tel (89) 29 66 06   Fax (89) 291 31   **H**

Maximilianstrasse 54 80538 Munich
Rooms 40   Double room from DM325

Located on a shop-till-you-drop boulevard, it is a great place to rest
your weary feet for just a cup of tea, or for the night. All the
major museums and theatres are also nearby and the main railway
station is a ten-minute taxi ride away. The rooms are decorated
in an elegant Bavarian baroque style, and filled with stylish
objects. But despite being seriously chic, they are very friendly
and most of the guests are regulars. *Private parking.* AMERICAN EXPRESS
Diners, Mastercard, Visa.

Munich   Tantris

Tel (89) 36 20 61   Fax (89) 361 84 69   **R**

Johann-Fichte-Strasse 7 80805 Munich
Seats 50   Meal for 2 approx DM200

Hans Haas has taken over in the kitchen at this glamorous,
glittering restaurant, but there was never any fear that the Tantris
would suffer from the change, as he came from the excellent
Weinhaus Brückenkeller in Frankfurt. Fish is served in a variety
of different ways, from a simple fish and vegetable terrine and
river salmon marinated in herbs and caviar, to Breton lobster
served with fresh noodles and a white truffle cream sauce. The
good dessert list, from semolina dumplings served with a ragout
of cherries, to caramelised fruit tarts, is very appealing, and their
home-made bread and fresh vegetables from their garden both
concontribute to a splendid dinner. Over 70,000 bottles fill their
cellars, which are renowned throughout Germany. *L 12-2 D 6.30-
11. Closed Sun, Mon, 1-10 Jan. Private parking.* AMERICAN EXPRESS
Diners, Mastercard, Visa.

★

Munich   Hotel Vier Jahreszeiten

Tel (89) 23 03 90   Fax (89) 23 03 96 93   **HR**

Maximilianstrasse 17 80539 Munich
Rooms 322   Double room from DM465

Classic and traditional, this 19th-century hotel stands proudly
on the central Maximilianstrasse, only two minutes walk from the
Opera House and theatre. It has been open since 1858, but in 1972
several new wings were added. The rooms have recently been
renovated, but many are still traditionally decorated. With ten
function rooms to choose from, catering for every conceivable
meeting, big business conference or jet-setters' ball is a major part
of the operation. *Cable TV/fax. theatre-style conference facilities for
up to 600. Secretarial/translation services on request. Indoor swimming
pool, sauna, solarium, massage, gym. Hairdresser. Private garage.*
AMERICAN EXPRESS *Diners, Mastercard, Visa.*

Restaurant
Seats 80   Meal for 2 approx DM105

The chef has been with the hotel since the 70s, serving a diverse
international menu with some reliably good combinations:
roasted medallions of monkfish with a butter sauce served with
sliced courgettes and carrots, seafood in a shellfish sauce on a bed
of linguine with fresh ricotta and tournedos of beef in a pepper
sauce. Light, tangy fresh fruit sorbets, chocolate mousse and lime
parfait – end the meal nicely. Wines are predominantly German,
with a few French offerings. *L 12-2.30 D 6-11. Private garage.*
AMERICAN EXPRESS *Diners, Mastercard, Visa.*

Around Munich

Aschau   Residenz Heinz Winkler

| Tel 08052 179 90   Fax 08052 17 99 66 | HR |

Kirchplatz 1 83229 Aschau im Chiemgau
Rooms 32   Double room from DM250

Some 80km south-east of Munich just off autobahn E 52 (actually
Salzburg airport across the Austrian border is much nearer) the
town itself has a romantic castle and baroque churches. The hotel
too is almost medieval in style with white arcades, vivid orange
roof tiles, pretty shutters and a large paved patio. Inside, there are
comfortable lounges and luxurious bedrooms, many with fantastic
views across to the foothills of the alps. Conferences for up to 60.
Ample parking. AMERICAN EXPRESS *Diners, Mastercard, Visa.*

Restaurant
Seats 120   Meal for 2 approx DM280

The elegant dining room is a fitting showcase for some of the best
cooking to be found in Germany. Chef-patron Heinz Winkler,
previously at Munich's *Tantris* (*qv*), cooks in almost classical
French style, albeit with Italian, and of course German (Bavarian)
influences. The five-course fixed-price (DM145) lunch menu, for
instance, might offer a salad of baby rabbit and leeks served in a
balsamic vinegar or salmon cakes with gherkins in a lemon
dressing, potato soup with lobster chunks, sole on a bed of julienne   ★
vegetables with basil, strips of venison in a port wine sauce and
apricot tart served with Amaretto cream. Choosing à la carte you
might be tempted by beef carpaccio served with a herby
vinaigrette, thin escalopes of veal in a white truffle oil sauce, and
a white chocolate mousse with strawberries. As well as German
wines, there are several burgundies and clarets on the list,
including vintage Latour and Lafite. *L 12-1.30 D 6.30-10.*

Stuttgart

Stuttgart   Der Goldene Adler

Tel (711) 640 17 62   Fax (711) 649 24 05   **R**

Böheimstrasse 38 70178 Stuttgart

Seats 120   Meal for 2 approx DM120

Right in the centre of Stuttgart, this restaurant mixes French
cuisine with regional German dishes. Marinated salmon could
be followed by roast rack of lamb served with green beans and
a gratin of potatoes. Crepes are seeped in Jack Daniels and served
with a bitter orange sauce. The menu changes seasonally. *L 11.30-
2.30 D 6-10.30. Closed L Sat, all Mon, school holidays. Private
parking.* AMERICAN EXPRESS *Mastercard, Visa.*

Stuttgart   Hirsch-Weinstuben

Tel (711) 711 375   Fax (711) 717 06 20   **R**

Maierstrasse 3 70567 Stuttgart

Seats 35   Meal for 2 approx DM150

This area is really the 'old village' of Stuttgart, opposite a church
and the town hall. Old mixes with new, with modern painted
walls and old German furniture. The restaurant has been run by a
family for the last 12 years and serves a well-balanced
combination of traditional regional food and nouvelle cuisine. The
ingredients are simple, the execution impeccable. Ragout of oxtail
is served in a red wine sauce, while turbot is served in a curry
sauce with roast potatoes. Home-made goose liver paté is the house
speciality. However, as in many German restaurants, the desserts
do not get much more adventurous than fresh fruit with home-
made honey ice cream. The wine list has some trusty Rieslings,
but also runs to some good French and Italian bottles. *L 12-1.30
D 6-9.30. Closed L Mon & Sat, all Sun. Private parking.*
AMERICAN EXPRESS *Diners, Mastercard, Visa.*

Stuttgart   Speisemeisterei

Tel (711) 456 00 37   Fax (711) 456 00 38   **R**

Am Schloss Hohenheim 70599 Stuttgart

Seats 45   Meal for 2 approx DM280

From 1770, German citizens used to make representations to the
Duke Karl Eugen of Würtemberg in these rooms; these days, the
chef, Martin Öxle, has been making his mark on the regional and
French culinary map since this restaurant opened here in 1993.
He changes the menu every day, but has a particular penchant for
fresh fish dishes: fillet of pike-perch is served as a soufflé on a lentil
cream and an escalope of monkfish rests on a bed of pesto noodles.
Meat and poultry also appear with dishes like calf's head salad
accompanied by green asparagus and lobster. He also creates some
tempting desserts: white wine mousse is wrapped in filo pastry
and served with fresh peaches. The European wine list has
a surprisingly comprehensive choice of rosés. *L 12-3 (Sun only)
D 6.30-12. Closed D Sun, all Mon. Private parking. No credit cards.*

Stuttgart   **Steigenberger Graf Zeppelin Hotel**

Tel (711) 204 80   Fax (711) 204 85 42   **H**

Amulf-Klett-Platz 7 70173 Stuttgart

Rooms 240   Double room from DM345

Only 3km away from the Trade Fair and central railway station,
and very near the Palace Gardens, this hotel is part of the
Steigenberger chain. Since it opened in the 30s, Kissinger,
Gorbachov and Yeltsin have all visited and many EU meetings
have been held here. Inside, it is very modern, with innocuous
pastels in the bedrooms, which are equipped with cable TV and
faxes. *24hr room service. Theatre-style conference facilities for up to
460. Secretarial/translation services on request. Swimming pool/sauna.
Public parking.* AMERICAN EXPRESS *Diners, Mastercard, Visa.*

Stuttgart   **Restaurant Top Air**

Tel (711) 948 21 37   Fax (711) 797 92 10   **R**

Flughafen 70621 Stuttgart

Seats 30   Meal for 2 approx DM190

This stylish art deco restaurant is actually inside the airport, and
one of the airport restaurants in Europe most worth
recommending. The menu combines light modern German
cooking with regional dishes. Grilled turbot and sea bass are
served alongside rumpsteak served in miso and basil sauce. Other
dishes lean towards more international cuisine, with cannelloni
filled with lobster and fresh tarragon and salmon, sturgeon and
artichoke carbonara. *L 11.45-2.30 D 5.45-10 (Sat 6-12). Closed
L Sat, 8-23 Aug.* AMERICAN EXPRESS *Diners, Mastercard, Visa.*

Stuttgart   **Hotel Wörtz**

Tel (711) 236 70 01   Fax (711) 236 70 07   **HR**

Hohenheimerstrasse 30 70184 Stuttgart

Rooms 35   Double room from DM155

Just off a main road in the centre of the city, this family-run hotel
is rightfully the official residence of visiting American Embassy
officials. But, despite being only five minutes from the main
railway station, it is relatively quiet inside with plenty of
protection and comfort given by the air-conditioning and double-
glazing. The building dates only from the 40s, but the ornate
frescoed ceilings are over 400 years old. As one might imagine,
there are no sports or conference facilities here, but the rooms
do now have cable TV. They are decorated with heavy old
German furniture and bronze-forged ornaments. As the family
collect more pieces, the rooms are changed and renovated. *Private
parking.* AMERICAN EXPRESS *Diners, Mastercard, Visa.*

Restaurant   **Zur Weinsteige**

Seats 60   Meal for 2 approx DM115

In this 19th-century converted wine cellar, with its old wooden
ceilings, ornately carved doors and heavy wooden tables,
a typically Southern German menu is served, with fresh rainbow
trout and Black Forest venison. On the main menu, sausages are
accompanied by creamed mushrooms and noodles and medallions
of veal and pork are cooked with chanterelles and baby vegetables.
They have a collection of more than 500 different wines, mostly
regional German. *Open L 12-2 D 6-10. Closed Sun, Mon, 18 Dec-
12 Jan.* AMERICAN EXPRESS *Diners, Mastercard, Visa.*

Elsewhere in Germany

Baden-Baden   Brenner's Park-Hotel & Spa

Tel (7221) 90 00   Fax (7221) 387 72   **H**

Schillerstrasse 6 76530 Baden-Baden
Rooms 100   Double room from DM450

A quiet, walkable distance from Baden-Baden, which has been
famous for its spas since the 1600s, this privately-owned hotel
in the Black Forest has been in existence for over 120 years. The
building, which has played host to countless important dignitaries
over the years, has been the scene for several momentous political
decisions, as well as accommodating such VIPS as de Gaulle,
Adenaeur, the Duke and Duchess of Windsor and the Aga Khan.
Inside, the rooms have great style, with classic period decor and
interesting antiques. Visitors still come to this very fashionable and
luxurious hotel, specifically for the Black Forest Clinic, which
pioneers all types of therapeutic medicine and rehabilitation. If you
just want exercise and relaxation, the sports facilities are excellent,
with an indoor swimming pool, saunas and gym as well as tennis,
riding and golf in the large private grounds surrounding the hotel.
*Cable/satellite TV. 2 Restaurants. Conference facilities. Beauty Salon.
Health clinic. Sports facilities.* AMERICAN EXPRESS® *Diners, Mastercard, Visa.*

Baiersbronn   Hotel Traube Tonbach

Tel (7442) 49 20   Fax (7442) 49 26 92   **HR**

Tonbachstrasse 237 72270 Baiersbronn
Rooms 300   Double room from DM250

Deep in the Black Forest, Baiersbronn is reached from the
Karlsruhe-Basel motorway by a 45km scenic route. The hotel
is beautifully situated in a green valley above the town. More than
a hotel, it is one of Germany's finest resorts, fully equipped to offer
guests a range of health and beauty treatments second to none.
Rooms are large and luxuriously furnished, and many have
balconies. The Finkbeiner family has been here for over 200 years.
*Theatre-style conference facilities for up to 60. Outdoor and indoor
swimming pools, saunas, gym, tennis courts, massage. No credit cards.*
See over for restaurants

Restaurant Schwarzwaldstube

Seats 70   Meal for 2 approx DM300

The jewel in the crown of the Traube-Tonbach resort is their
gourmet restaurant in the Schwarzwaldstube (Black Forest Room).
With only 12 tables seating 35 guests it's very popular and you
now have to book many weeks ahead to dine here. Lunch is easier
but booking is essential. Chef Harald Wohlfahrt, a youthful
looking 39, has built up a formidable reputation and a recent meal
was well up to expectation. After training with Eckart
Witzigmann in Munich and Alain Chapel in France he came
to the Schwarzwaldstube 17 years ago, and owner Heiner
Finkbeiner, a first-class chef himself, has given him a free hand
to develop his talents. Dishes to savour from the à la carte selection   ★
or the seven-course tasting menu in half portions are caviar with
sturgeon parfait, scallops with lemon sauce and potato pancakes,
lobster gratin with a tarragon sauce and a sensational quail with
foie gras and truffles. Try also sea bass fillet on a parsley purée
with a red wine sauce or partridge in puff pastry. To end, why not
choose an omelette soufflé and pears in red wine. The wine list
is very extensive with rare French vintages and, of course, a large
selection of Mosel, Rhine and Baden wines. There is also a useful
selection of half bottles. *L 12-2 D 7-10. Closed Mon, Tue, 9-31 Jan,
31 Jul-22 Aug. Private parking.* AMERICAN EXPRESS *Diners, Visa.*

Friedrichsruhe	Wald und Schlosshotel Friedrichsruhe

Tel (7941) 608 70   Fax (7941) 614 68   **HR**

74639 Friedrichsruhe
Rooms 51   Double room from DM295

In fairy tales, Germany is filled with fantastic giants and castles;
in reality there are now few castles one can actually stay in – but
this is one of them. Most of the bedrooms are in the 300-year-old
castle, with the rest of the guests staying in the porter's lodge
or garden house. Impressive antiques dramatically fill the rooms,
but the facilities are limited; the conference facilities only stretch
to 80 people sitting theatre-style. However, considering the place
is very remote, 90km away from Stuttgart and 20 minutes drive
from Heilbronn, the sports facilities are great – notably an 18-hole
golf course, outdoor and indoor swimming pool and four tennis
courts. *Conference facilities. Private parking.* AMERICAN EXPRESS *Diners,
Mastercard, Visa.*

Restaurant

Seats 85   Meal for 2 approx DM400

Chef Lothermann has been here for over 20 years and has created
a classical French menu, with a smattering of more refined
regional dishes. A chartreuse of quail breast and goose liver
is served in a truffle sauce; roasted fillet of turbot is served with
small chanterelles on a bed of spinach in a fish sauce; fillet of veal
with asparagus comes with hollandaise sauce and is accompanied
by flat dough cakes. *L 12-2.15 D 6.45-9.30. Private parking.*

Passau   **Holiday Inn**

Tel (851) 590 00   Fax (851) 590 05 29   **H**

Bahnhofstrasse 24a 94032 Passau

Rooms 129   Double room from DM280

Situated right on the Bavarian border, Passau is 170km from
Munich and 100km from Linz. Despite the hotel being part of an
international chain, the decor inside is typically and traditionally
Bavarian. The rooms are well equipped, with satellite TV, in-
house movies and large French beds. With nine conference rooms,
they can cater for theatre-style conferences and meetings of up
to 360 people. *Conference facilities. Secretarial/translation services
on request. Indoor swimming pool.* AMERICAN EXPRESS *Diners, Mastercard,
Visa.*

Scotch Beef Club Members: Germany

BADEN-BADEN: Privathotel Quissiana
BADEN-BADEN: Hotel Brenner's Park
BIELEFELD: Zum Mauseteich
BRAUNSCHWEIG: Mövenpick
BREMEN: Hotel Havenhaus Restaurant
BREMEN: Maritim Hotel Congress Centrum Bremen
COLOGNE: DOM-Hotel
COLOGNE: SAS Royal Hotel
CUXHAVEN: Silencehotel Deichgraf
DARMSTADT: Maritim Hotel Rhein-Main
DORTMUND: Mövenpick
DUSSELDORF: Mövenpick
EGLOFFSTEIN: Gasthaus Krone
ESSEN: Sheraton-Hotel
FRANKFURT: Bettina Eck
FRANKFURT: Mövenpick
GOTTINGEN: Gebhards Hotel
HAMBURG: Mövenpick
HAMBURG: SAS Royal Hotel
HAMELN-WESSER: Klütturm
KEITUM/SYLT: Beef und Lobster
LINDAU/BODENSEE: Hotel Bad Schachen
LINNESTADT OEDIGEN: Hotel Restaurant Haus Buckmann
LILENTHAL: Alte Posthalterei
MANNHEIM: Hotel Pfalz
MUNICH: Marriott Hotel
MUNICH: Park Hilton
MUNICH: Hotel Bayerischer Hof
MUNSTER-HANDORF: Hotel Deutscher Vater
NORDSEEINSEL JUIST: Hotel Worch
NURNBERG: Grand Hotel Nürnberg
PASSAU: Holiday Inn
PORTA WESTFALICA: Porta Berghotel
SIEGEN: Queens Hotel
STUTTGART: Mövenpick
WEGBERG: Molzmühle
WEINSTADT/BEUTELSBACH: Krone
ZEIL AM MAIN: Zeiler Bürgerstube

Germany Index

Greece

Currency: Greek Drachma   **Exchange Rate:** £1 = approx Dr 360

International dialling code: 010 30
(Athens + 1)

Passports/Visas: No visa required by British passport holders.

British Embassy & Consulate Tel: 1-723 6211/19

TRANSPORT
Airports:
Athens - West Air Terminal (Olympic Airways and domestic flights)
Tel: 1-989 2111
Athens - East Air Terminal (International and charter flights) Tel: 1-979
9466
Railway Stations: (Central information & tickets)
1 Karolou Street Tel: 1-522 2491 or 6 Sina Street Tel: 1-362 4402
Car Hire: Avis Tel: 1-322 4951 / Budget Tel: 1-921 4771 / Eurodollar
Tel: 1-922 9672 / Europcar Tel: 1-921 5788 / Hertz Tel: 1-961 3625

Banks open: 8.30am-2pm Mon-Fri.

Shops open: Mon/Wed 9am-5pm, Tue/Thu/Fri 9am-7pm, Sat 8.30am-
3.30pm.

National Holidays: New Year's Day, 6 Jan, 6 & 25 Mar, 21, 23 & 24
Apr, 1 May, 12 Jun, 15 Aug, 28 Oct, Christmas Day & Boxing Day

Tourist Offices:
Greek Tourist Board in London - Tel: 0171-734 5997
In Athens - Greek National Tourist Organisation Tel: 1-322 3111

American Express Travel Service Office:
Athens - AETS
   2 Hermou Street
   Syntagma Square
   GR 10225
   PO Box 3325
   Tel: 1-3244976 #

Athens

Athens   Andromeda Hotel

`Tel (1) 6437302-5`   **H**

Timoleontos Vassou Street 22 115 21 Athens
Rooms 30   Double room from Dr65,000

Five minutes from the city centre and within shuttling distance of
the airport, this hotel has changed very little over the years.
Persian rugs are still spread along the seven floors, dotted with
heavy old armchairs. The bedrooms are of a good size, with four
studios and three penthouse suites available. They are also well
equipped with faxes, mini-bars, satellite and cable TV. *24hr room
service. Cable and satellite TV/fax. Theatre-style conference facilities
for up to 110. Secretarial/translation services. Public/valet parking.*
AMERICAN EXPRESS *Diners, Mastercard, Visa.*

THE APARTMENT SERVICE
Tel in UK: (0181) 748 4207   Fax: (0181) 748 3972
The Apartment Service will find you the right apartment
worldwide to suit your needs, whether you are on a short or
long-term stay. A 96-page colour catalogue is free on request.
All budgets are catered for.

Athens   Athenaeum Intercontinental

`Tel (1) 9023 666   Fax (1) 9243 000`   **H**

Syngrou Avenue 89-93 117 45 Athens
Rooms 551   Double room from Dr58,700

A product of an early 80s boom in building, this hotel is new, but
with a traditional feel; marble lines the lobby and the eight floors
redecorated last year have been fitted with ruby red carpets and
subtle beige paintwork. The rooms, however, are modern with
simple, solid furniture. Despite being just five minutes away from
downtown Athens, there are good sports facilities here and a pool
to relax in away from the noisy, bustling street below. Many
waltzing couples have glided round their ballroom, the largest
in the capital. *24hr room service. Cable TV/fax. Theatre-style
conference facilities for up to 2000. Secretarial/translation services
on request. Private parking.* AMERICAN EXPRESS *Diners, Mastercard, Visa.*

Athens   Athens Chandris Hotel

`Tel (1) 9414 824   Fax (1) 9425 082`   **H**

Syngrou Avenue 385 Faliro 175 64 Athens
Rooms 366   Double room from Dr34,000

Between Piraeus and the airport, which is ten minutes away
by car, the hotel is also 10 minutes from the Acropolis and the
centre of Athens and a hotel shuttle regularly ferries guests in and
out of the city. Chandris' hotel group started up in the 70s and this
one appears a little dated now, with its plain beige and brown
material chairs and sofas and metal-legged chairs. There are plans
afoot to renovate the whole hotel in 1995. The rooftop swimming
pool offers great views of the hills, sea and Athens itself and

a chance to relax away from the heat of the streets. Alternatively, sit in the garden behind the reception. *24hr room service. Conference facilities for up to 500. Secretarial/translation/chauffeur services on request. Private parking.* AMERICAN EXPRESS *Diners, Mastercard, Visa.*

Athens   **Athens Hilton**

Tel (1) 7250 201   Fax (1) 7253 110   **HR**

Vassilis Sophias Avenue 46 115 28 Athens
Rooms 453   Double room from Dr46,000

Like many Hilton hotels, the one in Athens was a ten-floor tribute to modernity back in the 70s. King Constantine, Pierre Cardin and Jacques Delors have all stayed here, doubtless wooed by the reliability of service; the concierge was head doorman for 20 years before he took his present post. Five club suites have king-size and twin beds and are fitted with fax lines. All the rooms have pastel cotton linen and smart, recently renovated marble bathrooms. *24hr room service. Theatre-style conference facilities for up to 1600. Secretarial/translation/valet services on request. Swimming pool, sauna. Private parking.* AMERICAN EXPRESS *Diners, Mastercard, Visa.*

Restaurant Ta Nissia
Seats 85   Meal for 2 approx Dr8,000

The interior of this old taverna-style restaurant has been smartened up, the hand-carved wooden walls have been restored and porcelain pieces placed around the tables, but the food remains a pleasing mélange of traditional Greek taverna grilled food, with some fancier French dishes. Plenty of fresh fish and grilled steak and lamb are the main staples of the menu; their T-bone steak is a popular dish served with sautéed potatoes and salad. A large wine list stretches to some good French and Italian bottles. *D 7.30-12.30.*

Athens   **Boschetto**

Tel (1) 7210 893   Fax (1) 72223 598   **R**

Evangelismos off Elefterios Venizelou 106 75 Athens
Seats 214   Meal for 2 approx Dr11,000

The French windows look over a small park and across to the Hilton hotel right in the centre of Athens. This old summerhouse was a small taverna café, but became an Italian restaurant six years ago. Simple, straightforward Italian dishes, like gnocchi with gorgonzola or spinach, are served with grilled skewered salmon and swordfish marinated in herbs. The interior is as lush as the foliage in the gardens, with pine green walls and bright terracotta pots. *L 1-4 D 8.30-12.30. Closed 10-20 Aug.* AMERICAN EXPRESS *Visa.*

To dial overseas from the UK, 010 will change to 00
on 16th April 1995.

Athens   La Brasserie

Tel (1) 6716 572   **R**

Kifissias 292 (3rd floor) 154 51 Athens
Seats 90   .   Meal for 2 approx Dr20,000

True to its name, modern wooden tables and chairs give
an informal feel to this five-year-old French/Italian restaurant
which tends to place a great deal of emphasis on fish. Simple
grilled sea bass, red mullet and prawns and Italian-style dishes with
fish cooked in plenty of garlic and olive oil predominate.
A smattering of French wines accompany local bottles. *L 11-2
D 9-2. Closed Sun.* AMERICAN EXPRESS *Diners, Mastercard, Visa.*

Athens   La Fenice

Tel (1) 8949 454   **R**

Zisimopoulou Glifatha 10 TK 16674 Athens
Seats 90   Meal for 2 approx Dr12,000

Hand-made tiles and white and beige furniture add to the homely
feel of this new restaurant. The food is also home-made,
straightforward Italian cooking, with a good selection of fish and
meat dishes and fresh pasta. House specialities include: lobster
bisque, langoustines with pasta and chicken grilled in saffron and
served with zucchini. Some Italian bottles have joined the local
wine list. *D 8-2. Closed Sun. Private parking.* AMERICAN EXPRESS
Mastercard, Visa.

Athens   Hotel Grande Bretagne

Tel (1) 3230 251   Fax (1) 3228 034   **H**

Constitution Square 105 63 Athens
Rooms 364   Double room from Dr60,000

A beautiful mansion built after the Ottomans left the city in the
1830s. 160 years later, it is still an admirable piece of architecture,
standing imposingly opposite the Parliament. Stained-glass-
ceilinged halls, mirrored salons and a ballroom are all decorated
with restored, hand-carved furniture, brocade curtains and large
chandeliers. Since the Italian group, CIGA hotels, took over
in 1992, some of the bedrooms have been redecorated and
furniture re-upholstered. The bedrooms are elegantly
proportioned with old furniture and fabrics in muted yellows and
burgundies, but have modern marble bathrooms and double
glazing. *24hr room service. Satellite TV/fax. Theatre-style
conference/ballroom facilities for up to 1000. Secretarial/translation/valet
services. Public parking.* AMERICAN EXPRESS *Diners, Mastercard, Visa.*

Athens   Ledra Marriott

Tel (1) 9347 711   Fax (1) 93 58 603   **HR**

Syngrou Avenue 115 117 45 Athens
Rooms 255   Double room from Dr63,000

Situated in an exclusive residential avenue right between the sea
and the city centre, the modern Marriott has played host to stars
such as Leonard Bernstein, as well as several heavyweight
Government meetings. The whole hotel has recently been
refurbished and the rooms are now decorated in pastel pink shades

with blue rugs, and very well equipped, with reliable service from the experienced concierge and room service staff. *24hr room service. Cable TV/fax. Theatre-style conference facilities for up to 100. Secretarial/translation services. Swimming pool. Public parking.* AMERICAN EXPRESS *Diners, Mastercard, Visa.*

Restaurant Kona Kai
Seats 110   Meal for 2 approx Dr12,000

Polynesian cooking mixes with Japanese teppanyaki in this, Athens' authentic Far Eastern restaurant. Mongolian beef fried in soya and sesame oil, spring rolls, egg rolls, and seafood dragons (pancakes filled with cream cheese and crabmeat) all catch the attention. Fountains, flowers and other exotica add to the Oriental atmosphere. The hotel's other restaurant, *Zephyros*, specialises in Greek cuisine. *D 8-12.*

Athens   **Myrtia**   **R** ·
Tel (1) 7012 276
Trivonianou 32 116 36 Athens
Seats 170   Meal for 2 approx Dr16,000

This old taverna, with wooden tables and chairs, old Greek plates on the walls and numerous marble vases scattered throughout, has been serving traditional Greek food for 25 years. The menu offers plenty of grilled, fried and baked fresh fish, meatballs and lamb, and is livened up with the likes of baked quail pie. Mostly national wines are served with a few French and Italian. The guitar quintet strums a medley of international tunes. *D 8-1. Closed Sun, Aug. Private/valet parking.* AMERICAN EXPRESS *Diners, Mastercard, Visa.*

Athens   **Park**   **H**
Tel (1) 8832 711   Fax (1) 8238 420
Alexandras 10 106 82 Athens
Rooms 145   Double room from Dr245,000

Athenian traffic belts past this modern, family-run hotel right in the very heart of the city. Inside, classic sofas, carpets and wallpapers line the rooms, with a mirrored entrance. The rooms are a decent size, the majority of them being doubles, but do not have writing desks, except in the ten suites. *24hr room service. Theatre-style conference facilities for up to 500. Secretarial/translation services on request. Swimming pool. Public parking.* AMERICAN EXPRESS *Diners, Mastercard, Visa.*

The Golden Eurostar [★] denotes our pick of the restaurants. Cooking is the major consideration, but other factors are also taken into account, including ambience, comfort and service.

Athens   Pentelikon Hotel

Tel (1) 8080311   Fax (1) 8010314   **HR**

Deligianni Street 66 Kifissia 145-62 Athens
Rooms 43   Double room from Dr56,000

It is not only LaToya Jackson who has retreated from the press
inside this 1920s neo-classical building surrounded by extensive
gardens; President Papandreou has stayed here too. The old house
was renovated when it became a hotel in the 80s, but its
aristocratic air remains: marble floors sweep through the building,
frescoes decorate the ceilings and leather chesterfield sofas adorn
the halls. The bedrooms are equally grand, with marble
bathrooms and traditional wooden furniture. *Room service 6.30am-
1.30am. Satellite TV/fax. Conference facilities for up to 100.
Valet/secretarial/translation services.* AMERICAN EXPRESS *Diners, Mastercard,
Visa.*

Restaurant Vardi's
Seats 60   Meal for 2 approx Dr10,000

This garden setting is a perfect spot in which to while away long,
hot summer evenings. The cooking consists of suitably light
Mediterranean dishes with plenty of marinated fish and salad:
grilled foie gras served on an endive salad with grapes marinated
in white wine, salmon tartare with caviar and quail's eggs served
with marinated sweet red peppers. Sea bass and lobster are regular
favourites. If you would rather have a snack you can sit at the bar
and have salmon and caper canapés. *D 8.30-1.30. Closed Sun, 1-15
Aug.*

Athens   Precieux Gastronomie

Tel (1) 3608 616   Fax (1) 3608 619   **R**

Akadimias 14 10671 Athens
Seats 40   Meal for 2 approx Dr11,000

The family owners have many culinary strings to their bow:
a delicatessen on the other side of Athens and a buffet/snack bar
down below this restaurant. The Greek chef is regularly sent
to gastronomic seminars in France, where he has developed
a penchant for lightly cooked fish dishes, more delicately presented
than traditional Greek food. His specialities are fillet of sea bass
steamed with parsley and garlic and grilled salmon served in a
mushroom sauce. The menu changes only twice a year and the
ambience not at all; dim lighting and soulful guitar and piano
music are enhanced by romantic requests from the floor. *L 12-4
D (Nov-May) 8.30-late. Closed Sun.* AMERICAN EXPRESS *Diners,
Mastercard, Visa.*

Athens   St George Lycabettus

Tel (1) 7290 711   Fax (1) 7290 439   **H**

Kleomenous 2 106 75 Athens
Rooms 300   Double room from Dr34,000

Ornately decorated mirrors and shiny, ragged shell-coloured walls
add to the modern interior of this 70s building, 30 minutes from
the airport and ten minutes from the railways station. The rooms
have recently been redecorated with chintzy bedcovers and

curtains and a new wing has added extra bedrooms to the eight-floored building. Some rooms enjoy a view of the Acropolis. *24hr room service. Satellite TV. Boardroom-style conference facilities. Secretarial/translation services. Swimming pool. Private parking.* AMERICAN EXPRESS *Diners, Mastercard, Visa.*

Athens	**Varoulco**	
Tel (1) 4112 043		**R**

Deligiorgi Street 14 18533 Athens
Seats 65   Meal for 2 approx Dr20,000

Back in the 30s it was a small taverna, now it is a unique restaurant; it serves practically nothing but monkfish! Admittedly, it comes in a number of different ways: steamed and grilled, on skewers or filleted. The popular house speciality is steamed fillet of monkfish with a celery and onion sauce. Some Italian wines alongside the Greek. *D 9-2. Closed Aug. Public parking.* AMERICAN EXPRESS

Around Athens

Vouliagmeni	**Astir Palace Resort/Arion**	
Tel (1) 8960211-9 Fax (1) 8961902		**H**

Apollonos Street 40 166-71 Vouliagmeni
Rooms 560   Double room from Dr42,000

Secluded by a park of pine trees 25km out of Athens and a 5km shuttle ride from the airport, this is an extraordinary resort complex. It is quiet and generally a little cooler by the sea, with all the sports facilities one could possibly need, yet it is very well equipped for meetings and conferences. Conference meetings to try to resolve the Bosnian Crisis were staged here and EC meetings are regular events. At the time of going to press, all the rooms were being refurbished only a year after the hotel opened. When the work is finished, 50 of the rooms will be suites. *24hr room service. Fax/cable TV. Conference facilities for up to 900. Secretarial/translation/valet/limousine/safety deposit services. 3 private beaches/3 swimming pools (indoor and outdoor), tennis courts, saunas, gym, water sports. Private parking.* AMERICAN EXPRESS *Mastercard, Visa.*

Greece Index

Hungary

Currency: Hungarian Forint   **Exchange Rate**: £1 = approx Ft 165

International dialling code: 010 36
(Budapest + 1)

Passports/Visas: No visa required by British passport holders for stay of up to 30 days.

British Embassy in Budapest Tel: 1-266 2888   Fax: 1-266 0907

TRANSPORT
Airports:
Budapest-Ferihagy Tel: 1-157 9123
Railway Stations:
Keleti Tel: 1-113 6835 / Nyugati Tel: 1-149 0115 / Déli Tel: 1-155 8657
State Railways central ticket & information office Tel: 1-122 8405
Car hire in Budapest:
Europcar Tel: 1-113 1492/113 0207 / Hertz Tel: 1-122 1471 (airport 1-157 8618/157 8606) / Avis Tel: (airport) 1-147 5754/147 8470 / Budget Tel: 1-138 4205 (airport 1-157 9123)
Speed Limits: 80 km/h on trunk roads, 100 km/h on motorways, 50 km/h in towns.

Banks open: 8am-3pm Mon-Thu (Fri till 1pm).

Shops open: Food shops in general Mon-Fri 7am-7pm (Sat till 1pm). Other shops 10am-6pm Mon-Fri (Sat till 1pm). There are now some convenience stores open around the clock.

National Holidays: New Year's Day, 15 Mar, Easter Monday, 1 May, Whit Monday, 20 Aug, 23 Oct, Christmas Day & Boxing Day.

Tourist Offices:
Hungarian Embassy in London - Tel: 0171-235 4048
Tourist Board in Budapest Tel: 1-117 9800

American Express Travel Service Office:
Budapest - American Express Hungary Ltd
    Deak Ferenc U.10
    1052
    PO Box 698 (PO Box Post Code 1365)
    Tel: 1-2668680 #

Budapest

Budapest	**Atrium Hyatt**	

Tel (1) 266 1234   Fax (1) 266 9101   **H**

Roosevelt-ter 2 Budapest V

Rooms 353   Double room from Ft24,740

One of the big three hotels in the very centre of the city, this one
is on the Pest bank of the River Danube, next to the famous
tourist attraction, the Chain Bridge. The facilities are as excellent
as the location, with sufficient capacity to hold a theatre-style
conference for up to 750 people. Business guests on the seventh
and eighth floors can also use the Regency Club, an informal
lounge with great views. The rooms are well equipped, with
mini-bars, and the 27 suites also have fax and computer terminals.
*24hr room service. Cable TV/air-con. Conference facilities.
Sauna/solarium/indoor swimming pool. Beauty salon/massage. Private
garage.* AMERICAN EXPRESS *Diners, Mastercard, Visa.*

THE APARTMENT SERVICE
Tel in UK: (0181) 748 4207   Fax: (0181) 748 3972
The Apartment Service will find you the right apartment
worldwide to suit your needs, whether you are on a short or
long-term stay. A 96-page colour catalogue is free on request.
All budgets are catered for.

Budapest	**Bagolyvár Restaurant**	

Tel (1) 121 3550 (ext 222, specify Bagolyvár)   **R**

Állatkerti út 2 Budapest XIV

Seats 70   Meal for 2 approx Ft3000

Under the same ownership as *Gundel*, Bagolyvár is the Hungarian
version of the *cucina mamma*: you will find home-style cooking
(mostly Hungarian specialities), friendly service and an intimate
yet elegant atmosphere. Bagolyvár means Owl's Castle and refers
to the fanciful Transylvanian style of the building, whose interior
design evokes the feel of a turn-of-the-century Budapest home.
In addition to the dishes on the menu, there are daily specials
on the blackboard. Old-fashioned chicken and beef broth with
shell-shaped noodles would be a good starter, or in the summer,
have chilled fruit soup with sour cream. Goose dishes are
especially good here: roast goose with braised cabbage and
potatoes is superb. If you prefer a lighter dish, have pan-fried
breast of turkey with green salad. Home-made poppy seed noodles
– a Hungarian extravaganza – are worth trying, or if you want
to stay on more familiar ground, have a cottage cheese pancake
with vanilla sauce, or a strawberry torte for a dessert. *Open noon-
10.30pm. Public parking.* AMERICAN EXPRESS *Diners, Mastercard, Visa.*

Budapest   Casino Restaurant

Tel (1) 118 4576   R

Vigadó u 2 Budapest V
Seats 60   Meal for 2 approx Ft4500

The restaurant is in the same building as the Casino Vigadó and
the dinner guests get a free entry ticket to the Casino. The food
is good and prices are reasonable, *and* this is the only restaurant
open until 4am. Because of its central location, it is also
a convenient place for a light lunch. For dinner, try the goose liver
roulade with sesame seeds as an appetiser and then have *csorba* soup
with cabbage leaves and sour cream; for a main course choose
stuffed quails with almond sauce and for dessert, have the Casino
pancakes, filled with fresh fruit and served with a marzipan sauce.
Open 10am-4am. AMERICAN EXPRESS *Diners, Mastercard, Visa.*

Budapest   Corvinus Kempinsky

Tel (1) 266 1000   Fax (1) 266 2000   H

Erzsebet-ter 7-8 Budapest V
Rooms 369   Double room from Ft30,000

The newest and most impressive of Budapest's small collection
of 'luxury Western' hotels, it was built only two years ago. The
rooms are very well equipped and so are the conference rooms,
supported by a large business centre with secretarial and
translation services. It is also right in the centre of Budapest's
business district and therefore an ideal location for meetings.
24hr room service. Satellite/cable TV/safe/air-con. Restaurants.
Theatre-style conference facilities for up to 450. Business centre. Indoor
swimming pool/solarium/gym. Private garage. AMERICAN EXPRESS *Diners,*
Mastercard, Visa.

Budapest   Cyrano Restaurant

Tel (1) 266 3096   Fax (1) 118 4991   R

Kristóf tér 7-8 Budapest V
Seats 55   Meal for 2 approx Ft3000

A new restaurant – established in 1993 by a handful of young
people – in a beautiful old Baroque building in the centre of the
pedestrian zone of the city (off Váci Street and Vörösmarty
Square, where young artists, most of them students at the Budapest
Academy of Arts, sit in rows, drawing portraits of the passers-by).
The restaurant got its name from the chandelier which hangs
in the centre of the main room (it was used in the film, *Cyrano*
de Bergerac, which was shot in a Budapest studio) and was bought
by the present owners from the producers. The young chef's
cuisine is international, so you should come here to eat if you want
to give your stomach a rest after too many rich Hungarian dishes.
Start your lunch or dinner with veal paté and blueberry jam,
continue with a garlic cream soup and order trout with almonds,
or strips of steak with chili, if you prefer beef. There are always
various vegetarian dishes on the menu, like stuffed mushrooms
or broccoli with wild mushrooms. *Open 11am-11.30pm. Public*
garage parking. AMERICAN EXPRESS *Mastercard, Visa.*

Budapest   Fehér Bölény Restaurant

Tel (1) 112 2825   **R**

Bank utca 5 Budapest V

Seats 45   Meal for 2 approx Ft8000

Founded in 1987, this was the first steak house in Budapest
to discover the secret of a good steak: cattle reared the whole year
round in the open air and meat which is carefully marinated
before roasting. Tamás Rádi and Oszkár Pölös, the owners
of Fehér Bölény (White Bison) toured Great Britain and the USA
to find the recipe for a suitable marinade, and their research
resulted in 15 kinds of steaks garnished with potatoes, Texan
beans, and various salads. There are also starters and soups,
of course, but the real thing here is the steak: marinated for three
days, with each slice weighing about 25 dkgs (8oz). Peter Ceress,
the chef, will do the steak exactly as you want, you may have
it with green sauce, seasoned with pepper, or with cheese sauce,
seasoned with cumin. *D only 6-2. Closed Sun. No parking.*
AMERICAN EXPRESS *Diners, Mastercard, Visa.*

Budapest   Fészek Restaurant

Tel (1) 122 6043   Fax (1) 122 7652   **R**

Kertész utca 36 Budapest VII

Seats 350   Meal for 2 approx Ft3000

Fészek is an artists club which has been going since the turn of the
century (the name Fészek means both 'nest' and is also the
abbreviation of the club's name meaning painters, architects, actors
and other bohemians). The restaurant is on the main floor and
between spring and autumn meals are served in the big courtyard,
which has a nice garden with flowers and old trees. The cuisine
is international and there are also traditional Hungarian dishes
on the menu. Your choice could be cold goose liver with French
salad for starters, followed by a consommé *à la hongroise*; have
beef stroganoff for a main course and crepe Suzette for dessert.
Open noon-12.30am. Closed 24-25 Dec. No parking. AMERICAN EXPRESS

Budapest   Forum Hotel

Tel (1) 117 8088   Fax (1) 117 9808   **H**

Apaczai Csere-utca 12-14 Budapest V

Rooms 400   Double room from Ft21,800

An excellent location for a hotel, right on the Pest bank of the
River Danube, very near to the business and financial centre.
To add to that, they have recently opened their own new business
centre, where English-speaking secretaries will type all your notes
on computers (open 7am-8pm Mon-Fri). The rooms are some
of the most modern and up to date in Budapest, with good
facilities (this does not include fax machines, but these are
available in the business centre). *24hr room service. Satellite TV/air-
con. Theatre-style conference facilities for up to 250. Private parking.*
AMERICAN EXPRESS *Diners, Mastercard, Visa.*

Budapest   **Gellért Hotel**

Tel (1) 185 2200   Fax (1) 166 6631   **HR**

Szent Gellért tér 1 Budapest XI

Rooms 239   Double room from Ft20,200

The 75-year-old Gellért has great views over the Pest bank of the
River Danube. In true old European-style, the place was originally
a spa hotel and you can still use the thermal baths in the building
next door and receive a range of health and beauty treatments.
In the summer, you can cool off afterwards in the outdoor
swimming pool. The hotel is as good for business as it is for
health, with a conference room seating 160 delegates theatre-style
and a fully-equipped business centre, complete with secretarial and
translation services. Be careful to check what kind of room you
are booking as they vary tremendously: the small singles only
have showers and no mini-bars or air-conditioning, while the
suites and some of the doubles boast satellite TV and air-
conditioning. *24hr room service. Conference facilities. Business centre.*
Thermal baths/health and beauty treatments/indoor swimming pool.
Private parking. AMERICAN EXPRESS® *Diners, Mastercard, Visa.*

Duna Restaurant

Seats 200   Meal for 2 approx Ft10,000

Situated on the first floor, with an art-deco interior and
a magnificent view of the river, this is a pleasant place for a dinner
party with discreet background music. Between the two World
Wars, it was managed by the famous restaurateur, Károly Gundel,
and the gourmet specialities he created survived and are found
in the kitchen of the present excellent chef, Ferenc Novák. During
the summer, you may combine lunch or dinner with one or two
hours in the champagne bar, or the swimming pool with its
artificial waves. In the latter case, your meal will be served on the
terrace overlooking the pool. Try the cold *fogas* for a starter, with
a mixed salad and yoghurt dressing. Continue with the chilled
fruit soup, or with *gulyás* soup if the weather is not too hot. Fillet
of veal cooked Gellért-style is a good choice for your main course:
the fillets are sautéed, covered with slices of ham and bacon, and
a ragout of green peas, cream and egg yolks, which is all then
baked with some grated cheese. If you do not want meat have the
tokaji mushrooms: wild mushrooms filled with mushroom paté,
breaded and baked in olive oil and served with a Madeira sauce.
Excellent wines from the up-and-coming generation of Hungarian
vintners are sadly missing from the wine list. Try Nagyrédei
Pinot Blanc for a white choice, or a Gróf Nagyrédei Rosé for red,
to stay on the safe side. *L 12-4 D 7-11.30.*

Opening times are often liable to change at short notice,
so it's always best to book.

Budapest Gundel Restaurant

Tel (1) 121 3550 Fax (1) 142 2917 **R**

Állatkerti út 2 Budapest XIV
Seats 180 Meal for 2 approx Ft10,000

This historic restaurant is a 100-year-old palace in the romantic
City Park, with a view of the lake and Vadjahunyad Castle. It was
Károly Gundel who, between the two World Wars, made the
restaurant world famous and George Lang, the American-
Hungarian restaurateur, who took over in 1991 and brought back
its refined cuisine and elegance, deservedly receiving our award
for Best Restaurant, Eastern Europe. Choose the fowl soup
Ujházy-style (home-style) made by boiling a whole chicken with
a selection of vegetables and go on to George Lang's goose liver.
You should also try one of Károly Gundel's classical creations:
pike-perch and crayfish *pörkölt* or *Gundel Tokány*, which mixes
fillet of beef with various kinds of mushrooms, marjoram, green
peas and white asparagus, all garnished with crisp shoe-string
potatoes in a nest of scrambled eggs. For dessert, Gundel pancakes
are a must: filled with a mixture of raisins, candied orange peel
and rough-ground walnuts, and covered with a chocolate-rum
sauce. The House of Gundel own vineries at Tokaj and Eger – for
a white wine, Gundel Tokaji Furmint would be a good choice and
for a red wine, Gundel Bull's Blood of Eger. After dessert, a glass
of Gundel Tokaji Aszu or Gundel Tokaji Aszu Essence would
be delightful. *L 12-3 D 7-12. Public parking.* AMERICAN EXPRESS *Diners,
Mastercard, Visa.*

Budapest Hilton

Tel (1) 175 1000 Fax (1) 156 0285 **HR**

Hess András tér 1-3 Budapest 1
Rooms 323 Double room from Ft30,430

On the spectacular Castle Hill in Buda, overlooking the beautiful
city with its graceful bridges spanning the wide Danube, this
tastefully-built modern Hilton has the old chapel and cloisters of a
medieval Dominican monastery within its grounds (where open-
air concerts are held in the summer). Despite being 15 years old
and out of the main city business centre, the conference facilities
are good and spacious, with the capacity to seat 600 people
theatre-style. The bedrooms have colour TVs, mini-bars and air-
conditioning and the bathrooms have recently been refurbished.
24hr room service. Air-con. Conference facilities. Private garage.
AMERICAN EXPRESS *Diners, Mastercard, Visa.*

Kalosca Restaurant

Seats 55 Meal for 2 approx Ft12,000

You may start your gourmet tour of Budapest here on the sixth
floor, in a room decorated with motifs of Hungarian folklore.
Kalocsa offers a ravishing milieu for a Hungarian repast. Your fare
could be fish soup (*halászlé*) made with a variety of fish, then
perhaps beef with *letcho* (tomatoes, green and red peppers) or veal
chops stuffed with goose liver. For dessert have flambéed fruits,
or Transylvanian Varga strudel cake (*vargabéles*). For a red wine
a good choice would be Villányi Cabernet Sauvignon 1993. If you
want a demi-sec white wine after the dessert, try Nagyrédei
Hárslevelű 1986, from the Szőlőskert Vinery at Nagyréde. *L 12-3
D 7-11.30. Closed sometimes during the summer.*

Budapest   **100 Éves Restaurant**

Tel (1) 118 3608   Fax (1) 266 5240   **R**

Pesti Barnabás u 2 Budapest V
Seats 74   Meal for 2 approx Ft8000

Even though the restaurant's name, '100 Years Old', has remained
unchanged over the years, the Baroque house is actually about
three hundred years old and the restaurant has been open for 164
years. It is a small and intimate gourmet restaurant, with a great
variety of fish and game dishes. Your fare could be cold
Hungarian-style hors d'oeuvre, with goose liver, salami, cheese,
asparagus and other goodies, followed by a beef tea served *100
Years Old- style*. After this, have fillets of venison *à la Agnes Sorel*,
served with a ragout of ham and wild mushrooms cooked with
red wine. It will be flambéed at your table while gypsy music
plays in the background. If you want fish, however, order carp
in paprika sauce with dumplings, and for a dessert have pancakes
100 Years Old-style, filled with walnuts, pineapple and raisins and
accompanied by a punch sauce. *Open noon-11.30. Public parking.*
AMERICAN EXPRESS *Diners, Mastercard, Visa.*

Budapest   **Kisbuda Gyöngye Restaurant**

Tel (1) 168 6402/9246   Fax (1) 168 9227   **R**

Kenyeres utca 34 Budapest III
Seats 70   Meal for 2 approx Ft6000

After the house where Alice Mezõdy's previous gourmet
restaurant existed was demolished to make way for an office
building, Alice found for herself this charming old place in Óbuda
(Old Buda). She furnished it with turn-of-the century furniture,
old clocks and portraits of Óbuda burghers, successfully evoking
the atmosphere of a 19th-century Old Buda home. Now it is
a successful restaurant, with candles and lyrical violin-cum-piano
background music, and one that's popular with the locals. Start
your dinner with garlic soup, which is the *pièce de résistance* of the
chef, and after that have chicken *à la Kugler* – breast of chicken
with some exotic seasoning. Order cottage cheese dumplings for
dessert. The food is not exciting, but is tasty and filling. A good
choice of white wine would be Öreghegyi Chardonnay, from the
Tibor Báthory vineyard; for red wine, try the Cabernet
Sauvignon of the Saint Donatus cellar at Balatonborlár. Mezõdy's
other restaurant-coffee-house-beer hall, Remiz (meaning tram
depot) located in the depot for trams commuting between
Moszkva Square and the Buda Hills, is newer and even cheaper.
The cuisine is simple but delicious, with starters like goose liver
and crackling and main courses like knuckle of veal garnished
with baked onions and fried potatoes. *Open noon-midnight, (Sun
till 4). Closed D Sun. Public parking.* AMERICAN EXPRESS *Diners,
Mastercard, Visa.*

> To dial overseas from the UK, 010 will change to 00
> on 16th April 1995.

Budapest   Kispipa Restaurant

| Tel (1) 142 2587 | **R** |

Akácfa utca 38 Budapest VII

Seats   Meal for 2 approx Ft3000

This is a small restaurant with a rich and highly impressive *carte du jour*. People come here to enjoy reasonably-priced gourmet food, with agreeable background piano music every evening. It is difficult to make up one's mind as there are more than 100 dishes on the menu – a good choice would be pheasant soup cooked in 'housewife-style', veal *paprikás* Bakony-style (with wild mushrooms and sour cream), or medallions of pork Vintners-style (filled with plum and apple). Instead of dessert, try the cheese platter, with five different kinds of cheese (including some excellent goat's cheese). *Open noon-12.30am. Closed Sun & National Holidays.* AMERICAN EXPRESS

Budapest   Liget Hotel

| Tel (1) 269 5300   Fax (1) 269 5329 | **H** |

Dozsa Gyorgy-ut 106 Budapest VI

Rooms 139   Double room from Ft12,300

Overlooking Heroes Square, on the edge of City Park, this is a modest hotel, offering friendly service and the staff speak excellent English. Facilities in the bedrooms are limited to a mini-bar and radio but there's a small health centre for those wanting to relax and unwind. Don't worry about the absence of a restaurant here, there are plenty of places waiting to be discovered nearby. *Sauna/solarium/massage. Private garage.* AMERICAN EXPRESS *Diners, Mastercard, Visa.*

Budapest   Marriott

| Tel (1) 266 7000   Fax (1) 266 5000 | **H** |

Apaczai Csere-utca 4 Budapest V

Rooms 363   Double room from Ft16,000

The views are dramatic here: you can see right across the Danube and over Buda's Castle district, so make sure you have a room overlooking the river, preferably high up. All the rooms have been completely refurbished (and all are well equipped, with satellite TV and air-conditioning); there's a business lounge situated on the tenth floor. The Executive suites are all on the eighth, ninth and tenth floors. *24hr room service. Theatre-style conference facilities for up to 600. Sauna/indoor swimming pool. Private garage/parking.* AMERICAN EXPRESS *Diners, Mastercard, Visa.*

Budapest   Mátyás Pince Restaurant

| Tel (1) 118 1650/1693   Fax (1) 118 1650 | **R** |

Március 15 tér 7 Budapest V

Seats 300   Meal for 2 approx Ft8000

Mátyás Pince (Matthias Cellar) was founded 90 years ago by the renowned restaurateur, Mátyás Baldauf, who commissioned the artist, Jen Haranghy, to decorate the walls with scenes from the life of his namesake, the Hungarian Renaissance King Matthias. Inside it is attractive and typically Hungarian, with frescoes, stained-glass windows, folk embroideries and carved furniture.

★

There is a gypsy orchestra playing both at lunchtime and during the evening. The food is good; it consists of traditional Hungarian dishes, with some fresh-water fish, which the restaurant gets from the Tisza River. Order the Mátyás platter as a cold appetiser, with cold duck, pork, beef and goose liver. Continue with carp *Dorozsma*-style (sautéed with smoked bacon and ham and a ragout of mushrooms and sour cream poured over the top, all seasoned with paprika and garnished with home-made noodles).

An absolute must for dessert is the raspberry strudel, which is the house speciality. *Open noon-12.30am. Public parking.* AMERICAN EXPRESS® *Diners, Mastercard, Visa.*

Budapest   ## New York Café-Restaurant

| Tel (1) 122 1648   Fax (1) 122 3849 | R |

Erzsébet krt 9-11 Budapest VII

Seats 450   Meal for 2 approx Ft7000

You must visit the New York Café-Restaurant, even though it is now surrounded by scaffolding owing to the bad condition of the 100-year-old art nouveau building. It was the meeting place – almost a club – for writers, painters, musicians, actors and directors; some of them virtually lived here, as it was open day and night, seven days a week. The day it opened, a solemn procession led by Franz Molnár went to the banks of the Danube and threw the keys into the river demonstrating that it would never close. You should visit it like a museum: look around the coffee-house and look at the gallery, where caricatures of writers and journalists are hanging on the walls, and then go downstairs to the restaurant in the basement (called *mélyvíz*, 'deep water', by the regulars) if you want to have lunch or dinner. The food is satisfactory, but not outstanding, and it is better to just have a coffee or tea with some snacks, or sweets in the coffee house. *Open 9am-midnight (coffee house); L 12-3.30 D 6.30-11.30 (restaurant). No parking.* AMERICAN EXPRESS® *Diners, Mastercard, Visa.*

Budapest   ## Radegast Beer Hall

| Tel (1) 212 3746 | R |

Maros utca 16 Budapest XII (entrance on Pintér utca)

Seats 70   Meal for 2 approx Ft2000

If you want simple and good food in a family restaurant, among locals, visit the Radegast Beer Hall at Buda where you can eat your lunch or dinner in high-back booths made from darkly stained wood, or in the shadow of a tall tree in the courtyard, during the summer. Instead of appetisers, have one of the salads such as thinly sliced cucumber, or tomato and onion, both served with a sugared vinegar dressing (you may have Roquefort or yoghurt dressing instead, if you wish). Ask for pork fillets with peas, mushrooms and slices of onion in a creamy paprika sauce after that. Refuse the customary garnish of fried potatoes – which are disappointing – and ask for vegetables instead. For a dessert have cottage cheese-filled pancakes, or cherry or apple pie. Give the *somlói galuska*, (a rum-soaked multi-layered sponge) a miss – it is too rich. *Open 11-10.30. Public parking. No credit cards.*

Budapest   Robinson Restaurant

Tel (1) 142 0955   Fax (1) 142 3776   **R**

City Park Lake-side Budapest XIV
Seats 50   Meal for 2 approx Ft6000

A young restaurateur, Árpád László, nurtured the idea of opening
a restaurant jutting out over City Park lake for many years;
finally he succeeded, persuaded the city council and made his
dream come true. Swans and wild ducks swim almost under your
feet, while you are enjoying pork ribs grilled over charcoal,
or Robinson's special pancakes filled with fruit and accompanied
by vanilla sauce. The restaurant is quite comfortable, and the
service is friendly and personal. In summer, start your lunch
or dinner with chilled fruit soup and try the braised goose liver
with French toast. After this, you could choose grilled *fogas* (pike-   ★
perch) seasoned with rosemary and served with a crayfish ragout.
You may hesitate, however, considering the alternatives:
medallions of pork with calvados sauce, or grilled chicken, stuffed
with wild mushrooms, garnished with peaches and blueberries.
László entertains his guests with musical – and ballet –
programmes on a stage built over the lake, and every evening
there is guitar music in the restaurant. Do not expect a traditional
Hungarian meal, but come here if you want fun and light cuisine.
Open noon-11.30pm. Public parking. AMERICAN EXPRESS® *Diners,*
Mastercard, Visa.

Budapest   Taverna Hotel

Tel (1) 138 4999   Fax (1) 118 7188   **H**

Vaci-utca 20 Budapest V
Rooms 224   Double room from Ft13,500

A very popular hotel in the pedestrian-only part of the city, with
private parking beneath the building. Conferences can
be organised, but do note that they speak very little English here.
So tourists beware, as you may find that your sign language
is exhausted and you still have not found what you wanted. There
is a brasserie in the hotel, but since it is so central try one of the
numerous excellent restaurants nearby. *No room service. Satellite*
TV. Massage/sauna. Theatre-style conference facilities for up to 120.
Private garage. AMERICAN EXPRESS® *Diners, Mastercard, Visa.*

Budapest   Udvarház Restaurant

Tel (1) 188 6921   **R**

Hármashatárhegyi út 2 Budapest III
Seats 500   Meal for 2 approx Ft5000

This restaurant, on a hilltop, Hármasmatárhegy, about 17km from
the centre of the town, is worth visiting if you want to enjoy
nature and a unique view of the town. Take a taxi, or your own
car; a bus does run between the Újlaki Church and the hill, but
it takes about an hour to get there from downtown Budapest.
Lunch and dinner are served on the terrace overlooking the Buda
hills and the town and in the main restaurant whose name means
'Rose Arbour'. Nearly all the dishes are classically Hungarian. Start
with a herb soup, seasoned with marjoram, thyme, chives and
peppermint, followed by mushroom fritters. Try the sloppy

cabbage with *dagodó* (the meaty part of pork, just below the ribs)
a traditional Hungarian dish seasoned with tarragon, dill and sour
cream. Vanilla-flavoured *Pálffy* noodles should be your choice for
a dessert. Gypsy music plays every evening and quite often
folklore dance-shows are performed. If you want to talk, however,
make a reservation in one of the private rooms. *Open 11-10.30.
Closed Mon. Public parking.* AMERICAN EXPRESS *Diners, Visa.*

Budapest   **Vadrózsa Restaurant**

Tel (1) 135 1118   R

Pentelei Molnár u 15 Budapest II
Seats 100   Meal for 2 approx Ft8000

Here in a former well-to-do family residence on the Hill of Roses
(Rózsadomb), in an elegant residential district of Budapest, the
feeling its still like dining in someone's home. Solid wooden walls,
a crystal chandelier, soft piano music, fresh flowers and a rare sense
of space, along with amiable service, make the Vadrózsa the right
place to relax and enjoy yourself. Start with the appetiser platter,
with pieces of goose liver served either cold or grilled, caviar and
steak tartare. Follow with a consommé, if you want some soup,
after which have the fillet of *fogas* with tartare sauce, loaded with
chopped pickles. For a meat dish, the *lecsó* lamb is our advice:
perfectly grilled and served with a mixture of tomatoes, onions
and paprika – one of the most delightful Hungarian dishes.
Desserts are seasonal, from strawberries to peaches and pineapple,
served either plain or with ice cream. But in all probability, you
will not be able to resist the crepe, which comes filled with
a steamy mash of walnuts and topped with flambéed liqueured
chocolate. *D only 7-11.30. Closed Mon. Public parking.*
AMERICAN EXPRESS *Mastercard, Visa.*

Hungary Index

Italy

Currency: Italian Lira   **Exchange Rate:** £1 = approx L 2420

International dialling code: 010 39
(Rome + 6 Milan + 2 Florence + 55 Naples + 81 Turin + 11 Venice + 41
Genoa + 10 Pisa + 50)

Passports/Visas: No visa required by British passport holders.

British Embassy in Rome Tel: 6-482 5441   Fax: 6-487 3324

TRANSPORT
Airports:
Rome - Ciampino Tel: 6-794941 / Fiumicino Tel: 6-65951
Milan - Linate Tel: 2-74852200 / Malpensa Tel: 2-74852200
Turin - Caselle Tel: 11-5778362
Venice - Tessera Tel: 41-2606111
Genoa - Sestri Tel: 10-2411
Naples - Capodichino Tel: 81-7896111
Pisa - San Giusto Tel: 50-500707
Railway Stations:
Rome - Termini Tel: 6-4775
Milan - Centrale Tel: 2-67500
Venice - Santa Lucia Tel: 41-715555
Turin - Porta Nuova Tel: 11-561 3333
Genoa - Porta Principe Tel: 10-284081
Florence - Santa Maria Novella Tel: 55-288785
Naples - Centrale Tel: 81-553418
Car hire: Contact UK international branches for information - Avis Tel:
0181-848 8733 / Budget Tel: 0800 181181 / EuroDollar Tel: 0895
233300 / Hertz Tel: 0181-679 1799/1777.
Speed limits: 110 km/h on trunk roads, 90 km/h on secondary roads,
130 km/h on motorways, 50 km/h in towns.

Banks open: 8/8.30am-1.30pm & 2.30/3pm-4pm Mon-Fri

Shops open: 8/8.30am-12.30pm & 3.30pm/4-7/7.30pm Mon-Sat (Closed
Monday am)

National Holidays: New Year's Day, 6 Jan, Easter Sun/Mon, 25 April,
1 May, 15 Aug, 1 Nov, 8 Dec, Christmas Day & Boxing Day.

Tourist Offices:
Italian Tourist Board in London - Tel: 0171-408 1254
In Italy - Rome Tel: 6-49711 / Milan Tel: 2-809662

American Express Travel Service Office:
Rome - AETS
  Piazza Di Spagna 38
  00187
  Tel: 6-67641 #

Rome

Rome	**Alberto Ciarla**

Tel (6) 5818668 Fax (6) 5884377	**R**

Piazza San Cosimato 40 00153 Rome

Seats 70   Meal for 2 approx L200,000

Owner, Alberto Ciarla's colourful character has made its mark
on his restaurant in a big way; he chose a trendy, and lively part
of Rome, Trastevere. He loves the Mediterranean, and his hobby
is collecting wines. He is also President of the Sommelier's
Association, and his list of French and Italian wines is supported
by a good selection from the New World. The chef's 15-year-stint
here has marked the restaurant out as offering those consistently
traditional Italian fish dishes so popular in Rome: pasta with beans
and seafood, *cernia alla lampedusana* (grouper lightly cooked
in tomatoes and capers) and some excellent and very light steamed
fillets of fish with various sauces. Vegetables, like broccoli cooked
in fish stock, make excellent accompaniments. The restaurant's
decor is a striking one with a multitude of modern mirrors and
a red and black decor creating, along with candlelight, a quiet and
romantic atmosphere. *L 12.45-2.30 D 6-12.30. Closed 1st 15 days
Aug, 24 Dec-6 Jan.* AMERICAN EXPRESS *Diners, Mastercard, Visa.*

THE APARTMENT SERVICE
Tel in UK: (0181) 748 4207   Fax: (0181) 748 3972
The Apartment Service will find you the right apartment
worldwide to suit your needs, whether you are on a short or
long-term stay. A 96-page colour catalogue is free on request.
All budgets are catered for.

Rome	**Aldrovandi Palace Hotel**

Tel (6) 3223993 Fax (6) 3221435	**H**

Via Ulisse Aldrovandi 15 00197 Rome

Rooms 140   Double room from L500,000

An imposing hotel across the road from the zoo at the northern
side of the Villa Borghese Gardens. Originally a convent for the
daughters of the aristocracy, the hotel, which opened in the early
80s, has been completely refurbished. The interior is a stylish mix
of the contemporary and the classical, decorated in warm tones
and tasteful, well co-ordinated colourful furnishings. Bedrooms
have an elegant, old-fashioned ambience, being furnished with
splendid examples of period furniture. Those most recently
redecorated have a few more modern elements. The staff are very
helpful, especially the concierge, who has been here since the hotel
opened. Conference parties have eight equipped rooms to use and
then can relax in the gardens, or have a dip in the pool.
Secretarial/translation/valet services on request. Private parking.
AMERICAN EXPRESS *Diners, Mastercard, Visa.*

Rome   **Atlante Star**

Tel (6) 6873233   Fax (6) 6872300   **H**

Via Vittelleschi 34 00193 Rome

Rooms 70   Double room from L350,000

This 30s house, round the corner from St Peter's, has been
a family-run hotel for 30 years. Inside the smart, lacquered-wood
furniture is offset by tapestries on the walls. Being so central, it has
marvellous views, especially from the floodlit restaurant terrace,
edged with bright plants and flowers. The roof-garden restaurant,
Les Etoiles, is a great place for spotting famous landmarks. *24hr
room service. Cable TV. Conference facilities. Private parking.*
AMERICAN EXPRESS® *Diners, Mastercard, Visa.*

Rome   **Andrea**

Tel (6) 4821891   Fax (6) 4828151   **R**

Via Sardegna 28 00187 Rome

Seats 100   Meal for 2 approx L180,000

Located at the top of the fashionable Via Veneto, the restaurant,
which opened in the 20s and later was closely associated with the
glamorous '*La Dolce Vita*' set (Fellini and Mastroianni were
frequent visitors), retains an elegant, very chic atmosphere – a
perfect setting for the international menu. *L 12.30-3.30 D 7.30-
9.30. Closed 8-28 Aug. Public parking.* AMERICAN EXPRESS® *Diners,
Mastercard, Visa.*

Rome   **Camponeschi**

Tel (6) 6874927   **R**

Piazza Farnese 50A 00186 Rome

Seats 100   Meal for 2 approx L180,000

The owner, whose family have been in the restaurant business for
70 years, has done a great job maintaining the beauty of this 16th-
century building. Its garden spreads out into the *Piazza* named
after Michelangelo's Palazzo Farnese and its colourful terracotta
floors and hand-marbled walls makes it a really great spot from
which to admire the Palazzo. However, just as the architecture
accentuates the past, so does the food: traditional dishes like *astice
al tartufo nero con salsa di aceto ai lamponi* (crayfish with black
truffles in raspberry vinegar sauce), and *tagliolini ai fiori di zucca,
zafferano, prosciutto* (small tagliatelle with courgette flowers,
saffron and Parma ham) and sea bass with porcini mushrooms are
some of the interesting interpretations of old Italian dishes. The
owner has a collection of 350 wines. *D only 8-1 (L on request).
Closed Sun.* AMERICAN EXPRESS® *Mastercard, Visa.*

Meal prices for 2 are based on à la carte menus.
When set menus are available, prices will often be lower.

Rome   **Checchino dal 1887**

Tel (6) 5746318   Fax (6) 5743811   **R**

Via Monte Testaccio 30 00153 Rome
Seats 65   Meal for 2 approx L180,000

Very much a meat-lover's restaurant, in particular those who
appreciate a wide variety of animal products. This traditional
Roman trattoria opened in 1887 by a Mrs Ferminia, who began
using some of the offal from the slaughterhouse opposite. She
invented a great number of dishes like *il padellotto alla macellara*
(sautéed veal innards and spinal marrow in white wine), where
strong flavours were rendered, by careful cooking and spicing,
into delicacies of great refinement and which were, and still are,
greatly appreciated. Not all is quite so gutsy however – note
garofolato di bue (beef stuffed with cloves, garlic and pancetta,
braised in tomato sauce) or *braciollette d'abbacchio 'scottadito'* –
literally 'finger burners' – grilled baby lamb chops that you eat   ★
with your fingers. Roasted pork loin studded with porcini
mushrooms is another example of the more conventional dishes
available. Chef-owner Ninetta Ceccacci Mariani, from the
founding family, has maintained excellent standards; the vast wine
list has 400 bottles to choose from and is surprisingly international
– even with some from Thailand; and the 'cheese menu' is
tantalisingly unusual. If you get the chance check out the cellar
whose walls are full of Roman artefacts. A gastronomic and
historic must. *L 12.30-3 D 8-11.30. Closed L Sun & Mon (all Sun
& Mon Jun to Sep), Aug, 24 Dec-1 Jan. Public parking.*
AMERICAN EXPRESS® *Mastercard, Visa.*

Rome   **Columbus Hotel**

Tel (6) 6865435   Fax (6) 6864874   **H**

Via della Conciliazone 33 00192 Rome
Rooms 92   Double room from L245,000

The building was a 15th-century palazzo built by the influential
Della Rovere family, many of whom were Cardinals and Popes.
Nowadays, the hotel's regular guests stay here when visiting the
Vatican – only 100 yards away. Presidents and Popes have walked
through the colonnaded Roman Renaissance hall, which
is decorated with frescoes (reputedly by Pinturicchio). Three of the
bedrooms have original 16th-century furniture, others are
tastefully furnished with modern pieces, but all have been updated,
and fitted with a bathroom or shower, and air-conditioning. It is
a really sumptuous place for entertaining, with three splendid
reception rooms; one, decorated with frescoes, opens out on to
a private walled garden. *Cable TV. Theatre-style conference facilities
for up to 200. Secretarial/translation services. Private parking.*
AMERICAN EXPRESS® *Mastercard, Visa.*

Rome — Da Giggetto

Tel (6) 6861105 Fax (6) 683210

R

Via del Portico d'Ottavia 21a 00186 Rome

Seats 200   Meal for 2 approx L120,000

Deep in the Jewish quarter some 600 metres east of *Piazza Farnese*, this 17th-century building was converted into a restaurant by the family three generations ago; now the son is the chef and also the sommelier. Generations may have moved on, but the menu remains loyal to the family's Roman and Jewish roots. Go through the *peperino* (old Roman marble) entrance into the beamed, whitewashed dining rooms and you will be able to view the culinary preparations through a glass window into the kitchen. Dishes like *carciofi alla giudea* (Jewish-style artichokes), *fiori di zucca con pastella* (courgette flowers fried in batter) and *aliciotti fritti* (fried anchovies) as well as some hearty offal dishes are typical of the classical Roman style of cooking with a few additional Jewish recipes. The menu, like the character of the place, never seems to change. *L 12.30-3 D 7.30-11. Closed Mon, 2 weeks Aug.* AMERICAN EXPRESS® *Diners, Mastercard, Visa.*

Rome — De La Ville Intercontinental

Tel (6) 67331 Fax (6) 6784213

H

Via Sistina 67-69 00187 Rome

Rooms 190   Double room from L590,000

At the top of the Spanish Steps by Trinità dei Monti and enjoying excellent views, this is a hotel of style and distinction. The traditional decor is a tasteful blend of antiques with modern pieces, a theme repeated in well-equipped rooms which are uniformly elegant. There are no sports facilities, but there is a shopping arcade, beauty salon, and hairdressing as well as a travel agent. *Satellite TV/air-con. Theatre-style conference facilities for upto 110. Secretarial/translation services on request. Public parking.* AMERICAN EXPRESS® *Diners, Visa.*

Rome — Hotel Del Sole Al Pantheon

Tel (6) 6780441 Fax (6) 69940689

H

Piazza della Rotonda 63 00186 Rome

Rooms 26   Double room from L420,000

Open the wooden shuttered windows and look out over the small piazza with its neat cafés and white linen umbrellas to the impressive Pantheon and you cannot help falling in love with this location. There has been a hotel here, or rather a 'traditional inn', since 1476 (making it one of the oldest hostelries in Europe), but it was exquisitely modernised five years ago. The present minimalist decor incorporates white marble to create a cool airy ambience. In the bedrooms, terracotta tiled floors, and desks and bedside tables made of *travertino*, (an old Roman stone), are complemented by carved wooden beds with crisp white covers. Sartre and Simone de Beauvoir gained inspiration here. There is a garden for splendid alfresco breakfasts. *Cable TV. Private parking.* AMERICAN EXPRESS® *Diners, Mastercard, Visa.*

Rome   L'Elite

Tel (6) 8804503   Fax (6) 8804495   **R**

Via Salaria 1223 00138 Rome
Seats 150   Meal for 2 approx L160,000

The owner, who is also the chef, helped design this acclaimed
building, and has carved out his own niche within classical Roman
cuisine. He was awarded the Gold Medal by the Roman Academy
of Gastronomes for his fish and meat dishes. The building, with its
5m-high bay windows, pyramid-shaped fountain, sea blue fabric-
covered walls and aquariums filled with seafish, has also been
written about in architectural magazines. Classical Roman dishes
like *rigatoni con la pajata* (pasta with calf's offal in tomato sauce)
and *coda alla vaccinara* (oxtail) are served along with some super
fish dishes: *leone marino* (steamed shellfish with six different
sauces), *tagliolini alla vesuviana* (pasta with shellfish flambéd at the
table) and a winter-time favourite – *polenta con la padellaccia
di maiale* pork with polenta. A unique recipe is the *minestra
all'antica Civitavecchia* (a secret and very old fisherman's recipe for
a soup with beans and seafood). *L 12.30-3.30 D 7.30-11.30. Closed
Sun, 8-28 Aug.* AMERICAN EXPRESS *Mastercard, Visa.*

Rome   Forum Hotel

Tel (6) 6792446   Fax (6) 6786479   **H**

Via Tor de' Conti 25 00184 Rome
Rooms 76   Double room from L450,000

Ancient Rome, in the shape of the Imperial Roman Forum,
stretches out impressively in front of the hotel, giving great views
from some of the bedrooms and adding a sense of tranquillity
to the place. Inside, there is a traditional air with elegant Louis
XVI-style furniture in both public rooms and bedrooms. The staff
are long-serving, many having been here since the hotel opened
in 1962. Conference parties get a discount on their rooms
(L385,000 for a double room plus breakfast). *Theatre-style
conference facilities for up to 100. Secretarial/translation services
on request. Private garage.* AMERICAN EXPRESS *Diners, Mastercard, Visa.*

Rome   Hassler Villa Medici

Tel (6) 6782651   Fax (6) 6789991   **H**

Piazza Trinità dei Monti 6 00187 Rome
Rooms 100   Double room from L620,000

At the top of the Spanish Steps, with panoramic views of the city
and a unique view of *Piazza di Spagna*, the hotel, formerly a 19th-
century residence, has been run by the Wirth family for more
than 90 years. It has a comfortably clubby atmosphere, with
chesterfield sofas and Louis XIV-style furniture. The rooms are
spacious, some with French windows leading on to balconies;
paintings from the schools of Tintoretto and Titian decorate the
walls. Marble bathrooms have gold-plated fittings. They do not
have any sports facilities of their own, but arrangements can
be made to use nearby facilities. *Satellite TV/air-con. Theatre-style
conference facilities for up to 100. Hairdresser. Private parking.*
AMERICAN EXPRESS *Mastercard, Visa.*

Rome   **Lord Byron Hotel**

Tel (6) 3220404   Fax (6) 3220405   **HR**

Via Giuseppe de Notaris 5 00197 Rome

Rooms 37   Double room from L320,000

Chic, smart and discreet; this beautiful villa, once belonging to a
Roman Count, is situated in a quiet residential area immediately
north of the Villa Borghese Gardens. The locality is one of the
smartest in Rome. The hotel's style is that of a small, exclusive
town house. The splendid hallway is lined with books and
numerous old oil paintings. The rooms have all recently been
redecorated with hand-painted Florentine-style white furniture
and pretty, bright floral fabrics giving them a summery
appearance. The piano bar is renowned for its 'Le Jardin'
champagne cocktail. There are nine apartments. *24hr room service.
Satellite TV/air-con. Theatre-style conference facilities for up to 80.
Public parking.* AMERICAN EXPRESS *Mastercard, Visa.*

Relais Le Jardin

Seats 60   Meal for 2 approx L300,000

A stunning restaurant, with superb place settings featuring
gleaming silverware and sparkling crystal glassware
complemented by beautiful flower arrangements. Chef Antonio
Sciullo with his entourage of ten staff has been here many years
and consistently creates highly imaginative and well-presented
dishes. The seasonal menu could begin with a dish of swordfish
marinated in citrus fruits with a selection of sweet and sour
vegetables, quail and mushroom terrine with a celery salad and
a black and redcurrant sauce or even courgette flowers stuffed
with an aubergine and basil mousse and accompanied by a
parmigiana tartlet. Pasta dishes range from superb ravioli stuffed
with a skate, endive and potato mixture with fresh anchovies
subtly flavoured with wild fennel to a pasta called *tonnarelli* served
with mushrooms and aubergines and accompanied by tomato,   ★
basil and quail's eggs. Main dishes include roast turbot in a potato
crust with a broad bean and chicory purée, a millefeuille
of scallops, scampi and cod steamed in a spinach leaf parcel, roast
loin of lamb with thyme, served with endive, pesto and semolina
gnocchi or breast of partridge stuffed with mushrooms, grapes and
pistachios and accompanied by a little strudel of corn and spinach.
Sweets are no less enterprising, typical examples being a lemon
and ricotta cheese parfait with poppy seeds and a small baba
soaked in Rosolio – a wonderful extra-sweet, flowery liqueur – or
a warm coffee and bitter chocolate torte served with a sage and
aniseed sauce. *L 12.30-2.30 D 7.30-10.30. Closed 3 weeks around 15
Aug.*

The Golden Eurostar [★] denotes our pick of the
restaurants. Cooking is the major consideration, but
other factors are also taken into account, including
ambience, comfort and service.

Rome   **Majestic**

Tel (6) 486841   Fax (6) 4880984   **H**

Via Veneto 50 00187 Rome

Rooms 100   Double room from L580,000

Self-consciously stylish, this was the very first hotel on the *Via Veneto* back in 1889. It was renovated in 1990 by Italian architect, Sturchio, who stripped the old building down to its bare essentials and opted for an art deco style. The original marble and wood floors have been retained with the addition of art deco furniture. The splendid Giuseppe Verdi saloon with its original paintings remains. The hotel enjoys an excellent bustling central location. *Theatre-style conference facilities for up to 150. Private parking.* AMERICAN EXPRESS *Diners, Mastercard, Visa.*

Rome   **Quinzi Gabrieli**

Tel (6) 6879389   Fax (6) 6874940   **R**

Via delle Coppelle 5 00187 Rome

Seats 40   Meal for 2 approx L140,000

This restaurant in a 15th-century building located just north of the Pantheon is like a little seaside oasis; the inside is done out as the terrace of a villa overlooking the sea, while the ceiling is decorated to depict the sky. One wall represents the sea and the others, palms and a tropical beach. Added to all this are yellow sand-coloured tablecloths and a menu that is exclusively fish which is so fresh that if bad weather prevents fishermen getting out in their boats, the restaurant closes. There are some great dishes, many prepared in front of you, like *spaghetti con crostacei e pomodorini* (pasta with shellfish and cherry tomatoes). The selection of wines stretch from New Zealand to California. *D 8-12. Closed Sun, Aug.* AMERICAN EXPRESS *Mastercard, Visa.*

Rome   **Rosetta**

Tel (6) 6861002   Fax (6) 6872852   **R**

Via della Rosetta 8-9 00186 Rome

Seats 50   Meal for 2 approx L250,000

35 years ago, Massimo Riccoli's family started the first fish-only restaurant in Rome in this 19th-century house near the Pantheon. Decorated in the style of a French bistro and with modern paintings, low lampshades and Lalique plates, it still has an unrivalled reputation for imaginatively prepared fish. Try their specialities: *filetto di cernia con pomodori e olive* (fillets of grouper with tomatoes and olives), or *moscardini con carciofi, broccoli o funghi porcini* (baby squid stewed with seafood, artichokes, mushrooms or broccoli depending on the season). A speciality of note is the *pasta alla Sarde* from Sardinia, but originally an Arabic dish of sardines, pasta, sultanas, pine nuts, juniper and wild fennel. Spanish and Chilean wine appear along with French and Italian bottles on an extensive wine list. *L 1-2.45 D 8-11.30. Closed Sun, 12 Aug-5 Sept.* AMERICAN EXPRESS *Mastercard, Visa.*

Rome   Sabatini

Tel (6) 5818307   Fax (6) 5898386   **R**

Vicolo Santa Maria in Trastevere 00153 Rome

Seats   Meal for 2 approx L170,000

The chef, Pio del Castro, has been here since the place opened and
cooks a selection that includes traditional Roman dishes: *bucatini
alla matriciana* (pasta with a spicy bacon and tomato sauce), and
saltimbocca alla romana (veal and parma ham with Marsala) feature,
for example, on an extensive and varied menu. Every wine region
from Piedmonte to Sicily is well represented. *L 1-3 D 8-11.30.
Closed 15 days in Aug, 1 week Christmas.* AMERICAN EXPRESS *Diners,
Mastercard, Visa.*

Rome   Sans Souci

Tel (6) 4821814   Fax (6) 4821771   **R**

Via Sicilia 20 00175 Rome

Seats 80   Meal for 2 approx L240,000

Signor Borghesi, the owner for the last 32 years, can recall the
heady *La Dolca Vita* days and among his patrons are the influential
and affluent who frequent his smart late-night, taverna whose
walls are decorated with 17th-century paintings and wooden
panelling. Have an aperitif in the American bar while your order
is taken. The food is a mixture of traditional French and Italian,
with terrine of foie gras and tartare of fish vying with *tartufo
in crosta* (truffle in crispy pastry) as starters. To follow try the
pigeon also in crisp pastry (this time with foie gras), lobster,
Aberdeen Angus beef or the home-made pasta with artichoke
sauce. 380 Italian, plus major French chateaux wines. *D 8-1.30.
Closed Mon, Aug.* AMERICAN EXPRESS *Mastercard, Visa.*

Rome   Ai Tre Scalini di Rossana e Matteo

Tel (6) 7096309   Fax (6) 7002835   **R**

Via dei Santi Quattro 30 Rome

Seats 35   Meal for 2 approx L150,000

An outstanding restaurant, all the more so when you discover that
the head chef, Rossana, never had any formal training as a chef
(she studied for an engineering degree instead) and back in the 60s
decided to open this restaurant with some close friends. Her menu,
described as 'a great adventure', is imaginative and varied, ranging
from classical Italian and regional dishes to international
specialities. Everything is beautifully executed, framed around the
pick of the day's markets. Wines are patriotically Italian with
a dry Tuscan house white and just a smattering of French and
Californian offerings. With only seven tables and soft background
music, it is a very private sort of place, close to the Colosseum
in an ancient and colourful building. *L 12.30-3 D 7.30-10. Closed
3 weeks Aug.* AMERICAN EXPRESS *Mastercard, Visa.*

Rome   Valadier

Tel (6) 3611998   Fax (6) 3610559   H

Via della Fontanella 15 00187 Rome
Rooms 38   Double room from L405,000

This 300-year-old building was converted into a high-class
modern hotel in 1991. The bedrooms have large wall mirrors,
modern furniture and fabrics, and for Italy, are remarkably well
equipped. It is small and family run, with an elegant and exclusive
ambience. *24hr room service. Theatre-style conference facilities for
up to 40. Secretarial services.* AMERICAN EXPRESS *Mastercard, Visa.*

Florence

Florence   **Pensione Annalena**

Tel (55) 22 24 02   Fax (55) 22 24 03   **H**

Via Romana 34 50125 Florence

Rooms 20   Double room from L205,000

Ring to gain admittance to a former convent located a few minutes from the Palazzo Pitti and Boboli Gardens. Inside, a wide stone staircase leads up to this first-floor budget hotel at the rear. The spacious reception area, decorated with oil paintings and a few sculptures, is also the bar, lounge and breakfast area (though breakfast can be taken in rooms if preferred). Decor throughout is simple, bedrooms being delightfully old-fashioned, with basic comforts. They are also very, very quiet. Bathrooms are compact; some have showers only (no bathtubs) but all have bidets. *Satellite TV. Terrace.* AMERICAN EXPRESS *Diners, Mastercard, Visa.*

Florence   **Hotel Aprile**

Tel (55) 21 62 37   Fax (55) 28 09 47   **H**

Via Della Scala 6 50123 Florence

Rooms 29   Double room from L140,000

Just around the corner from the southern end of Piazza Santa Maria Novella, the hotel is a former Palazzo Medici (with external traces of some ancient frescoes still just about visible below the eaves). The interior reflects the antiquity of the buildings, being very traditional and quaint. Highly-polished floors strewn with colourful rugs, fine paintings on the walls and lots of comfortable seating create a pleasantly homely ambience. There's a cosy bar-cum-lounge to the rear which opens on to an enclosed courtyard garden – a fine spot for an alfresco breakfast. Bedrooms are high-ceilinged, most having boldly patterned wallpapers and old-fashioned furniture. There are however mini-bars, TVs and phones and five rooms even have air-conditioning. *Satellite TV/air-con. No parking.* AMERICAN EXPRESS *Mastercard, Visa.*

Florence   **Bernini Palace**

Tel (55) 288621   Fax (55) 268272   **H**

Piazza San Firenze 29 50122 Florence

Rooms 86   Double room from L380,000

Parliamentarians must have been impressed by this hotel back in the 1850s, when they came to hold court in the magnificent vaulted main room (now a breakfast room), adorned with fine frescoes on the ceiling. Breakfast is a splendid affair, with a buffet laid out around the room. One of the great attractions of staying here is that from some of the front bedrooms there are wonderful views – from the Bargello and Badia Fiorentina to the rear of the Palazzo Vecchio. Otherwise, all the bedrooms are well equipped, offering a good range of modern amenities. *24hr room service. Cable TV. Secretarial/translation services. Private parking.* AMERICAN EXPRESS *Visa, Diners, Mastercard.*

Florence   **Hotel Brunelleschi**

Tel (55) 56 20 68   Fax (55) 21 96 53   **H**

Piazza Santa Elisabetta 50122 Florence
Rooms 96   Double room from L390,000

Down a narrow street to the east of Via de' Calzaiuoli, very close
to the Duomo in the direction of the Palazzo Vecchio, is one of the
city's tiniest squares. It is dominated by the Byzantine Torre
Pagliazza, which has been skilfully incorporated into the hotel,
whose main entrance is immediately next to it. Occupying such
an ancient site has entailed the construction of a most unusual
hotel, with several quite different properties combined to create
a supremely comfortable, modern establishment. A spacious lobby
leads to public rooms arranged on many different levels with
ample lounge space. Bedrooms are first-rate, decorated with
impeccable good taste – smart limed furniture and soft peach
upholstery with matching drapes and bed covers. They feature all
the expected extras, including multilingual satellite TV and mini-
bars. Bathrooms, with marble fittings and double handbasins, also
lack for nothing. Top-floor rooms enjoy splendid views over the
rooftops with glimpses of the cathedral from north-facing rooms.
One south-facing suite has its own private sun terrace. Breakfast
may be taken in the tower. Superb standards of service with
friendly, helpful staff. *24hr Room service. Satellite TV/air-con.
Theatre-style conference facilities for up to 110. Translation and
secretarial services. Public parking.* AMERICAN EXPRESS *Diners, Mastercard,
Visa.*

Florence   **La Capannina Di Sante**

Tel (55) 688345   Fax (55) 6580841   **R**

Piazza Ravenna 50126 Florence
Seats 40   Meal for 2 approx L80,000

Long before the Arno was polluted and grey, fishermen used
to sell small fish from the river, grilled in this wooden *capanna*. It's
now a popular fish restaurant on the banks of the Arno with
a flower-filled garden. Sante Collesno, who trained with Lorenzo
Borni at *San Lorenzo* in London, runs it. He's Sicilian, so the dishes
aren't traditionally Tuscan. His specialities are *rombo all'isolana*
(turbot cooked with green vegetables, potatoes, tomatoes and
onions) and *spaghetti alla Sante* (spaghetti with a rich assortment
of seafood). The fish on offer changes constantly, but Collesno
likes lightly prepared lobster, fillets of sea bass and smoked
sturgeon. For ice cream lovers who haven't discovered Vivoli's –
Collesno serves it here. *D 8-12. Closed 10 days around 15 Aug.*
AMERICAN EXPRESS *Diners, Mastercard, Visa.*

Florence   **Il Cibreo**

Tel (55) 2341100   Fax (55) 244966   **R**

Via dei Macci 118 50122 Florence
Seats 60   Meal for 2 approx L180,000

Florentine food is not normally noted for its imaginative flair,
or any real breakaway from its traditional Tuscan roots, but chef
and part-owner Fabio Picchi's cooking is a marked exception.

He started this restaurant in the 70s with three friends and since then has opened a trattoria (*Il Cibreo dei Poveri*) next door which shares the same kitchen, but with simpler ingredients the prices are a third lower. At Cibreo the dishes to look out for are the *passato di pomodori gialli* (mashed yellow tomatoes), *sformato di patate e ricotta con ragu di carni bianche* (soufflé of potatoes and ricotta with a white meat ragu) and the *piccione ripieno di pere arrostite* (pigeon stuffed with roasted pears). The wine list remains staunchly traditionally Italian, just like the old Florentine family-style dining room. *L 12.50-2.30 D 7.30-11.15. Closed Sun, Mon, 26 Jul-4 Sept, 1 week Jan.* AMERICAN EXPRESS *Diners, Mastercard, Visa.*

> The Golden Eurostar [★] denotes our pick of the restaurants. Cooking is the major consideration, but other factors are also taken into account, including ambience, comfort and service.

Florence   **Dino**   R

Tel (55) 241452   Fax (55) 24136

Via Ghibellina 51 rosso 50122 Florence
Seats 100   Meal for 2 approx L100,000

The restaurant's setting is a 14th-century palazzo and the family who run it (mother is the chef and father the wine specialist, having been the President of the regional Sommelier Association) have revived many old-fashioned traditional Tuscan recipes, previously buried deep in dusty family recipe books. Try the *stracotto del granduca* (a 16th-century stewed beef dish prepared with chianti and green vegetables), the *garretto* (shin of pork braised in aromatic herbs), or the more subtle *risotto della Renza* named after the chef (cooked with five aromatic fresh herbs). *L 12-3 D 7.30-10.30. Closed D Sun, all Mon.* AMERICAN EXPRESS *Diners, Visa.*

> Meal prices for 2 are based on à la carte menus. When set menus are available, prices will often be lower.

Florence   **Don Chisciotte**

Tel (55) 47 54 30   Fax (55) 48 53 05   **R**

Via Ridolfi 4r 50129 Florence
Seats 50   Meal for 2 approx L170,000

One could say this restaurant was slightly off the beaten track, as it
is in a largely residential area just north-west of the city centre
a few paces from Piazza Della Indipendenza. It possesses a good
measure of style and elegance with its light, pretty decor of soft
pink napery and walls hung with a collection of fine paintings,
some depicting Don Quixote. There's also a fine malt whisky
collection. The menu is imaginative and very well thought-out
with ample choice – almost too much as it all sounds
so mouthwatering. The food on the plate lives up to all
expectations, highlighted by careful seasoning and subtle flavours.
An antipasto could be herbed rabbit salad, courgette flowers
stuffed with grouper on a tomato sauce or a wonderfully simple
carpaccio of prawns served split with a superb orange-flavoured
olive oil. Choices for later on range from fresh tagliatelle with
scampi and asparagus or green gnocchi (*malfatti*) with salmon and   ★
a squid sauce to salmon with smoked *scamorza* cheese, sea bass with
aubergines and tomatoes or a baked fillet of turbot with courgette
flowers on a bed of creamy courgette sauce – a remarkable dish
of very refined, delicate flavours. Meat dishes are equally
innovative, as in an entrecote with shallots and pine nuts and
pigeon breast in a Vin Santo sauce. Sweets are exceptional too:
examples are a very delicate lemon bavarois topped with
a strawberry jelly and served with a very fresh tasting strawberry
purée, or a warm, delicate pastry filled with fruit and served with
a hot, dark, rich chocolate sauce. The prices for such food are very
reasonable and, with extremely warm and friendly staff as another
plus, the experience is one that would be nice to repeat over and
over. *L 1-2.30 D 8-10.30. Closed L Mon, all Sun, Aug. No Parking.*
AMERICAN EXPRESS *Diners, Mastercard, Visa.*

Florence   **Enoteca Pinchiorri**

Tel (55) 24 27 77   Fax (55) 24 49 83   **R**

Via Ghibellina 87 50122 Florence
Seats 70   Meal for 2 approx L540,000

Due east of the Palazzo Bargello in a magnificent 15th-century
building is one of Italy's foremost restaurants. Giorgio Pinchiorri,
his Niçoise wife Annie Feolde and head chef Italo Bassi have,
together, created a restaurant of international repute. Of the two
dining rooms, the main one at the front of the ground floor is the
grander, with its beautiful stucco walls hung with exquisite
paintings, and a large Murano crystal chandelier. On the tables are
silver-vased flower arrangements with a particularly exuberant
display under the chandelier. The other dining room is an   ★
attractive candle-lit split-level room. However, for a fine summer's
evening the inner courtyard is the perfect sanctum from the
outside world. Here is modern Italian cooking in its most refined
(and expensive) form. Ingredients are assembled with immense
care and precision ensuring a perfect all-round harmony of texture
and flavour. The excitement of anticipating the composition
of each ordered course persists from start to finish. True to the

basics of Italian cooking this is seductively simple cooking – the frisson from each mouthful coming from the ingenuity with which the dishes are assembled. There's a splendid carte as well as two set menus (both L 150,000 a head) – a tasting menu and a menu composed of regional specialities. A typical selection from the carte could be *astice e orzo all' aceto balsamico* – a marvellous salad of lobster and barley, the combination a brilliant one – the lobster, soft, in contrast to the slight nuttiness of the grains, the balsamic vinegar, a thickened essence dribbled around the plate. Next *gnocchi di patate farciti di pesto, calamaretti al vino bianco* – not the usual gnocchi at all but very thinly rolled and made into ravioli-like parcels filled with a delicate pesto with tender sautéed squid for a subtle contrast. For a main course sea bass is baked under a salt crust and served with a gateau of crunchy-topped potato slices. Other choices are loin of veal with an aubergine soufflé; duck, its skin spiced and crispy, served with caramelised apples, and lamb cutlets wrapped in lettuce with a garlic cream. Desserts are delicious – in particular an iced jasmine mousse layered with fine, crisp wafer biscuits and a cinnamon ice with a strudel of apples and plums. Giorgio has amassed a stupendous wine cellar with a superfine collection of Italian, French and Californian vintages. *L 12.-15-1.30 D 7.30-10. Closed L Mon, all Sun, Aug.* AMERICAN EXPRESS *Mastercard, Visa.*

Florence   **Grand Hotel Villa Cora**

Tel (55) 2298451   Fax (55) 2290086   HR

Viale Nicolo Machiavelli 18/20 50125 Florence
Rooms 48   Double room from L587,000

The Emperor of Japan came here on a state visit in 1993, just the latest in a long line of famous visitors to enter these 19th-century neo-Classical portals. Originally a private country villa belonging to Baron Oppenheim, it was converted into an elegant hotel in 1974, with extravagant frescoed ceilings and Venetian glass chandeliers throughout the salons. The Imperial Suite is quite something with its frescoes, a chandelier and a rare Siena marble bath tub. The rooms are equally beautifully restored and impressively fitted: gilt mirrors, carved wooden beds and elegant dressing tables. It really is an extraordinarily beautiful place and definitely one of the loveliest hotels in Europe – a worthy winner of our Best Hotel Western Europe award. *24hr room service. Outdoor swimming pool. Private parking.* AMERICAN EXPRESS *Mastercard, Visa.*

Taverna Machiavelli
Seats 100   Meal for 2 approx L160,000

Simple decor (plain vaulted ceilings and marble floors) meets even simpler rustic Tuscan fare here. The light modern Italian menu has plenty of choices with no particular surprises, and there's a good selection of fresh pasta. *L 12-2.30 D 7.30-11.*

Florence   Helvetia e Bristol

Tel (55) 287814   Fax (55) 288353   **H**

Via dei Pesconi 2 50123 Florence
Rooms 52   Double room from L365,000

'Unique' is a much-used word – but even for Florence this hotel
is just that; it has added modern amenities, yet kept the charming
hotch-potch of antiques, paintings, and bookcases that characterise
19th-century old Florentine hotels and make them so appealingly
lived-in. Unusually, it has nine singles and 43 suites, some
of which have jacuzzis. Each suite is still individually designed
with floral wallpaper, antique furniture and fitted carpets.
Breakfast and lunch are served in the Winter Garden, with its
interesting plants and relaxing rattan chairs and it turns into
a piano bar in the evening. Nor could the hotel be in a better,
more central location, close to the couture shops on *Via
Tornabuoni. 24hr room service. Private garage.* AMERICAN EXPRESS
Mastercard, Visa.

Florence   J & J Hotel

Tel (55) 240951   Fax (55) 240282   **H**

Via di Mezzo 20 50121 Florence
Rooms 19   Double room from L240,000

J & J's is a real retreat, and has been since the 16th century, when
it was a monastery belonging to the curate of Fiesole. Spanish
princes and Italian actors have holed up inside these high-ceilinged,
arched rooms, with balconies overlooking the cloistered reception
rooms below. Restored wooden floors and frescoes on the ceilings
add to the air of *ancien régime*. The bathrooms are parquet-floored
and decorated with hand-painted tiles, some with old-fashioned
baths, others more up to date with jacuzzis. The owners, James
and Jacqueline Cavagnali, have spread rugs over the floors and
bought soft sofas, all adding to the homely, relaxed atmosphere.
Porter service until 10pm (tea/toast). Public parking. AMERICAN EXPRESS
Mastercard, Visa.

Florence   Il Latini

Tel (55) 21 09 16   **R**

Via dei Palchetti 61 50123 Florence
Seats 110   Meal for 2 approx L100,000

Book, or queue to squeeze on to one of the long trestle tables
at this perennial favourite of Florentines. Hustle, bustle and great
food for the price are its hallmarks. Baskets of roughly cut
country bread and bottles of red or white local wine are left
on the table – no-one seems to bother too much how much you've
drunk – and the food is served in very tasty, generous portions.
There is a menu, but leave the ordering to the jovial waiters,
who'll recommend superb melon and prosciutto, crostini topped
with a fresh tomato, garlic and herb sauce, ravioli filled with
spinach and ricotta with a rich tomato sauce, and then roast rabbit,
chicken or veal or a lean and succulent *stracotto alla fiorentina* – a
chunky couple of slices of meat loaf, sometimes cooked in white
wine, though the more usual method is with fresh tomato,
rosemary and other herbs. This isn't a refined style of cooking but

is highly enjoyable for its sheer simplicity. *Zuccotto*, supposedly a *semifreddo* (half-frozen), can turn out totally frozen – so who's perfect! *L 12.30-3 D 7.30-11. Closed Mon, mid July-mid Aug, 10 days Christmas. No parking.* AMERICAN EXPRESS *Visa.* 🐂

Florence   La Loggia

Tel (55) 2342832   Fax (55) 2345288   R

Piazzale Michelangelo 1 50126 Florence

Seats 120   Meal for 2 approx L120,000

Florence is one great big collection of things to see and here is yet another great spot from which to view the city centre. The building was intended to be a museum, but with the notoriously poor record of the Italians for maintaining their antiquities, and their great love affair with food, it is hardly surprising that it is now a thriving restaurant. The seven owners are also the seven chefs who manage to work together to create consistent traditional Italian fare, including *ribollita* (Tuscan bean soup) and *gnocchi verdi di verdure* (green vegetable gnocchi). They have some great wines from tiny Italian vineyards. The Loggia is a great place for dinner on a warm evening. *L 12-3 D 7-10.30. Closed Wed, 15-29 Aug.* AMERICAN EXPRESS *Diners, Mastercard, Visa.*

Florence   Hotel Loggiato Dei Serviti

Tel (55) 28 95 92   Fax (55) 28 95 95   H

Piazza S.S. Annunziata N3 50122 Florence

Rooms 29   Double room from L225,000

The front of the hotel overlooks Giambologna's majestic statue of the Grand Duke Ferdinand I, which stands in the centre of a square bordered on three sides by two colonnades and the church of S.S. Annunziata. The hotel's modest entrance is in one corner of the Sangallo colonnade which he built around 1525 for the confraternity of the Servants of Mary. It is virtually a mirror image of the more renowned Hospital of the Innocents across the way, a fine example of Florentine Renaissance architecture by Filipo Brunelleschi, built some 100 years earlier. The rear of the hotel backs on to another famous institution – the Gallery of the Academy, with its statue of Michelangelo's *David*. The hotel fits perfectly into this wonderful location, offering very high standards of service and comfort. Polished stone floors, antiques and fine furnishings feature throughout, along with stucco walls and beautifully vaulted ceilings. On the upper floors some of the ceilings are heavily beamed. Even though there's great antiquity all around modern comforts have been unobtrusively incorporated. Thus all rooms are air-conditioned and all have the likes of mini-bars and televisions. The constraints of the building means that no two bedrooms are alike and bathrooms, splendid though they are, sometimes appear to have been squeezed in – some have showers and no tubs. *24hr room service. Satellite TV/air conditioning. Public parking.* AMERICAN EXPRESS *Diners, Mastercard, Visa.*

Florence   Al Lume Di Candela

| Tel (55) 29 45 66 | R |

Via Delle Terme 23r 50123 Florence
Seats 35   Meal for 2 approx L140,000

'By the Light of the Candle' is in one of the very narrow streets
that run parallel with the river north of the Ponte Vecchio. The
candle-light comes from small table lamps in what is a smart yet
quite informal restaurant with crisp pink napery and walls hung
with large, very abstract works of art. The latter contrast with the
largely traditional character of the rest of the decor. The menu too
has some modern elements as in home-made macaroni flavoured
with thyme and accompanied by squid, pecorino cheese and
a sauce of tomato and sherry, or roast salmon with fennel seeds
and potato vinaigrette. Meat dishes include rack of lamb with
porcini mushrooms and a fillet of beef with rosemary, extra virgin
olive oil and a cannellini bean cream. Desserts include a delicious
trio of mousses – coffee, white chocolate and plain chocolate –
served on three crisp biscuit bases with a banana custard cream
in the centre. *D only 7.30-10.45. Closed Sun, Aug. No parking.*
AMERICAN EXPRESS *Diners, Mastercard, Visa.*

Florence   Hotel Monna Lisa

| Tel (55) 247 97 51   Fax (55) 247 97 55 | H |

Borgo Pinti 27 50121 Florence
Rooms 34   Double room from L230,000

Almost due east of the Duomo and only some ten minutes walk
away, the hotel is housed in a grand Renaissance Palazzo. The
present owners are descendants of Giovanni Dupré and as a result
the whole place is virtually a gallery of fine classical paintings,
drawings and sculptures, including Giambologna's first model
of the *Rape of the Sabine Women*. Public rooms as a result are truly
splendid and are additionally cool and spacious with beautiful
antique furniture complementing the artwork. To the rear is a
very fine, large, enclosed garden. Bedrooms, all individually
decorated, are furnished with style and character. To find they are
also air-conditioned and feature such amenities as colour
televisions, mini-bars, phones and spotless bathrooms is an added
advantage. *Satellite TV/air-con. Private parking (L20,000 per night).*
AMERICAN EXPRESS *Diners, Mastercard, Visa.*

Florence   Omero

| Tel (55) 220053   Fax (55) 2336183 | R |

Via Pian de' Giullari 11r 50125 Florence
Seats 150   Meal for 2 approx L110,000

The Vecchio Borgo hills are where Florentines escape the heat
of the city, to enjoy the views, and this traditional trattoria's
Tuscan cooking. The building was a local grocer's store, before
becoming a restaurant 80 years ago. For the past 17 years it has
been run by three cousins. *Antipasti misti alla fiorentina* is a good
traditional starter, with Tuscan salami and paté on crostini or a
deliciously thick Tuscan soup *pappa al pomodoro*. Some of the finest
traditional fare are the *pappardelle al sugo di coniglio* (pasta with
rabbit ragu served in the hunting season with a piquant wild boar

and hare sauce) and a fritto misto of chicken, rabbit and brains. Tuscan wine, along with 100 other wines, is informally served to the checked-clothed tables inside these brick-walled, wooden-floored rooms. *L 12.30-3.30 D 6-12. Closed Tue, Aug. No parking.* AMERICAN EXPRESS® *Mastercard, Visa.*

Florence   **Regency Hotel**

Tel (55) 245247   Fax (55) 245247   **HR**

Piazza Massimo d'Azeglio 3 50121 Florence
Rooms 35   Double room from L320,000

This discreet hotel, sister to the *Lord Byron* in Rome, feels like a private home, set in a quiet residential square, opposite a lush park. Cars are banned, except for the President's. The whole district originates from the early 1870s when Florence was, for a brief period, the capital of Italy, and the building became the smart city residence of politicians. Inside it is stylish and smart but also very cosy; small drawing rooms have deep sofas to sink into; while light patterned wallpaper sets off the heavier Edwardian furniture. The bedrooms are similarly furnished – but some are a little narrow. The lawns provide ample opportunity for relaxing outdoors too. *24hr room service. Cable TV. Private garage.* AMERICAN EXPRESS *Diners, Mastercard, Visa.*

Relais Le Jardin
Seats 40   Meal for 2 approx L160,000

The tables spread into two rooms: a light, sunny conservatory overlooking the hotel garden and an old wood-ceilinged dining room fitted with a luxurious carpet and decorated with the original stained-glass windows. As in the sister restaurant in Rome, the menu starts from a traditional base of regional Italian cooking, but branches out into more adventurous realms: the smoothly satisfying warmed soufflé of Sicilian broccoli served with a velouté of tomatoes, or the fillet of *triglia* (red mullet) braised with fennel seeds, capers and lemon stand out. The menu changes constantly, a reflection of the freshest market ingredients. Washed down with the light house Chianti and finished off with some wild berries, a meal will tickle even the most refined taste buds. *L 12.30-2.30 D 7.30-10.30. Closed Sun.*

> The Golden Eurostar [★] denotes our pick of the
> restaurants. Cooking is the major consideration, but
> other factors are also taken into account, including
> ambience, comfort and service.

Florence   Sabatini

Tel (55) 28 28 02   Fax (55) 21 02 93   **R**

Via Panzani 94 50123 Florence
Seats 180   Meal for 2 approx L195,000

Established in 1924 and still with a fine reputation, the restaurant,
which is a short stroll from the Duomo towards the station, has
a decor of traditional style and character. The split-level dining
rooms have polished wood-panelled walls, smart green and white
ceramic-tiled floors and views on to two small, sunny, plant-filled
patios. The menu, which varies with the seasons, has changed little
down the years, offering prime produce, quite simply prepared
and featuring all the expected Tuscan specialities. Midsummer
offerings could include a salad of fresh raw porcini mushrooms
dressed with a herby mayonnaise followed perhaps by *spaghettini*
with baby clams in olive oil and white wine then a main course
of baked sea bass or turbot. There's a good selection of quite
familiar meat alternatives. Good desserts and super coffee. Old-
fashioned standards of service. *L 12.30-3 D 7.30-10.30. Closed
Mon, also L 25 Dec.* AMERICAN EXPRESS *Diners, Mastercard, Visa.*

Florence   Torre di Bellosguardo

Tel (55) 298145   Fax (55) 229008   **H**

Via Roti Michelozzi 2 50124 Florence
Rooms 16   Double room from L330,000

Visitors come to Florence to bathe in its history and here, in this
villa from the 1500s perched on the hillside surrounded by a park,
guests can sleep in surroundings that evoke a true sense of the past.
The house, once the home of Cavalcanti (Dante Alighieri's close
friend), was a cultural hothouse for Italy's 14th-century literati.
Until 20 years ago it was an American college, where the
infamous Erica Yong became inspired to write about Europe. The
beamed bedrooms may not be equipped with satellite TV, but
they are adorned with far more inspiring frescoes, and some even
have four-poster beds. For the best views choose one of the
bedrooms in the 14th-century tower. The swimming pool is a
godsend, an escape from the sweltering heat of the summer. They
do not have a restaurant, but can cater for diners with advance
notice. *24hr room service (breakfast, drinks only). Private parking.*
AMERICAN EXPRESS *Diners, Mastercard, Visa.*

Florence   Villa Carlotta

Tel (55) 220530   Fax (55) 2336147   **H**

Via Michele di Lando 3 50125 Florence
Rooms 27   Double room from L240,000

From here, some of the most delightful sights of Florence are
a short stroll away: the Ponte Vecchio, Palazzo Pitti and the
elegant Giardino di Boboli as well as the Forte Belvedere. The
hotel was once part of a villa belonging to a knight of the old
Florentine capital and his former stables are now the restaurant.
The stuccoed ceilings and deep fireplaces remain, but the Egyptian
owner has recently redecorated the rooms with 19th-century
furniture, pale pink silk on the walls and floral curtains and sofas.
It is all very cosy and relaxing, especially the balcony, where one

can recline on a chaise-longue and listen to the sound of the fountain. *No room service. Theatre-style conference facilities for up to 60. Closed 1-24th Aug. Private parking.* AMERICANEXPRESS® *Diners, Mastercard, Visa.*

Florence   **Villa Le Rondini**

Tel (55) 4000081   Fax (55) 268212   **H**

Via Bolognese Vecchia 224 50139 Florence
Rooms 43   Double room from L230,000

The Reali family have run this hotel, comprising three 17th and 18th-century country villas on the road to Trespiano, since 1969. The district, Monterinaldi, overlooks Florence, 7km to the south. The hotel is extremely quiet, set in a 20-hectare park of cypress and fruit trees. The rooms are typically Florentine, with painted antique furniture and hand-carved bedheads, simple white curtains and marble floors. They are cosy and comfortable, but do not offer any modern luxuries. *Theatre-style conference facilities for up to 150. Outdoor swimming pool, tennis courts, gym, sauna. Private parking.* AMERICANEXPRESS® *Mastercard, Diners, Visa.*

Around Florence

Borgo San Lorenzo   **Il Feriolo**

Tel (55) 840 99 28   **R**

Via Faentina 32 50032 Borgo San Lorenzo
Seats 60   Meal for 2 approx L90,000

Pick up the Via Faentina leading almost due north out of Florence city centre and follow it for about a further two kilometres the other side of the village of Olmo in the direction of Borgo San Lorenzo. The restaurant is signposted on the right and is found at the end of a long, narrow, winding lane at the summit of a small hill. It was once a fortified monastery, and there are superb views from the outside terraces over the surrounding wooded hills. Inside, however, with only few windows, there's rather less of a view in what is a series of small rustic, farmhouse-style dining rooms. The food matches, with hearty portions and robust flavours. The menu is short, with choices recited at the table. Excellent prosciutto with melon, even better crostini topped with the likes of mushrooms, chicken livers and garlicky mayonnaise are followed by wonderful ravioli balls, the lightest of pasta filled with spinach and ricotta dressed with butter and fresh sage. More substantial are *pappardelle* with *ragu* of goat. Main dishes include excellent game such as grilled venison steaks or wild boar as well as veal escalopes with porcini mushrooms. Excellent desserts too, including an irresistible *torta della nonna* – grandmother's tart. A very popular restaurant with locals so it's best to book. *L 12.30-3 D 7.30-10. Closed Tues, 3 weeks end Jan, 2 weeks end Aug. Private parking.* AMERICANEXPRESS® *Diners, Mastercard, Visa.*

Fiesole   San Michele

Tel (55) 594512   Fax (55) 598734   **H**

Via Doccia 4 50014 Fiesole

Rooms 28   Double room from L870,000

Fiesole is a beautiful, unspoilt village which looks down over
terraces of vines to Florence; the moonlight ballets and operas
in the Roman amphitheatre are stunning. So it is fitting that there
should also be an amazing hotel to stay in. This villa began life as a
Franciscan monastery with a facade designed by Michelangelo. It is
a grand example of Renaissance architecture, with loggias
surrounding the building, and the original chapels still nestling
amongst the vintage oak, olive and cypress trees. The reception
was the original chapel, and in the private dining room a fresco
of *The Last Supper* (by Tito da Titi) decorates the wall. Monastic
simplicity still pervades the bedrooms, though Persian carpets now
cover the wooden floors, whitewashed walls and curved archways.
Altogether romantic and charming. *24hr room service (drinks),
6.30am-12pm (food). Restaurant (Tuscan/nouvelle cuisine). Outdoor
swimming pool. Closed Nov-Mar. Private parking.* AMERICAN EXPRESS
Mastercard, Visa.

Siena   Castello Di Spaltenna

Tel (577) 74 94 83   Fax (577) 74 29 69   **RR**

Gaiole in Chianti 53013 Siena

Seats 60   Meal for 2 approx L160,000

From Florence follow the very winding S222 through Grassina,
Greve and the very heart of Chianti Classico country, turning
on to the S408 to find this imposing ancient hill-top fortified
monastery now owned by Seamus de Pentheny O'Kelly, who
is also the chef. In fine weather the characterful inner courtyard
is used for alfresco dining, otherwise the lofty, galleried dining
room with its huge open fireplace is the setting for some true and
very fine Tuscan country cooking. The menu features a series
of well-balanced set menus as well as a comprehensive carte.
Typical dishes from a very meat- and vegetable-orientated menu
include *crostini* with chicken livers, *pappardelle* with a rich duck
and wild fennel sauce, venison with a juniper sauce and roast leg
of lamb with rosemary. Virtually all the vegetables are organically
grown on the premises and the wine list majors on excellent local
vintages. There's a wine cellar in the basement where wine tastings
are a regular feature and it's here too that snacks and light lunches
are served. *L 12.30-2 D 7.30-9.45. Closed all Mon, L Tues (except
residents).* AMERICAN EXPRESS *Diners, Mastercard, Visa.*

Rooms   Double room from L215,000

Twenty-one splendid rooms, each quite different in shape and size,
are furnished to a high and very comfortable standard. Located
on the upper floors, they have polished quarry-tiled floors, heavy
beamed ceilings and colourful fabrics that ooze character and good
taste. Many have fine views over the surrounding hills and all are
well equipped, having mini-bars, televisions and air-conditioning.
Bathrooms, too, are immaculate and modern. Guests have the use
of a beautifully located outdoor swimming pool, while on the
ground floor next to the dining room is a simple lounge for the
relaxation of both residents and diners. *Satellite TV/air-
conditioning. Outdoor swimming pool. Closed 6 Jan-mid March.*

Milan

Milan	**Aimo e Nadia**

Tel (2) 416886   Fax (2) 48302005   **R**

Via Montecuccoli 6 20147 Milan

Seats 35   Meal for 2 approx L250,000

A little out of the city centre in a quiet residential locality easily
reached on Line 1 of the underground (get out at Primaticcio),
Aimo Moroni's restaurant has an attractive, modern appearance
with a clean, simple, yet elegant decor. It comprises two smallish
dining rooms whose otherwise plain walls are hung with bold,
colourful artwork. Well-spaced tables have their own multi-hued
splashes of colour in the form of pretty flower posies. The menu
takes Italian cooking into a realm of fantasy where imagination
and cooking skills are combined to create dishes of superb quality.
Even the breads are excellent, particularly the one with pine nuts.
For lunch there's a good-value 3-course set menu which includes
two glasses of wine. There is also the full à la carte and *menu
degustazione*. Changing daily, typical fare could begin with slivers
of marinated raw sea bass dressed with olive oil, basil and curly
lettuce. A pasta course could be dainty filled bows flavoured with
watercress, served with thin fingers of fresh ewe's milk ricotta,
fresh tomato and basil – a wonderfully light and very cooling dish
on a hot summer's day. Sea bream fillets are carefully wrapped
round a mixture of the fish and herbs then placed on a bed of very
finely diced aubergines, tomato and capers. Veal rump from
Piedmont has a filling of layers of prosciutto and *quartirolo* – a
particularly fine version of Taleggio cheese. This is served with
a very delicate honey-flavoured onion purée. A typical sweet is a
jellied cherry terrine with a chilled plum mould and an apricot
sauce as well as a refreshing fresh mint sorbet. A charming family-
run establishment with booking essential in the evening. *L 12.30-
2.30 D 8-10.30. Closed L Sat, all Sun, Aug, 1 week Jan. Public
parking.* AMERICAN EXPRESS *Diners, Mastercard, Visa.*

The Golden Eurostar [★] denotes our pick of the
restaurants. Cooking is the major consideration, but
other factors are also taken into account, including
ambience, comfort and service.

To dial overseas from the UK, 010 will change to 00
on 16th April 1995.

Milan   L'Ami Berton

Tel (2) 713669   Fax (2) 7423476   R

Via Nullo 14 20129 Milan
Seats 50   Meal for 2 approx L350,000

Established nine years ago east of the city centre close to Piazza
Novelli, this is a very elegant and classy restaurant with a beautiful
sage green and pale grey interior. As well as the expected fine
ornaments and decorations, walls have glass-shelved cabinets
displaying an extensive selection of Scotch whiskies and rare
brandies. The menu is a relatively short one, featuring classics
presented in a very attractive and modern fashion. Cooking
is first-rate, with superbly defined flavours adding to the visual
appeal of the food. Dishes are uncomplicated, this simplicity very
positively demonstrating the excellent quality of the raw
materials. A typical meal could begin with a wonderful courgette
flower fritter or carpaccio of duck, rabbit and mushrooms
followed perhaps by a small selection of out-of-the-ordinary pasta
dishes such as cold *tagliolini* with caviar and spring onions
or *lasagnette* with porcini mushrooms. Fish dominates the main
courses, with monkfish and wild rice, turbot with porcini and
a mixed grill of large scampi and prawns. Beef fillet comes rare,
thinly sliced and arranged with tiny, raw cherry tomatoes and
a light olive oil dressing. There are extremely good desserts, too,
such as apple millefeuille with *crème chantilly*, peach poached
in moscatel and served with a strawberry sauce or a coffee
semifreddo with white chocolate. Smooth, accomplished service.
L 12-2.30 D 8-10.15. Closed L Sat & Sun, 3 weeks Aug.
No parking. AMERICAN EXPRESS® *Visa.*

★

Milan   Antica Trattoria della Pesa

Tel (2) 6555741   Fax (2) 6555741   R

Viale Pasubio 10 20100 Milan
Seats 60   Meal for 2 approx L160,000

Since the 1880s the Fassi family have been serving up traditional
Milanese cooking in this rustic trattoria: risotto with saffron,
breaded veal cutlet and osso buco. Desserts run to vanilla soufflé
with hot chocolate sauce; while the wine list of mainly Italian reds
includes some well-known French vintages. *L 12.30-3 D 7.30-11.*
Closed 22 Jul-22 Aug. Public parking. AMERICAN EXPRESS® *Diners,*
Mastercard, Visa.

Milan   Biffi Scala

Tel (2) 866651   Fax (2) 86461060   R

Piazza della Scala 20121 Milan
Seats 140   Meal for 2 approx L200,000

The restaurant was opened soon after *La Scala*, in the same
building, and became the haunt of multitudes of international
artistes. As the chef and restaurant manager are Sicilian, the food
is a mixture of Milanese and Sicilian dishes. *Risotto al salto* (rice
cooked with saffron and fried to a crunchy brown on the outside),
beef tournedos with bacon and pepper and steamed sea bream
served with sautéed courgettes and thyme are typical. The desserts
are worth a standing ovation: pear and pistachio torte, or perhaps

torta Biffi Scala (puff pastry with raspberries and cream), their special house dish. *L 12.30-2.45 D 7.30-11.30. Closed Aug, 24 Dec-7 Jan. Public parking.* AMERICAN EXPRESS *Diners, Mastercard, Visa.*

Milan   Boeucc

Tel (2) 76020224   R

Piazza Belgioioso 2 20121 Milan
Seats 140   Meal for 2 approx L160,000

Longevity is one of their strong points: the restaurant has been going since 1820 and they have been in this 18th-century Piermarini building since 1932; the chef has been producing classic Milanese dishes for a little less time, in fact a 16-year stint. His repertoire has changed very little, perhaps veering slightly towards more international cuisine, but osso buco with risotto and small penne with sea bass and courgette flowers are still the norm here. Located in a quiet and attractive square, the restaurant is extremely elegantly decorated, with high ceilings from which hang glittering antique chandeliers. *L 12.40-2.40 D 7.40-10.40. Closed Aug, 25 Dec, Easter.* AMERICAN EXPRESS

Opening times are often liable to change at short notice, so it's always best to book.

Milan   Brunelleschi Hotel

Tel (2) 8843   Fax (2) 804924   H

Via Baracchini 12 20123 Milan
Rooms 75   Double room from L380,000

The name may have changed (it was called the Select Hotel until five years ago), but the 50s building remains very much the same, despite its recent renovation. It is right in the centre of Milan, close to the Duomo square. The rooms are modern and smart, with all the mod cons and even small balconies decorated with greenery. *Cable/satellite TV. Theatre-style conference facilities for up to 60. Secretarial/translation services on request. Private parking.* AMERICAN EXPRESS *Diners, Mastercard, Visa.*

Meal prices for 2 are based on à la carte menus.
When set menus are available, prices will often be lower.

Milan   Calajunco

Tel (2) 2046003   R

Via Stoppani 5 20129 Milan
Seats 45   Meal for 2 approx L250,000

Named after a tiny islet off Panarea, one of the most beautiful
of the Lipari islands, this is the culinary domain of Dr Renato
Carnevale, owner, bon viveur and master of his kitchens. Ring the
door bell and you gain access to a stylish, modern, split-level
dining room whose stark white walls (even the windows have
wide floor-to-ceiling translucent white screens) are hung with
huge misty blue pictures of the islands. The sky blue napery
at lunchtime gives way to white in the evening, when discreet
lighting and azure candles provide a suitably romantic touch. The
cooking captures the simple, sunny character of the islands, with
Dr Carnevale adding flashes of inspiration to create dishes of great
brilliance. There is no menu proper, the choice being explained
at the table, where dinner begins with a glass of bubbly and
perhaps an appetiser of the juiciest of fresh raw scampi, marinated
in lemon juice and extra virgin olive oil. Next, a warm slice
of moist lobster tart is followed by a most unusual way with
aubergines: they are sliced paper-thin and baked with a stuffing
of herbs and cheese and served with a tomato sauce made solely
from pulped and reduced fresh tomatoes. For the marriage of his   ★
eldest son he created the most wonderful risotto – of scampi
(cooked this time) and orange, creating an outstanding
combination of flavours. *Conchiglia del pescatore* evokes the sea
coming in a giant clam shell packed with linguine in a rich
tomato sauce with baby clams and *scorfano* (scorpion fish). There
are a few meat dishes but you get the impression that the
restaurant majors on fish. A speciality is *involtini* of three fish each
with its own character and meant to be eaten in a particular order
– first baked sole fillets wrapped around lettuce, pecorino and
Parmesan, next grilled swordfish folded around a pine nut
mixture and served on orange slices and finally fried red mullet
with a filling of capers, and a little pounded red mullet. A simple
rocket salad accompanies. Sweets include a magnificent almond
semifreddo, served with the darkest and richest of hot chocolate
sauces. Stunning *cannolichi* (dainty little cream-filled pastries)
precede the desserts and wonderful coffee ends a truly memorable
meal. *L 12.30-2.30 D 8-10.30. Public parking. Closed L Sat, all Sun.
Diners, Visa, Mastercard.*

Milan   Hotel De La Ville

Tel (2) 867651   Fax (2) 866609   H

Via Hoepli 6 20121 Milan
Rooms 104   Double room from L350,000

Few hotels are right in the heart of a city and also blissfully quiet.
Situated a short distance from the Duomo, it offers classic
comforts: elegant rooms filled with antique furniture, but also
equipped with cable and satellite TV and a mini-bar. Renovations
have been under way; there is a gleaming new hall featuring
cherrywood, but, at the time of going to press, the rooms had yet
to be started. *No room service. Theatre-style conference facilities for
up to 50. Closed Aug. Public parking.* AMERICAN EXPRESS *Diners,
Mastercard, Visa.*

Milan   Diana Majestic

Tel (2) 29513404   Fax (2) 201072   **H**

Viale Piave 42 20129 Milan
Rooms 94   Double room from L320,000

The jewel in the crown of Milan's *Belle Epoque*, this is the oldest
hotel in the city, dating back to 1905. *Viale Piave* is very
conveniently on the circle route of the 29 and 30 trams but
it might be advisable to avoid the bedrooms that look over it.
Instead, choose one of the quieter rooms overlooking the garden,
where you can have breakfast and lunch on a terrace in the
summer. The hotel interior is chic, with huge original art deco
windows, marble floors and fine old pieces of furniture. *Theatre-
style conference facilities for up to 50.*
AMERICAN EXPRESS *Mastercard, Visa.*

Milan   Al Garibaldi

Tel (2) 6598006   Fax (2) 6555413   **R**

Viale Monte Grappa 7 20124 Milan
Seats 95   Meal for 2 approx L120,000

Of the two rooms that comprise this north-of-centre restaurant the
rear is the preferred one – the front is more of a locals' rendezvous.
White walls are hung with all manner of paintings and drawings
of the Italian hero – there's even a huge portrait of him riding
on horseback. The menu is a conventional one featuring a short
list of familiar favourites from excellent prosciutto with juicy
melon and various risotti – the one with courgette flowers (an
early- to mid-summer special) is particularly good. Here they
major more on meat than fish so opt for grilled fillet or T-bone
steak or some quite good veal. *L 12.30-2.30 D 8pm-1am. Closed
L Sat, all Fri, Aug, 1 week Christmas. No parking.* AMERICAN EXPRESS
Diners, Mastercard, Visa.

Milan   Al Genovese

Tel (2) 8373180   **R**

Via Ettore Troilo 14 20136 Milan
Seats 38   Meal for 2 approx L240,000

The owner of this restaurant close to the Pavese canal trained with
Gualtiero Marchesi, and hails from the coast of her home region.
She has converted this old trattoria into a leading restaurant
specialising in the dishes of Liguria, with plenty of fish and
vegetables. *Spuncia corrente* (baby squid gently stewed with fresh
tomatoes and basil), *branzino crudo con lenticche* (sea bass served
raw with lentils) and *musciame* (a salame of tuna eggs served with
vegetables) are typical of the style of cooking. Another Genoese
house speciality is *torta pasqualina* – a delicious savoury millefeuille
pie filled with vegetables, soft cheese, whole eggs and Parmesan –
traditionally an Easter dish. Eat in the garden in the summer.
*L 12.30-2.30 D 7.30-10. Closed 1st 3 weeks in Aug, 23 Dec-2 Jan.
Public parking.* AMERICAN EXPRESS *Diners, Mastercard, Visa.*

Milan   Giannino

Tel (2) 545 27 65   **R**

Via A Sciesa 8 20135 Milan

Seats 250   Meal for 2 approx L120,000

A very grand restaurant in true flamboyant Italian style, much
beloved by the Milanese for this very reason. Cars enter to the
side with secured parking provided, while patrons arriving at the
main entrance proceed down a long, wide hallway past open-plan
kitchens visible behind glass screens and rack upon rack of fine
wines as well as huge, bubbling lobster tanks. In summer the place
to eat is in the splendid winter garden with its caged singing
canaries and cool, leafy arbour. The interior dining rooms are
characterised by resplendent Murano crystal chandeliers and fine
furniture. The lengthy menu is a very traditional one and the food
is competently prepared. The charcoal grill renders a good
selection of meats and seafood while the restaurant's own classic
dishes include the likes of risotto with saffron and marrow
flowers, veal paupiettes with a truffle sauce and osso buco with
gremolata. *Tagliolini* (thin noodles) flavoured with lobster coral
come with scampi and asparagus. When in season, fresh porcini
mushrooms are served baked with a sprinkling of parsley,
breadcrumbs and garlic. Booking is advisable. *L 12.30-2.30
D 7.30-10.30. Closed Sun, Aug. Private parking.* AMERICAN EXPRESS ®
Diners, Mastercard, Visa.

Milan   Bistrot Di Gualtiero Marchesi

Tel (2) 877120   Fax (2) 877035   **R**

Via San Raffaele 2 20121 Milan

Seats 120   Meal for 2 approx L 110,000

The recent arrival of Gualtiero Marchesi's new venture on the
very top (7th) floor of La Rinascente, Milan's foremost
department store, has opened his style of exceptional gastronomy
to a much wider public by offering a wide range of relatively
inexpensive foods. The setting is ultra-modern, with a direct lift
operating in the evening from the street. The huge curved
skylight takes full advantage of a unique view of the Duomo with
its 135 white marble spires and 2,200 sculptures. By day there's
a choice of three locations – the Cafè for counter service, open
9.30am to 9pm daily; the Brunch for informal waitress service,
open noon-10pm, and the Bistrot, which offers a more extensive
selection of food including three fixed-price menus – vegetarian,
meat and fish. Each comes with a small carafe of wine and half   ★
a litre of mineral water per person. There's also a short, but
exciting and varied carte featuring a selection of remarkably
stylish and exceptionally well-prepared dishes. The simplicity
of the preparation and the use of prime ingredients is instrumental
in the creation of the wonderful textures and flavours you
encounter on the plate. A very fine carpaccio of vegetables dressed
with truffle oil; spinach and ricotta ravioli with a shallot butter
or a classic dish of pan-fried *risotto al salto alla milanese* are to be
found alongside roast fillet of sea bream on an aubergine purée
in what are superb, albeit slightly abridged versions of his style
of cooking. The *costoletta di vitello alla milanese* is unmissable and
there's an excellent *semifreddo* of peaches with Amaretto or a

yoghurt bavarois with morello cherries to round things off
magnificently. *L 12.30-2.30 D 7.30-10.30. Closed L Mon, all Sun,
3 weeks Aug. Public parking.* AMERICAN EXPRESS® *Diners, Mastercard, Visa.*

Milan   Al Porto

Tel (2) 8321481   R

Piazzale Cantore 20123 Milan
Seats 90   Meal for 2 approx L210,000

Not far from Porta Genova station, the restaurant stands alone
on an island at the southern end of a large square. What little
remains nowadays of Milan's canal system comes to a head in a
small dock very close by and large black anchors either side of the
smart entrance gives a suitably nautical theme to what is a good,
simple fish restaurant, serving the freshest of fish. Appetisers
include charcoal-grilled scallops and a plate of mixed shellfish
followed by a choice of several fishy risotti including one with
squid ink and even a curried one with prawns. There are also
soups – mussel, clam or fish – as well as pasta dishes with scampi
or baby clams for instance. The *fritto misto* with scampi and young
squid is delicious as are the various simply grilled fish such as sea
bass, monkfish and gilt-head bream – each moistened with
a dribbling of olive oil before being served. Simple desserts to end
as well as excellent coffee. Quite rapid service. *L 12.30-2.30
D 7.30-10.30. Closed L Mon, all Sun, Aug. No parking.*
AMERICAN EXPRESS® *Diners, Mastercard, Visa.*

Milan   St Andrews

Tel (2) 76023132   Fax (2) 798565   R

Via Sant'Andrea 23 20121 Milan
Seats 70   Meal for 2 approx L250,000

In sharp contrast to the haute couture shops on every side, this
restaurant, with its staunchly British name, is a bastion of tradition
and classicism. The sombre, dark club-like decor is in a definite
time-warp with its brown leather-clad walls, varnished darkwood
strip ceiling and very deep-cushioned black leather chairs. It's very
much a favourite with well-established executives, either
on business or with their spouses, who come to savour its quiet
civility. The menu, with versions in several languages, is of simple,
enjoyable dishes with the emphasis very much on luxury
ingredients. Among the antipasti is a splendid warm lobster salad
and among farinaceous dishes is a classic version of *risotto alla
milanese.* There's an equal measure of mostly grilled meat and fish
dishes such as lamb cutlets trimmed of all fat and cooked
to perfection. *L 12-3.30 D 7-12.30. Closed Sun, Aug. Valet parking.*
AMERICAN EXPRESS® *Diners, Mastercard, Visa.*

Milan   Il Sambuco

Tel (2) 33610333   Fax (2) 3317399 **R**

Via Messina 10 20100 Milan

Seats 80   Meal for 2 appprox L180,000

The restaurant of the Hotel Hermitage is located north-west of the
city centre, a few streets from the very splendid Monumental
cemetery. The hotel was built two years ago and the restaurant
is decorated in pretty shades of pink and red with soft lighting and
attractive table settings. It is favoured by a well-heeled,
conservative clientele who come for the fish, which is all they
serve here. It is of the freshest and finest quality and includes
a delicious starter of steamed *cannochie* and *totani* (Adriatic shrimps
and flying squid from the Ligurian sea). Other typical dishes from
a menu which changes twice yearly are scallops sautéed with
vegetables and a superb fritto misto of all manner of beautifully
cooked fish. The wine list is predominantly white and Italian but
with a few French vintages and very few reds. *L 12-2.30 D 8-
10.30. Closed Aug, 27 Dec-5 Jan.* AMERICAN EXPRESS® *Diners, Mastercard,
Visa.*

Milan   Santini

Tel (2) 782010   Fax (2) 76014691 **R**

Corso Venezia 3 20121 Milan

Seats 65   Meal for 2 approx L250,000

Younger sister of London's *Santini* and *L'Incontro*, this is an
extremely fashionable and elegant restaurant close to Milan's top
designer boutiques. From the street entrance with its uniformed
doorman a long passageway leads into a splendid anteroom and
bar with the stylishly appointed restaurant beyond. Decor is a cool
combination of glittering whites and creams. The menu is modern
and also Venetian including some excellent fish and shellfish such
as salt cod (*baccala*), scallops and baby squid. *Tagliolini* come with
fresh crab followed perhaps by the classic calf's liver Venetian style
or superb chargrilled swordfish steak. *L 12.30-2.30 D 5.30-11.
Closed Sun, 3 weeks Aug. No parking.* AMERICAN EXPRESS® *Diners,
Mastercard, Visa.*

Milan   Savini

Tel (2) 72003433   Fax (2) 86461060 **R**

Galleria Vittorio Emanuelle II 20121 Milan

Seats 100   Meal for 2 approx L340,000

Established over 60 years ago in the heart of one of Milan's
grandest settings, the restaurant has in the past had the reputation
of being one of the city's most expensive, fashionable and
exclusive. The turn-of-the-century decor features glittering
chandeliers and plush red carpets on the inside while the terrace,
now completely enclosed and fully air-conditioned, has window
boxes brimming with exotic plants. A few cut-backs have been
made of late which do not detract too much from the overall
grandeur of the place. The cooking is firmly rooted in tradition
with a few minor modern touches such as steamed lobster served
lukewarm but the rest includes the likes of *risotto alla milanese*,
turbot with tomato and thyme, fillets of sole with scampi and

mixed vegetables or rack of lamb with black truffle. Results
on the plate don't always hit the mark but service is as smooth and
efficient as you could hope for. *L 12.15-3 D 7-10.30. Closed L Sat,
all Sun. No parking.* AMERICAN EXPRESS *Diners, Mastercard, Visa.*

Milan   **Starhotel Rosa**

Tel (2) 8831   Fax (2) 8057964   **H**

Piazza Fontana (Duomo) 20122 Milan
Rooms 185   Double room from L 270,000

Located in an attractive square with central fountain a couple
of streets behind the Duomo, the hotel has to have the most
unattractive exterior ever – a building in front of the hotel was
demolished and the city council haven't yet agreed what should
be in its place. The drab remains of that building for the moment
form the front outside wall of the hotel: a long red canopy
extends over the pavement and is the only indication that there
is anything here at all. Once inside however there are all the
trappings of a modern city-centre hotel with a smart lobby area
fitted with buttoned black leather seating. At the rear is an
attractive if windowless bar with a breakfast room beyond (there
is currently no restaurant as the hotel's in a state of change owing
to the exterior). Bedrooms are smart and comfortable, all air-
conditioned, with some top-floor rooms having a splendid view
of the cathedral's magnificent spires. Decor is modern, and rooms
are equipped with mini-bars and remote-control TVs. Bathrooms,
all with bidets and both bath and shower facilities, are bright and
clean. *24hr room service. Satellite TV/air-con. Theatre-style conference
facilites for up to 120. Private parking.* AMERICAN EXPRESS *Diners,
Mastercard, Visa.*   *See over for Around Milan*

Around Milan

Abbiategrasso   **Antica Osteria del Ponte**

| Tel (2) 9420034   Fax (2) 9420610 | **R** |

Piazza G Negri 9 Cassinetta di Lugagnano 20081 Abbiategrasso

Seats 40   Meal for 2 approx L210,000

In the heart of a sleepy village, 20-odd kms south west of Milan,
the characterful 15th-century stone inn that stands next to a small
bridge over the Milan canal is the exalted domain of Renata,
Maurizio and Ezio Santi, Ezio being in charge of what is one
of the very best kitchens in Italy. Getting here is the problem.
Either take a taxi the whole way from Milan (very expensive)
or else catch one of the hourly trains from Porto Genova in the
direction of Montara, an easy and pleasant 25-minute journey.
Be sure, however, when booking your table, to order a taxi
to pick you up at the station to take you the short, but circuitous
2kms from Abbiategrasso to Cassinetta. In fine weather, the only
place to eat is on the terrace, sheltered by a heavily beamed roof
and a surrounding wall of lush greenery with a trickling waterfall
in one corner. Even the tables are fresh and summery, with bold
orange rose-patterned napery and pretty scented rose posies.
At other times you dine in very elegant simplicity inside, under
more beams, with thick, white-painted walls all around. The
menu descriptions are short and exact, and the choice, though not
extensive, is sufficiently varied. Dishes while not complex, display ★
a great degree of refinement and immense attention to detail. After
a complimentary glass of sparkling wine, a tiny pre-appetiser
of smoked swordfish on radicchio with a red pepper cream
precedes the likes of the tenderest, plumpest scampi coated and
fried in fine breadcrumbs subtly flavoured with orange and served
on a small mixed leaf salad. Next a risotto of the most
wonderfully creamy consistency, here flavoured with saffron
pistils and courgette flowers, a sublimely delicate combination. For
a main course the choice could be a bourride made with soft,
succulent fillets of turbot and sea bass with prawns. Other choices
could be a saddle of rabbit with a sauce of aged balsamic vinegar,
guinea fowl lacquered with green pepper and rib of veal with
a porcini mushroom sauce. To finish, a dessert such as a wild
strawberry millefeuille served with an almond sauce is the
culmination of an experience well worth the trip out of Milan.
Staff couldn't be kinder. *L 12-2 D 8-10. Closed Sun & Mon, Aug.*
AMERICAN EXPRESS *Diners, Mastercard, Visa.*

Erbusco   **Gualtiero Marchesi L'Albereta**

| Tel (30) 77 60 550   Fax (30) 77 60 573 | **HR** |

Via Vittorio Emanuele II 25030 Erbusco (Brescia)

Rooms 26   Double room from L240,000

1½ kilometres from the centre of Erbusco is an area very aptly
named Bellavista. The hotel is perched on a hilltop overlooking
lush vineyards, wooded slopes and the distant Alps in a totally
unspoiled, timeless setting. Here there is ample opportunity for
relaxation and tranquillity. Created from a mansion built in the
early 1800s, this brand-new hotel fits perfectly into its setting
offering, in addition, almost every conceivable modern amenity,
from spacious and elegantly appointed day rooms, including
several smart, comfortable lounges, even a library, to fabulous
bedrooms and bathrooms all decorated in the best possible taste.

Not only is the whole place beautifully furnished and immaculately maintained but there are exemplary standards of service too. All the bedrooms are fully air-conditioned and are furnished with antique furniture in a heavy, traditional country style which fits in well with the thick white walls and polished floors. Five bedrooms, with twin beds, have balconies and the best rooms have jacuzzi baths and separate showers. There's an amazing indoor pool on the lowest level with patio doors that open on to a sunny south-facing terrace overlooking the gardens. The breakfast room takes full advantage of the early-morning sun with breakfasts, themselves a treat. *Satellite TV/air-con. Indoor swimming pool/sauna/keep-fit equipment. Theatre-style conferences for up to 50.* AMERICAN EXPRESS® *Diners, Mastercard, Visa.*

Restaurant

Seats 50   Meal for 2 approx L250,000

For those who can't or won't make the 60-odd kilometre journey from Milan to Erbusco there is some consolation in the excellent Bistrot (qv) on the 7th floor of *La Rinascente* in the very heart of Milan. Otherwise, as there's no direct means of access, it's hire a chauffeur or a car for the day and head straight up the Viale Zara from the centre of Milan, ignoring pointers to Bergamo, until you reach the A4 Autostrada and head in the direction of Venice. After passing Bergamo take the Rovato exit. Turn left after the tollgate and continue through Erbusco heading for Sarnico. In the village centre a sign for the restaurant on the right points up a narrow lane which eventually leads into the hills. Once you arrive you can see why the Marchesis exchanged their restaurant in central Milan for this idyllic spot. Surrounded by the Franciacorta vineyards, it is at the summit of a hill commanding magnificent views northwards towards Lake Iseo and the Italian Alps. The dining room has a splendid enclosed terrace with the most wonderful view. The rear wall has a splendid fresco in muted colours and the roof is supported by huge beams providing a rustic touch in contrast to the chandeliered elegance of the internal dining room. Gualtiero Marchesi's reputation is for advancing the cause of Italian gastronomy into the realm of studied innovation. Working with the wealth of first-class produce so readily at hand, he fashions the simplest of dishes that capture the living essence of the ingredients. The cooking is light and fresh, delicately seasoned and with everything in perfect balance. The use of differing, sometimes contrasting, constituents produces new and unusual taste sensations. A typical meal begins with a complimentary glass of sparkling wine, here of exceptional Franciacorte spumante, then a pre-appetiser of a few paper-thin slivers of raw beef fillet laid on a tiny, lightly-dressed, crisp-leaved salad. Next comes a dish such as fine slices of raw, very fresh sturgeon, dressed only with extra virgin olive oil and a generous sprinkling of caviar. The pasta course could be raviolo of a layer of green and white pasta with, in between, a small selection of tender scallops and scampi. For a main course the choice includes turbot baked in a salt crust served with a sauce of fresh oranges, milk-fed lamb baked with potatoes and artichokes, steamed rib of beef with vegetables served with pickles, candied fruit in mustard syrup and salsa verde, stuffed veal medallions accompanied by a wild mushroom sauce and spiced duck breast with caramelised baby turnips. The desserts are further examples of his approach to the fusion of unusual flavours – as in a hot chocolate pudding with a gratinated rich, creamy saffron sauce or thyme ice cream with a lemon and honey sauce. *L 12-2 D 8-10. Closed D Sun, all Mon, 3 weeks Aug.*

Naples

Naples	**La Cantinella**	

Tel (81) 7648684	**R**

Via Cuma 42 Lungomare di Santa Lucia 80132 Naples
Seats 120   Meal for 2 approx L140,000

An idyllic spot for a long, lazy lunch, or as the G7 meeting found
recently, ideal for a power-lunch, thrashing out the world's
problems. Picture the scene: rattan chairs and white linen-clad
tables arranged on the veranda, looking out over the bay
to Vesuvius and Sorrento. Then the food: a regional cuisine,
mainly of fish, but with a few meat dishes (some of the meat
is imported from Scotland). The fish dishes include an old
fishermen's recipe, *pesce acqua pazza* (gurnard baked with cherry
tomatoes – fishermen added seawater in the past), *scaloppina alla
cantinella* (ham, palm hearts and black truffle) and *gamberi con
rucola e polpa di granchio* (prawns in a crab sauce with rocket,
home-made linguine with squid and prawns in a tomato sauce and
baked sea bass). A total of eight chefs prepare these dishes, and also
fresh Neapolitan sweet pastries. The international wine list is one
of the most extensive and interesting in Italy. *L 12.30-3.30 D 7.30-
12.30. Closed Sun, 13-31 Aug, 24 Dec-6 Jan.* AMERICAN EXPRESS
Mastercard, Visa.

Naples	**Don Alfonso 1890**	

Tel (81) 8780026 Fax (81) 5330226	**R**

Piazza Sant'Agata sui due Golfi 80064 Naples
Seats 40   Meal for 2 approx L190,000

The same family have run this restaurant since 1890 and the
present owner has been running it and cooking here for 20 years.
The combination of original 19th-century recipes and a fresh
interpretation of regional dishes makes for an interesting menu
which sways towards fish dishes like *astice agli agrumi* (crayfish
with citrus fruits), but also includes ravioli with cherry tomatoes,
basil, caciotta cheese and tomato sauce and *costoletta di agnello alle
erbe aromatiche* (lamb cutlets with aromatic herbs). The speciality
is rib of veal with raisins, pine nuts and tomato. *L 12.30-2.30
D 7.30-10.30. Closed Mon, also Tue Oct-May, 10 Jan-25 Feb.
Private parking.* AMERICAN EXPRESS *Mastercard, Visa.*

Naples	**San Germano**	

Tel (81) 5705422 Fax (81) 570 1546	**R**

Via Beccadelli 41 80125 Naples
Seats 150   Meal for 2 approx L160,000

Neapolitan cooking with lashings of seafood is very much the
order of the day in a grand hotel restaurant on the outskirts of the
city on the road to Pozzuoli. The seafood pasta is definitely worth
looking out for. The menu changes seasonally, but always has
a predominance of fish. *L 12.30-2.30 D 7.30-9.30. Closed Aug, 24
Dec-7 Jan. Private garage.* AMERICAN EXPRESS *Diners, Mastercard, Visa.*

Naples   Giuseppone a Mare

Tel (81) 5756002   R

Via Ferdinando Russo 13 Capo Posillipo 80123 Naples
Seats 200   Meal for 2 approx L120,000

Antonio di Martino has been in the kitchen for the last 13 years, cooking an international repertoire but with more of a leaning towards Mediterranean dishes. Fish is mostly featured, though the odd meat dish also appears. Both are quite simply treated, mostly plain grilled or roasted with a dribble of olive oil. The lemon profiteroles to finish are refreshingly different. The setting, overlooking the Bay of Naples, is a splendid one and the restaurant, on a seaside road above a beach, makes the most of the location. *L 12.30-4 D 5.30-11. Closed 1st 15 days Aug. Private parking.* AMERICAN EXPRESS *Diners, Mastercard, Visa.*

Naples   Grand Hotel Parker's

Tel (81) 7612474   Fax (81) 663527   H

Corso Vittorio Emanuele 135 80121 Naples
Rooms 83   Double room from L280,000

A panoramic spot for a hotel; and in fact, there has been one here since 1860. The present hotel was reopened four years ago, completely renovated, with additional conference rooms. Each of the six floors has a completely different style, the bedroom decor ranging from Louis XVI to modern furniture. All are well equipped and have splendid bathrooms, marble floors and antique pictures gracing the walls. Public rooms and areas are particularly elegant with some French period-style furniture as well as a few more modern pieces. Front-facing bedrooms on the upper floors have particularly splendid views over the bay with Vesuvius on the left and Ischia just about visible on the right. *Theatre-style conference facilities for up to 250. Secretarial/translation services. Private parking.* AMERICAN EXPRESS *Mastercard, Visa.*

Naples   La Sacrestia

Tel (81) 7611051   Fax (81) 664186   R

Via Orazio 116 80122 Naples
Seats 120   Meal for 2 approx L130,000

Set in a 19th-century villa, surrounded by a garden full of orange and lemon trees, the restaurant is ornate; original religious frescoes decorate the ceilings, and the windows and furniture have come from an old church. The terrace is a great place to eat, sitting looking over the garden. The light regional cooking takes every advantage of the fresh fish available for example baby squid with capers and *bottarga* (a dried tuna roe delicacy). A good local dish is *polpettone alla napoletana* (a chunky meat loaf with ham, cheese, sultanas and pine nuts). *L 1-3.30 D 8-12.30. Closed Mon (also Sun in Jul), Aug.* AMERICAN EXPRESS *Mastercard, Visa.*

Around Naples

Capri   La Capannina

| Tel (81) 8370732   Fax (81) 8376990 | R |

Via Le Botteghe 12-14 80073 Capri

Seats 110   Meal for 2 approx L160,000

After World War II, the De Angelis family moved their
restaurant from the Piazza to *Via Le Botteghe*, where it is now, and
it is still run by them. They also own a rather splendid gourmet
deli, *La Capannina Più*, where you can purchase salami, cheeses
and Capri's speciality – lemon liqueur. Like most of the food
on Capri, the menu is heavily weighted towards fish, including
fish soup, linguine in a sauce of scorpion fish, calamari filled with
a mixture of cheese, capers and breadcrumbs as well as ravioli
filled with local cheese, marjoram and raisins with a tomato and
basil sauce. The two rustic but elegant dining rooms have marble
floors and walls hung with pictures by local artists. Most of the
wines are local. *L 12-3 D 7.30-12. Closed Wed, 6 Nov-24 Mar.*
AMERICAN EXPRESS *Mastercard, Visa.*

Capri   Casanova

| Tel (81) 8377642   Fax (81) 8377642 | R |

Via Le Botteghe 46 80073 Capri

Seats 60   Meal for 2 approx L120,000

In winter, when they are closed to casual customers, they run
promotions for local cooking. Their kitchen is traditional, with
a few concessions towards the creative. Fish and shellfish form the
basis of the menu: octopus, clams and prawns are among a wealth
of local fish which feature in simply prepared dishes. Home-made
pasta is a particular house speciality with *ravioli Capresi* (ravioli
with fresh tomatoes, basil, marjoram and local cheese); while *pasta
afrodisiaco* is fettucine tossed with baby shrimps and cherry
tomatoes. Meat dishes include fillet steak with a sauce of Marsala
and porcini mushrooms, veal chop with sage and butter or veal
escalope with mozzarella and tomatoes. Simple sweets include
a local speciality, a delicious chocolate and almond torte. Their
cellar is as indigenous as their kitchen. *L 12-3 D 7-11.30. Closed
Thur, also Oct-June.* AMERICAN EXPRESS *Diners, Mastercard, Visa.*

Capri   Grand Hotel Quisisana

| Tel (81) 8370788   Fax (81) 8376080 | HR |

Via Camerelle 2 80073 Capri

Rooms 122   Double room from L310,000

The varied former lives of this establishment include a residence
for Sicilian nobility and a wealthy Mexican's second home, before
it was converted into a hotel in 1878. Unlike many hotels
on Capri, this place has concentrated on appealing to businessmen,
with a vast conference capacity of up to 500 people seated theatre-
style and secretarial and translation services on request. The other
facilities are equally up to date, with an indoor and outdoor
swimming pool, two tennis courts, a gym and sauna. The rooms
have that stylish simplicity found in the Mediterranean, with cool
white-washed walls and slabbed ceramic floors; all rooms have
satellite TV. The place feels very spacious as it is surrounded
by acres of parkland. *24hr room service. Conference facilities. Closed
Nov-Mar.* AMERICAN EXPRESS *Diners, Mastercard, Visa.*

Restaurant Quisi
Seats 50   Meal for 2 approx L300,000

The restaurant was set up by Gualtiero Marchesi, who has
organised the kitchen, trained the staff and arranged the menu.
This is an extremely stylish place, very elegantly furnished, with
a classical decor of antiques including beautiful paintings of the
abundant marine life found round the island. A fine terrace too,
is available for alfresco dining. There is an excellent and well-
balanced fixed-price, no-choice menu which changes daily.
A typical meal could begin with a scampi salad with a ginger
confit followed by fresh tagliolini with courgettes and marjoram,
then roast lamb with an accompaniment of mushrooms, potatoes
and onions and rounded off by a delicious crème brulée flavoured
with Grand Marnier. The carte offers superb modern Italian
cooking with Marchesi's stamp firmly on it. The food is a little
more conservative however than at *L'Albereta* (see under Around
Milan Erbusco) in the North. Appetisers include a dish
of asparagus with caviar, baby clams and boiled egg and warm
lobster with cucumber and a yoghurt sauce. First courses include
his famous *risotto alla milanese* topped with a gold leaf as well
as the likes of deep-fried ravioli with a sauce of red peppers. Main
dishes include a baked fillet of sea bass with a small stew
of vegetables and an olive sauce, deep-fried Dover sole fillets in a
sweet and sour sauce, steamed fillet of beef with bone marrow and
a herb sauce or roast duck with peaches. Splendid desserts round
off a superb experience. *D only 7.30-11.*

Restaurant Colombaia
Seats 80   Meal for 2 approx L120,000

Eating an alfresco lunch here is a relaxed and very enjoyable affair.
The chef, a relation of Marchesi's, prepares typically
Mediterranean dishes, with plenty of grilled fish, veal and light
pasta and rice dishes. Every day, a buffet of salads and hot dishes
is laid out for the light price of L35,000. The wine list
is dominated by Italian whites. *L only 12.30-2.30.*

Capri   Luna

Tel (81) 8370433   Fax (81) 8377459   **H**

Viale Matteotti 3 80073 Capri
Rooms 54   Double room from L270,000

The company which runs this hotel can recommend a reliable
garage in Sorrento where guests can leave their cars while they are
on Capri. Most people take a taxi or the funicular railway from
the port to the hotel, but if guests do want to walk, they can
arrange for a porter to come down to carry their baggage. The
Luna is very smart and chic, yet has a relaxed and informal
ambience. Alternatively, the terrace makes a perfect supper setting,
but you pay an extra £20, approximately, for the privilege. The
views are breathtaking as the hotel is perched on a cliff,
overlooking the sea. The old-fashioned rooms have period
furniture and ceramic-tiled floors. Capri is a relaxing place, and
here it is especially quiet, close to an ancient monastery as well
as the Giardino d'Augusto. *24hr room service. Satellite TV/air-con.
Restaurant (International). Outdoor swimming pool. Closed Nov-Easter
Sun.* AMERICAN EXPRESS *Diners, Mastercard, Visa.*

Capri   **Punta Tragara**

Tel (81) 8370844   Fax (81) 8377790   H

Via Tragara 57 80073 Capri

Rooms 35   Double room from L240,000

Ten minutes walk from the centre of Capri with a friendly,
homely atmosphere, this hotel is popular with holidaymakers (but
do note that children under 12 are not allowed). It has some good
health facilities including a beauty salon, hydromassage in the
outdoor swimming pools as well as a large garden. The rooms are
spacious, with a small sitting room on a separate level from the
bedroom and bathroom. *Closed end Oct-Good Fri.* AMERICAN EXPRESS
Diners, Mastercard, Visa.

Capri   **Scalinatella**

Tel (81) 8370633   Fax (81) 8378291   H

Via Tragara 10 80073 Capri

Rooms 30   Double room from L460,000

A tranquil retreat with large gardens and plenty of gentle sporting
activities. The bedrooms are well equipped, with cool ceramic
floors and 16th-century furniture. But for those with more
weighty matters on their mind than the latest in haute couture,
there are no conference facilities. Not a suitable plasce for children.
*24hr room service. Satellite TV. Restaurant (regional). Outdoor
swimming pool/2 tennis courts/gym. Closed 30 Oct-28 Mar.*
AMERICAN EXPRESS *Visa.*

Turin

Turin   Del Cambio

Tel (11) 546690   Fax (11) 543760   **R**

Piazza Carignano 2 10123 Turin

Seats 90   Meal for 2 approx L200,000

Opposite the Renaissance museum in a quiet city square, the
restaurant first opened its doors in the mid 18th century and
as such is one of the oldest in Italy. The present decor reflects some
of this ancient character, a stylish mix of classical and Baroque
with much rich velvet in evidence as well as polished wood, old
gilt-framed mirrors, and beautiful frescoes. Every Friday there
is music from a string quartet. Specialising in the cooking of the
region, the menu offers the likes of courgette flowers stuffed with
creamed truffles, risotto with white truffles, filled pasta with
simple sauces and beef braised in Barolo with spices. The pasta
is home-made and delicious. Desserts include a very special
chocolate cake with a delicious chocolate cream. The excellent
wine list features mainly Piedmontese wines wtih Barbaresco
vintages going back to 1947. *L 12-2.30 D 7.45-10.30. Closed Sun,
28 Jul-28 Aug. Public parking.* AMERICAN EXPRESS *Diners, Mastercard,
Visa.*

Turin   Due Lampioni da Carlo

Tel (11) 8179380   Fax (11) 887260   **R**

Via Carlo Alberto 45 10123 Turin

Seats 80   Meal for 2 approx L250,000

Converted from a wine shop 50 years ago, the restaurant is located
in a beautiful 17th-century palazzo. The chef, Carlo Bagatin,
is loyal to his Piedmontese roots, but has been heavily influenced
by the time he spent working at the *Bristol* in Paris. Plenty
of grilled fish like sea bass, swordfish, sole and salmon are served
in a variety of light, interesting sauces – for example grilled sea
bass with an orange sauce or with pesto and pine nuts. The meat
dishes are equally interesting: fillet of beef is served with
a creamed black olive sauce and veal escalopes are layered with
melted, grated Parmesan and asparagus. The *bollito misto piemontese*
is a mix of gently poached meats – beef, calf's head and capon and
is offered alongside other Piedmont specialities such as stuffed rib
of very young veal and *finanziera torinese* – a rich dish of poached
various diced meats cooked with wild mushrooms, butter and
Marsala. Wines are healthily split between well-known Italian and
French names, with a French house Chardonnay. *L 12.30-2.30
D 7.30-11. Closed Sun. Public parking.* AMERICAN EXPRESS *Mastercard,
Visa.*

To dial overseas from the UK, 010 will change to 00
on 16th April 1995.

Turin   **Neuv Caval 'd Brons**

| Tel (11) 5627483   Fax (11) 543610 | R |

Piazza San Carlo 157 10123 Turin

Seats 65   Meal for 2 approx L280,000

Despite reopening in 1988 advertising itself as an international
restaurant, it still serves plenty of Piedmontese specialities:
Castelmagno cheese flan with a rich sauce of the same cheese,
noodles tossed with a veal and orange sauce, quail stuffed with
goose liver on a potato nest, and roast breast of duck with pears
baked in wine. Other dishes do lean towards the international,
with fillet of beef in a juniper berry sauce and fillet of trout
on toasted brioche and a cider sauce. Desserts range from rice flour
crepes filled with peach and lemon meringue tart to orange terrine
with a Grand Marnier jelly. *L 12.30-2.30 D 8-10.30. Closed L Sat,
all Sun, 10-25 Aug. Public parking.* AMERICAN EXPRESS *Diners,
Mastercard, Visa.*

Turin   **Palace Hotel**

| Tel (11) 5625511   Fax (11) 5625511 | H |

Via Sacchi 8 10128 Turin

Rooms 123   Double room from L291,000

A splendid 19th-century hotel that has been in the same family
since 1872. Near the main railway station, it has all the trappings
of a grand hotel with a stylish and very elegant traditional decor.
Early 18th-century French furniture with silks and other fine
fabrics on the walls create a refined and luxurious ambience.
Bathrooms are spacious and beautifully appointed with white
marble. *Cable/satellite TV. Private parking.* AMERICAN EXPRESS
Mastercard, Visa.

Turin   **La Prima Smarrita**

| Tel (11) 3179657   Fax (11) 3179191 | R |

Corso Unione Sovietica 244 10125 Turin

Seats 70   Meal for 2 approx L280,000

The menu here has long been a successful and playful mix
between Tuscan cooking, for example *ribollita*, and fine Piedmont
cuisine, which includes wild mushrooms, fillet of beef, squid and
white truffles. House specialities like *triglia con purée di fave
e basilico* (red mullet with a purée of broad beans and basil),
costoletto di agnello alle erbe (lamb cutlet roasted with herbs) and
a chateaubriand of swordfish. Several different set menus are
on offer, including Tuscan, Mediterranean and vegetarian.
*L 12.30-3 D 7.30-11.30. Closed Mon, 1st 3 weeks Aug. Diners,
Visa.*

Turin   **Vecchia Lanterna**

Tel (11) 537047   Fax (11) 530391   **R**

Corso Re Umberto 21 10128 Turin

Seats 145   Meal for 2 approx L200,000

Right on Piazza Solferino, this elegant and stylish restaurant has
a quiet, romantic ambience. It is decorated in warm, muted
colours, with 19th-century Murano crystal chandeliers suspended
from the ceilings and fine oil paintings on the walls. Pre-dinner
drinks and orders are taken in the smart American bar where
there is occasional live music entertainment. The family who own
the restaurant have been in the business for three generations and
took over the running of this place in 1970. The father is the chef
and offers a menu that combines a classical repertoire with some
regional specialities. Noteworthy dishes are goose liver with
lightly sautéed apples and a wonderful sherry sauce, *agnolotti* with
a delicious filling of duck forcemeat and a rich truffle sauce and sea
bass accompanied by a Barolo sauce. Nougat glacé makes
a splendid finale. There are usually three menus to choose from – a
seasonally changing carte, a fish menu and a *menu degustazione*
(tasting menu). Occasionally they also offer a special menu of a
well-balanced selection of the dishes of a particular region of Italy.
The wine list is mainly Italian though there are a few French and
German vintages too. *L 12-2.30 D 8-11.30. Closed L Sat, all Sun,
1 week Aug.* AMERICAN EXPRESS *Mastercard, Visa.*

Around Turin

Costiglione d'Asti   **Da Guido**

Tel (0141) 966012   Fax (0141) 966012   **R**

Piazza Umberto I 27 Costiglione D'Asti

Seats 50   Meal for 2 approx L250,000

Lidia Alciati cooks in the kitchen now helped by one of her sons
while husband Guido oversees the dining room. She has never
undergone any formal training, but learnt the art of cooking
from her mother, and today offers superb examples of traditional
Piedmontese food in a fine restaurant which as well as being in a
quiet square has a glass frontage overlooking a wooded park.
Decor is classical, with antique furniture, though there are a few
abstract paintings on the walls. This, perhaps, reflects the nature
of the menu, which incorporates modern influences with the
classic cuisine of the region. Examples are a superb cold starter
of *vitello tounato* – tender veal slices served in a creamy tuna sauce   ★
(the Piedmontese version as served here has cream rather than
mayonnaise), turkey fillets marinated with black olives, courgette
flowers stuffed with a vegetable mousse, *agnolotti* – a local variant
of ravioli, here filled with minced lamb and served with a simple
gravy, and *stracotto*, braised beef in red wine. To finish there are
fine local cheeses as well as dainty petits fours and a cold
zabaglione accompanied by amaretti biscuits. From mid-
September to December a speciality to look out for is dishes using
the splendid white truffles from the region. *D only 8-late. Closed
20 Dec-10 Jan, 1-20 Aug. Diners, Mastercard, Visa.*

Venice

Venice   Antico Martini

Tel (41) 5224121   Fax (41) 5289857   **R**

Campo San Fantin 1983 30124 Venice
Seats 120   Meal for 2 approx L180,000

Few restaurants can claim, like this place, that they have been
going since 1700. It is also quite central just to the west of Piazza
San Marco. The menu mixes international and local dishes, with
gratinated onion soup found alongside Venetian bean and pasta
soup; ravioli with brie and walnut sauce and chateaubriand with
béarnaise sauce. The fish and seafood risotto is a popular dish for
two people and takes 20 minutes to prepare. The carte is a
comprehensive one. Also featured are a number of good set
menus. To finish, a selection of home-made desserts as well
as crepes Suzette with Grand Marnier. *L 12-2.30 D 7-11.30. Closed
Tue. Private parking.* AMERICAN EXPRESS *Diners, Mastercard, Visa.*

Venice   Hotel Des Bains

Tel (41) 5265921   Fax (41) 5260113   **H**

Lungomare Marconi 17 30126 Lido Venice
Rooms 191   Double room from L488,000

Occupying a splendid location on the Lido, this is a grand hotel
in every sense of the word. Thomas Mann, the author of *Death
in Venice* – subsequently made into a film by Visconti – set the
action in and around the hotel. The rooms are luxurious, with
lavish curtains, high ceilings and fine furniture. The receptions
rooms too, are elegant in the style of the 'Belle Epoque'. There are
splendid views from the terrace, down on to the beach. The sports
facilities, especially water sports, golf and riding, are excellent.
*Theatre-style conference facilities for up to 400. Outdoor swimming
pool, tennis courts, golf, riding, waterskiing, windsurfing, beach. Beauty
salon, sauna, massage. Closed Nov-Apr. Private parking.*
AMERICAN EXPRESS *Mastercard, Visa.*

Venice   La Caravella

Tel (41) 5208901   Fax (41) 5207131   **R**

Calle Larga 22 Marzo 2397 30124 Venice
Rooms 80   Meal for 2 approx L148,000

This is the restaurant of the Hotel Saturnia-International, which
has been in the same family ownership for three generations. Both
are housed in a building which dates from the early 14th century,
when it was the private home of Doge Pisani. The restaurant's
decor is unusual, themed on Christopher Columbus and boats,
with a wooden floor and walls, even a rudder. Aided by soft
candlelight and gentle background music, the atmosphere
is romantic and in summer the garden provides a beautiful
location for alfresco dining. The cooking is Venetian in character,
offering the likes of calf's liver with polenta, scallops au gratin, sea
bass baked with herbs and *grasseola* – a species of large spider crab
whose flesh is mixed with lemon and olive oil. A speciality is their
filetto alla Caravella – beef fillet with mustard, cognac and cream.
Sweets include the familiar but delicious tiramisu and zabaglione.
L 12-3 D 7-12. AMERICAN EXPRESS *Mastercard, Visa.*

Venice   **Hotel Cipriani**

Tel (41) 5207744   Fax (41) 5203930   **HR**

Giudecca 10 30133 Venice

Rooms 92   Double room from L720,000

The Cipriani is almost as much a Venetian landmark as the Doge's
Palace or Piazza San Marco. Only a five minute *vaporetto* (water
bus) ride away from San Marco across on the Giudecca island, the
hotel has views in all directions: of the lagoon, the Palladian San
Giorgio Maggiore, the vineyards and the Redentore. Giuseppe
Cipriani opened it in the late 50s with the Guinness family and
despite having up-to-date facilities little has changed since those
early days. Almost unrivalled standards of service, luxury and
comfort abound in this tranquil and beautiful setting. The beige-
pink stucco, terracotta-tiled and deep green shutters have
a uniquely Italian soft, worn look; while the rooms have been
classically redecorated in keeping with the building itself. Meals
are still normally eaten alfresco, on three terraces spread alongside
the waterfront. In the Palazzo Vendramin next door, also owned
by the Cipriani, guests can stay in one of the nine apartments. *24hr
room service. Satellite TV. Theatre-style conference facilities for up to
100. Olympic-sized swimming pool, tennis court, sauna, yacht. Closed
3-10 Jan.* AMERICAN EXPRESS *Diners, Mastercard, Visa.*

Restaurant

Seats 130   Meal for 2 approx L380,000

Started, like the hotel, by Venetian restaurateur Giuseppe Cipriani,
who also opened Harry's Bars in Venice and New York, the
restaurant offers a refreshingly re-interpreted Venetian menu with
plenty of interesting fish dishes: black risotto with cuttlefish; fillets
of baby sole from the Adriatic marinated in a Venetian sweet and
sour sauce with onions, sultanas and white polenta. House
specialities are home-made pasta and carpaccio. The long wine list
is predominantly Italian, with a good house red and white.
L 12.30-2.30 D 8-10. Closed 11 Nov-24 Feb.

Venice   **Hotel Danieli**

Tel (41) 5226480   Fax (41) 5200208   **H**

Castello 4196 30122 Venice

Rooms 230   Double room from L612,000

One of many CIGA hotels, both in this city and elsewhere in Italy,
the Danieli opened as a hotel at the beginning of the last century.
The original building dates back to the late 14th century when
Doge Dandolo built it as a palazzo for visiting dignitaries. The
hotel comprises three once separate, but now connected, buildings.
The main, and central, one is the original palazzo, and retains its
beautiful facade while on the inside it is furnished in great style
with colourful mosaics, a columned entrance hall with a gold
frieze and splendid antique Venetian furniture. On one side is an
18th-century building furnished with handsome painted furniture
while on the other is the Danielino, built in the 40s and therefore
lacking some of the style and character of the other two.
Conferences for up to 120 are held in a beautiful room lined with
red damask – the same colour as a doge's hat. *Theatre-style
conference facilities for to 200. Secretarial/translation services. Public
parking.* AMERICAN EXPRESS *Mastercard, Visa.*

Venice   Excelsior

Tel (41) 5260201   Fax (41) 5267276   **H**

Lungomare Marconi 41 30126 Lido Venice
Rooms 174   Double room from L290,000

Venice's film festival is centred around this magnificent hotel,
which opened in 1907 on the Lido. It has splendid gardens,
a swimming pool, and 2km of sandy beach dotted with hundreds
of beach huts. Being on the beach does, of course, make the
atmosphere more relaxed, but this hotel is still rather splendid and
grand with its '1001 nights-style' Moorish decor. Everything is on
a vast scale, with theatre-style conference facilities for up to 600,
in a new conference centre with nine halls. This obviously attracts
businesses organising in-house seminars but the sheer
impressiveness of the building also makes it a popular place for
tourists. The rooms are light and cool, reflecting the colours of the
Italian summer, the Arab influences extending to the style
of furniture, and the room decor. Facilities are fantastic, with
everything from safes to multilingual information services
available. *24hr room service. Satellite TV/air-con. Conference facilities.
Tennis courts, swimming pool, water sports, beach. Closed Nov-Mar.
Private parking.* AMERICAN EXPRESS *Diners, Mastercard, Visa.*

Venice   Flora

Tel (41) 5205844   Fax (41) 5228217   **H**

Calle Larga 22 Marzo 2283/a 30124 Venice
Rooms 38   Double room from L160,000

Off one of the main routes west of St Mark's Square, the hotel
enjoys a pleasantly quiet, yet central location and has the added
advantage of a pretty, flower-filled garden. It has been in the same
family ownership for 30 years and it possesses a very traditional
ambience that is both relaxed and friendly. Decor throughout
is attractively old-fashioned and quite simple. There are few
modern amenities, some rooms having TVs and hairdryers.
However all are air-conditioned. Bathrooms, all with bidets, have
either bath-tubs or showers. *24hr room service.* AMERICAN EXPRESS
Diners, Mastercard, Visa.

Venice   Gritti Palace

Tel (41) 794611   Fax (41) 5200942   **H**

Campo Santa Maria del Giglio 2467 30124 Venice
Rooms 95   Double room from L730,000

Facing the Grand Canal, this is another CIGA hotel and one
of their most splendid. The Doge Andrea Gritti built it in the
15th century as his private residence. Since it became a hotel
in 1948, Queen Elizabeth II has stayed and Hemingway has lived
here – a suite bears his name. Public rooms are beautifully
decorated with very fine artwork on the walls including a large
portrait of the Doge. The bedrooms are elegantly traditional with
18th-century antiques, and original Venetian floors have been
retained in some. *Theatre-style conference facilities for up to 100.
Secretarial/translation services.* AMERICAN EXPRESS *Mastercard, Visa.*

Venice   Harry's Bar
Tel (41) 5285777   Fax (41) 5289299   R
Calle Vallaresso 1323 30124 Venice
Seats 90   Meal for 2 approx L170,000

There have been pressures to popularise the menu following the
restaurant's heightened celebrity status but Arrigo Cipriani has
resisted it. Traditional Venetian cooking is still prepared by the
two longstanding stalwarts of the kitchen, with risotto dishes
being one of the house specialities, for instance, squid ink risotto.
Other specialities include Venetian style calf's liver, and chicken
curry with pilaff rice. Carpaccio was invented here, so is well
worth trying. The bar serves light snacks and some truly excellent
cocktails. There's also a splendid wine list featuring a fine selection,
mostly from the north of Italy. *Open 10.30am-11pm. Closed Mon.*
AMERICAN EXPRESS *Diners, Mastercard, Visa.*

Venice   Londra Palace
Tel (41) 5100533   Fax (41) 5225032   H
Riva degli Schiavoni 30122 Venice
Rooms 68   Double room from L280,000

Built as two hotels, the Londres and the D'Angleterre in 1858,
it became the Londra Palace after the last war. Tchaikovsky
composed his Fourth Symphony in one of the bedrooms, which
has been kept more or less as it was then and now features
a collection of his memorabilia. Other rooms are furnished
in 19th-century Biedermaier style and are full of character with
a fine collection of pictures, fragments of antique fabrics, letters
and photographs of famous guests. Most of the bathrooms have
jacuzzis. *Theatre-style conference facilities for up to 80.*
AMERICAN EXPRESS *Mastercard, Visa.*

Venice   Caffè Quadri
Tel (41) 5289299   Fax (41) 791661   R
Piazza San Marco 121 30100 Venice
Seats 80   Meal for 2 approx L90,000

A truly historic café where Signor Quadri served his first cup
of coffee in 1725, the café proper opening some 40 years later.
It wasn't until after the First World War that it became
a restaurant as well. This is a grandiose and splendid room with
mirror and burgundy damask-lined walls, and gilt beamed ceilings
from which hang Murano crystal floral chandeliers. The furniture
in the café is Baroque and paintings from the Tintoretto school
hang on the pale green stucco walls. The barman here – Massimo
Barnabei – can compose any cocktail. Food is limited to six
lunchtime dishes including carpaccio, blinis with brie and walnuts
and spaghetti with tomato and basil. The restaurant, the only one
in St Mark's Square, offers traditional Venetian specialities such
as seafood risotto, squid-ink spaghetti, scallops with saffron and
fillet of beef with black pepper and Parmesan. Desserts include
hazelnut ice cream baked under a meringue crust and jelly with
fruits of the forest. A few French and German wines supplement
a comprehensive Italian list. *Open 10am-midnight. Closed Mon.*
AMERICAN EXPRESS *Mastercard, Visa.*

Venice   **Quattro Fontane**

Tel (41) 5260227   Fax (41) 5260726   **H**

Via Quattro Fontane 16 Lido 30126 Venice
Rooms 60   Double room from L145,000

Small cars can arrive by ferry at this isolated spot on the Lido. The
house looks like a large family country home and was built in the
50s. The rooms are rather old-fashioned, furnished with beautiful
chintzy fabrics. Most of the staff, including the concierge, have
been here 25 years and organise the place as they would their
home. The hotel doesn't have a lift and there are 66 steps up to the
3rd floor. Once you get there, however, there are superb views
down over the park surrounding the hotel. Facilities in the hotel
may be limited but people come here for the peace and quiet.
No room service. Closed Nov-Apr. Private parking. AMERICAN EXPRESS
Mastercard, Visa.

Around Venice

Torcello   **Locanda Cipriani**

Tel (41) 730150   Fax (41) 730757   **R**

Piazza Santa Fosca 30012 Torcello
Seats 400   Meal for 2 approx L260,000

Take the *vaporetto* from Fondamenta Nuove on the north shore
for the 45-minute crossing to this island in the Venetian lagoon.
The restaurant, an offshoot of *Harry's Bar* (*qv*), has been going
since 1938. One of its finer features is the opportunity for alfresco
dining in the large, well-tended garden. As well as a selection
of well-balanced and reasonably priced fixed menus (from
L44,000) there is a comprehensive carte of modern Venetian
dishes. Seafood dominates, ranging from gratinated scallops with
hollandaise, crab dressed with olive oil and lemon, and squid ink
risotto to grilled bream, monkfish flavoured with thyme and
curried scampi with pilaff rice. The few simple meat dishes
include fillet of beef with green peppercorns and veal escalopes
with peas. The selection of desserts isn't elaborate either,
strawberry mousse and melon with port being typical. Excellent
coffee concludes an enjoyable experience. *L 12-3 D 7-10.30.*
Closed 15 Nov-15 Mar. AMERICAN EXPRESS *Visa.*

Elsewhere in Italy

Castrocaro Terme   La Frasca

Tel (543) 76 74 71   Fax (543) 76 66 25   **RR**

Via Matteotti 38 47011 Castrocaro Terme Forli
Seats 60   Meal for 2 approx L250,000

Castrocaro, an ancient and still much used spa town, is where the
fertile plains of Romagna's Po Valley meet the Apennine foothills.
Here, in a delightful 'village' setting, Gianfranco Bolognesi, his
wife Bruna and head chef Marco Cavallucci have, together,
created one of Italy's finest and most renowned restaurants. In
summer, you dine alfresco under a cool, leafy canopy – hence the
name *La Frasca* (leafy evergreen bough), a sign used once upon a
time by inns. Otherwise, the bar and dining rooms of the solidly
built stone house offer cosy, tradtitional splendour. The best of
local produce – game, white and red meats, truffles (predominantly
white), diverse mushrooms, all manner of cheeses from the region
and vegetables a-plenty as well as seafood direct from the coast,
40-odd kilometres away, and not forgetting the specially hand-
made breads and pasta, are all fashioned into the most sublime
dishes. The cooking follows the principles of Artusi, with modern,
lighter touches incorporated involving shorter cooking times, the
elimination of heavy sauces and a reduction and variation in the
quantity of fats and seasonings used. This is cooking of the very
highest level where flavours and textures are so carefully married
that the palate and senses are transported almost into a state
of rapture. Yet all is so unbelievably simple and straightforward.
As well as a short carte there are fixed-price menus including   ★
il Sapore della Tradizione (renewed tradition) – a meat menu, and
il Profumo del Mare e dell'Orto (the perfumes of the sea and garden)
– an exquisite seafood menu of unsurpassable quality. The latter
began on a recent visit with a sliver of sea-trout terrine which is
followed by a beautifully presented small lobster salad – the flesh
laid on a very tiny dice of fruit and surrounded by a dribbling of
smooth tomato-ey gazpacho. Next, ravioli filled with prawns and
fennel and very delicately flavoured with dill, which precedes
fillets of sole flavoured with a hint of rosemary and black truffle
and garnished with crisp deep-fried beet leaves. The main course is
roast sea bass served on a smooth, luscious basil purée with an
Artusi classic, *sformato di zucchini* – a featherlight courgette
moulded mousse – a simple and magical combination of great
precision. Desserts, including a stunning lemon and strawberry
terrine accompanied by an apricot compote, and a marvellous
selection of petits fours with fine coffee are the perfect ending to a
perfect meal. Mr Bolognesi, originally Italy's top sommelier, has
amassed an amazing wine cellar that features a superb selection of
the finest Italian vintages. *L 12.15-2.30 D 8-10. Closed Mon, 1st
2 weeks Aug, 1st 3 weeks Jan.* AMERICAN EXPRESS *Diners, Mastercard, Visa.*

Rooms   Double room from L400,000

There are two magnificent apartments some 200 metres away in a
converted ancient fortress which have been fitted out in a truly
luxurious manner. One is furnished in great style with furniture
by some of Italy's top designers, the other features beautiful 19th-
century pieces from Romagna. Both have every conceivable
comfort, with private terraces, spacious lounges, phone, radio and
TV as well as modern kitchens. Bathrooms have jacuzzi tubs and
are well-equipped and very up-to-date.

Scotch Beef Club Members: Italy

VAL D'AOSTA
ISSOGNE: Al Maniero

PIEMONTE
CALUSO: Hotel Daniel's Rist. La Fiaba de Marghy
CUORGNE: Hotel Astoria
TORRE CANAVESE: Italia
TURIN: Jolly Hotel Il Ligure Rist. Il Birichino
TURIN: Jolly Hotel Principi di Piemonte Rist. Il Gentilom
TURIN: Jolly Hotel Ambasciatori Rist. Il Diplomatico
VALMADONNA: Le Fonti

LOMBARDIA
BUSTO ARSIZIO: Moreno
CUSAGO: Da Orlanda
FIGINO SERENZA: Park Hotel e Hotel Villa Argenta
GORLAGO: Bella Italia
MADESIMO: Dogana vegia di Vitali Dario
MILAN: Jolly Hotel President Rist. Il Verziere
MILAN: Jolly Hotel Touring Rist. Amadeus
MILANO 2 SEGRATE: Jolly Hotel Rist. I Papaveri
MILANOFIORI ASSAGO: Jolly Hotel Milanofiori Rist. Quadrifoglio
MONTESPLUGA: Hotel Vittoria Akros
OSTIGLIA: Pontemolino
PAVIA: Locanda Vecchia Pavia
RECORFANO DI VOLTIDO: Gianna
RHO: Al Rhotaia
TREZZANO SUL NAVIGLIO: Green Grey

FRIULI V.G.
AVIANO: Hotel Aliva
CORNO DI ROSAZZO: Il Mulino
FONTANAFREDDA: Fassina
MAGNANO IN RIVERA: Hotel Green
OPICINA (TS): Dina
PORDENONE: Hotel Palace
RAGOGNA: Locanda Vuanello
TARVISIO: Italia
TRIESTE: Hosteria Bellavista
TRIESTE: Jolly Hotel Rist. Cavour
TRIESTE: Trattoria Città di Londra

TRENTINO
ARCO: Hotel Villa delle Rose
GAVAZZO DI TENNO: Albergo Stella d'Italia
PINZOLO: Primo o Poi
TRENTO: Chiesa
TRENTO: Doria

LIGURIA
CHIAVARI: Antica Osteria da U Dria
GENOVA: Jolly Hotel Plaza Rist. Villetta di Negro
GENOVA: Montallegro
LA SPEZIA: Jolly Hotel Rist. Del Golfo

VENETO
ALTAVILLA VICENTINA: Al Passeggio/Essevi
AURONZO DI CADORE: Lerois
BERGANTINO: Hotel Ristorante da Luciano
CADEGLIOPPI: Casa di Valle
CAERANO S MARCO: Enoteca Benzi
CALDIERO: Renato
CIMADOLMA: Le Calandrine
CORNEDO: 2 Platani
CRESPADORO: Le Meridiana
FARRA D'ALPAGO: Hotel Rifugio S Osvaldo
FELTRE: Sagittario
FOLLINA: Al Caminetto
GIAVERA DEL MONTELLO: La Baita
GIAVERA DEL MONTELLO: Ponte di Rialto
MIANE: Da Gigetto
MONFUMO: Osteria Alla Chiesa
NEGRISIA PONTE DI PIAVE: Ai Sette Nani
NERVESA DELLA BATTAGLIA: Da Roberto Miron
ROMANO D'EZZELIO: Ca'Takea
SCHIO: For a Man
SERREN DEL GRAPPA: Al Pentagono
SOLIGHETTO: Locanda da Lino
TREVISO: Alle Beccherie
VALDAGNO: Al Pezzo
VALDAGNO: Hostaria A le Bele
VENICE: Ai Gondolieri
VERONA: La Lampara
VERONA: Torcoloti
VICENZA: Remo
VOLPAGO DEL MONTELLO: Sbeghen

EMILIA ROMAGNA
BELLARIA: Azienda Agrituristica Chretien a Pippo
BOLOGNA: Jolly Hotel Rist. Amarcord
CASADIO: La Grigliata
CORTEMAGGIORE: Antica Corte
GRAGNANO: Luna Nuova
RAVENNA: Jolly Hotel Rist. La Veranda
REGGIO EMILIA: Antica trattoria La Favella
REGGIO EMILIA: Il Pozzo
RIMINI: Cucina della Nonna
RONCOPASCOLO: Il Gufo
SORBOLO: Spiga d'Oro

TOSCANA
AULLA: Il Rigoletto
CAMAIORE: Osteria Il Vignaccio
FLORENCE: Il Latini
FLORENCE: Jolly Hotel Rist. Carlton
PISA: Jolly Hotel Rist. Il Cavaliere
SIENA: Jolly Hotel Rist. La Rotonda
TERRANUOVA BRACCIOLINI: Amicorum

MARCHE
ANCONA: Jolly Hotel Rist. Miramare
BABARA: Hotel La Chiocciola
PORTO D'ASCOLI: Cogningi

LAZIO
ROME: Jolly Hotel L da Vinci Rist. Giovannini
ROME: Jolly Hotel Midas Rist. Baiocco
ROME: Jolly Hotel V Veneto Rist. Il Giardino
FIUGGI FONTE (FR) Hotel Gran Palazzo della Fonte Fiuggi

CAMPANIA
AVELLINO: Jolly Hotel Rist. Ippocampo
CASERTA: Jolly Hotel Rist. La Reggia
GUGLIONESE: Ribo
ISCHIA: Jolly Hotel Ischia
NAPLES: Jolly Hotel Rist. Il Grattacielo
NOCERA SUPERIORE (SA): Europa
SALERNO: Jolly Hotel Rist. La Scaglio

PUGLIA
BARI: Executive restaurant S.t.l.
BARI: Jolly Hotel Rist. La Tiella
BARI: Hotel Sheraton Nicolaus
BARI: Piccinni
FOGGIA: In Fiera Cicolella
FOGGIA: Hotel Cicolella
LAMA (TA): Le Vecchie Cascine

CALABRIA
CROTONE: Hotel Costa Tiziana

SICILIA
AGRIGENTO: Jolly Hotel Rist. Il Buon Gustaio
CATANIA: Jolly Hotel Rist. Gourmet
ERICE: Il Cortile di Venere
MESSINA: Jolly Hotel Rist. Dello Stretto
PALERMO: Forst
PALERMO: Jolly Hotel Rist. I Paladini
SIRACUSA: Jolly Hotel Rist. Il Giardinetto
TAORMINA: Jolly Hotel Diodoro

SARDEGNA
QUARTU s ELANA (CA): Pizzeria Sant'Andrea

Italy Index

Recommended by

EGON RONAY'S GUIDES

1995

YOUR GUARANTEE
OF
QUALITY AND INDEPENDENCE

- Establishment inspections are anonymous

- Inspections are undertaken by qualified
  Egon Ronay's Guides inspectors

- The Guides are completely independent
  in their editorial selection

- The Guides do not accept advertising,
  hospitality or payment from listed
  establishments

Hotels & Restaurants   Pubs & Inns
Europe   Just a Bite
Family Hotels & Restaurants   Paris
Oriental Restaurants   Ireland
New Zealand & South Pacific   Australia

Egon Ronay's Guides are available from all good bookshops or can be
ordered from Leading Guides, 35 Tadema Road, London SW10 0PZ
Tel: 071-352 2485 / 352 0019   Fax: 071-376 5071

Latvia

Currency: Latvian Lat   **Exchange Rate:** £1 = approx Ls 0.85
Not obtainable in UK. Travellers cheques/US dollars/DM
recommended.

International dialling code: 010 371
(Riga + 2)

Passports/Visas: No visa required by British passport holders for stay
of less than 30 days.

British Embassy in Riga Tel: 2-320 737

TRANSPORT
Airports:
Riga-Skulte Tel: 2-207 661/207 009
Car hire in Riga:
Hertz Tel: (airport) 2-207 980 / Avis Tel: 2-225 876 (airport 2-207
353)
Speed limits: 70 km/h on trunk roads, 110 km/h on motorways,
60 km/h in towns.

Banks open: Hours vary, but banks are generally open between 10am
& 6pm. Exchange bureaus may stay open later.

Shops open: Hours vary, but shops are generally open between 9am &
6pm (some later) and many close for lunch.

National Holidays: New Year's Day, Good Friday, Easter Day,
1 May, 2nd Sunday in May, Jun 23 & 24, 18 Nov, Christmas Day,
Boxing Day & New Year's Eve.

Tourist Offices:
Latvian Embassy in London - Tel: 0171-727 1698
Tourist Board in Riga Tel: 2-229 945 / 2-213 011 / 2-327 542

(further information available from Intourist London - Tel: 0171-538
8600/538 5965)

American Express Travel Service Offices or Representative (R):
Riga - Latvia Tours (R)
   Grecinieku Str 22/24
   Tel: 2-213652/220047

Latvia   Riga

Riga   **Hotel de Rome**

Tel (2) 82 00 50   Fax (2) 82 00 58   **HR**

Kalku iela 28 1050 Riga

Rooms 90   Double room from $200

In the 1920s Riga was called the 'Paris of the East' and this hotel
was the glamorous *Grand Hotel*. Today, it still aims to keep that
stylish image and is the venue for local fashion shows and
exhibitions. Most of their guests are German and linked to the
new Latvian-German business initiatives being forged here. The
rooms, some of which look over the Opera House and public
gardens opposite, were all renovated in 1991 refurnished and
decorated with floral prints. The reception also aims at a
contemporary Western look, with a huge sculptural pyramid
hanging from the wall and local market garden flowers filling
every available space. *Theatre-style conference facilities for up to 100.
Translation services. Sauna, massage.* AMERICAN EXPRESS *Diners,
Mastercard.*

Restaurant Otto Schwarz

Seats 60   Meal for 2 approx $106

Like every aspect of Latvian life, this restaurant has been heavily
influenced by recent German investment; the head chef is from
North Germany and his cooking, despite being in many ways
traditionally Latvian, has plenty of German idiosyncrasies and
is far more comprehensive than any other restaurant in Riga.
Stuffed fillet of veal is served in a cherry sauce with maize
dumplings, while calf's liver comes in a balsamic vinegar sauce
with potato noodles. The specials change all the time, but always
veer towards the German influence, like fillet of trout served in a
rich carrot and butter sauce with sautéed potatoes or salmon with
grapefruit sauce. The dining room itself is panelled, with heavy
old carved mahogany, and looks over Riga's rooftops. *Open noon-
11pm.*

Lithuania

Currency: Lithuanian Lita   **Exchange Rate:** £1 = approx Lt 6
Not obtainable in UK. Travellers cheques/US dollars/DM
recommended.

International dialling code: 010 370
(Vilnius + 2)

Passports/Visas: No visa required by British passport holders for stay
of less than 1 month.

British Embassy in Vilnius: Tel: 2-222 070

TRANSPORT
Airports:
Vilnius Tel: 2-669 481/630 201
Railway Stations:
Vilnius Tel: 2-356 225
Car hire:
Vilnius - Eva Car Rental Tel: 2-649 428 / Balticar Tel: 2-460 998 /
Hertz Tel: 2-227 025 / Avis Tel: 2-733 226 (airport 2-291 131)
Speed limits: 70 km/h on trunk roads, 110 km/h on motorways,
60 km/h in towns.

Banks open: Hours vary, but banks are generally open between 10am
& 6pm. Exchange bureaus may stay open later.

Shops open: Hours vary, but shops are generally open between 9am &
6pm (some later) and many close for lunch.

National Holidays: New Year's Day, 16 Feb, Easter weekend, first
Sunday in May, 6 July, 1 Nov, Christmas Day & Boxing Day.

Tourist Offices:
Lithuanian Embassy in London - Tel: 0171-938 2481
Tourist Board in Vilnius Tel: 2-627 118

(further information available from Intourist London - Tel: 0171-538
8600/538 5965)

American Express Travel Service Offices or Representative (R):
Vilnius - Lithuanian Tours (R)
  Seimyniskiu Str. 18
  2005
  Tel: 2-353931/354163 #

Lithuania   Vilnius

Vilnius   **Restaurant Ida Basar**

Tel (2) 62 84 84   Fax (2) 62 78 34   R

Subacius gatré 3 Vilnius
Seats 32   Meal for 2 approx $40

A grand piano resounds through the upstairs restaurant, where the
more formal tables are arranged; while downstairs, more tables
surround a noisy bar. Being in the centre of the city, the scene can
be equally lively outside. German cooking dominates the extensive
menu. Chicken fricassee is fried with pineapple and bananas and
the pancakes are filled with the likes of fresh asparagus and wild
mushrooms. Daily specials are nearly always traditional Lithuanian
dishes. The blueberry dumplings with sour cream on the side are
great when the fruit are in season. Western European wines
(French, Italian and Spanish). *Open noon-1am. No parking. Diners,
Visa.*

Vilnius   **Lietuva Hotel**

Tel (2) 35 60 74   Fax (2) 35 62 70   H

Ulitsa Ukmerges Paleckio 20 2600 Vilnius
Rooms 200   Double room from $75

This 22-storey, state-owned hotel dating from the early 1980s
is just across the river from the old town of Vilnius. The
bedrooms are simple and functional, with telephones but few
other accessories. *Theatre-style conference facilities for up to 300.
Translation services. Hairdresser/chemist/post office. Private parking.*
AMERICAN EXPRESS® *Diners, Mastercard, Visa.*

THE APARTMENT SERVICE
Tel in UK: (0181) 748 4207   Fax: (0181) 748 3972
The Apartment Service will find you the right apartment
worldwide to suit your needs, whether you are on a short or
long-term stay. A 96-page colour catalogue is free on request.
All budgets are catered for.

Vilnius   **Restaurant Stiklai**

Tel (2) 22 23 18   Fax (2) 22 38 70   R

Ulitsa Gaono 7 Vilnius
Seats 70   Meal for 2 approx $35

The first privately-owned enterprise to open in Lithuania, this
place has been run by a co-operative since 1987. The 17th-century
building is sandwiched between two lively, winding streets right
in the heart of the old town. Surprisingly, the chefs trained
at *Lenotre* school in Paris and have introduced vegetarian choices
on to the menu – a rare feat for Slavic countries. Stuffed peppers
with fish and mushroom and potato pie are two of the more solid
Slavic dishes, but other more refined alternatives are goose breast
in cranberry sauce and pancakes filled with asparagus in a white
wine sauce. Veal is their main speciality, for example, veal
'Cipriani' (stir-fried veal cooked with peaches and cherries and
served in a cherry wine sauce). *Open 11am-late. Visa.*

Luxembourg

Currency: Luxembourg Franc **Exchange Rate:** £1 = approx FLux 50

International dialling code: 010 352 (for whole country)

Passports/Visas: No visa required by British passport holders.

British Embassy in Luxembourg Tel: 22 9864

TRANSPORT
Airports:
Findel Airport Tel: 47 98 2315
Railway Stations:
Gare Centrale Tel: 49 2424
Car hire in Luxembourg:
IDEM Car Rental Tel: 48 7684 (airport 43 4588) / Avis Tel: 48 9595/6
/ Budget Tel: 44 1938 (airport 43 7575)
Speed limits: 90 km/h on trunk roads, 120 km/h on motorways, 50
km/h in towns.

Banks open: Mon-Fri 8.30/9am-12/12.30pm & 1.30-4.30pm.

Shops open: Mon-Sat 9am-6pm. Many shops are closed Monday
mornings.

National Holidays: New Year's Day, 2 & 27 Jan, 17 April, 1 & 25
May, 5 & 23 Jun, 15 Aug, 4 Sep, 1 Nov, Christmas Day & Boxing Day.

Tourist Offices:
Luxembourg Tourist Board in London - Tel: 0171-434 2800
In Luxembourg (City) Tel: 48 1199 / 22 2809 / 47 1961 / 22 3296
(airport 40 0808)

American Express Travel Service Office:
Luxembourg City - AETS
    34 Avenue De La Porte Neuve
    L-2227
    Tel: 228555 #

Luxembourg

Luxembourg   Clairefontaine

Tel 46 22 11   Fax 47 08 21   **R**

9 Place de Clairefontaine 1341 Luxembourg

Seats 60   Meal for 2 approx FLux6000

Tony Tintinger is justifiably proud of his restaurant in the old part
of Luxembourg City: he has an exciting menu that changes every
week and a comprehensive wine cellar in an 11th-century tower
near the restaurant. His foie gras is served with caramelised apples
and calvados, his langoustine salad comes with finely chopped
leeks and a warm shellfish vinaigrette. Main dishes concentrate
on fish, veal, lamb and pigeon, with baby pigeon grilled and
served with potato ravioli and a light rape seed sauce. The four-
course fish menu with lobster and monkfish (FLux2560)
is excellent value, or lunchers can try *les menus d'affaires*. The long
list of desserts is also equally appetising: try the warm banana
soufflé served with a bitter orange coulis. *L 12-2 D 7-10. Closed
L Sat, last 2 weeks Aug. Private parking.* AMERICAN EXPRESS *Diners,
Mastercard, Visa.*

Luxembourg   Le Royal

Tel 4 16 16   Fax 22 59 48   **H**

12 Boulevard Royal 2449 Luxembourg

Rooms 80   Double room from FLux8900

This modern hotel, built only ten years ago, is right in the city
centre overlooking the park. Despite the location, it is quiet,
thanks to double-glazing throughout. The rooms, as expected, are
well equipped and even have Japanese satellite television and
Reuters financial information. Other facilities are also excellent,
with an indoor swimming pool, saunas, and a gym. *24hr room
service. Theatre-style conference facilities for up to 350.
Secretarial/translation/valet services on request. Public parking.*
AMERICAN EXPRESS *Diners, Mastercard, Visa.*

Luxembourg   Sheraton Aérogolf

Tel 34 05 71   Fax 34 02 17   **H**

Route de Trèves 1019 Luxembourg

Rooms 146   Double room from FLux8200

This modern hotel is very conveniently located, only 1km away
from the airport and 8km from the city centre. Rooms are up to
date and furnished with smart reproduction furniture and
matching carpets and curtains. The bar has live piano music every
night except Sunday, and in the summer you can take your drink
up to the terrace. *Satellite/cable TV. Theatre-style conference facilities
for up to 100. Secretarial/translation services on request. Private
parking.* AMERICAN EXPRESS *Mastercard, Visa.*

Echternach — La Bergerie

Tel 728 50 41   Fax 728 508   **H**

47 Route de Luxembourg 6450 Echternach
Rooms 15   Double room from FLux3400

Only 30 minutes from the airport and the City of Luxembourg,
this small family-run hotel was started after the considerable
success of their restaurant (*see below*). Despite its convenient
location it is in a quiet spot, five minutes away from a lake and
surrounded by gardens. The few bedrooms (mostly doubles) are
intended for visitors to their nearby restaurant and are plain, with
modern furniture. The atmosphere is very friendly and informal;
the owner's wife works on reception and his mother in the
restaurant. *Closed Jan, Feb. Solarium/sauna. Private parking.*
AMERICAN EXPRESS® *Diners, Mastercard, Visa.*

THE APARTMENT SERVICE
Tel in UK: (0181) 748 4207   Fax: (0181) 748 3972
The Apartment Service will find you the right apartment
worldwide to suit your needs, whether you are on a short or
long-term stay. A 96-page colour catalogue is free on request.
All budgets are catered for.

Geyershaff — La Bergerie

Tel 794 64   Fax 797 71   **R**

6251 Geyershaff
Seats 35   Meal for 2 approx FLux4800

This restaurant is part of the La Bergerie hotel in Echternach (*see
above*) although it is 6.5km away. In this 200-year-old farmhouse
in the middle of the countryside, the chef-owner has been cooking
French dishes, mostly fish, for years. His menu still excites with
house specialities such as lobster roasted with a selection of herbs,
fresh foie gras, saddle of young rabbit stuffed with herbs and
medallions of monkfish baked in saffron. Try the home-made
apple tart with cinnamon. The three set menus are also very
inviting and, starting at FLux2400, are excellent value. *L 12-2
D 7-9. Closed D Sun, Mon, 2 weeks from 1 Jan.* AMERICAN EXPRESS®
Diners, Mastercard, Visa.

★

Hesperange — L'Agath

Tel 48 86 87   Fax 48 55 05   **HR**

274 Route de Thionville 5884 (Howald) Hesperange
Rooms 5   Double room from FLux3300

5km outside the City of Luxembourg, this place offers a few lucky
diners in their French restaurant a comfortable bed for the night.
There are only five bedrooms so book well in advance. The
rooms are old-fashioned, but have been recently redecorated with
flowery curtains and bedcovers. They all overlook the quiet park
surrounding the building. Two small rooms can be used for
informal meetings, but there are really no other specific
conference facilities. *Swimming pool/tennis court/golf. Closed 2 weeks
from mid-Jul, 10 days from 21 Dec. Private parking.* AMERICAN EXPRESS®
Diners, Mastercard, Visa.

See over

Restaurant
Seats 40   Meal for 2 approx FLux5500

This Louis XVI dining room, with its glittering antique
chandeliers and wall tapestries, is intimate, comfortable and cosy;
the cooking too is homely and traditional, with a hint
of modernity. The predominantly fish menu has dishes like perch
cooked in basil and served with a compote of aubergines and
turbot *en croute* with a confit of tomatoes; or for those less keen
on fish: rabbit, pigeon, lamb or veal sweetbreads. *L 12-2 D 7-9.30.
Closed Sun, Mon.*

Hostert   Le Gastronome
`Tel & Fax 34 00 39`   R
90 Rue Andethana 6970 Hostert
Seats 55   Meal for 2 approx FLux4000

The chef-owner still adheres to his classic French training and
prepares traditional dishes like mousseline of asparagus, ravioli
stuffed with quail, foie gras, fillets of sole braised with bacon and
fillet of bass cooked in a star anise butter. This is definitely a place
for eating fish and most of the main dishes concentrate on it. *L 12-
2 D 7-10. Closed 7-13 Aug, 25 Dec. Private parking.* AMERICAN EXPRESS
Diners, Mastercard, Visa.

Kockelscheuer   Patin d'Or
`Tel 22 64 99   Fax 40 40 11`   R
40 Route de Bettembourg 1899 Kockelscheuer
Seats 35   Meal for 2 approx FLux7000

Buried deep in the forest, this restaurant, opened by the Berrings
in the 70s, brings new meaning to eating alfresco; half the tables
are outside on the terrace in the summer, while the rest look out
through vast windows into the forest. Monsieur Berring's cooking
owes a lot to the 15 years he spent working with Vergé in France,
but he has built on his traditional base and added plenty
of imaginative touches all of his own. *Filets de rouget de roche poelés,
pates à l'huile de homard* (fried rock mullet fillets on a bed of home-
made pasta with lobster-flavoured olive oil) and *pied de porc farci
à l'ancienne et sa fricassée de lentilles* (stuffed pig's trotters with
a traditional mix of green lentils and fresh vegetables) are two
notable house specialities. The menu changes constantly
to incorporate the best fresh ingredients with plenty of game
dishes on offer during the hunting season. Exclusively French
wines. *Open 12-9. Closed Sat, Sun. Private parking. Diners,
Mastercard, Visa.*

★

Limperstberg   Bouzonviller
`Tel 47 22 59   Fax 46 43 89`   R
138 Rue Albert Unden 2652 Limperstberg
Seats 30   Meal for 2 approx FLux3000

Bouzonviller continues, 35 years after he started cooking, to be
inspired by French food. His menu changes seasonally and has
a balanced variety of modern French dishes like pigeon sausages
served with a mixed green salad, smoked char (salmon-trout) with
fried leeks and for dessert, nougat ice cream with a bergamot

coulis. All the herbs and spices come from their garden at the back. The wines are predominantly French, with a dry white house bourgogne and a house red Minervois. *L 12-2 D 7.30-10. Closed 3 weeks Aug, 1 week end Dec. Public parking. Mastercard, Visa.*

Strassen   L'Olivier

Tel 31 36 66   Fax 31 36 27   H

140a Route d'Areon 8008 Strassen

Rooms 46   Double room from FLux4900

Purpose-built two years ago, L'Olivier has bedrooms which are well equipped and spacious enough to accommodate three to four people in the doubles. Even though it is surrounded by fields the hotel is only 3km from Luxembourg and ten minutes drive from the airport. Barbecues on the terrace are a regular feature. *Boardroom & theatre-style conference facilities for up to 70. Private parking.* AMERICAN EXPRESS *Mastercard, Visa.*

Scotch Beef Club Members: Luxembourg

CHAMPLON: Hostellerie de la Barrière de Champlon
DURBUY: Hotel de Prévot
NASSOGNE: Beau-Séjour

Luxembourg Index

Recommended by

EGON RONAY'S GUIDES

1995

Hotels & Restaurants
Europe
Family Hotels & Restaurants
Oriental Restaurants
New Zealand & South Pacific

Pubs & Inns
Just a Bite
Paris
Ireland
Australia

Egon Ronay's Guides are available from all good bookshops or can be
ordered from Leading Guides, 35 Tadema Road, London SW10 0PZ
Tel: 071-352 2485 / 352 0019   Fax: 071-376 5071

Malta

Currency: Maltese Lira   **Exchange Rate:** £1 = approx Lm 0.6

International dialling code: 010 356 (for whole island)

Passports/Visas: No visa required by British passport holders for stay of less than 3 months.

British High Commission in Malta Tel: 233 134/8

TRANSPORT
Airports:
Luqa airport Tel: 243 455
Car hire in Malta:
Avis (Msida) Tel: 246 640/225 986
Hertz (Gzira) Tel: 314 630/314 636
Budget (Marsa) Tel: 247 111/241 517
Budget, Europcar, Hertz & Avis at Luqa airport Tel: 249 600
Speed limits: 64 km/h on trunk roads, 40 km/h in towns.

Banks open: Mon-Fri 8.30am-12.30pm (to 11.30am Saturdays).

Shops open: 9am-7pm Mon-Sat (closed 3-4 hours at lunchtime).

National Holidays: New Year's Day, 10 Feb, 19 & 31 Mar, Good Friday, 1 May, 7 & 29 Jun, 15 Aug, 8 & 21 Sep, 8 & 13 Dec, Christmas Day.

Tourist Offices:
Maltese Tourist Board in London - Tel: 0171-323 0506
In Malta –
Luqa Airport Tel: 239 915
Valletta Tel: 224 444/5 or 225 048/9
Sliema Tel: 313 409
Gozo Tel: 556 454

American Express Travel Service Offices or Representative (R):
Valletta - A & V Von Brockedorff Ltd (R)
    14 Zachary Street
    Vlt 10
    PO Box 494
    Tel: 232141/230517/230763 #

Valletta

Valletta   The Carriage

Tel 24 78 28   R

68 South Street Valletta
Seats 50   Meal for 2 approx Lm25

One of Malta's leading restaurants, strongly supported by
prominent businessmen – and the kitchen also services the Prime
Minister's lunch room. The views from the windows are
spectacular and from here one can see the whole of the bay, the
capital Valletta and Manoel Island. The owner trained with
Alastair Little in London and in the last nine years has continued
to update and innovate the modern Mediterranean cooking
he serves. Carriage crab fishcakes are served with a mustard and
dill mayonnaise, ravioli are stuffed with artichoke purée and
chicken and artichoke roulade is decorated with mustard and
chives. The main menu and the set business lunch (Lm5.50)
change four times a year. A small, but select wine list offers
European and New World wines, with burgundy and champagne
served by the glass. *L 12.30-3.30 D Sat only 8-11. Closed Sun, Aug.
Public parking.* AMERICAN EXPRESS *Diners, Mastercard, Visa.*

★

THE APARTMENT SERVICE
Tel in UK: (0181) 748 4207   Fax: (0181) 748 3972
The Apartment Service will find you the right apartment
worldwide to suit your needs, whether you are on a short or
long-term stay. A 96-page colour catalogue is free on request.
All budgets are catered for.

Valletta   Hotel Phoenicia

Tel 22 52 41   Fax 23 52 54   HR

The Mall Floriana Valletta 16
Rooms 136   Double room from Lm58

The beautiful, fan-vaulted lounge, now painted in striking pastels,
highlights the architecture and grandeur of this 1920s hotel.
Although thoroughly modernised and comfortably up to standard
of a Forte Grand hotel, there is still a nice feeling of maturity and
comfort in the old vein. Its position, just outside the main gates of
the citadel of Valletta, makes it convenient for visiting
businessmen. Although it has no direct access to the harbour or
beach, there are beautiful terraced gardens, with an all-year-round
swimming pool. All this is situated just above the bastions and
there are magnificent harbour views. In accordance with its status,
it has full conference facilities and a fine ballroom. We
recommend the small supplement for rooms with a harbour view.
*24hr room service. Air-con, fax, satellite TV, mini-bar. Crazy golf.
Conference facilities for up to 600.* AMERICAN EXPRESS *Diners, Mastercard,
Visa.*

Phoenix Restaurant
Seats 400   Meal for 2 approx Lm30

The main hotel offers table d'hote lunch and dinner plus à la carte.
Executive chef Paul Pattersen, an Irishman, has arrived from the
Balmoral Hotel in Edinburgh. His repertoire includes marinated
wild salmon topped with beetroot and Oriental spices served on a
fine apple salad; a chilled tomato and basil consommé with soft
herb dumplings; roast breast of duck with a compote of lentils and
glazed baby onions enhanced by a sauce infused with lime.
Desserts include 'chocolate indulgence', which is a milk chocolate
bavarois with wild berries and Drambuie cream. Summer lunch
can be taken on the terrace and is a modestly price Lm5.50
carvery. Meals are regularly accompanied by a live pianist
or string trio or a classical guitarist, all playing at reasonable
decibels (not too intrusive). Mercifully the compulsory jacket and
tie regulation has now been rescinded. *L 12.30-2.30 D 7.30-10.30.*

Gozo

Gozo   Hotel Ta'Čenč

`Tel 55 68 19   Fax 55 81 99`   **HR**

Sannat 6020 Gozo
Rooms 82   Double room from Lm37

Imposing and situated on the highest point on Gozo, surrounded
by farmland and only 200m from the cliffs, this hotel opened
back in the 70s. However, since then, the place has had
a glamorous facelift, with the wooden-floored, farmhouse-style
rooms updated to include mini-bars and 12 suites complete with
their own terraces. Set just above its own private beach, Kantra,
the hotel is easily accessible by helicopter from the mainland,
or by ferry and the hotel's complimentary shuttle service. Every
conceivable water sport can be arranged here, so there is no excuse
to lounge under an umbrella. *Theatre-style conference facilities for
up to 300. Secretarial/translation/valet services on request. 2 tennis
courts/volleyball/2 swimming pools/water sports. Private parking.*
AMERICAN EXPRESS *Mastercard, Visa.*

Carruba Restaurant
Seats 150   Meal for 2 approx Lm24

Inside this old farmhouse with stone walls and marble floors,
a Maltese and an Italian chef prepare traditional Italian cooking
with 'Maltese influences' (very much Italian anyway). The daily
set menu serves simple Italian dishes like pasta with fresh pesto,
entrecote in a rich red wine and bone marrow sauce and sautéed
calf's kidneys, plus a few regional dishes like risotto served with
salmon. The home-made desserts are equally straightforward:
creme caramel, fresh fruit salad and crepes Suzette. *L 1-2.30
D 7.30-9.30.* AMERICAN EXPRESS *Diners, Mastercard, Visa.*

Gozo   L-Imġarr Hotel

`Tel 56 04 55   Fax 55 75 89`   **H**

Mgarr GSM 104 Gozo
Rooms 74   Double room from Lm56

Towering up above the cliffs on the Mgarr Harbour, this
impressive hotel in old farmhouse style was built in 1992.
Balconies look out over the harbour, the swimming pool or the
tiny old fishing village. The rooms are softly lit, with plain
windows which maximise the stunning views. They are modern,
but tastefully and individually furnished, with air-conditioning
throughout. For a cooling swim, there are good-size pools with
sun loungers set around the edge. The hotel offers a courtesy
shuttle service to the beach and the capital, Victoria, but the
quickest way to the airport on Malta is by helicopter. *24hr room
service. Satellite TV. Theatre-style conference facilities for up to 150.
Secretarial/translation services on request. 2 swimming pools (1 with
hydro-massage)/sauna/gym. Private parking.* AMERICAN EXPRESS *Mastercard,
Diners, Visa.*

Restaurant

Seats 140   Meal for 2 approx Lm30

The main hotel restaurant has been cleverly divided by arches into separate, intimate, semi-vaulted areas. It is nice to be immediately offered the table d'hote menu, changed daily, which offers both international and local dishes. Antipasto includes grilled peppers, aubergine and baby marrows. This is followed by a selection of pasta dishes such as pumpkin gnocchi prepared with butter and sage, rigatoni pasta with sausages, tomatoes and garlic or a stracciatella soup. Main courses include an excellent Gozitan rabbit stew, flavoured with thyme, and normally a good selection of fresh fish. Unusually for Malta they sometimes serve a really tender, pink calf's liver, which comes with polenta, spinach and tomatoes. The dessert house speciality is Grand Marnier soufflé. Hotel offers diners free pick up/drop off service to ferry to Malta. The table d'hote menu at Lm9 plus VAT is good value but drinks are expensive. *L 1-2.30 D 7-9.30 (Summer 7.30-10)*.

Elsewhere in Malta

Marsascala　　Christopher's

Tel 82 91 42　Fax 82 9142　　　　　　　　**R**

29 Marina Street Marsascala
Seats 32　　　　　　　　　　Meal for 2 approx Lm35

It may be difficult to believe, but this little restaurant has recently
been extended to its present size. The decor, however, remains the
same: natural brick walls, terracotta-tiled floors and classic
mahogany furniture. The owner-chef has an impressive pedigree,
having worked at the Grill Room in the London *Savoy* and with
Marco Pierre White at *Harveys* in London. He returned home
to start cooking imaginative French and Italian dishes, which
change daily. Starters range from ravioli filled with veal
sweetbreads and wild mushrooms to a chartreuse of avocado and
smoked salmon served with a warm goat's cheese sauce, to main
courses like stuffed pig's trotters, roast sea bass, breast of wood-
pigeon or steamed salmon. The wine list is as balanced as the
menu. Finish with a home-made sorbet or *tarte au chocolat. D 7.30-
10.30. Closed 2 weeks end Jul-Aug, 1st week Nov. Public parking.*
AMERICAN EXPRESS® *Mastercard, Visa.*

Melleiha　　The Arches

Tel 57 34 36　Fax 52 05 33　　　　　　　　**R**

113 Gorgborg Olivier Melleiha
Seats 80　　　　　　　　　　Meal for 2 approx Lm28

Dining here in the centre of Melleiha, in this elegant, colonnaded
room with arched windows looking out over the roof, is very
much a French affair combined with a light flirtation with
nouvelle cuisine. Specials like smoked trout with salmon mousse
and asparagus sauce, or grilled lamb cutlets with a rich ragout
of vegetables, change every week. The main à la carte menu has
a classic choice of dishes – beef stroganoff, *chateaubriand* and Dover
sole meunière – but also offers some more imaginative
alternatives. Fish of the day, lightly grilled with saffron and
paprika, pink duck breast served with a redcurrant sauce and
carpaccio served with a cold lettuce and olive oil sauce are typical
examples. Dessert is ice cream. *D 7.30-10.30. Closed Sun. Public
parking.* AMERICAN EXPRESS® *Mastercard, Visa.*

St Julians　　Hilton International

Tel 33 62 01　Fax 34 15 39　　　　　　　　**H**

St Julians
Rooms 204　　　　　　　　　　Double room from Lm57

The head concierge and many of the other staff have been here for
20 years, adding to the relaxed family-orientated atmosphere not
always found in a chain hotel. The Hilton is situated in 30 acres
of land and gardens, with its own private beach. The town and
the nearest nightlife are five minutes walk away. There are seven
suites available along with the bedrooms, which were being
refurbished and updated at the time of going to press. *24hr room
service. Theatre-style conference facilities for up to 450.
Secretarial/translation/valet services on request. 3 swimming pools
(heated in winter)/2 floodlit tennis courts/mini golf/sauna. Private
parking.* AMERICAN EXPRESS® *Diners, Mastercard, Visa.*

St Julians   Peppino's

Tel 37 32 00   **R**

31 St Georges Road St Julians
Seats 40   Meal for 2 approx Lm22

Ever since it opened in December 1991, this has been a very
popular meeting place; there is a bar on the ground floor and the
restaurant is on the first and second floors, overlooking St Julians
Bay and the fishing boats in the harbour. The menu
is straightforward and Italian, with the expected selection of pasta,
grilled fresh fish, veal and chicken. *L 12-3 D 7-11. Closed Sun,
2 weeks Jan. Public parking.* AMERICAN EXPRESS *Diners, Mastercard, Visa.*

St Paul's Bay   Le Pilier

Tel 57 68 87   Fax 57 68 87   **R**

14 Mosta Road St Paul's Bay SPB 07
Seats 66   Meal for 2 approx Lm24

Sitting in this arched stone building feels like being in an airy
Norman chapel, with its solid stone floors and wooden beams.
The menu is essentially French, with the occasional Italian dish
and some Maltese specialities such as rack of lamb encrusted with
mixed herbs and served with a mushroom timbale, breast
of duckling surrounded by a rich mushroom and port sauce, or a
filo pastry parcel of leg of duckling. The main menu
is complemented by ever-changing specials, like mussels served
in garlic and white wine or fillet of sole with a seafood and cider
cream sauce. *D 7-11. Closed Sun. Public parking.* AMERICAN EXPRESS
Diners, Mastercard, Visa.

San Anton   Corinthia Palace Hotel

Tel 44 03 01   Fax 46 57 13   **H**

De Paule Avenue San Anton BZN 02
Rooms 155   Double room from Lm68

New, palatial and fantastically well equipped, this colonnaded
villa, with its balustraded balconies, fountains and acres of foliage,
is a real retreat right in the centre of Malta, only 20m from the
Presidential Palace and the San Anton public gardens. The
conference facilities are excellent, with a 24-hour business centre
with up-to-date information on the financial markets. Extensive
facilities are also to be found in the bedrooms, decorated with
plain curtains, simple modern wooden furniture and flowery
quilts. For those looking to return home completely revitalised,
there is a unique health spa; unusual treatments like relaxing
Reiki, Rasul mud, and oxygen therapies are offered along with
a choice of four saunas, a therapy pool with jacuzzi, gym and
a natural solarium. Water workouts, natural beauty treatments and
meditation all combine to make this a particularly comprehensive
health centre. *24hr room service. Cable TV/fax. Theatre-style
conference facilities for up to 500. 2 secretaries/translation/valet services.
Health spa. Diners, Mastercard, Visa.*

Malta Index

Monaco

Currency: French Franc   **Exchange Rate:** £1 = approx Fr8

International dialling code: 010 33

British Consulate in Monte Carlo Tel: 93 50 99 66

TRANSPORT
Airports:
Nice Cote-D'Azur Tel: (general enquiries) 93 21 30 30 / (flight enquiries) 93 21 30 12
Railway Stations:
Monte Carlo Station Tel: (passenger information) 93 25 54 54 / (reservations) 93 30 74 00
Car hire:
Avis Tel: - city 93 30 17 53 / airport 93 21 36 33
Budget Tel: - city 92 16 00 70
Hertz Tel: - city 93 50 79 60 / airport 93 21 36 72
Europcar Tel: - city 93 50 74 95 / airport 93 21 36 44
Speed limits: 75 km/h on voie rapide (by-pass), 53 km/h in built-up areas.

Banks open: Mon-Fri 9am-12pm & 2-4.30pm (except afternoons preceding legal Bank Holidays)

Shops open: Daily from 9-12am and from 3-7pm except Sundays and Bank Holidays.

National Holidays: 2 & 27 Jan, 28 Feb, 17 April, 1 & 25 May, 5 jun, 15 Aug, 1 & 19 Nov, 8 Dec, Christmas Day, New Year's Day.

Tourist Offices:
Monaco Tourist Board in London - Tel: 0171-352 2103
In Monaco
Monte Carlo (Direction du Tourisme et des congres) Tel: 92 16 61 16

American Express Travel Service Office:
Monte Carlo - AETS
    35 Boulevard Princesse Charlotte
    Mc 98000
    Tel: 93 25 74 45 #

Monaco

Monte Carlo	Hotel de Paris

Tel 92 16 30 00   Fax 93 25 59 17   **HR**

Place du Casino MC 98000 Monaco

Rooms 251   Double room from Fr2300

Opened in 1864, this is a grand and imposing hotel that oozes
glamour, especially at the time of the Grand Prix when the jet-
setters stay in harbourside suites, with all the trappings of luxury.
An ongoing refurbishment programme has seen all the bedrooms
(184) in the newer part of the hotel redecorated; the old part (67
bedrooms) was in line for similar treatment during the winter
of 1994/1995. Satellite TV and mini-bars are standard in all
rooms, some eighty rooms have fax lines, and many enjoy
panoramic views. The stunning indoor swimming pool has heated
sea water, a shuttle takes you to an outdoor pool at the beach, and
tennis is available at the Monte Carlo Country Club, just 2km
away. Apart from the *Louis XV* restaurant (see below), there's the
rooftop *Grill* with its sliding roof and sensational views of the
Principality, and the *Terrasse-Empire,* open only during the season
and at Christmas/New Year. *24hr room service. Theatre-style
conference facilities for up to 100. Secretarial/translation services
on request. Indoor swimming pool. Ample parking (150 cars).*
AMERICAN EXPRESS *Diners, Mastercard, Visa.*

Restaurant Louis XV

Seats 70   Meal for 2 approx Fr2200

Arriving in 1987 to revitalise the cooking at this opulent and
grand dining room, with its ornately painted ceiling and Louis
XV-style panelling, Alain Ducasse had begun his career with Alain
Chapel, undoubtedly the greatest influence in his passion and taste
for haute cuisine. Now there are lots of Mediterranean
interpretations, using virgin olive oil, local fish and vegetables –
indeed there's a vegetarian menu *Les Jardins de Provence*, a snip
at Fr730! The other fixed-price menu (both change every day)
is even more steeply priced at Fr820, or else you can choose à la
carte or from *les suggestions.* Expect to see dishes (described
at length) such as *homard breton de nos viviers, grosses pates et vongole
en cocotte lutée au simple jus de la presse* (Brittany lobster fresh from
their own tanks, thick pasta and Italian clams in pastry, served
with a sauce made from the juices of the compressed lobster shell),
*chapon de la peche locale du jour tartiné de gamberoni hachés, pommes
à la boulangère, jus de bouillabaisse, salades de l'arrière-pays et crostini
frottés d'ail nouveau* (a locally caught pink fish spread with mashed-
up king prawns, with potatoes sliced and baked with onions,
a bouillabaisse sauce and a salad of vegetables with garlic croutons),
*pigeonneau des Alpes de Haute-Provence et foie gras de canard sur
la braise, pommes nouvelles à la peau* (young pigeon and foie gras
cooked over charcoal), or *quasi de veau de lait fermier cuisiné
en prenant le temps qu'il faut, légumes en gros morceaux gratinés au suc
de roti* (slow-cooked veal with caramelised chunky vegetables).
The dessert menu comes in two parts, based on either fruits
or chocolate/coffee; wiz patissier Frédéric Robert might offer wild
strawberries served in their warm juices with a mascarpone sorbet,
or a strong chocolate sorbet with white meringue and macerated
oranges surrounded by nougatine. *L 12.30-2 D 8-10.30. Closed
Tue, Wed (but open D Wed in summer), 2 weeks Feb, Dec.*

Netherlands

Currency: Dutch Guilder   **Exchange Rate:** £1 = approx Gld 2.7

International dialling code: 010 31
(Amsterdam + 20 Hague + 70 Rotterdam + 10)

Passports/Visas: No visa required by British passport holders.

British Embassy in Amsterdam Tel: 20-676 4343 Fax: 20-676 1069

TRANSPORT
Airports:
Amsterdam-Schiphol Tel: 20-601 9111 / Rotterdam-Zestienhoven Tel: 10-446 3444 / Eindhoven Tel: 40-524 255 / Maastricht-Beek Tel: 43-666 444
Railway Stations:
For all rail and transport information Tel: 69-292 (domestic) / 69-296 (international)
Car hire:
Amsterdam - Avis Tel: 20-564 1611 (airport 20-604 1301) / Europcar Tel: 20-665 4141 (airport 20-604 1566) / Budget Tel: 2503 71200 (airport 20-604 1349)
Rotterdam - Budget Tel: 10-411 3022 (airport 10-427 8196)
The Hague - Budget Tel: 70-382 4386/382 0609
Speed limits: 50 km/h on secondary roads, 80 km/h on trunk roads, 120 km/h on motorways, 30 km/h in towns

Banks open: 9am-4pm Mon-Fri (Thu from 5pm-8pm). Some banks close at 5pm.

Shops open: Mon 1-6pm, Tue-Fri 9am-6pm, Sat 9am-5pm. Some stores in main cities stay open until 9pm on Thursdays.

National Holidays: Good Friday, Easter, 30 April, 5 & 25 May, 4 & 5 Jun, Christmas Day & Boxing Day.

Tourist Offices:
Dutch Tourist Board in London - Tel: 0171-931 0707
In Holland –
Amsterdam Tel: 634-034 066 / Rotterdam Tel: 634-034 065 / The Hague Tel: 634-035 051

American Express Travel Service Offices or Representative (R):
The Hague - AETS
  Venestraat 20
  2511 AS
  Tel: 70-3701100 #
Amsterdam - AETS
  Van Baerlestraat 38
  1071 AZ
  Tel: 20-6738550 #

The Hague

The Hague	Auberge De Kieviet	
Tel (1751) 19232 Fax (1751) 10969		**HR**

Stoeplaan 27 2243 CX Wassenaar The Hague
Rooms 24   Double room from Gld250

Wassenaar is a smart district of the Hague and this small hotel
down a quiet street is beautiful and exclusive. Two top floors have
recently been built, adding an extra suite and more double rooms.
The decor is determinedly functional and plain, with the antique
furniture being the real highlight. Friendliness abounds. *24hr room
service. Cable TV. Theatre-style conference facilities. Private parking.*
AMERICAN EXPRESS *Diners, Mastercard, Visa.*

Restaurant
Seats 80   Meal for 2 approx Gld130

Functional rather than elaborate accurately describes this
restaurant; white linen and silver cutlery cover the tables neatly
and discreet paintings are dotted around the walls. If you choose
from one of the six set menus and long French wine list, there
is little room for disappointment. Gravlax with a rosemary
dressing, *espresso aux champignons* and baked quail in a sage sauce
served with noodles, finished off with baked apples caramelised
in honey, typifies the balanced, light menus. The sauvignon and
merlot house wines are extremely palatable. *L 12-2 D 6-10.*

THE APARTMENT SERVICE
Tel in UK: (0181) 748 4207   Fax: (0181) 748 3972
The Apartment Service will find you the right apartment
worldwide to suit your needs, whether you are on a short or
long-term stay. A 96-page colour catalogue is free on request.
All budgets are catered for.

The Hague	Corona	
Tel (70) 3637930 Fax (70) 3615785		**H**

Buitenhof 39-42 2513 AH The Hague
Rooms 26   Double room from Gld275

In a stylish, tree-lined street in the political heart of The Hague
(next to the Parliament buildings), three 17th-century Dutch
houses offer cosy, comfortable accommodation at a reasonable
price. The rooms are as inviting as the building, with flowery
decor and plain reproduction furniture. *24hr room service.
Conference facilities for up to 100. Secretarial/translation services
on request.* AMERICAN EXPRESS *Mastercard, Visa.*

The Hague   De Hoogwerf

Tel (70) 3475514   Fax (70) 3819596   **R**

Zijdelaan 20 2594 BV The Hague
Seats 250   Meal for 2 approx Gld220

Situated near the Queen's Palace and surrounded by a park, this
centuries old Dutch farmhouse bulging with antiques produces
simple but excellent French food. Each season, the menu changes
according to great national events. The 400th anniversary of the
tulip was being celebrated in 1994, and 1995 is the year of the
painter Mondrian. Grilled chicken livers on a bed of mixed leaf
salad, smoked sole in a dill sauce and beef stroganoff are typical
items. *Open 9am-midnight. Closed Sun, National holidays. Private
parking.* AMERICAN EXPRESS *Diners, Mastercard, Visa.*

The Hague   Des Indes

Tel (70) 3632932   Fax (70) 3451721   **H**

Lange Voorhout 54-56 2514 EG The Hague
Rooms 76   Double room from Gld490

The Inter-Continental chain took over this hotel in the early 80s
and were in the process of renovating the rooms at the time
of going to press. However, they will remain plain and elegant,
with their old fireplaces intact, decorated in light modern fabrics
and reproduction limed furniture. The building itself has a more
colourful history; back in 1880, a baron entertained his royal
guests in this, his stately home, and the sweeping staircase and
marble pillars still remain. The ballerina Pavlova (the famous
dessert was named after her) and the spy Mata Hari are among the
illustrious guests who have stayed here. *24hr room service. Theatre-
style conference facilities for up to 60 (fully equipped).
Secretarial/translation/valet services on request.* AMERICAN EXPRESS *Diners,
Mastercard, Visa.*

The Hague   Da Roberto

Tel (70) 3464977   **R**

Noordeinde 196 2514 GS The Hague
Seats 40   Meal for 2 approx Gld200

Roberto has been cooking in his restaurant in the heart of The
Hague for the last 15 years, and his menu is still loyal to his
traditional Italian culinary roots: warmed *carpaccio*, home-made
Tuscan pasta, *pappardelle* served with fresh cream, sardines and
anchovy paste and *osso buco alla milanese. L 12-2 D 6-10. Closed
Sun. Public parking.* AMERICAN EXPRESS *Diners, Mastercard, Visa.*

Opening times are often liable to change at short notice,
so it's always best to book.

The Hague   **Steigenberger Kurhaus Hotel**

Tel (70) 4162636   Fax (70) 4162646   **HR**

Gevers Deynootweg 30 2586 CK Scheveningen The Hague
Rooms 241   Double room from Gld425

Scheveningen is a famous Dutch beach resort and the hotel, an old
Grand Municipal Bathing House, is equally famous. In the 1900s
the Club de Schevinique in the hotel was a well-known club
where guests gambled at écarté and baccarat. Nowadays, this
seafront hotel is still a lively hotspot, and the Casino re-opened
in the 70s. But, despite its traditional recreational atmosphere, the
hotel has excellent conference facilities with 14 air-conditioned
conference rooms and European Community summit meetings
have been held here. Most of the rooms are doubles, but there are
two bridal suites for honeymooning couples. They were all
completely renovated in 1990 and are modern and well equipped.
*24hr room service. Cable TV. Theatre-style conference facilities for
up to 450. Secretarial/translation services on request. Florist.
Public/valet parking.* AMERICAN EXPRESS *Mastercard, Diners, Visa.*

Restaurant Kandinsky
Seats 55   Meal for 2 approx Gld180

A great deal of effort and attention to detail has gone into creating
this restaurant; the Kurhaus even purchased four signed lithos
by Kandinsky to decorate the walls. The *nouvelle cuisine* menu fits
in well with these modern art surroundings. It changes daily, with
such delicate dishes as confit of duck and raisins steeped
in armagnac, poached monkfish in a curried, white butter sauce
and home-smoked salmon with an olive oil, anchovy and basil
purée. The desserts are equally exquisite: a chartreuse bombe with
scrolls of chocolate and a vanilla sauce, and sesame mousse served
with port jelly. *L 12-3 D 6.30-10.30. Closed L Sat & July, Aug.
Valet parking.*

Around The Hague

Leidschendam   **Villa Rozenrust**

Tel (70) 3277460   Fax (70) 3275062   **R**

Veursestraatweg 104 2265 CG Leidschendam The Hague
Seats 100   Meal for 2 approx Gld130

Father and daughter have run this large 18th-century mansion as a
restaurant for 23 years. The arrival of a new chef five years ago
has moved the menu away from the traditionally French, towards
more rustic Italian cooking such as salmon lasagne and spinach and
ricotta ravioli. However, house specialities stick to their French
roots. The lightly cooked fillet of skate served with langoustines   ★
and a rich langoustine sauce and calf's sweetbreads in a white wine
sauce are fine examples. A large but cosy place, with rich red
carpeted floors and wooden tables: it comes as quite a surprise in a
quiet residential street. *L 12-2.30 D 6-10. Closed 2 weeks Aug,
National holidays.* AMERICAN EXPRESS *Diners, Mastercard, Visa.*

Voorburg   **Vreugd en Rust**

Tel (70) 3872081   Fax (70) 3877715   **RR**

Oosteinde 14 L2271 EH Voorburg The Hague
Seats 80   Meal for 2 approx Gld160

The candles glow in this 17th-century mansion and flicker across
the park surrounding it. Diners quietly enjoy the light French
dishes with simple starters like smoked mackerel and watercress
salad, crab soup with coriander and cheese and equally
straightforward main courses: roast beef cooked with potatoes and
marinated salmon served with rice. The head chef's forte
is cooking fish and beef, but his team make great patisserie – so try
the apricot tart served with pistachio ice cream before retiring for
the night to one of the fourteen comfortable bedrooms. *D only 7-
12. Closed 27 Dec-10 Jan.* AMERICAN EXPRESS *Mastercard, Visa.*

Amsterdam

Amsterdam   **Ambassade**

Tel (20) 6262333   Fax (20) 6245321   H

Herengracht 341 1016 AZ Amsterdam
Rooms 46   Double room from Gld275

Ten 17th- and 18th-century merchant houses make up this
traditional hotel (there's no restaurant), which is truly the pride
and joy of the lady who owns it; every winter she redecorates one
of the houses and continues to search for antique furniture to fill
the bedrooms. It is quite as romantic as a Venetian palazzo, the
canals surround the old buildings on all sides and narrow staircases
wind round up to the low-ceilinged bedrooms inside. It is hardly
surprising that so many writers have stayed here. The breakfast
room has a perfect view of the Herengracht canal and so do some
of the understated, excellently decorated rooms – so pick carefully.
24hr room service. Secretarial/translation services on request.
AMERICAN EXPRESS *Diners, Mastercard, Visa.*

Amsterdam   **American Hotel**

Tel (20) 6245322   Fax (20) 6253236   H

Leidsekade 97 1017 PN Amsterdam
Rooms 188   Double room from Gld475

Most locals visit this hotel to sit and admire the stunning art deco
café in the centre of the 19th-century listed building. The rooms
are also filled with art deco pieces and colourfully decorated. The
hotel enjoys a good location next to the Stadsschouwburg theatre
and almost facing the hustle and bustle of Leidseplein. *24hr room
service. Cable TV. Conference facilities. Secretarial/translation services
on request. Gym, sauna, solarium. Public parking.* AMERICAN EXPRESS
Mastercard, Visa.

Amsterdam   **Amstel Hotel Inter-Continental**

Tel (20) 6226060   Fax (20) 6225808   HR

Professor Tulpplein 1 1018 GX Amsterdam
Rooms 79   Double room from Gld850

One of the more elegant of Inter-Continental hotels, the Amstel
sits beside the canal and its terraces slope down to the very edge
of the water. Visiting heads of state and royalty tend to stay here
so locals consider this 19th-century building to be the 'the royal
palace of Amsterdam', with its imposing, classically designed
entrance hall and a recent £30 million renovation. Bedrooms are
now equipped with faxes and videos, and are traditionally
furnished with old desks and chintzy fabrics. *24hr room service.
Theatre-style conference facilities for up to 180.
Secretarial/translation/valet services on request. Indoor swimming pool,
sauna, jacuzzi.* AMERICAN EXPRESS *Diners, Mastercard, Visa.*

Restaurant La Rive
Seats 130   Meal for 2 approx Gld250

Mr Kranenborg, one of Holland's top chefs, has been brought into
the kitchen since the recent renovations and subsequent re-opening
in October 1993. Its 19th-century structure is still classically
charming, with beautiful views of the Amstel river (one can even

arrive here by boat). However, the menu remains French with appetising dishes such as baked sweetbreads and snails served with truffles, courgettes and chervil and baked red mullet in a shellfish sauce with tomato butter and polenta. He particularly favours pigeon, fish and duck. *L 12-3 D 6.30-10.30.*

Amsterdam   **Beau Bourg**

Tel (20) 6640155 Fax (20) 6640157   **R**

Emmalaan 25 1075 AT Amsterdam
Seats 60   Meal for 2 approx Gld40

This is the family's second restaurant, opened last year following the tremendous success of their first place, La Duchesse in Schiedam (see entry). Here they are in a chic, residential area of Amsterdam. Inside, it is a relaxed brasserie with a hotch-potch of tables and the soft sound of background jazz. The food, as in their more formal place, is traditionally French with *confit de canard* vying with *fruits de mer* as the house specialities. Try the good Beaujolais house wine. *L 12-3 D 6-11.30pm. Closed 31 Dec. Public parking.* AMERICAN EXPRESS *Mastercard, Visa.*

Amsterdam   **Christophe**

Tel (20) 6250807 Fax (20) 6389132   **R**

Leliegracht 46 1015 DH Amsterdam
Seats 80   Meal for 2 approx Gld200

Frenchman Christophe Royer loves Southern French regional cooking and slow old-time music – so his modern restaurant is a celebration of both. He cooks Mediterranean dishes such as duck foie gras marinated in Jurançon wine and served with a jelly of the wine as well as roast lobster with garlic and potatoes and monkfish with bacon, fresh noodles and a creamy mushroom sauce. There are also some Dutch dishes, notably the local catch grilled with coriander and fennel or smoked salted pork. Royer has collected a comprehensive selection of French chardonnays. *D only 7-11pm. Closed Sun. Public parking.* AMERICAN EXPRESS *Diners, Mastercard, Visa.*   ★

Amsterdam   **Hotel Dikker en Thijs**

Tel (20) 6267721 Fax (20) 6258986   **H**

Prinsengracht 444 1017 KE Amsterdam
Rooms 25   Double room from Gld315

Get a room with a view of the Prinsen canal outside this 19th-century canal house on the corner with Leidaestraat. Inside, the whole hotel was updated in the 80s, the bedrooms painted throughout with modern pastel colours and air-conditioning installed. Certainly, the marble reception area with its minimalist black leather sofas is quite a contrast to the typical canal house hotel. *24hr room service. Theatre-style conference facilities for up to 30. Secretarial/translation services on request.* AMERICAN EXPRESS *Diners, Mastercard, Visa.*

Amsterdam   Hotel de l'Europe

Tel (20) 6234836   Fax (20) 6242962   **HR**

Nieuwe Doelenstraat 2-8 1012 CP Amsterdam

Rooms 100   Double room from Gld555

Marble stretches along the floors and up the pillars in the
reception of this 19th-century hotel, which is part of the Concorde
Hotel Group. All the bedrooms have large, light windows, the
best overlooking the Muntplein and the canals. Some are modern
with white-painted furniture, the rest have heavy curtains, old-
fashioned blankets and four-poster beds. If you want to see the
sights of Amsterdam, this hotel is in a great location in the city
centre. *24hr room service. Cable TV/video. Theatre-style conference
facilities for up to 500. Secretarial/translation/valet services on request.
Swimming pool(indoor). Private parking.* AMERICAN EXPRESS *Diners,
Mastercard, Visa.*

Restaurant Excelsior

Seats 90   Meal for 2 approx Gld130

The meal's excellent value – four courses, an apéritif, wine and
coffee for Gld130 – has not been lost on the locals so this high-
ceilinged, chandelier-filled salon is often busy. Nevertheless, the
subdued piano music still makes it a quiet place for a romantic
evening. The set and à la carte menus are both faithfully French,
with starters like pan-fried duck liver served with a sweet and
sour pear sauce and grilled red mullet served with fresh Italian
tomatoes. The main courses also offer no great surprises: grilled
turbot served with a mustard sauce and roast saddle of lamb
cooked in thyme and honey. Shellfish is their main speciality: try
langoustine curry or lobster salad. The wine list is also religiously
French. *L 12.30-2 D 7-10.*

Amsterdam   The Garden Hotel

Tel (20) 6642121   Fax (20) 6799356   **H**

Dijsselhofplantsoen 7 1077 BJ Amsterdam

Rooms 90   Double room from Gld465

Amsterdam's green belt stretches around this aptly-named small
hotel close to the Amstel canal and a short stroll from Vondelpark.
It's popular with opera stars, and the staff are incredibly helpful
with extra services, such as valet parking. The rooms have all been
inspired by food and are either caviar grey, salmon pink or salad
green. Whichever you choose, all rooms have been modernised
recently, and the bathrooms now all have jacuzzis. *24hr room
service. Conference facilities (fully equipped). Public/valet parking.*
AMERICAN EXPRESS *Diners, Mastercard, Visa.*

Amsterdam   The Grand

Tel (20) 5553111   Fax (20) 5553222   **HR**

Oude Zijdse Voorburgwal 197 1012 EX Amsterdam

Rooms 182   Double room from Gld625

Two canals flow through the courtyard gardens of this 16th-
century hotel, which was once a convent. Despite being so central,
it enjoys a very secluded location. All the bedrooms overlook
either the canal or the courtyard and are tastefully furnished

in light colours with some original 17th-century pieces. Quite
a few changes have occurred recently; it has been taken over
by the French chain, Demeure Hotels, who have renovated the
rooms, closed the Admiralty restaurant and improved the menu
of the bistro, Café Roux. It is a comfortable place to stay, especially
with the variety of sports facilities. The conference rooms have all
been personally designed by Monique Roux (Albert Roux's wife,
Albert being the proprietor of London's Le Gavroche restaurant)
with Dutch antique vases and glass. *24hr room service. Fax. Theatre-
style conference facilities for up to 200. Secretarial/translation services
on request. Spa, sauna, Turkish baths, whirlpool bath. Private parking.*
AMERICAN EXPRESS *Mastercard, Visa.*

Café Roux

Seats 65   Meal for 2 approx Gld90

The chef Andrew Turner came here from London's Le Gavroche
two years ago, and works very closely with Albert Roux, who
acts as an advisor and mentor. But even with the recent changes
and the closure of the Admiralty restaurant, the Café remains loyal
to the classic Roux roots: fish terrine, crab soufflé, fillet of sole
with mussels and prawns, fillet of cod in a garlic sauce, and rum
and chocolate mousse are all regulars on the menu. As a brasserie,
it does not aim to match the variety and quality of the raw
ingredients previously used in the Admiralty, but it still serves
some finely prepared dishes. *Open 6.30am-11.30pm.*

Amsterdam   **Grand Hotel Krasnapolsky**   **H**

Tel (20) 5549111   Fax (20) 6228607

Dam 9, 1012 JS Amsterdam
Rooms 322   Double room from Gld485

Krasnapolsky originally had a Polish café here, but, unusually,
extended it into a hotel. The rooms are stylish and well equipped,
with faxes, safes and elegant writing desks. A new bedroom wing
will be opened in 1995. *24hr room service. Theatre-style conference
facilities for up to 1500. Secretarial/translation/valet services. Private
parking.* AMERICAN EXPRESS *Mastercard, Visa.*

Amsterdam   **Halvemaan**   **R**

Tel (20) 6440348   Fax (20) 6441777

van Leyenberghlaan 20 Buitenveldert 1082 GM Amsterdam
Seats 65   Meal for 2 approx Gld275

Modern architecture meets modern menu in this unusual 80s
purpose-built restaurant, designed by the leading Dutch architect
also responsible for the new wing of the Boymans van Beuningen
Museum in Rotterdam. Inside, leading Dutch artists exhibit their
recent work. The owner-chef cooks a selection of shellfish, meat
and fish dishes that do not vary a great deal throughout the year.
His cooking has traditional French influences, but remains
essentially Dutch. Steak tartare and veal sweetbreads compete with
smoked salmon with lentils and veal kidneys served with garlicky
mashed potatoes. Wines are French, German and Australian; there
are no house wines. *L 12-2.30 D 6-10.30. Closed Sat & Sun. Private
parking.* AMERICAN EXPRESS *Diners, Mastercard, Visa.*

Amsterdam   Hilton

Tel (20) 6780780   Fax (20) 6626688

H

Apollolaan 138-140 1077 BG Amsterdam

Rooms 271   Double room from Gld440

Hilton acquired this hotel in the 60s and famously had John Lennon and Yoko Ono honeymooning in one of their suites. 20 minutes from the airport but a long walk from the city centre, the hotel, which borders the Amstel canal benefits from being in a quiet and largely residential location. The traditional rooms are due to be redecorated in 1995. *24hr room service. Cable TV. Secretarial/translation services on request. Theatre-style conference facilities for up to 650. Marina and yacht club. Private parking.* AMERICAN EXPRESS *Mastercard, Visa.*

Amsterdam   De Hoop Op D'Swarte Walvis

Tel (75) 165629 Fax (75) 162476

R

Kalverringdijk 15 1509 BT Amsterdam

Seats 100   Meal for 2 approx Gld250

As in many good Dutch restaurants, the chef marries French food with Dutch specialities in an eclectic menu: *zaanse mosterdsoup* (traditional creamy mustard soup) and *texels lam* (lamb stewed in its own stock) are served alongside turbot in a mustard and saffron sauce and fillet of veal in a tomato and basil sauce. A real bonus here is the superb location: ten minutes outside Amsterdam in an old whaling village with 17th-century wooden houses – this one was an old orphanage. The beamed restaurant, full of old fishing tackle and brass lamps, spreads out on to a conservatory (with nine more tables). *L 12-2.30 D 6-10.30.* AMERICAN EXPRESS *Diners, Mastercard, Visa.*

Amsterdam   De Jonge Dikkert

Tel (20) 6411378   Fax (20) 6459161

R

Amsterdamseweg 104A 1182 HG Amsterdam

Seats 100   Meal for 2 approx Gld160

This rustic restaurant – ten minutes from Amsterdam – was a 17th-century windmill; now the floors are polished red stone and Dutch paintings hang on the walls. But the cooking is not just the usual combination of Dutch herrings, mustard soup and *sauerkraut*; French dishes include wild duck and tournedos. They also produce their own home-smoked salmon. Jazz music makes this quite a lively spot in the evening. *L 12-3 D 6-10. Private parking.* AMERICAN EXPRESS *Diners, Mastercard, Visa.*

Amsterdam   Keyzer

Tel (20) 6620778   Fax (20) 6737353

R

Van Baerlestraat 96 1071 BB Amsterdam

Seats 100   Meal for 2 approx Gld200

Do not be put off by the run-down street; the atmosphere inside is chic and arty. This art deco restaurant plays host to bohemian diners and regular exhibitions by local young artists. It is very cosy, with the tables squeezed close together. Traditional French fare is served to the loyal clientele; regular dishes like sole meunière and lamb provençale are the order of the day and game comes on to the menu in its season. *Open 9am to midnight. Closed Sun. Public parking.* AMERICAN EXPRESS *Diners, Mastercard, Visa.*

Amsterdam	Lucius	
Tel (20) 6241831 Fax (20) 6276153		**R**

Spuistraat 247 1012 VP Amsterdam
Seats 75   Meal for 2 approx Gld200

A no-nonsense fish restaurant appropriately set in a 19th-century salvage warehouse building. They serve a wide variety of seafood and fish: Dutch salted herrings, *gefillte fisch* (carp served with a salty gherkin and horseradish sauce), fried plaice, fresh mussels and oysters. Drink *jenever* (an aromatic gin) with the herrings, and a cool glass of Dutch beer with the rest. The place is usually packed, but not noisy, so as you sit at a small, blue-and-white-checked table you can watch the busy street life go by. *D 5-12. Public parking.* AMERICAN EXPRESS *Mastercard, Visa.*

Amsterdam	Sichuan Food	
Tel (20) 6269327 Fax (20) 6277281		**R**

Regulierdwarsstraat 35 1017 BK Amsterdam
Seats 61   Meal for 2 approx Gld200

It is a real find to discover a traditional Sichuan restuarant in the heart of a city whose main foray into Eastern cuisine has been Indonesian. Dim sum, Peking duck and fish, especially fresh lobster out of their fish tank are the specialities, along with spicy fried oysters. French Bordeaux and strong, sweet Chinese wines are served with the strongly flavoured food. *D 5-11. Public parking.* AMERICAN EXPRESS *Mastercard, Visa.*

Amsterdam	De Silveren Spieghel	
Tel (20) 6246589 Fax (20) 6203867		**R**

Kattengat 4 & 6 101252 Amsterdam
Seats 120   Meal for 2 approx Gld170

Right in the heart of Amsterdam's Montmartre-style district with busy squares and the Singel canal nearby, this 17th-century building was originally the premises of a soap manufacturer. Not long after, Spieghel, the Mayor at the time, converted it into one of Amsterdam's first proper restaurants. The chef is influenced by French cuisine, but still serves traditional Dutch dishes, like mustard soup and lamb poached in its own stock. Like many Dutch restaurants they are not open for lunch, except by arrangement. An amazing 5000 bottles of wine fill the cellars, collected by the sommelier-owner. *D 6-10.* AMERICAN EXPRESS *Mastercard.*

> Meal prices for 2 are based on à la carte menus.
> When set menus are available, prices will often be lower.

Amsterdam   **Vermeer**

Tel (20) 5564885 Fax (20) 6243353	**R**

Prins Hendrikkade 59 1012 AD Amsterdam

Seats 55   Meal for 2 approx Gld300

Inside the Hotel Barbizon Palace is a setting just like a Vermeer –
and copies of his paintings hang in the lounge. Two 17th-century
houses have been joined together to create this homely restaurant:
antiques are dotted round the rooms and original wooden panels
line the walls. The cooking looks to southern Italy for its
inspiration; among the most mouthwatering of the dishes
is vanilla-flavoured mascarpone soufflé topped with crushed and
minted raspberries. Other choices on the à la carte menu are also
appetising: lightly sautéed terrine of goose liver and potatoes
sprinkled with hazelnut oil makes a delicious starter, and the
prawn fishcakes with garlic and saffron a tasty main course. *L 12-3
D 6.30-10.30. Closed Jul-mid Aug, 25 Dec-2 Jan. Private parking.*
AMERICAN EXPRESS *Diners, Mastercard, Visa.*

Around Amsterdam

Hoorn   **De Oude Rosmolen**

Tel (2290) 1 47 52 Fax (2290) 1 49 38	**R**

Duinsteeg 1 1621 ER Hoorn

Seats 35   Meal for 2 approx Gld250

Old culinary secrets have passed from father to son; and the latter
now cooks in the kitchen of this 17th-century building in the
centre of Hoorn. The cooking is as cosy as the small restaurant
with its old paintings and casual Italian furniture and the menus
change almost every day. The three and four-course set menus
offer good value and plenty of interest, with such delights
as *terrine de ris de veau asperges, et mousseline à l'huile de truffe* and   ★
homard aux macaronis, crémette de homard. The 'Petit Faim Grand
Plaisir' *dégustation* menu particularly appeals. Try the light
profiteroles stuffed with foie gras mousse. Unusually for Holland,
most of the raw ingredients come directly from France. *D 6-9.30.
Closed Thur, 2 weeks Aug depending on local fair. Public parking.*
AMERICAN EXPRESS *Diners, Mastercard, Visa.*

Overveen   **De Bokkedoorns**

Tel (23) 263600 Fax (23) 273143	**R**

Zeeweg 53 2051 EB Overveen Haarlem

Seats 45   Meal for 2 approx Gld200

Deep in the dunes on a remote corner of a lake, this restaurant has
been passed down from father to son for generations. Back in the
60s, they ran a café as well, but now it is only the traditional
French restaurant that they built themselves which has survived.
The fish comes fresh from the coast every day and the turbot and
shellfish are very popular. But some unusual meat dishes can also   ★
be enjoyed: pigeon is served in a strong meat sauce and rack
of lamb is cooked with herbs and vegetables and served in a rich
gravy. Chardonnays from Chile meet German rieslings on an
eclectic wine list. *L 12-2.30 D 5.30-12. Closed 2 weeks after
Christmas. Private parking.* AMERICAN EXPRESS *Diners, Mastercard, Visa.*

Rotterdam

Rotterdam	**Le Coq d'Or**

Tel (10) 4366405   Fax (10) 436 59 06   R

Van Vollenhovenstraat 25 3016 BG Rotterdam

Seats 150   Meal for 2 approx Gld170

The strong, traditionally French and extensive à la carte menu
is extremely inviting, with some interesting hors d'oeuvre,
particularly the *bouillon* of duck with morel mushrooms and fried
goose liver served with slices of green apple, marinated in port.
The fish dishes also create some imaginative combinations: pike-
perch is grilled with scallops and strips of leek and served with
a warm goose liver sauce and fried monkfish comes with
an unusually rich red wine sauce. The French wines go down very
well with the food, so take time to enjoy them, the 19th-century
Dutch surroundings and famous collection of paintings. *L 12-3
D 6-12. Closed Sun. L valet parking/D public parking.* AMERICAN EXPRESS®
Diners, Mastercard, Visa.

Rotterdam	**Old Dutch**

Tel (10) 4360344   Fax (10) 4367826   R

Rochussenstraat 20 3015 EK Rotterdam

Seats 110   Meal for 2 approx Gld200

Ever since this restaurant was rebuilt after World War II, it has
been one of the main meeting places for Rotterdam's industrial
elite; the Bodega Bar has seen many deals done over a few
cocktails. The old Dutch country-style house serves both rich and
light dishes on a menu that changes seasonally. Home-smoked and
marinated salmon, lobster bisque and home-made goose liver paté
are followed by dishes such as grilled sole and turbot and fried
monkfish served with the market's freshest vegetables. The French
wine list is short, but comprehensive, with two good house wines.
Open 11.30am-midnight. Closed Sat, Sun. Valet parking.
AMERICAN EXPRESS® *Diners, Mastercard, Visa.*

Rotterdam	**Parkheuvel**

Tel (10) 4360530   Fax (10) 4367140   R

Heuvellaan 21 3016 GL Rotterdam

Seats 60   Meal for 2 approx Gld260

A cosy restaurant whose large glass window gives you a splendid
view over the harbour. The chef-patron's French and Dutch
cuisine is splendidly executed, from the traditional terrine
of Dutch herrings, served with potatoes, gherkins and dill, and
fried cod with shrimps and browned butter, to modern French
dishes like monkfish with coriander and veal fried in truffle oil
and served with creamed kidney beans and truffle sauce. *L 12-3
D 6-10. Closed Sun. Private parking with valet service.* AMERICAN EXPRESS®
Diners, Mastercard, Visa. 🐂

Opening times are often liable to change at short notice,
so it's always best to book.

Rotterdam   **Ràden Mas**

Tel (10) 4117244   Fax (10) 4119711   **R**

Kruishade 72 3012 EH Rotterdam
Seats 120   Meal for 2 approx Gld200

Not on the face of it the most congenial location for eating: right
in the centre of a busy shopping centre in the centre of Rotterdam.
But step in away from the shopping crowds and you will find
an appealing array of Indonesian delicacies on the menu. The
Indonesian rijstafel (rice table) starts with a fragrant herb *bouillon*
served with miniature meat balls, moving on to shrimps, spicy
traditional Dutch-Indonesian chicken satay, grilled beef fillet and
stir-fried roast pork in a piquant sauce. If, instead, you decide
to create your own *mini-dégustation*, try the more unusual oyster
satay grilled on skewers with a fragrant sauce or the colourful
combination of artichokes stuffed with prawns and crab meat on a
bed of spinach sauce. They offer an extensive French wine list, but
a cool Indonesian beer goes down equally well. *Open noon-
10.30pm. Closed 24-31 Dec. Public parking.* AMERICAN EXPRESS
Mastercard, Visa.

Rotterdam   **Rainbow Hotel**

Tel (10) 4134790   Fax (10) 4127890   ·   **H**

Willemsplein 1 3016 DN Rotterdam
Rooms 104   Double room from Gld150

Having recently become part of the Norwegian chain, 'Rainbow
Hotels', the hotel, which sits prettily alongside the banks of the
Nieuwe Maas river, has been extensively renovated. The rooms
are now rather colourful, with simple, modern wooden writing
desks and beds. Rotterdam railway station is two kilometres away
(the No 5 tram takes you door to door). *24hr room service. Theatre-
style conference facilities for up to 60. Closed 24 Dec-2 Jan.*
AMERICAN EXPRESS *Diners, Mastercard, Visa.*

Rotterdam   **Savoy Hotel**

Tel (10) 4139280   Fax (10) 4045712   **H**

Hoogstraat 81 3011 PJ Rotterdam
Rooms 94   Double room from Gld175

The industrial noise and smells of Rotterdam are thankfully left
behind outside the Savoy, due to its new double-glazed windows
and subdued, discreet atmosphere. This Savoy is relatively new,
originating from the 60s; the rooms are all modern, plain and
functional, and regularly redecorated. Despite its modernity, the
hotel does not have any of its own health or conference facilities,
but guests can use the fitness club across the road and hold
meetings at their sister hotel, the *Atlanta. 24hr room service. Cable
TV. Fax/secretarial/translation services on request.* AMERICAN EXPRESS
Mastercard, Visa.

Around Rotterdam

Ommoord   **Keizershof**

| Tel (10) 4551333   Fax (10) 45568023 | **R** |

Martin Luther Kingweg 7 3069 EW Rotterdam

Seats 90   Meal for 2 approx Gld200

Restaurants with truly international menus are quite rare, but here a Burgundy food festival follows a Dutch one, while other dishes on the menu are Indian, Japanese and traditional French. To complement this eclectic menu, the owner has a huge collection of wines, one of the largest in the country, including some good French house bottles. It is a big restaurant, decorated like an old German farmhouse with a vast fireplace surrounded by antiques. Popular with parties. *Open 11am-10pm.* AMERICAN EXPRESS® *Diners, Mastercard, Visa.*

Schiedam   **Auberge Hosman Frères**

| Tel (10) 4264096   Fax (10) 4730008 | **R** |

Korte Dam 8-10 3111 BG Schiedam

Seats 50   Meal for 2 approx Gld180

Built on the foundations of a 12th-century convent, the inn itself goes back to 1547. It's in an area with many active windmills including the Walvirch, reputedly the largest in the world. For the last 20 years, the Hosman family have owned the auberge and bistro next door, as well as running a wine importing business, and the wine list features some particularly good burgundies. French dishes are the order of the day, with traditional French *bouillabaisse*, or crab served with a ragout of duck and pilau rice. Finish with some sweet Dutch strawberries. For an even cheaper menu with similar beef, fish and seafood dishes, you can eat in the more buzzing bistro, where large wooden tables make it a great venue for parties. *L 12-2 D 6-10, Sat 6-10 only. Closed Sun, Mon, 24 Dec, 31 Dec-1 Jan. Public parking.* AMERICAN EXPRESS® *Diners, Mastercard, Visa.*

Schiedam   **La Duchesse**

| Tel (10) 4264626   Fax (10) 4732501 | **R** |

Maasboulevard 9 3114 HB Schiedam

Seats 80   Meal for 2 approx Gld200

A husband-and-wife team have been running this restaurant on the banks of the Meuse for the last five years – and it is very popular with the locals. The extensive French menu includes traditional favourites: snails, oysters, fillet of monkfish and grilled salmon. However, it also branches out beyond the standard French repertoire to include interesting dishes such as *fricassée de lapin, tournedos de boeuf* with wild mushrooms in a port sauce. Look out for the long list of liqueurs. *L 12-3 D 6-10.30. Closed D Sat, all Sun, 31 Dec. Private parking.* AMERICAN EXPRESS® *Diners, Mastercard, Visa.*

Scotch Beef Club Members: The Netherlands

GRONINGEN
OUDESCHANS: De Piekenier

FRIESLAND
APPELSCHA: La Tourbe
BAKKEVEEN: De Slotplaats
BOLSWARD: De Doele
DRACHTEN: De Wilgenhoeve
HEERENVEEN: Sir Sebastian

OVERIJSSEL
BLOKZIJL: Kaatje bij Sluis
DALFSEN: Pien
DE LUTTE: De Wilmersberg
ENSCHEDE: Het Koetshuis Schuttersveld
ENTER: De Twentsche Hoeve
OOTMARSUM: De Wiemsel
ZWOLLE: Barbara

GELDERLAND
ARNHEM: De Menthenberg
BRUCHEM: Landgoed Groenboven
EDE: Het Pomphuis
GARDEREN: De Bonte Koe
's HEERENBERG: Le Loup
NUNSPEET: Het Roode Wold
OLDENBROEK: Herkert
WAGENINGEN: Steakhouse

UTRECHT
HARMELEN: De Kloosterhoeve
HOUTEN: De Hofnar
MONTFOORT: De Schans
UTRECHT: Jean d'Hubert
VINKEVEEN: Le Canard Sauvage
WOERDEN: De Schutter

NOORD HOLLAND
AMSTERDAM: Bartholdy
AMSTERDAM: Beddington's
AMSTERDAM: De Boekanier
AMSTERDAM: Chez Georges
AMSTERDAM: Forte Crest Apollo
AMSTERDAM: The Grand
AMSTERDAM: Intermezzo
AMSTERDAM: SAS Royal Hotel
AMSTERDAM: Swissotel Ascot
AMSTERDAM: Teppan Yaki Hosokawa
AMSTERDAM: De Trechter
AMSTERDAM: Het Tuynhuys
BENTVELD: Blanje Bleu
BEVERWIJK: 't Gildehuys
BEVERWIJK: In'd Hooge Heeren
CALLANTSOOG: De Vijverhut
HAARLEM: Peter Cuyper
HEEMSKERK: De Vergulde Wagen
HEEMSTEDE: Le Cheval Blanc

HEERHUGOWAARD: De Zandhorst
HILVERSUM: Chablis
HOORN: Portofino
KUDELSTAART: De Kempers Roef
LISSERBROEK: Het Oude Dijkhuys
MONNICKENDAM: Nieuw Stuttenburgt
SCHAGEN: Igesz
SCHIPHOL: Hilton Airport
SCHOORL: Merlet
TEXEL DEN HOORN: Het Kompas
ZANDVOORT: Riche
Z.O. BEEMSTER: La Ciboulette

ZUID HOLLAND
BERGAMBACHT: Onder de Molen
DELFT: L'Orage
DEN HAAG: Julien
DEN HAAG: Rousseau
DEN HAAG: Sauvage
DEN HAAG: Sequenza
DEN HAAG: Shirasagi
HOEK VAN HOLLAND: De Blaasbalg
LEIDEN: Holiday Inn
LEIDERDORP: Elckerlyc
MIDDELHARNIS: De Hooge Heerlykheid
OEGSTGEEST: De Beukenhof
OOSTVOORNE: Parkzicht
OUDDORP: Beau Rivage
ROTTERDAM: Hilton
ROTTERDAM: Parkheuvel
SPIJKENISSE: 't Ganzegors
WADDINXVEEN: 't Baarsje
WARMOND: De Stad Rome

NOORD BRABANT
BREDA: Le Canard
DEN BOSCH: Chalet Royal
EINDHOVEN: Holiday Inn
EINDHOVEN: De Luytervelde
ETTEN-LEUR: De Zwaan
OIRSCHOT: La Fleurie
UDEN: De Druiventros

LIMBURG
HIEJEN: Mazenburg
MAASTRICHT: 't Plenske
NUTH: Pingerhof
VAALS: Ambiente
VAALS: Gillissen
VALKENBURG: Les Cupidos
VALKENBURG: Eduards
VALKENBURG: 't Hooght-Thermaetel
VALKENBURG: Lindenhorst
VALKENBURG: Prinses Juliana
WEERT: l'Auberge

ZEELAND
SCHUDDEBEURS: Schuddebeurs
SLUIS: Oud Sluis

Netherlands Index

Norway

Currency: Norwegian Krona
Exchange Rate: £1 = approx NKr 10.50

International dialling code: 010 47
(Oslo + 22)

Passports/Visas: No visa required by British passport holders.

British Embassy in Oslo Tel: 22-55 2400

TRANSPORT
Airports:
Oslo-Fornebu (international & regular flights) Tel: 67-53 8566
Oslo-Gardemoen (charter flights) Tel: 63-97 8448
Railway Stations:
Oslo Central Station Tel: 22-36 8000 (reservations: international 22-36 8111 / domestic 022-36 8085) / Nationaltheateret Station (tel information service) Tel: 22-17 70 30
Norwegian State Railways (central office) Tel: 22-83 8850 (Reservations: 22-17 1400)
Car hire in Oslo:
Hertz Tel: 22-20 0121 (airport 67-53 3647) / Avis Tel: 22-83 5800 (airport 67-53 0557) / Budget Tel: 22-17 1050 (airport 67-7924)
Speed limits: 80 km/h on trunk roads, 90 km/h on motorways, 50 km/h in towns.

Banks open: Winter hours Mon-Fri 8.15am-3.30pm (Thu till 3pm). Summer hours (15 May-15 Sep) Mon-Fri 8.15am-3pm (Thu till 5pm).

Shops open: Mon-Fri 9am-4/5pm, Thu till 6/8pm, Sat till 1/3pm.

National Holidays: New Year's Day, 9, 13, 14, 16 & 17 April, 1, 17 & 25 May, 4 & 5 June, Christmas Day & Boxing Day.

Tourist Offices:
Norwegian Tourist Board in London - Tel: 0171-839 6255
In Oslo - (main office) Tel: 22-83 0050 / (Central Station) Tel: 22-17 1124

American Express Travel Service Office:
Oslo - American Express
    Karl Johansgatan 33/35
    PO Box 1705
    0121
    Tel: 2-2861300 #

Oslo

Oslo	**Ambassadeur Hotel**	
Tel 22 44 18 35 Fax 22 44 47 91		**H**

Camilla Colletts vei 15 0258 Oslo 2
Rooms 41   Double room from NKr1500

Within easy reach of the park, museums and city's shopping
centre, this hotel also has the added advantage of being in a quiet,
civilised residential area. There is a welcome departure from the
uniform minimalist Norwegian decor, with rooms decorated
in Dutch, Roman or seafaring styles. Conference facilities are
limited to one theatre-style meeting room that can seat 25 people.
No room service. AMERICAN EXPRESS® *Diners, Mastercard, Visa.*

Oslo	**Babette's Gjestehus**	
Tel 22 41 64 64 Fax 22 41 64 63		**R**

Rådhispassagen 0160 Oslo 1
Seats 40   Meal for 2 approx NKr1000

The restaurant is internationally famous for inspiring Karen
Blixen's book, *Babette's Feast*, subsequently made into an engaging
film. Norway has some of the best fish in Scandinavia, so the
almost wholly fishy menu comes as little surprise, and is very
enjoyable. Fish soup is served with peppers in a garlic sauce;
poached monkfish is cooked with spring cabbage; a token meat
dish such as fillet of veal *marengo* with tomatoes, onions and
mushrooms appears on the menu. Desserts are delicious – try
chocolate tart with mocca sauce. The international wine list has
a predominance of French bottles. *D 4-12 (Mon-Fri) 5-12 (Sat).
Closed Sun. Public parking.* AMERICAN EXPRESS® *Diners, Mastercard, Visa.*

Oslo	**Bagatelle**	
Tel 22 44 63 97 Fax 22 43 64 20		**R**

Bygdøy Allé 3 0257 Oslo 2
Seats 70   Meal for 2 approx NKr2000

Eyvind Hellstrøm has been cooking since 1965 and in 1982
he bought this old 30s French restaurant, one of the best in
Scandinavia. His pedigree is impeccable: he trained with Girardet
among others and has taken the rudiments and flair of French
cuisine and adapted it to Norwegian ingredients, with plenty
of shellfish and game. Oysters, lobster, turbot, scallops and crayfish
are all regular features on the seasonally changing menu. Grilled   ★
Norwegian lobster is served with a light herb butter; monkfish
tails are served with a mustard and cabbage-shrimp stew. The
wine list is vast and well selected, with an all-encompassing list
of burgundies and Bordeaux. *D 6.30-10.30. Closed Sun.
No parking.* AMERICAN EXPRESS® *Diners, Mastercard, Visa.*

Oslo   Bondeheimen Hotel

Tel 22 42 95 30   Fax 22 41 94 37   **H**

Rosenkrantzgate 8 0159 Oslo 1
Rooms 76   Double room from NKr990

A typically Norwegian hotel offering homely touches like bread
baked on the premises. Not only is the decor quite arty but
Norwegian authors regularly meet here for literary lunches. Being
right in the city centre, the bedrooms can be a little noisy, so ask
for a room at the back, overlooking the courtyard. The decor
in the rooms is minimalist and modern. The only sports facilities
are a Scandinavian sauna and solarium. The cafeteria is a pleasant
spot: quite chic and serving simple home-made food. *24hr room
service. Closed 22 Dec-2 Jan. Public parking.* AMERICAN EXPRESS *Diners,
Mastercard, Visa.*

Oslo   Le Canard

Tel 22 43 40 28   Fax 22 55 65 65   **R**

Oscarsgate 81 0256 Oslo 1
Seats 60   Meal for 2 approx NKr1500

Chef Lucien Mares, offers a traditional French menu. Duck,
chicken and game dishes are favourites, with house specialities
being roasted duck with olives, Madeira roasted roebuck, confit
of duck, and braised leg of veal with a caper sauce. The setting,
however, is more typically Norwegian, rustically decorated with
heavy 19th-century wooden furniture. *D 7-1am (Mon-Thur) 6-
1am (Fri, Sat). Closed Sun. Public parking.* AMERICAN EXPRESS *Diners,
Mastercard, Visa.*

★

THE APARTMENT SERVICE
Tel in UK: (0181) 748 4207   Fax: (0181) 748 3972
The Apartment Service will find you the right apartment
worldwide to suit your needs, whether you are on a short or
long-term stay. A 96-page colour catalogue is free on request.
All budgets are catered for.

Oslo   Continental Hotel

Tel 22 41 90 60   Fax 22 42 96 89   **HR**

Stortinsgaten 24-26 0161 Oslo 1
Rooms 163   Double room from NKr1900

Centrally located midway between the Royal Palace and the City
Hall, this is a traditional, family-run place. The old-fashioned
rooms have been renovated over the last three years and are now
equipped with cable TV and modern pine furniture. The hotel has
large conference facilities and secretarial and translation services.
*Theatre-style conference facilities for up to 300. Secretarial/translation
services on request. Closed 23 Dec-2 Jan. Private garage.* AMERICAN EXPRESS
Diners, Mastercard, Visa.   *See over for restaurant*

Restaurant Annen Etage
Seats 80   Meal for 2 approx NKr1400

A very grand Belle Epoque dining room with a high ornate
ceiling, columns and chandeliers, the restaurant offers French
cuisine alongside Norwegian specialities, as typified in the six-
course autumn Kr580 *menu dégustation*, starting perhaps with
breast of pheasant and grilled scallops served with balsamic
vinegar, marinated trout and pickled pumpkin, a refreshing
Campari and grapefruit sorbet, followed by a main course
of white grouse and wild mushrooms served with a stag cutlet in a   ★
red wine sauce with pears, Norwegian cheeses, and glazed apples
with caramel ice cream. More conventional dishes include
a mushroom bouillon with crayfish tails, sole *belle meunière*, wild
duck served with stuffed cabbage and a peppery sauce, and desserts
such as a classic crème brulée or passion fruit soufflé. Some
Californian wines on an otherwise European-only wine list. *L 12-2
D 7-10 Closed Sat, Sun, July, 23 Dec-2 Jan.*

Oslo   **D'Artagnan**

| Tel 22 41 50 62   Fax 22 42 77 41 | R |

Øvre Slottsgate 16 0157 Oslo 1
Seats 55   Meal for 2 approx NKr1600

Norwegian chef Freddie Nielsen has been running his restaurant
since the late 70s. He trained in Copenhagen and also in France
and his culinary heroes are Raymond Blanc and Michel Guérard.
He aims to emulate their modern French menus, using Norwegian
ingredients, leading to an obvious bias towards fish. Home-smoked
salmon fillets are served with a delicate sea urchin tart; truffles,
oysters and scallops come in a consommé; grilled fillet of halibut   ★
is served with a crayfish sauce. Game dishes like fillet of venison
and breast of partridge make seasonal appearances. The French-
only wine list has a house burgundy on offer. *Open 4.30pm-
midnight. Closed Sat, Sun, 7-31 Jul, 22 Dec-3 Jan. No parking.*
AMERICAN EXPRESS *Diners, Mastercard, Visa.*

Oslo   **Feinschmecker**

| Tel 22 44 17 77   Fax 22 56 11 39 | R |

Balchensgate 5 0265 Oslo 2
Seats 70   Meal for 2 approx NKr1000

The chef here is on the Norwegian national culinary team,
competing all over the world – so there's no guarantee that
he personally will be cooking your dinner. But the menu remains
the same in his absence. From the large, traditional open-plan
kitchen come grilled scallops with a celeriac purée and crispy
potato slices served in a saffron *bouillon* flavoured with fresh herbs.
Baked turbot is served with crispy potatoes and a fennel and apple
compote. His house specialities tend to be more local delicacies   ★
like marinated raw salmon served with caviar and salmon roe,
roast breast of duck with glazed endives and salt-baked pine-nuts,
baked turbot and grilled monkfish with a creamy sorrel sauce.
The place is ten minutes walk from the National Theatre, off
a small side street. *D 4.30-10.30. Closed Sun, 9-16 Apr, 7-31 Jul,
22 Dec-2 Jan. No parking.* AMERICAN EXPRESS *Diners, Mastercard, Visa.*

Oslo   Gabelshus Hotel

Tel 22 55 22 60   Fax 22 44 27 30   **H**

Gabelsgate 16 0272 Oslo 2

Rooms 45   Double room from NKr1000

The same family has run this place since the '40s and it has
a relaxed, informal air. There are 15 rooms in an extension built
in 1960 and these have bathrooms, while the others just have
showers. It is a good quarter of an hour out of the city, on the
road towards the airport. *Cable TV. Theatre-style conference
facilities for up to 65. Closed 21 Dec-2 Jan. Private parking.*
AMERICAN EXPRESS *Diners, Mastercard, Visa.*

Oslo   Grand Hotel

Tel 22 42 93 90   Fax 22 42 12 25   **H**

Karl Johansgate 31 0159 Oslo 1

Rooms 289   Double room from NKr1850

Part of the pleasure of staying here is that everywhere is a short
stroll away: the sights, the theatre, the park and Parliament. The
vast number of rooms are perhaps not up to international business
hotel standards, facilities-wise, but are stylishy set out. However,
the conference facilities are unusually large and well equipped for
Oslo. *Theatre-style conference facilities for up to 300.
Secretarial/translation services on request.* AMERICAN EXPRESS *Diners,
Mastercard, Visa.*

Oslo   Bristol Hotel

Tel 22 41 58 40   Fax 22 42 86 51   **H**

Kristian IV's gate 7 0164 Oslo 1

Rooms 141   Double room from NKr1490

Friendly and traditional, this Norwegian-run hotel, part of the
Inter Nor chain, makes a real effort to make your visit a pleasant
one, but with limited conference and other sports facilities, they
are not really suited to entertaining large business parties.
However, conferences can be organised across the road, where
there is room for up to 300 people theatre-style. The location
is excellent, two or three minutes walk from the Castle in the
middle of Oslo. *Cable/satellite TV. Theatre-style conference facilities
for up to 30.* AMERICAN EXPRESS *Diners, Mastercard, Visa.*

Oslo   Kastanjen

Tel 22 43 44 67   Fax 22 55 48 72   **R**

Bygdøy Allé 18 0262 Oslo 2

Seats 55   Meal for 2 approx NKr1000

This place offers Norwegian and European food on an eclectic
menu (translated into English). Starters like fish and shellfish soup
with garlic mayonnaise and duck confit with sweet pickles could
be followed by steamed salmon with cabbage in a light shellfish
broth. Main dishes include a good mix of fish and meat, a typical
meat dish being shoulder of lamb stuffed with fresh herbs and
served with aubergines and tomatoes. Chocolate honey terrine
with a raspberry sauce makes a fine dessert. *D 6-12. Closed Sun, 22
Dec-4 Jan, 1-4 Apr.* AMERICAN EXPRESS *Diners, Mastercard, Visa.*

Oslo   Kyoto

Tel 22 83 05 79   Fax 22 83 20 09   R

Bryggetorget 1 Aker Brygge 0250 Oslo 2
Seats 176   Meal for 2 approx NKr800

Any restaurant in Oslo which deviates from the Norwegian norm
is refreshing, and here an internationally-trained Japanese chef
produces authentic teppanyaki, sushi and teriyaki that breaks the
narrow gastronomic boundaries imposed on this capital. Starters
like skewered prawns and vegetables in a teriyaki sauce are
followed by sushi served on fragrant rice and slices of grilled
reindeer steak with a teriyaki sauce. Kyoto boasts one of the
largest international wine lists in Oslo. *Open 11.30am-11.30pm*
(Mon-Fri) 11.30am-11pm (Sun). Closed 23 Dec-1 Jan. Public
parking. AMERICAN EXPRESS *Diners, Mastercard, Visa.*

Oslo   Norum Hotel

Tel 22 44 79 90   Fax 22 44 92 39   H

Bygdøy Allé 53 0265 Oslo 2
Rooms 59   Double room from NKr870

A third generation, family-run hotel in a peaceful location
overlooking a park 15 minutes walk from the city centre. The
rooms are surprisingly well equipped, considering it is quite
a small place, and have recently been redecorated. Sixty people can
be accommodated for a theatre-style conference. *24hr room service.*
Closed 20-30 Dec, 26 Mar-4 Apr. AMERICAN EXPRESS *Diners, Mastercard,*
Visa.

Oslo   Ritz Hotel

Tel 22 44 39 60   Fax 22 44 67 13   H

Frederik Stangs Gate 3 0272 Oslo 2
Rooms 100   Double room from NKr990

A Ritz franchise that has been family-run since 1981. The
building originally was an early 20th-century inn. It is surrounded
by a garden and the rooms are quiet, despite the hotel
(incidentally, without a restaurant) being right in the city centre.
The facilities are pretty minimal with limited conference
amenities. *Cable/satellite TV. Theatre-style.conference facilities for*
up to 60. Closed 3-13 Apr, 23 Dec-3 Jan. Private parking.
AMERICAN EXPRESS *Diners, Mastercard, Visa.*

Oslo   Vika Atrium

Tel 22 83 33 00   Fax 22 83 09 57   H

Munkedansveien 45 0250 Oslo 1
Rooms 91   Double room from NKr955

Minutes away from the harbour and situated on a busy street, the
hotel is nevertheless reasonably quiet as the well-equipped modern
bedrooms are at the back of the building. However, sports and
conference facilities are limited. *No room service. Cable TV.*
Theatre-style conference facilities for up to 10. Gym. Private parking.
AMERICAN EXPRESS *Diners, Mastercard, Visa.*

Around Oslo

Sandvika	**Rica Hotel Oslofjord**

Tel 67 54 57 00   Fax 67 54 27 33   **H**

Sandviksveien 184 1300 Oslo 2

Rooms 242   Double room from NKr1270

15 minutes out of the city centre, near a fiord, this fantastic hotel is part of a Norwegian chain of business hotels. The original parts of the house were built in Ancient Dragon style in 1894, with splendid wood-panelled carvings depicting traditional Norwegian sagas in the main hall and fine sculptures and artwork elsewhere. The towering timber staircase is extraordinary. All the facilities, from the gym, sauna and whirlpool to the conference facilities are up to the minute; an added attraction is the hotel yacht, which can be hired to sail the waterways (for up to 30 people). There's also a large new shopping centre down the road. *Cable/satellite TV. Theatre-style conference facilities for 400. Private parking.* AMERICAN EXPRESS *Diners, Mastercard, Visa.*

Norway Index

Poland

Currency: Polish Zloty   **Exchange Rate:** £1 = approx Złt 36,400
Not usually obtainable in UK. Travellers cheques recommended.

International dialling code: 010 48
(Gdansk + 58 Poznan + 61 Krakow + 12 Wroclaw + 71
Warsaw + 22(6fig) + 2(7fig) Bydgoszcz + 52)

Passports/Visas: No visa required by British passport holders for stay
of less than 6 months.

British Embassy in Gdansk Tel: 58-628 1001/5   Fax: 58-621 7161

TRANSPORT
Airports:
Warsaw Tel: (International) 22-461 731/22-465 603 (Domestic) 2-650
1750/2-650 1953
Railway Stations:
Warsaw Tel: (International) 22-204 512/22-259 942 (Domestic) 22-200
361/369
Car hire in Warsaw:
Avis Tel: 2-630 7316 (airport 2-650 4871) / Budget Tel: 2-630 7280
(airport 22-467 310) / Europcar Tel: (airport) 22-249 772
Speed limits: 90km/h on trunk roads, 110 km/h on motorways,
60 km/h in towns.

Banks open: 8am-noon Mon-Fri (varies from town to town).

Shops open: (for groceries) 6am-6/7pm (Sat 7am-1pm), some shops
stay open for late-night shopping and on Sundays and holidays. Other
shops 10/11am-6/7pm, department stores generally 9am-8pm.

National Holidays: New Year's Day, Easter Sunday & Monday, 1 & 3
May, movable feasts, Corpus Christi, 15 August, 1 & 11 Nov, Christmas
Day & Boxing Day.

Tourist Offices:
Polish Tourist Board in London - Tel: 0171-637 4971
In Poland -
Warsaw Tel: 2-635 1881/22-316 356
Gdansk Tel: 58-314355/316637
Krakow Tel: 12-226091

American Express Travel Service Office:
Warsaw - AETS
  Dom Bez Kantow Krakowskie
  Przedmiescie 11
  Pl-34500
  PO Box 159
  Tel: 22-6352002 #

Warsaw

Warsaw   Ambasador

Tel (22) 25 99 61   **R**

Matejki 2 00-478 Warsaw

Seats 70   Meal for 2 approx Złt650,000

The 'ambassadorial' name of this restaurant is probably more
appropriate to its location, near the American Embassy (and,
incidentally, within walking distance of the Lazienki Park), rather
than being considered an ambassador for Polish cuisine. However,
it's fine for straightforward staples, such as meat platters, though
presentation can seem rather passé, particularly to Western diners
who have long said good-bye to the 'radish flower' school
of garnishing. The staff are warm and friendly, the colour scheme
bright, with traditional, decorative panels, and there's plenty
of greenery springing out from baskets and pots. For an alternative
vista look out of the long picture window overlooking the street.
Next to the dining room is the restaurant's coffee house, which
is worth visiting for ice cream and patisserie, particularly if it's
taken in the charming garden. Entrance in Aleje Ujazdowskie 8.
Open 11am-11pm. Public parking. AMERICAN EXPRESS *Diners, Mastercard,
Visa.*

THE APARTMENT SERVICE
Tel in UK: (0181) 748 4207   Fax: (0181) 748 3972
The Apartment Service will find you the right apartment
worldwide to suit your needs, whether you are on a short or
long-term stay. A 96-page colour catalogue is free on request.
All budgets are catered for.

Warsaw   Bazyliszek

Tel & Fax (22) 31 63 47   **R**

Rynek Starego Miasta 3/7 00-950 Warsaw

Seats 130   Meal for 2 approx Złt800,000

Walk straight past the snack bar (salads, vegetarian food, 40
different beers) on the ground floor of this distinguished burgher's
house and continue up to the first floor, where Bazyliszek offers
an altogether more substantial experience. Interconnecting dining
rooms with double wooden doors and period-style furniture have
more the air of a hunting lodge than a central city location
overlooking the old town market square. Moreover, paintings are
merely a side-show to the medieval armour, curved swords, cross-
bows and other aggressive accessories which decorate the walls.
Not surprisingly, game dishes are prominent on the menu
together with many long-standing favourites of native cuisine.
Presentation can appear extravagant, even rather over-elaborate,
but who cares – it's the taste that counts, and that is consistently
impressive. Attentive service combines smoothly with all the
other elements to make this one of Warsaw's best restaurants. *Open
noon-late. Public parking.* AMERICAN EXPRESS *Diners, Mastercard, Visa.*

Warsaw   Belvedere

Tel (22) 41 48 06   Fax (22) 41 71 35   R

Lazienki Krolewskie Park 00-460 Warsaw

Seats 70   Meal for 2 approx Złt2,000,000

The Lazienki Park setting is very romantic, incorporating the
magnificent Palace-on-the-Isle, together with various other palaces
and pavilions, an amphitheatre and Egyptian temple, as well as the
orangery which now contains the Belvedere restaurant. The
Belvedere's menu is a sterling pact between classic Polish and
modern European, and there are rewards for having a foot in both
camps. Sophisticated presentation draws on the best elements
of *nouvelle cuisine*, with flavour at full volume. When booking,
specify that you want a table actually in the orangery (where
greenery flourishes amongst period style), as there's always
a chance of being seated in the adjoining neo-classical section –
which spoils some of the point of going. Belvedere has also
revived the spirit of the 'Thursday dinners' which Poland's last
King, Stanislaus Poniatowski, held for the likes of writers, artists
and politicians at the adjacent Palace-on-the-Isle, the King's
summer residence. However, you're just as likely to sit next
to intellectuals and diplomats on any other day of the week. *Open
noon-midnight. Private parking. Fri & Sat dancing in the summer.*
AMERICAN EXPRESS *Diners, Mastercard, Visa.*

Warsaw   Hotel Bristol

Tel (2) 625 25 25   Fax (2) 625 25 27   HR

Ul Krakowskie Przedmiescie 42/44 00-325 Warsaw

Rooms 206   Double room from Złt5,280,000

When the sublime Hotel Bristol re-opened in 1992, it was
immediately re-established as one of Europe's grandest hotels, just
as in the past when luminaries such as Marlene Dietrich and Pablo
Picasso used to check in. The art nouveau building (with
matching interiors) is listed as a national monument, though it also
incorporates just as much culinary as artistic excellence. *24hr room
service. Business centre. Private parking.* AMERICAN EXPRESS *Diners,
Mastercard, Visa.*   *See over for restaurant*

Restaurant Malinowa
Seats 55   Meal for 2 approx Złt1,600,00

Very much at the forefront of 'new wave' Polish cuisine, the
Malinowa restaurant begins by sourcing traditional recipes
(including some from 19th-century cookbooks). And while
leaving their national identity intact, recipes are also given the
necessary update for modern palates, and the result is the best food
in Warsaw. *Barszcz* (Polish-style borscht) has been elevated into
a beetroot julienne with a gently jellied consommé and soured
cream, while *pierogi* (akin to ravioli) with seaweed is another
exciting development, served with a white wine and veal sauce,
in place of the usual melted butter and fried breadcrumbs. For
creative, full-flavoured Italian food (including carpaccio of veal
loin in truffle dressing, and veal escalopes on saffron risotto with
a light lemon sauce), the *Marconi* restaurant comes complete with
formal wooden panelling and views over a delightful courtyard.
Additionally the *Café Bristol* serves Austrian-style light meals and
patisserie in a Viennese-inspired setting, while leisure is catered for
by the indoor swimming pool, and the Cartier boutique. A joint
venture between Forte and Orbis, the Polish State Tourist
Organisation, the Hotel Bristol really is the peak of chic –
something which has long been missing in Warsaw. A short walk
from the old town. *Open noon-11pm.*

★

Warsaw   Ejlat

| Tel (2) 628 54 72 | R |

Ujazdowskie 47 Warsaw 00-536
Seats 60   Meal for 2 approx Złt400,000

Particularly recommended for an inexpensive and satisfying lunch,
Ejlat is centrally located, within the premises of the Polish-Israeli
Friendship Society. Not surprisingly, the menu offers typical
favourites from both schools of cooking, together with some
European items, and appeals as much to diplomats, politicians and
journalists as to anyone else. *Open 10am-late. Public parking.*
AMERICAN EXPRESS® *Diners, Mastercard, Visa.*

Warsaw   Hotel Europejski

| Tel (22) 26 50 51   Fax (22) 26 11 11 | HR |

Krakowskie Przedmiescie 13 00-065 Warsaw
Rooms 200   Double room from Złt350,000

Housing one of Warsaw's better restaurants, this is also one of the
city's oldest hotels, built in 1857 in a handsome, classical style.
Once through the pillared entrance, however, its clear that the
Europejski, although it has all the raw ingredients, is in need
of thorough refurbishment (particularly as it is opposite the Hotel
Bristol, which fully illustrates the heights that restoration can
achieve). The large main restaurant, *Europejski-Lux*, is too tired
to carry off its original colonnaded splendour. Fortunately, the
food has resisted the overall decline, revelling in classic Polish
as well as flambéed dishes. Many locals still head for the *Europejski*,
for the the less expensive and more comfortable *U Ossolinskich*
restaurant, where staple Polish fare and more international dishes
are served. The hotel's coffee house is also well-worth visiting.

Only minutes walk from the Royal Castle and old town, the
Europejski overlooks the Ogrod Saski (Saxon Gardens) on one
side, and on the other, Krakowskie Przedmiescie, one of the city's
most imposing thoroughfares. *24hr room service. Theatre-style
conference facilities for up to 50 (no secretarial services). Private garage.*
AMERICAN EXPRESS *Diners, Mastercard, Visa.*

Warsaw   **Foksal**

| Tel (22) 26 53 37   Fax (22) 27 87 16 | **R** |

Ul Foksal 3/5 00-366 Warsaw
Seats 50   Meal for 2 approx Złt800,000

Once a journalists' club, this central restaurant is now an altogether
different story, welcoming a much faster set, with a modern
sophisticated interior that concentrates on marble and flowers,
as well as a water garden. The cooking aims at a similar level
of modernity offering a choice of European, particularly French,
and international dishes. However trying to embrace such a broad
spectrum means the Foksal can be overwhelming. *Open noon-late.
Private parking.* AMERICAN EXPRESS *Diners, Mastercard, Visa.*

Warsaw   **Restauracja Fukier**

| Tel (22) 31 10 13   Fax (22) 31 10 13 | **R** |

Rynek Starego Miasta 27 00-272 Warsaw
Seats 160   Meal for 2 approx Złt1,000,000

Warsaw doesn't as yet have many pioneers of 'new wave' Polish
cuisine, but within that elite band Fukier is a formidable player.
This position reflects the proprietor's extensive culinary experience
in Europe – and Warsaw is now lapping it up. While respecting
the best elements of historic Polish favourites, such as *bigos*
(hunters' stew), dishes emerge from the kitchen with innovative,
well-defined flavours, and are composed carefully. Fukier's setting
also maximises the best of Polish tradition, being resplendent
within a burgher's house in the old town market square. Formal
aspects, such as oak panelling, a vaulted ceiling, chandeliers and
period-style furniture, are wittily combined with touches of folk
art. In summer you can dine alfresco in Fukier's patio courtyard.
Needless to say all this comes at a price, but it's well worth it.
Open noon-late. No parking. Diners, Mastercard, Visa.

The Golden Eurostar [★] denotes our pick of the
restaurants. Cooking is the major consideration, but
other factors are also taken into account, including
ambience, comfort and service.

Warsaw   Gessler's In The Garden

Tel (22) 27 06 63   Fax (22) 26 60 24   **R**

Ogrod Saski (Saxon Gardens) approached from Senatorska 37 00159 Warsaw

Seats 50   Meal for 2 approx Złt1,000,000

There are many individual benefits to be enjoyed at this restaurant, but they don't always add up to give a total package. Delightfully set on the edge of the Ogrod Saski (Saxon Gardens), a wooded park only a short stroll from the old town, Gessler (the last in a long line of Polish restaurateurs) also makes the best of a period building that has elements of a classical villa. The tree-lined terrace (with a necklace of coloured bulbs hanging between them) has plenty of pulling power in summer, whether it's to enjoy specialities such as fish (particularly herring and smoked trout), or to come after dinner, in typical local style, for the marvellous ice creams with fruit. The extravagantly phrased menu can be as mystifying as it is enticing – less could definitely mean more, while service can be less than it should be. Nevertheless, whether it's foreign diplomats or local trade, the appeal of Gessler's In The Garden remains perennial. *Open 11am-1am. Private garage.* AMERICAN EXPRESS *Diners, Mastercard, Visa.*

Warsaw   Hotel Grand

Tel (22) 29 40 51   Fax (2) 621 97 24   **HR**

Ul Krucza 28 00-522 Warsaw

Rooms 327   Double room from Złt1,805,000

It sounds encouraging, but beware. This hotel is in fact a prime example of post-war Socialist architecture and that's only a compliment if you happen to like this stark type of approach. However, it does at least offer an approximation of grandeur, with an indoor swimming pool and sauna. Meanwhile, the Turkosowa restaurant won't let you down, so long as all you expect is a competent meal at a reasonable price. Make sure you don't blow any money saved by eating at the Turkosowa with a spin in the hotel's casino. A central location means that this hotel, which is something of a period piece, is within walking distance of the principal business and shopping areas, and even the old town. *24hr room service. Theatre-style conference facilities for up to 80. Private parking.* AMERICAN EXPRESS *Diners, Mastercard, Visa.*

Warsaw   Hotel Jan III Sobieski

Tel (2) 658 44 44   Fax (2) 659 88 28   **HR**

Plac Artusa Zawiszy 1 02025 Warsaw

Rooms 425   Double room from Złt6,000,000

Something of a *cause célèbre* when it opened in 1992, the Jan III Sobieski's design was considered so avant-garde that locals streamed in to check it out for themselves. Not surprisingly, this hotel is unique in Warsaw, which really heightens the appeal. There are some traditional elements, a stately portrait of the eponymous 17th-century Polish King is one, but modern design dominates with variously coloured marble and wood animating the open plan lay-out. This approach continues in what is termed a 'restaurant landscape' complete with atrium, greenery and fountain bubbling down marble steps. Food is equally interesting with modernised Polish dishes, together with European and international numbers. Native game is a particular success – wild boar steak, venison consommé with mushroom ravioli, hare terrine with cranberry sauce, are all carefully cooked and delivered. If you want to taste the traditional 'blow-out' style of Polish cooking (knuckle in beer for instance) there are also regular buffets with folk dancing displays. This is one of several recurring themed-buffets, together with Russian, Spanish, even Country and Western. Only moments from the central railway station, the *Hotel Marriott* and the Palace of Culture, the Hotel Jan III Sobieski is on the opposite side of Warsaw from the old town. *24hr room service. Theatre-style conference facilities for up to 250. Business centre: secretarial, translation services. Private parking.* AMERICAN EXPRESS *Diners, Mastercard, Visa.*

Warsaw	**Hotel Marriott**	
Tel (2) 630 63 06 Fax (2) 630 52 39		**HR**

Al Jerozolimskie 65-79 00-697 Warsaw

Rooms 521	Double room from Złt3,500,00

With around 4500 people eating daily at the Marriott, this hotel manages to balance quality and quantity. With a choice of 11 restaurants and lounges, variety is obviously an attraction, and while there's nothing recognisably Polish about this five-star international-style tower block, that's not really the point. What really registers is a sense that this is where the action is. There are, however, plenty of Polish dishes to choose from in the main restaurant *Lilla Weneda* (for instance tripe soup, roast duck with red cabbage and apple, and beef roulade with buckwheat). Dishes are well prepared and professionally served; the Marriott's American style has translated very successfully, with the local employees being friendly and attentive. A good bet for Italian food is *Parmizzano's* (with live music) while the *Chicago Grill* is hot on steaks. Additionally, the *O'Hare* offers a pub experience, and the *Club Panorama* on the 40th and 42nd floors provides drinks, desserts and a big city view. The *Vienna Café* speaks for itself, while late-night swingers can find light meals at the *Orpheus* nightclub. Facilities include an indoor swimming pool and fitness centre. The Marriott, a joint venture with LOT (Polish Airlines), soars above central Warsaw, opposite the main railway station and the Palace of Culture, close to the main shopping and business districts. *24hr room service. Theatre-style conference facilities for up to 1000. Business centre: secretarial/translation services. Private parking.* AMERICAN EXPRESS *Diners, Mastercard, Visa.*

To dial overseas from the UK, 010 will change to 00 on 16th April 1995.

Warsaw   **Swietoszek**

Tel (22) 31 56 34	**R**

Ul Jezuicka 6/8 Warsaw

Seats 70   Meal for 2 approx Złt1,000,000

Rather than playing on its name, which means saintly and pious,
Swietoszek bills itself as a restaurant 'where Royalty meet'. This
is undoubtedly more effective. Indeed, Queen Sofia of Spain,
as well as Hollywood star Robert de Niro have descended into this
charming cellar, perfectly located by the old town market square.
A vaulted ceiling edged with darker brickwork is essentially all
there is to see. Yet this is all you really need to create a mellow,
candlelit atmosphere. Actually, it's so mellow that Swietoszek
is rather more appropriate for dinner than lunch. Booking is also
advisable as the restaurant fills up quickly. Although technically
a club, you don't need to worry about membership. Swietoszek's
long-established reputation rests on friendly, though sometimes
over-eager staff, and a menu that accommodates well-presented
and well-prepared Polish staples, such as *zurek* (sour rye soup) and
pike-perch. International flourishes include the likes
of *chateaubriand* and fondues. *Open 1pm-midnight. No parking.*
AMERICAN EXPRESS *Diners, Mastercard, Visa.*

Warsaw   **Tsubame**

Tel (22) 26 51 27 Fax (22) 26 48 51	**R**

Foksal 16 00636 Warsaw

Seats 60   Meal for 2 approx Złt500,000

A highly-regarded Japanese restaurant which also includes a sushi
bar and tempura dishes. Dishes are well presented in authentic
Japanese style, with sake on hand too. *Open noon-midnight. Closed
Easter Mon, 26 Dec. No parking.* AMERICAN EXPRESS *Diners, Mastercard,
Visa.*

Warsaw   **Hotel Victoria**

Tel (22) 27 92 71 Fax (22) 27 98 56	**HR**

Ul Krolewska 11 00-065 Warsaw

Rooms 363   Double room from Złt3,900,000

Resembling a giant radiator, this modern concrete-block-style
hotel has a far more cordial interior and staff, with a good line-up
of facilities, such as an indoor swimming pool, fitness centre and
sauna. The Victoria also benefits from a central location,
overlooking the Ogrod Saski (Saxon Gardens), only a short walk
from the old town. The most distinguished of the hotel's three
restaurants is the *Canaletto*, and the artist's views of Warsaw
provide the focus in an otherwise plain dining room. Polish
specialities, especially game, take flight alongside more
international numbers to make this one of Warsaw's finer
restaurants. Playing a supporting role to the *Canaletto* is the
Hetmanska restaurant, with its range of grilled dishes. *24hr room
service. Theatre-style conference facilities for up to 800. Business centre:
translation services. Private parking.* AMERICAN EXPRESS *Diners, Mastercard,
Visa.*

Bydgoszcz

Bydgoszcz   **Hotel Pod Orlem**

Tel (52) 22 18 61   Fax (52) 22 89 88   **H**

Aleja Gdanska 14 85006 Bydgoszcz

Rooms 74   Double room from Złt1,600,000

The *Secession* architecture (Poland's answer to art nouveau) dates
back to 1896, with the hotel surrounded by delightful gardens, yet
still within the centre of the city. Recent renovation has jaded its
charms somewhat, but also given it a sauna, solarium and fitness
centre. The restaurant is well-known throughout Poland for its
distinguished local and international cuisine. *Theatre-style conference
facilities for up to 60. Secretarial services. Private parking.*
AMERICAN EXPRESS *Diners, Mastercard, Visa.*

Gdansk/Gdynia/Sopot

Gdansk   **Hotel Hevelius**

Tel (58) 31 56 31   Fax (58) 31 19 22   **H**

Ul Heweiusza 22 80-890 Gdansk
Rooms 286   Double room from Złt1,870,000

This hotel is ideal if you want an old city location, although it is
a rather unimaginative, unappealing modern tower block, but
at least it places proper emphasis on comfort. The restaurant, with
its European and Polish menu, is popular. *No room service. Theatre-
style conference facilities for up to 120. Private parking.* AMERICAN EXPRESS
Diners, Mastercard, Visa.

Gdansk   **Hotel Marina**

Tel (58) 53 20 79   Fax (58) 53 04 60   **H**

Ul Jelitkowska 20 80-341 Gdansk
Rooms 79   Double room from Złt1,950,000

A modern, functional hotel close to the beach and marina, with
well-prepared international and Polish dishes in the restaurant. The
facilities inside are excellent, including boutiques, galleries,
an indoor swimming pool, gym, tennis courts, sauna and solarium.
Yet the theatre-style conference capacity, despite the business
centre, is limited to 50 people. *Conference facilities. Business centre:
translation services.* AMERICAN EXPRESS *Diners, Mastercard, Visa.*

Gdansk   **Pod Lososiem**

Tel (58) 31 76 52   Fax (58) 31 56 48   **R**

Szeroka 54, 80-835 Gdansk
Seats 120   Meal for 2 approx Złt600,000

Situated right in the old town, with its magnificent squares
of burgher's houses and historic docks, is this up-market and
expensive restaurant, which specialises in grilled salmon, though
other fish and meat dishes are also available. *Open 11-late.*
AMERICAN EXPRESS *Diners, Mastercard, Visa.*

Gdansk   **Tawerna**

Tel (58) 31 41 14   Fax (58) 31 41 14   **R**

Powroznicza 19/20, 80-828 Gdansk
Seats 66   Meal for 2 approx Złt500,000

In the historic heart of the old city, this place is renowned for its
fish dishes all cooked Polish-style. Other classics include duck
cooked with apples. *Open 11am-11pm. Public parking.*
AMERICAN EXPRESS *Diners, Mastercard, Visa.*

Gdynia   **Hotel Gdynia**

Tel (58) 20 66 61   Fax (58) 20 86 51   **H**

Ul Armii Krajowej 22 81-372 Gdynia
Rooms 300   Double room from Złt2,000,000

This comfortably modern hotel is close to the marina and beach.
It has some great facilities, including a business centre, with
translation services, boutiques and galleries, together with

an indoor swimming pool, sauna and solarium. The theatre-style conference facilities stretch to 200 people; while the restaurant offers a comprehensive selection of European and Polish dishes. *Conference facilities. Private parking.* AMERICAN EXPRESS® *Diners, Mastercard, Visa.*

Sopot	**Hotel Grand Sopot**

Tel (58) 51 00 41 Fax (58) 51 61 24	H

Ul Powstancow Warszawy 12/14 81-718 Sopot

Rooms 112   Double room from Złt1,600,000

This majestic hotel opened in 1926 in grand period style, in a fabulous location: not only in the centre of Sopot, but right by the beach (with a beach bar just to hand). If you want to play billiards, or try your luck gambling in the casino, you won't need to leave the hotel. So it is a place for unwinding and having fun, not really for business meetings, considering the limited conference facilities. *Theatre-style conference facilities for up to 20. No parking.* AMERICAN EXPRESS® *Diners, Mastercard, Visa.*

Krakow

Krakow	Da Pietro

Tel (12) 22 32 79   Fax (12) 21 28 80   **R**

Rynek Glowny 17 (Main Market Square 17) 31-008 Krakow
Seats 120   Meal for 2 approx Złt700,000

Italian food has considerable cachet in Poland, and this
establishment offers a comprehensive selection in a lively setting.
Open 12.30-midnight. No parking, ▓▓▓▓▓▓▓ *Diners, Mastercard,
Visa.*

Krakow	Hotel Forum

Tel (12) 66 95 00   Fax (12) 66 58 27   **HR**

Ul M Konopnickiej 28 30-302 Krakow
Rooms 277   Double room from Zlt3,292,000

A modern hotel block offering an up-to-date package: indoor
swimming pool, fitness centre, sauna, solarium, casino, travel desk
and boutiques. The views are inspiring too, as it is located opposite
the Royal Castle – though it's rather more than walking distance
to the main historic centre. Well-prepared French and Polish
dishes (such as pork cutlet and beef tenderloin) are a major
attraction at the restaurant. Moreover, the typically Polish
breakfast buffet incorporates all the favourites, with platters
of sliced meats, cheeses and so on. Alternative dining options are
grills in the *Rotisserie* and snacks in the roof-top coffee shop. *24hr
room service. Theatre-style conference facilities for up to 600.
Translation services.* ▓▓▓▓▓▓▓ *Diners, Mastercard, Visa.*

Krakow	Hotel Francuski

Tel (12) 22 51 22   Fax (12) 22 52 70   **H**

Ul Pijarska 13 31-015 Krakow
Rooms 42   Double room from Złt2,200,000

The *Secession* period (Polish art nouveau) is one of the most
delightful in Poland's architectural history, and this hotel built
in 1912 is a particularly handsome 'town-house' example.
Comfortable, traditional interiors add to the appeal, while the
restaurant's growing reputation rests on the flair of its Polish and
French cuisine. In a prime position, within the historic centre and
only a short walk from the Main Market Square. *Theatre-style
conference facilities for up to 30. Public parking.* ▓▓▓▓▓▓▓ *Diners,
Mastercard, Visa.*

Krakow	Hotel Grand

Tel (12) 21 72 55   Fax (12) 21 83 60   **HR**

Slawokowska 507 31-016 Krakow
Rooms 50   Double room from Złt2,400,000

One of a growing band of privately-owned hotels in Krakow, this
place is ideally located: only minutes from the Main Market
Square. Conference facilities here, however, are strictly limited
to catering for an informal meeting for a handful of people.
A pearl of the *Secession* period, from the facade right down to its
elegant restaurant, where traditional Polish dishes, such
as mushroom soup and duck, are enticingly presented and
professionally served. *24hr room service.* ▓▓▓▓▓▓▓ *Diners,
Mastercard, Visa.*

Krakow   **Hawelka Tetmajerowska**

Tel (12) 22 47 53   Fax (12) 22 58 64   **R**

Rynek Glowny 34 (Main Market Square 34) 31-010 Krakow
Seats 120   Meal for 2 approx Złt1,200,000

Rapidly becoming up-market, with a European menu that also
shows off vernacular classics, like pork tenderloin with prunes. It's
also perfectly placed within a burgher's house in the Main Market
Square, with a light, contemporary decor. *Tetmajerowska* is the
smarter dining room on the first floor (cost as above) and
Hawelka is on the ground (cost Złt 400,000). There's also a cellar
café/wine bar. *L 10-4 D 6-late (ground floor open 10am-11pm, cellar
noon-10pm). Public parking.* AMERICAN EXPRESS *Diners, Mastercard, Visa.*

Krakow   **Leonard**

Tel (12) 21 98 94   **R**

Rynek Glowny 25 (Main Market Square 25) 31-008 Krakow
Seats 55   Meal for 2 approx Złt500,000

Its distinguished cellar setting with Ludwig XVI furniture and
a European repertoire makes it a popular place with expatriates.
The staples on the menu are onion soup and pork cutlet, and other
traditional Polish food. *Open noon-11pm.* AMERICAN EXPRESS *Diners,
Mastercard, Visa.*

Krakow   **Wierzynek**

Tel (12) 22 98 96   Fax (12) 22 12 96   **R**

Rynek Glowny 15 (Main Market Square 15) 31-008 Krakow
Seats 240   Meal for 2 approx Złt600,000

This is the culinary grandee of Krakow and, in fact, one
of Poland's best known restaurants, with a 600-year-old history
that says it all. It has survived and thrived, though latest visits
do indicate occasional minor lapses. Otherwise the traditional
Polish food is rich, of the type that has sustained many a knight
and VIP over the centuries. Set in a stately burgher's house in the
Main Market Square, the atmosphere is also high on tradition,
complete with suits of armour, panelling and a creaking wooden
staircase. *Open noon-midnight. No parking.* AMERICAN EXPRESS *Diners,
Mastercard, Visa.*

Poznan

Poznan	**Meridian**	
Tel (61) 41 12 01 Fax (61) 47 34 41		**R**

Ul Litewska 60-605 Poznan
Seats 100   Meal for 2 approx Złt1,000,000

An inspiring setting on the edge of the Solacki Park, within
an attractive country-style building with modern interiors. The
service is excellent, as is the menu, which combines local and
national as well as French characteristics. 'Royal-style pheasant' is a
particular winner. *Open 1pm-2am. Private parking.* AMERICAN EXPRESS
Mastercard, Visa.

Poznan	**Novotel**	
Tel (61) 77 00 11 Fax (61) 77 36 54		**HR**

Ul Warszawska 64/66 61-028 Poznan
Rooms 153   Double room from Złt1,430,000

Set within the Malta Lake Park, this modern, low-rise building
also offers an outdoor swimming pool, tennis courts and an all-
year-round skiing facility, while still being close to the city centre.
Regional cuisine (like pork knuckle cooked in beer or cabbage
with mushrooms) adds interest in the restaurant, while boutiques
add extra colour to the facilities. *Theatre-style conference facilities for
up to 220. Private parking.* AMERICAN EXPRESS *Diners, Mastercard, Visa.*

Poznan	**Orbis Merkury**	
Tel (61) 55 80 00 Fax (61) 55 89 55		**H**

Ul Rossevelta 20 60-829 Poznan
Rooms 314   Double room from Złt1,330,000

Only a few minutes walk from the international fair grounds
in the centre of the city, this modern, flat-fronted hotel has a good
restaurant focusing on Polish cuisine. There's also a coffee shop,
together with the requisite facilities: boutiques, car rental and
night club. Conference facilities come complete with a business
centre offering translation services. *Theatre-style conference rooms for
up to 250. Translation services. Parking.* AMERICAN EXPRESS *Diners,
Mastercard, Visa.*

Poznan	**Hotel Polonez**	
Tel (61) 69 91 41 ˚ Fax (61) 52 37 62		**HR**

Aleja Niepodleglosci 36 61-714 Poznan
Rooms 406   Double room from Złt1,330,000

An attractively modern hotel, with casino, boutiques, sauna and
solarium, it's also conveniently located for the old town. *Theatre-
style conference facilities for up to 200.* AMERICAN EXPRESS *Diners,
Mastercard, Visa.*

Restaurant
Seats 300   Meal for 2 approx Złt400,000

Polish cuisine, such as veal and pork cutlets, stars here, with lighter
fare also available from the coffee shop. *Open 1pm-midnight.*

Poznan	**Hotel Poznan**

Tel (61) 33 20 81   Fax (61) 33 29 61 ┃ **HR**

Plac Gen H Dabrowskiego 1 61-898 Poznan

Rooms 500   Double room from Złt1,780,000

Generally regarded as the city's premier hotel: smart, modern
comfort comes complete with boutiques, galleries, a sauna,
solarium and night club. In the restaurant a Polish menu includes
veal cutlets with potatoes or *sauerkraut* and roasted pheasant,
ideally preceded by aperitifs at either of the two bars. Standing tall
in the centre of Poznan, it's only walking distance from the
international fair grounds. (Please note, prices and availability
of hotel rooms are significantly affected by the trade fairs – check
in advance.) *24hr room service. Private garage.* ▪AMERICAN EXPRESS *Diners,
Mastercard, Visa.*

Poznan	**U Dylla**

Tel (61) 52 17 76 ┃ **R**

Stary Rynek 37/39 61-772 Poznan

Seats 56   Meal for 2 approx Złt200,000

Fortunately prices aren't as high as the quality of the food, with
plenty of native classics such as hare with prunes, turkey, sausage
in batter and buckwheat pancakes. Poignant old Market Square
location. *Open 9am-10pm (to midnight during trade fairs).*
No credit cards.

Wroclaw

Wroclaw   **Hotel Monopol**

Tel (71) 370 41   Fax (71) 44 80 33   **HR**

Ul Modrzejewskiej 2 50-071 Wroclaw

Rooms 70   Double room from Złt1,390,000

An enchanting *Secession* (art nouveau) hotel, completed in 1892,
with character and a central city location that's as handy for
business as visiting the historic core. The popular *Monopol*
restaurant, with sour rye soup and pork cutlet with cabbage
amongst its Polish repertoire, also offers familiar international
numbers. *Public parking.* AMERICAN EXPRESS *Diners, Mastercard, Visa.*

Wroclaw   **Hotel Wroclaw**

Tel (71) 61 46 51   Fax (71) 61 66 17   **HR**

Ul Powstancow Slaskich 7 53-332 Wroclaw

Rooms 300   Double room from Złt2,600,000

The city's premier venue, with a restaurant serving international
and Polish food (rolled veal, pork with prunes). It's modern and
large, and the facilities include an indoor swimming pool, sauna
(with bar) and solarium, coffee shop and boutiques. Centrally
located within walking distance of the business area. *24hr room
service. Theatre-style conference facilities for up to 200. Business centre:
translation services. Swimming pool, sauna and solarium. Private
parking.* AMERICAN EXPRESS *Diners, Mastercard, Visa.*

Poland Index

Recommended by

EGON RONAY'S GUIDES

1995

YOUR GUARANTEE OF QUALITY AND INDEPENDENCE

- Establishment inspections are anonymous

- Inspections are undertaken by qualified Egon Ronay's Guides inspectors

- The Guides are completely independent in their editorial selection

- The Guides do not accept advertising, hospitality or payment from listed establishments

Hotels & Restaurants
Europe
Family Hotels & Restaurants
Oriental Restaurants
New Zealand & South Pacific

Pubs & Inns
Just a Bite
Paris
Ireland
Australia

Egon Ronay's Guides are available from all good bookshops or can be ordered from Leading Guides, 35 Tadema Road, London SW10 0PZ
Tel: 071-352 2485 / 352 0019   Fax: 071-376 5071

Portugal

Currency: Portuguese Escudo **Exchange Rate:** £1 = approx Esc 250

International dialling code: 010 351
(Lisbon + 1 Oporto + 2)

Passports/Visas: No visa required for British passport holders.

British Embassy in Lisbon Tel: 1-396 1191/396 1122

TRANSPORT
Airports:
Lisbon-Portela Tel: 1-841 5000
Oporto-Pedras Rubras Tel: 2-948 2291
Faro International Airport Tel: 89-81 8982
Railway Stations:
Lisbon Tel: Rossio (local/Lisbon Coast) 1-346 5022 / Santa Apolonia (international) 1-888 4181
Oporto Tel: Campanha 2-565 645 / Sao Bento 2-200 2722
Car hire:
Lisbon - Avis Tel: 1-356 1176 / Hertz Tel: 1-579 027 (airport 1-80 1496) Budget Tel: 1-53 7717 (airport 1-80 3981)
Oporto - Avis Tel: 1-31 5947 / Hertz Tel: 2-31 2387 (airport 2-948 1400) Budget Tel: (airport) 2-948 5714
Faro - Avis Tel: 89-81 8625
Speed Limits: 90 km/h on trunk roads 120 km/h on motorways, 60 km/h in towns.

Banks open: 8.30am-3pm Mon-Fri.

Shops open: Mon-Fri 9am-1pm & 3-7pm, Sat till 1pm (in December shops stay open until 7pm on Saturdays). Shopping Centres 10am-11pm 7 days.

National Holidays: New Year's Day, 28 Feb, 14 & 25 April, 1 May, 10 & 15 Jun, 15 Aug, 5 Oct, 1 Nov, 1 & 8 Dec, Christmas Day.

Tourist Offices:
Portuguese Tourist Board in London - Tel: 0171-494 1441
In Portugal –
Lisbon Tel: 1-352 5800 (airport 1-849 3689)
Oporto Tel: 2-317 514 (airport 2-941 2534)
Faro Tel: 89-80 0400/80 3604 (airport 89-81 8582)

American Express Travel Service Offices or Representative (R):
Lisbon - Top Tours (R)
  Av.Duque De Loule 108
  1000
  Tel: 1-3155885 #

Lisbon

Lisbon	**Albergaria Senhora do Monte**

Tel (1) 886 60 02   Fax (1) 87 77 83   **H**

Calçada do Monte 39 Lisbon 1100
Rooms 24   Double room from Esc15,000

Looking down from the hill, you can see St George's Castle and
the River Tejo and all the other tourist attractions that are within
walking distance away from this small, friendly hotel (without a
restaurant), open since the late 60s. The modern building has been
recently redecorated in up-to-date, flowery colours and designs.
24hr room service. AMERICAN EXPRESS *Mastercard, Visa.*

Lisbon	**Casa da Comida**

Tel (1) 388 53 76   Fax (1) 387 51 32   **R**

Travessa das Amoreiras 1 Lisbon 1100
Seats 55   Meal for 2 approx Esc20,000

In a restaurant just a 15-minute stroll away from the centre
of Lisbon, the chef, who has been here since it opened, prepares
a multitude of different grilled fish dishes. *Bacalhao* (salted cod)
comes with a tomato and garlic sauce, while crayfish, squid and
lobster are just lightly grilled and served with a squeeze of lemon
and some crunchy rock salt. *Mariscada* (shellfish) are a favourite   ★
dish and his speciality; so try the king prawns cooked on an open
grill. The exclusively Portuguese wine list has a house red,
Carvalho Pubeiro. Afterwards walk off your meal in the
courtyard garden. *L 12.30-3 D 7.30-12.* AMERICAN EXPRESS *Diners,*
Mastercard, Visa.

Lisbon	**Casa Do Leão**

Tel (1) 87 59 62   Fax (1) 87 63 29   **R**

Castelo São Jorge Lisbon 1100
Seats 60   Meal for 2 approx Esc6000

Inside the famous 800-year-old St George's Castle, one of Lisbon's
main attractions, the chef has been cooking traditional Portuguese
cuisine for ten years and little is set to change. Casseroles and
grilled fish dishes are very much the order of the day; but many
other choices are available: roasted kid, monkfish in a light lemon
sauce and clams served with potatoes, garlic and olive oil.
Cataplana (a medley of seafood served with tomatoes, potatoes and
garlic) is a particular house favourite. All the wines are,
as expected, Portuguese, with a Southern Portuguese house wine.
L 12.30-3.30 D 8-10.30. Public parking. AMERICAN EXPRESS *Diners,*
Mastercard, Visa.

Lisbon	**Chester**

Tel (1) 65 73 47   Fax (1) 388 78 11   **R**

Rua Rodrigo da Fonseca 87 Lisbon 1200
Seats 50   Meal for 2 approx Esc10,000

A peasant pub-styled place, given a British name and decor
to draw in the locals. However, the daily menu changes are
a better reason to come here. Dishes of the day, like chargrilled sea
bass and grilled beef steak served in a garlic sauce with sautéed

potatoes, are deservedly popular. Look out for the good selection
of *vinhos verdes*. *L 12-3 D 7.30-10.30. Public parking.* AMERICAN EXPRESS
Diners, Mastercard, Visa.

Lisbon   **Clara**

| Tel (1) 355 73 41   Fax (1) 885 20 82 | R |

Campo dos Mártires de Patria 49 Lisbon 1100
Seats 75   Meal for 2 approx Esc12,000

This elegant, 100-year-old private home was converted into
a restaurant back in 1980. Right next to the chic Pombelino
district, the owners lured a new head chef from the *Ritz Hotel*
to come and work for them. He has not, like so many chefs
in Lisbon, been tempted to produce an international menu, but has
stuck to simple Portuguese fish dishes. The menu changes with the
available fresh fish in the market, but popular dishes are cod,
salmon, sole and sea bream, all baked or grilled in olive oil, garlic
and herbs. All the wines are Portuguese. *L 12-4 D 7-12. Closed 1-
15 Aug, National Holidays.* AMERICAN EXPRESS *Diners, Mastercard, Visa.*

THE APARTMENT SERVICE
Tel in UK: (0181) 748 4207   Fax: (0181) 748 3972
The Apartment Service will find you the right apartment
worldwide to suit your needs, whether you are on a short or
long-term stay. A 96-page colour catalogue is free on request.
All budgets are catered for.

Lisbon   **Clube da Empresarios**

| Tel (1) 796 63 80   Fax (1) 797 41 44 | R |

Avenida da Republica 38 Lisbon 1100
Seats 60   Meal for 2 approx Esc8000

An eclectic mix of French, Portuguese and international cooking
finds its home in this 19th-century house, converted only ten years
ago and now one of Lisbon's more popular restaurants. Fish soups,
fruit cocktail and smoked salmon starters, followed by dishes like
grilled salmon with green peppers, rich partridge and peasant
casseroles and the traditional salted cod cooked Lisbon-style, with
tomatoes, parsley, garlic and white wine are all found on the
menu. In the piano bar next door, music and dancing go on until
dawn. *L 12-3 D 7.30-12. Private parking.* AMERICAN EXPRESS *Diners,
Mastercard, Visa.*

The Golden Eurostar [★] denotes our pick of the
restaurants. Cooking is the major consideration, but
other factors are also taken into account, including
ambience, comfort and service.

Lisbon   Conventual

Tel (1) 60 91 96   **R**

Praça das Flores 45 Lisbon 1200
Seats 70   Meal for 2 approx Esc7000

This place started life as a humble bakery in the old, quarter
of Lisbon and was converted into a restaurant 11 years ago. Now,
businessmen and politicians fill the wooden tables and chairs,
as the building is opposite the Houses of Parliament. Plain
Portuguese cooking comes out of the kitchen prepared by just one
chef. The traditional fish dishes are all there and also *cozido*
(a traditional stew made with beef, chicken and sausage and served
with rice cooked in stock and vegetables). The dry red or white
Cavares Teodoseo goes well with the simple cooking. *L 12.30-3
D 7.30-11.* AMERICAN EXPRESS *Diners, Mastercard, Visa.*

Lisbon   Da Lapa

Tel (1) 395 00 05   Fax (1) 395 06 65   **HR**

Rua do Pau de Bandeira 4 Lisbon 1200
Rooms 94   Double room from Esc35,000

Since this 17th-century palace was restored and converted into
a hotel two years ago, extensive building has gone on and the
place now has a new wing. The rooms in the old palace are only
suites or de luxe doubles, all decorated in different styles: colonial,
Arabian, or Portuguese, and filled with antique furniture; while
the new wing has modern decor. There are limited conference
facilities, but really this is an idyllic spot for tourists rather than
businessmen. The beautiful gardens surrounding this hotel give it a
feeling of utter isolation. *24hr room service. Theatre-style conference
facilities for up to 36. Secretarial/translation services. Outdoor
swimming pool. Private parking.* AMERICAN EXPRESS *Diners, Mastercard,
Visa.*

Embaixada
Seats 60   Meal for 2 approx Esc6000

Grilled fish from *bacalhao* to fillets of salmon is the basis of the
traditional Portuguese menu. However, for diners tired of the
perennial Portuguese offering of fish, there are some more meaty
alternatives; pork marinated in garlic, onions and olive oil and
cooked with wine and clams is a tasty peasant Portuguese dish.
On hot, sticky evenings, opt for a poolside table. *L 12.30-3
D 7.30-11.*

Lisbon   Escorial

Tel (1) 346 44 29   Fax (1) 346 37 58   **R**

Rua das Portas de Santo Antão 47 Lisbon 1100
Seats 65   Meal for 2 approx Esc9000

The building, with its Portuguese-tiled walls, is as traditional
as the cooking. Not surprisingly, fish predominates, with
swordfish, sole and salted cod, chargrilled lobster and *mariscada*
(a mix of chargrilled crayfish, lobster and king prawns). A few
international dishes are also thrown in: beef stroganoff and paella
are two worth looking out for. *L 12-3.30 D 7pm-1am. Public
parking.* AMERICAN EXPRESS *Diners, Mastercard, Visa.*

Lisbon   Espelho D'Agua

Tel (1) 301 73 73   Fax (1) 36 32 92   **R**

Avenida da Brasilia Lisbon 1400

Rooms 86   Meal for 2 approx Esc9000

Out in the subdued suburbs of Lisbon, a small family team have
been running this traditional Portuguese restaurant for the last ten
years. They mostly serve fish and seafood: grilled salmon, lobster,
prawns, squid, sea bass, sole etc – the list is long. All dishes are
simply cooked: placed on an open grill with a little olive oil,
lemon and garlic. The wines are as conservative as the cooking,
with a Portuguese red and white house wine. *L 12.30-4 D 7.30-
10.30. No parking. Mastercard, Visa.*

Lisbon   Gambrinus

Tel (1) 342 14 66   Fax (1) 346 50 32   **R**

Rua das Portas de Santo Antão 25 Lisbon 1100

Seats 60   Meal for 2 approx Esc12,000

Four friends opened this lively restaurant in the 60s and since then
have built up quite a reputation for themselves. The leather
upholstery, old fireplaces and tapestries depicting the four seasons
are a little severe, but it is filled with businessmen during the day
and serious Portuguese party-goers at night. Classical Portuguese
food comes with *sopa rica de peixes* (mixed fish soup) and a
national dish, suckling pig roasted on a spit, served with your
choice from a vast list of 420 Portuguese wines. *Open noon-2am.
Public parking.* AMERICAN EXPRESS *Diners, Mastercard, Visa.*

Lisbon   Hotel Méridien Lisbon

Tel (1) 69 04 00   Fax (1) 69 32 31   **HR**

Rua Castilho 149 1000 Lisbon

Rooms 300   Double room from Esc29,000

The Meridien Group opened this hotel ten years ago in a new
building right in the very centre of Lisbon, 15 minutes by car
from the airport. Various business meetings are held here
throughout the year, either in the large conference room, or in the
smaller boardrooms for up to 30 people. The rooms, described
as 'modern executive', have modern, practical and plain furniture.
*Satellite TV. Theatre-style conference facilities for up to 500.
Secretarial/translation services on request. Private parking.*
AMERICAN EXPRESS *Diners, Mastercard, Visa.*

La Brasserie des Amis

Seats 145   Meal for 2 approx Esc8000

The chef has come from another Meridien hotel in Canada,
so despite claims that the dishes served are Portuguese, his cooking
tends more towards the international. They place great emphasis
on watching their diners' figures, with special low-calorie meals.
However, if calorie-counting does not appeal, try the grilled sea
bass with a béarnaise sauce, rolled fillets of salmon in a saffron
butter sauce, or sirloin steak. House specialities are more typically
Portuguese, with suckling pig and roasted cod served with onions,
potatoes, olive oil and garlic. Wines are French and Portuguese.
L 12-3 D 7-11.

Lisbon   Mister Cook

`Tel (1) 80 72 37   Fax (1) 793 71 52`   **R**

Avenida Guerra Junqueiro 1 Lisbon 1000
Seats 70   Meal for 2 approx Esc10,000

Down a commercial street, near the *Plaça do Londres*, this place
is cool and modern with marble floors, freshly-painted walls and
an international menu, dotted with a few traditional dishes, to go
with its recent facelift. On offer are grilled entrecote and spare
ribs, along with *bacalhao* (salted cod cooked with a wine and garlic
sauce) and also *cataplana* (assorted seafood served in a large flat
shell with potatoes, tomatoes, onion and garlic). As so often in
Portugal, grilled sole and seafood are definitely the best options
to take. *L 12-3 D 7-11. Public parking.* AMERICAN EXPRESS *Diners,
Mastercard, Visa.*

Lisbon   Hotel Ritz Inter-Continental

`Tel (1) 69 20 20   Fax (1) 69 17 83`   **HR**

Rua Rodrigo da Fonseca Lisbon 88 1093
Rooms 303   Double room from Esc30,000

Many people desperately searching for a reliable hotel in foreign
countries cling to names like *Ritz*; but this hotel is no relation
to the *Ritz*, London or *Ritz*, Paris, but part of the Inter-
Continental Group. It is very central and therefore an attractive
place for EU and Presidential meetings. It was built in the 50s, and
many of the original team of staff are amazingly still here, as is
most of the original furniture. However, half the rooms have
recently been refurbished with new Italian pieces. They all also
have up-to-date facilities. There are 40 suites. *24hr room service.
Theatre-style conference facilities for up to 500.
Secretarial/translation/fax services on request. Private parking.*
AMERICAN EXPRESS *Diners, Mastercard, Visa.*

Varanda
Seats 100   Meal for 2 approx Esc10,000

The international menu in this large restaurant (with 25 extra
seats on the terrace outside in the summer) has few surprises, but
a comprehensive choice of dishes like pork cutlets, beef stroganoff,
roast chicken and even monkfish served with an orange and
saffron sauce. The open grill is popular, with about ten different
grilled fish and several steaks on offer. Only Portuguese wines are
served. *L 12.30-3.30 D 7.30-10.30. Private parking.*

Lisbon   Senora Vinho

`Tel (1) 397 26 81   Fax (1) 396 20 72`   **R**

Rua do Meio-à-Lapa 18 Lisbon 1200
Seats 120   Meal for 2 approx Esc6000

Eight years ago this old building became a restaurant, as busy
as the street outside, and took on the chef, who still cooks a variety
of Portuguese fish and meat dishes. Grilled lobster and prawns
served with rice are his speciality. *D only 8-12. Closed Sun.*
AMERICAN EXPRESS *Diners, Mastercard, Visa.*

Lisbon   **Sheraton Lisbon Hotel and Towers**

Tel (1) 57 57 57   Fax (1) 54 71 64   **H**

Rua Latino Coelho 1 Lisbon 1000
Rooms 384   Double room from Esc2000

Conveniently located in the centre of Lisbon, this Sheraton has
been here for 23 years; the concierge has been here for just as long
and is a great source of local information. The majority of their
guests are on business, so the rooms are modern and understated,
with good facilities. All the rooms are doubles, and there are seven
suites. The *Panorama Bar* on the 35th floor, as its name suggests,
has great views over the capital, as do some of the rooms. The
meeting rooms (or ballrooms) can open up into one large room
for 520 people. *24hr room service. Satellite TV/fax. Conference
facilities. Secretarial/translation services on request. Hairdresser/barber.
Outdoor swimming pool, sauna, gym, massage. Private parking.*
AMERICAN EXPRESS *Diners, Mastercard, Visa.*

Lisbon   **Tagide**

Tel (1) 342 07 20   **R**

Largo Academia Nacional de Belas Artes 18-20 Lisbon 1200
Seats 60   Meal for 2 approx Esc7000

Right in the historical heart of Lisbon, this restaurant still has
a fountain dating from 1677 in the corner, and antique blue and
white tiles on the walls, painted with Greek mythological figures.
Overlooking St George's Castle, the Tagide has on the whole stuck
loyally to Portuguese dishes, but still makes the occasional
overtures towards more international cuisine. But their strength
is their traditional fish dishes, with well-presented plates of stuffed
squid, escalopes of salted cod and baby octopus in a red wine sauce.
Look out for the occasional house specialities like pork and clams
marinated in garlic and coriander. There is a choice of 200 bottles
on the Portuguese and French wine list. *L 12.30-3 D 7.30-11.
Private parking.* AMERICAN EXPRESS *Mastercard, Visa.*

Lisbon   **Tavares**

Tel (1) 342 11 12   Fax (1) 347 81 25   **R**

Rua da Misericordia 37 Lisbon 1200
Rooms 60   Meal for 2 approx Esc7000

Certainly a well-established restaurant – it was opened back
in 1784 – run and owned by eleven members of the same family.
The 16th-century building has been renovated, but the the long
Empire-style mirrors and chandeliers still give the place a glitzy,
glamorous feel. French dishes sit alongside Portuguese ones, with
plenty of fish: fillet of sea bass is cooked in a champagne sauce,
fresh sardines are marinated in an onion sauce, prawns are served
in a garlic sauce and clams come casseroled. The menu will take
a good ten minutes to read, with eight soups, from seafood bisque
to Italian minestrone, and a selection of grilled meats from
chateaubriand to spare ribs. Bordeaux and burgundy wines
complement the Portuguese list (with some good *vinho verde*).
L 12.30-3.30 D 7.30-11. Public parking. AMERICAN EXPRESS *Diners,
Mastercard, Visa.*

Lisbon — **York House**

| Tel (1) 396 25 44   Fax (1) 397 27 93 | **HR** |

Rua Janelas Verdes 32 1st Floor Lisbon 1200

Rooms 35   Double room from Esc23,000

Formerly a convent, and then a private home, this house was
rebuilt by the Marquis of Pombal after an earthquake destroyed
the old part of the city. The building is on three levels, divided
by low stone steps and surrounded by beautiful courtyard gardens
and pathways, where guests can stroll peacefully after dinner. The
simple, old-fashioned rooms are in keeping with the building,
with stone floors, spartan decor and floral curtains. This is,
without doubt, a real find, but for laid-back tourists, not busy
businessmen. *No room service. Satellite TV. No parking.*
AMERICAN EXPRESS *Diners, Mastercard, Visa.*

Restaurant

Seats 40   Meal for 2 approx Esc7000

The chef has been preparing traditional Portuguese dishes in the
kitchen for the last 20 years – and the menu has changed very
little. *Bacalhao* (salted cod, a Portuguese favourite) can be served
in hundreds of different ways: here it is baked in corn bread,
or served Lisbon-style, in a tomato, parsley, garlic and white wine
sauce. Other dishes include octopus and shrimp salad with peppers
and fresh coriander, assorted Portuguese smoked meats and
sausages, with main courses such as browned fillets of hake with
tomato rice and pork ribs with country sausages and cabbage.
On Sundays they offer only a cold buffet spread of fish, meat and
salad. The wine list has Portuguese wines from tawny ports to
vinho verde. *L 12.30-2.30 D 7.30-9.30.*

Around Lisbon

Cascais — **Hotel Albatroz**

| Tel (1) 483 28 21   Fax (1) 484 48 27 | **HR** |

Rua Frederico Arouca 100 Cascais 2750

Rooms 37   Double room from Esc35,000

The Duke of Loulé built this palace in 1873, when it was known
as his 'Almond Box'. It was only in the 60s that the place became
a simple inn and then years later, in 1983, re-opened as a modern
hotel. Some of the 11 rooms in the original house overlook the
Cascais Bay and the beach below. They are still decorated in 19th-
century style, while the 29 rooms in the new wing are modern.
All the rooms have been fitted with modern facilities. There are
two reception rooms, but not fully equipped for conferences. *24hr
room service. Satellite TV. Private parking.* AMERICAN EXPRESS *Diners,
Mastercard, Visa.*

Restaurant

Seats 50   Meal for 2 approx Esc13,000

The impressive Cascais and Estoril coastlines are visible from the
windows of this quiet, traditional Portuguese restaurant. Salmon,
sole and seafood are some of the regular dishes served on an à la
carte menu that changes twice a year. All the fish is grilled and
served with fresh vegetables and light sauces. For a change, start
with one of the soups, or *escargots à la bourguignonne.* Champagne
is the only alternative to Portuguese wine. *L 12.30-3 D 7.30-10.*

Cascais   **Estalgem Senora da Guia**

Tel (1) 486 91 91   Fax (1) 486 92 27   **HR**

Strada do Guinchio apartado 197 Cascais 2750

Rooms 40   Double room from Esc20,000

Right out on the coast near Cascais, with a magnificent view
of the sea, this place is far away from the noise and bustle of the
resort. Originally, it was an old family inn, and it was renovated
and turned into a hotel ten years ago. At the time of going
to press, a new wing was being added to the three-floored
building, which will give – 44 rooms in total. The bedrooms are
already surprisingly well equipped, with mini-bars and satellite
TV, but other facilities in the hotel only run to a swimming pool.
Satellite TV. Outdoor swimming pool. Private parking. AMERICAN EXPRESS®
Diners, Mastercard, Visa.

Restaurant

Seats 50   Meal for 2 approx Esc10,000

Sitting at wooden tables and chairs outside, or in the old inn,
diners eat a mixture of grilled fish and meat, with some traditional
Portuguese dishes like *bacalhao*, or they can choose from the large
cold buffet (Esc 3000). Wines are traditionally Portuguese, with
no house wine on offer. *L 12.30-3 D 7.30-10. Private car park.*

Galamares   **Quinta da Santiago Guest House**

Tel (1) 923 29 23   Fax (1) 923 43 29   **R**

Quinta da Santiago Galamares 2710

Seats 30   Meal for 2 approx Esc5000

A set dinner is offered to the diners, all seated together on long
tavern-style tables in this small, family-run guest house in a village
between Lisbon and Sintra. French, Spanish and Portuguese dishes
make up the set menu, which changes every day. Watercress soup
or gazpacho will be followed by grilled sole, poached salmon
or *bacalhao*. The dishes may be simple, but they're good, and there
is always plenty of fresh fish, lightly grilled, with a little lemon
and salt. Have a good look at the building itself; it used to be
a retreat for 16th-century Catholic monks and the original hand-
painted ceiling can still be seen. *D only 8-8.30. Private parking.*
No credit cards.

Oporto

Oporto	**Infante de Sagres**

Tel (2) 01 90 31   Fax (2) 31 49 37   **H**

Praça Dona Felipa Lancastra 62 Oporto 4000
Rooms 74   Double room from Esc23,000

The same family have run this hotel, in the centre of Oporto, since
the early 50s; and it is still small, relaxed and informal. The rooms
are all doubles (there are six suites) and are equipped with satellite
TV and mini-bars. Surprisingly, they have a theatre-style
conference room for up to 120 people, even though this
is definitely not a businessman's hotel. *Conference facilities.*
No parking. AMERICAN EXPRESS *Diners, Mastercard, Visa.*

Oporto	**Mal Cozinhado**

Tel (2) 208 13 19   Fax (2) 202 26 38   **R**

Rua do Outeniu 11 Oporto 4000
Seats 65   Meal for 2 approx Esc7000

A perfect and picturesque setting for a long lunch; an old stone
stable has been converted into a restaurant surrounded by gardens
and overlooking a flowing river with a small bridge arching over
it. Traditional fish and meat dishes and regional wines do not
change. *Open 10am-late. Closed Sun. Private parking. No credit cards.*

Oporto	**Portocale**

Tel (2) 57 07 17   Fax (2) 57 02 06   **R**

Rua Portocale 598 Oporto 4000
Seats 60   Meal for 2 approx Esc12,000

Named after the two towns on either side of it, Oporto and Cale,
this restaurant is on the 13th floor of a modern building,
overlooking Oporto and the sea. The menu is traditionally
Portuguese, with tripe served with white beans, stewed kid in a
red wine sauce and dried cod baked in the oven with turnips and
clams. Plenty of fresh, grilled fish is also served. The wine list
is extensive, but typically Portuguese. *L 12.30-2.30 D 7.30-10.*
Closed 1 May, 25 Dec. Private parking. AMERICAN EXPRESS *Diners,*
Mastercard, Visa.

Portugal Index

Recommended by

EGON
RONAY'S
GUIDES
1995

YOUR GUARANTEE
OF
QUALITY AND INDEPENDENCE

- Establishment inspections are anonymous

- Inspections are undertaken by qualified
  Egon Ronay's Guides inspectors

- The Guides are completely independent
  in their editorial selection

- The Guides do not accept advertising,
  hospitality or payment from listed
  establishments

Hotels & Restaurants	Pubs & Inns
Europe	Just a Bite
Family Hotels & Restaurants	Paris
Oriental Restaurants	Ireland
New Zealand & South Pacific	Australia

Egon Ronay's Guides are available from all good bookshops or can be
ordered from Leading Guides, 35 Tadema Road, London SW10 0PZ
Tel: 071-352 2485 / 352 0019   Fax: 071-376 5071

Republic of Ireland

Currency: Irish Punt   **Exchange Rate:** £1 = approx Pt (Ir £)1

International dialling code: 010 353
(Dublin + 1 Cork + 21)

Passports/Visas: No visa required by British passport holders.

British Embassy in Dublin Tel: 1-269 5211

TRANSPORT
Airports:
Dublin Tel: 1-844 5039
Cork Tel: 21-313 131
Railway Stations:
Dublin-Heuston Tel: 1-836 6222
Cork Tel: 21-504 777
Car hire:
Dublin - Budget Tel: 1-837 9802 (airport 1-837 0919/842 0793) /
Hertz Tel: 1-660 2255 Europcar Tel: 1-668 1777 (airport 1-844 4179)
Cork - Budget Tel: 21-274 755 (airport 21-314 000) / Hertz Tel: 21-
965 849 Europcar Tel: (airport) 21-966 736
Speed Limits: 55 mph on trunk roads, 70 mph on motorways, 30
mph in towns.

Banks open: Mon-Fri 10am-5pm (can vary: 10am-12.30pm & 1.30-
3pm, Thu till 5pm).

Shops open: Mon-Sat 9/9.30am-6pm.

National Holidays: New Year's Day, 2 Jan, 17 Mar, 14, 16 & 17
April, 5 Jun, 7 Aug, 30 Oct, Christmas Day, Boxing Day & 27 Dec.

Tourist Offices:
Irish Tourist Board in London - Tel: 0171-493 3201
In Ireland –
Dublin Tel: 1-284 4768 / Cork Tel: 21-273 251

American Express Travel Service Offices or Representative (R):
Dublin - AETS
    116 Grafton Street
    PO Box 1184
    Dublin 2
    Tel: 01-6772874 #
Cork - Heffernan's Travel (R)
    Pembroke House
    Pembroke Street
    Tel: 021-271081 #

Dublin

Dublin   Hotel Conrad

Tel (1) 676 5555   Fax (1) 676 5424

H

Earlsfort Terrace Dublin 2

Rooms 191   Double room from £220

Opposite the National Concert Hall, just off St Stephen's Green,
the Conrad is very much a modern international-style hotel with
an impressive array of business facilities. It caters largely
to a corporate clientele – although concessions to the locality
include Alfie Byrne's bar, themed along the lines of a traditional
Dublin pub. Bedrooms, while decoratively uninspiring, are
eminently comfortable and well planned with large beds, good
easy chairs, decent work space, three telephones (including sockets
for fax), and every modern comfort. Excellent marble bathrooms
have large tubs with good showers above them, comprehensive
toiletries and ample towelling with generously-sized bathrobes.
Levels of service are high, from free valet parking and
comprehensive 24hr room service to a proper turn-down service
in the evenings, when a bottle of mineral water and a hand-made
Irish chocolate are left at the bedside. Banqueting for 150,
conference facilities for 250. *Hair salon, news kiosk, brasserie (7am-
11.30pm).* AMERICAN EXPRESS *Diners, Mastercard, Visa.*

Dublin   Le Coq Hardi

Tel (1) 668 9070   Fax (1) 668 9887

R

35 Pembroke Road Ballsbridge Dublin 4

Seats 50   Meal for 2 approx £95

John and Catherine Howard run a classic restaurant in a classic
Georgian building at the end of a terrace. Inside are high ceilings
and handsome mirrors, brasswork and ornate plasterwork, and the
immaculately set tables put the seal on a setting that's entirely
fitting for John's serious French-based cooking. Many of his dishes
are from the traditional repertoire – terrine of foie gras with
brioche, cod boulangère, Venetian-style lamb's liver, entrecote
with a shallot and bone marrow sauce. 'Le Coq Hardi' is a breast
of chicken filled with potato, wild mushrooms and herbs,
wrapped in bacon, oven-roasted and finished with Irish whiskey
sauce. Other dishes are more contemporary in style, such as warm
salad with game, pink grapefruit and pine nuts, strudel
of vegetables on a light curry sauce with mint, or darne of salmon
steamed with tomato, black olives, olive oil and sea salt. Bread-
and-butter pudding with Irish whiskey custard is a favourite
dessert. Particularly famous for its Bordeaux cellar, which includes
an 1870 Chateau Mouton Rothschild for the modest sum
of £5000+, do not ignore the exceptional selection of cognacs and
armagnacs, nor the rest of the list that has plenty of good wines
from ofrom outside France; really, though, this is a connoisseur's
list to drool over. Set L £16 Set D £28.50. *L 12-2.30 D 7-11.
Closed L Sat, all Sun, Bank Holidays, 1 week Christmas, 2 weeks
Aug.* AMERICAN EXPRESS *Mastercard, Diners, Visa.*

★

Dublin   **Patrick Guilbaud**

Tel (1) 676 4192   Fax (1) 660 1546   R

46 James Place off Lower Baggot Street Dublin 2
Seats 60   Meal for 2 approx £100

Approaching this purpose-built, air-conditioned restaurant, you
might wonder if you are in the right street, so unprepossessing
does the building look from a distance. But once inside there's
no mistake – a comfortable reception lounge with several striped
sofas, lots of greenery in both the plant-filled atrium and high-
ceilinged dining room, decent art (mostly abstract paintings), and,
above all, very smartly attired and professional staff. For well over
a decade this has been *the* place in which to enjoy classical French
cuisine with a light, modern touch. Despite the restaurant's name,
Patrick is not the chef/patron – the cooking is left to a team
of French chefs, led by Guillaume Le Brun (visible in a glass-
fronted kitchen); indeed, most of the staff are French. The
ingredients, naturally, are mostly Irish, notably as in seafood
dishes, such as pan-fried king scallops served with seasonal salad
and bacon, Dublin Bay prawns in crisp pastry cases served with
mango and capers, or steamed sea bass on a saffron purée with red
pepper oil. Also highly recommended as starters are the home-
made lemon pasta with salmon and hot lobster tourte with chive
sauce, while game dishes in season (roast wild venison with sauce   ★
poivrade and morello cherries or roast breast of pheasant with
parcels of mushrooms) are eagerly awaited by regulars. The table
d'hote lunch and dinner menus (both exclusive of a service charge
of 15%, as is the à la carte) are particularly good value, and though
there's a somewhat limited choice at dinner (four courses and
coffee), lunch offers four selections among both starters and main
courses. And for a table whose occupants cannot make up their
minds, why not try the *menu surprise* (£45 per person)? Desserts
(a tart lemon mousse, berry cheesecake or poached pear in red
wine) and French cheeses are quite splendid, as is the variety
of breads offered, the amuse-gueule, the coffee and petits fours.
Service is impeccable. As you would expect, the wine list
is predominantly French, but not exclusively so, and – for
a restaurant of this class – prices are reasonable; note the old
classics in the 'Specialist Cellar'. Set L £18.50 Set D £25 & £45.
L 12.30-2 D 7.30-10.15. Closed Sun & Mon, Bank Holidays.
AMERICAN EXPRESS *Diners, Mastercard, Visa.*

THE APARTMENT SERVICE
Tel in UK: (0181) 748 4207   Fax: (0181) 748 3972
The Apartment Service will find you the right apartment
worldwide to suit your needs, whether you are on a short or
long-term stay. A 96-page colour catalogue is free on request.
All budgets are catered for.

Dublin   Roly's Bistro

Tel (1) 668 2611   Fax (1) 660 8535   **R**

7 Ballsbridge Terrace Ballsbridge Dublin 4
Seats 120   Meal for 2 approx £50

The combination of proven individuals – restaurateur Roly Saul
and chef Colin O'Daly – makes for a successful restaurant,
deservedly popular since opening. On two floors, upstairs perhaps
has a more authentic bistro atmosphere, while the ground floor
is a little more sedate, and there's a real buzz about the place. First
comes an excellent variety of breads, followed by an eclectic
selection of dishes from crab bisque and guinea fowl terrine
to roast pork with apple sauce and Dublin Bay grilled black sole,
spicy stir-fry chicken and Cajun-style steamed fillet of plaice
on a bed of spinach with sun-dried tomatoes and a dash of chili.
Good accompanying salads and vegetables as well as the puddings
(super orange crème brulée), coffee and inexpensive wines – there
are several under £10 a bottle. *L 12-3 D 6-10 (Sun to 9).*
Closed Good Friday, 25 & 26 Dec. Set L £10.50. AMERICAN EXPRESS®
Mastercard, Visa.

Dublin   Shelbourne Hotel

Tel (1) 676 6471   Fax (1) 661 6006   **H**

St Stephen's Green Dublin 2
Rooms 164   Double room from £245

Situated on St Stephen's Green, Europe's largest garden square, the
Forte-owned Shelbourne has been at the centre of Dublin life since
opening its doors early in the 19th century. The hotel has retained
much of its original grandeur, with a magnificent faux-marbre
entrance hall and a sumptuous lounge where morning coffee and
afternoon tea are taken. The famous Horseshoe Bar and the newer
Shelbourne Bar are among the favourite gathering places for
Dubliners, especially on a Friday night, and many a scandal has
originated from their walls. Spacious, elegantly furnished superior
and de-luxe rooms and suites have traditional polished wood
furniture and impressive drapes, while standard rooms in a newer
wing are smaller. All rooms are well appointed, with bathrobes,
mini-bars and three telephones as standard. Valet parking. 12
function rooms can cater for up to 500 for a reception. *Beauty
salon, gents' hairdressing.* AMERICAN EXPRESS® *Mastercard, Diners, Visa.*

Dublin   La Stampa

Tel (1) 677 8611   Fax (1) 677 3336 .   **R**

35 Dawson Street Dublin 2
Seats 160   Meal for 2 approx £55

Noisy (but unobtrusively), bustling, lively and frenetic – just how
a restaurant of this *genre* should be. Sited in a spacious high-
ceilinged room with large mirrors and plain wood floor, there's
a Renaissance feel about the place, which also has a fully licensed
bar where drinks can be enjoyed while waiting for a table. What's
more, the staff smile and besides being genuinely cheerful are   ★
efficient as well; combine this with decent food at fair prices, and
you have a winning and successful formula, as here. Chef Paul
Flynn spent several years working in top London restaurants, and

though the dishes on the menu are altogether more rustic and substantial than served in those establishments, his background and pedigree stand him in good stead. Starters include freshly made pasta strips with a chunky tomato sauce, chopped Toulouse sausage and coriander (also available as a main course), an authentic Caesar salad, or a spicy terrine of duck with onion compote, while main courses might feature roast monkfish with basil purée, tomato and pepper olive oil, boiled bacon with traditional Irish colcannon (curly kale and mashed potato) and a caper and parsley sauce, or herb-crusted roast rack of lamb served with Provençal tomatoes and potato dauphinois in a light garlic sauce. Desserts are no less abundant in the true sense of the world – try the sticky toffee pudding or chocolate truffle cake. Set L £12.50. *L 12.30-2.30 D 6.30-11.30. Closed L Sat & Sun, Good Friday, 2 days Christmas.* AMERICAN EXPRESS® *Diners, Mastercard, Visa.*

Dublin   The Westbury

Tel (1) 679 1122   Fax (1) 679 7078   **HR**

Off Grafton Street Dublin 2

Rooms 203   Double room from £190

The Westbury is located within walking distance of many Dublin landmarks. The major shops are also close at hand, and the hotel has its own shopping mall. Among the day rooms are the Terrace Bar and the Sandbank Seafood Bar. Pinks and blues are key colours in the bedrooms, which offer a high standard of comfort and accessories; they range from modernised singles to luxury penthouse suites. Business gatherings and banquets (to a maximum of 170) are accommodated in elegantly furnished boardrooms and function suites. Here, as elsewhere, the Westbury has the atmosphere of a top-class hotel with legions of staff providing a good level of service. *Gymnasium, beauty & hair salon, news kiosk, coffee shop (10am-10pm, Sun to 3pm).* AMERICAN EXPRESS® *Diners, Mastercard, Visa.*

Russell Room

Seats 100   Meal for 2 approx £85

The traditional French menu holds few surprises, though the cooking is sound and both service and surroundings suitably stylish. Seafood makes a strong showing, and flambéed crepes Suzette is a completely apposite dessert for the setting. A three-course table d'hote lunch (four courses at dinner) offers a choice of five or so dishes at each course. Set L £18.50 Set D £23.50. *L 12.30-2.30 D 6.30-10.30 (Sun to 9.30).*

Meal prices for 2 are based on à la carte menus.
When set menus are available, prices will often be lower.

Dublin   **Zen**

Tel (1) 497 9428   **R**

89 Upper Rathmines Road Dublin 6
Seats 85   Meal for 2 approx £50

An unusual Chinese restaurant in many respects, not least that the
south-city premises occupy what was once a Church of England
meeting hall – the lofty hammer-beam roof is still evident. The
other reason it's unusual is because it's owned by an Irishman,
Dennis O'Connor, who doesn't speak a word of Chinese, yet
imports his chefs and staff directly from Beijing. The cooking
is mainly Szechuan with the particularly hot and spicy dishes
asterisked on the menu, such as the hot (in both senses) appetiser
of dumplings in a ginger, garlic and chili sauce, guaranteed to burn
(in a tasteful manner) the roof of your mouth! For the less
adventurous there are more conventional starters: sesame prawn
toast, crispy spring rolls and orange-flavoured sliced beef. Main
dishes include succulent and carefully prepared prawns (fried with
cashew nuts or in a garlic sauce), steamed whole black sole
in ginger sauce or various sizzling meats. Aromatic or smoked
duckling arrive less highly seasoned, or you could give a day's
notice and order crispy Beijing duck, roasted whole, its skin and
meat mixed with spring onions and bean paste, then rolled
in wheat pancakes. Set D from £17.50. *L 12.30-2.30 D 6-11.30.*
Closed L Mon-Wed & Sat, 25 & 26 Dec, Good Friday.
AMERICAN EXPRESS *Diners, Mastercard, Visa.*

Cork

Cork   Arbutus Lodge

Tel (21) 501237   Fax (21) 502893   **HR**

Montenotte Cork Co Cork

Rooms 20   Double room from £85

Considerable improvements and refurbishment have taken place
in most of the bedrooms at this former home of a Lord Mayor
of Cork, high above the city with views of the River Lee and the
surrounding hills. The hotel gets its name from the Arbutus tree,
one of the many rare trees and shrubs growing in the spectacular
terraced gardens. The house is full of genuine antique furniture
(note the four-poster in the Blue Room) and some marvellous art,
both old and new, the modern paintings by Irish artists much
in demand by galleries and museums. Declan and Patsy Ryan, here
since 1961, extend a warm welcome to all their guests, ably
backed up by charming staff. Whether you choose to relax in the
cosy lounge or the panoramic bar with its own terrace, you'll feel
at home and the cleverly designed and smartly decorated
bedrooms, utilising all possible space, provide both comfort and
tranquillity. Bathrooms boast quality towels, bathrobes and
toiletries and you'll start the day with as good a breakfast as you'll
find anywhere. Conference facilities for up to 120. *Garden, tennis.*
AMERICAN EXPRESS *Diners, Mastercard, Visa.*

Restaurant

Seats 50   Meal for 2 approx £80

Alongside Myrtle Allen (see entry for *Ballymaloe House*), Declan
Ryan has trained and brought on more chefs in this country than
anyone. Back in the kitchen from early morning until service
commences, he has currently moulded together an enthusiastic
young team headed by the talented Helen Ward, who is only in
her very early 20s! Here is a restaurant that has remained loyal
to its roots – no slavish copying of French trends but a reliance
on local produce including herbs and soft fruit from the hotel's
own garden and traditional Cork dishes – spicy beef, tripe and
drisheen. Game in season and the freshest of fish are also a feature
(inspect the seafood tank in the bar) and always a fine example
of the kitchen's style is the nightly-changing, seven-course tasting   ★
menu – no mini-portions, but enough to satisfy the hungriest
of souls with spiced beef and mushroom filo parcels, nage
of scallops and prawns, escalope of salmon on sorrel sauce, very
tender roast mallard with blackcurrants, finishing with chocolate
and rum log or gargantuan floating islands. Service is as caring
and professional as you'll find anywhere, the cheeseboard promotes
Irish cheeses in tip-top condition, and the sweet trolley will tempt
even the faint-hearted. A variety of breads is baked on the premises
daily, and the wine list has been lovingly nurtured for three
decades. Set L £14.50 Set D £21.50/£27.75. *L 1-2 D 7-9.30.
Closed Sun, 1 week Christmas.*

Cork	**Cliffords**	
Tel (21) 275333		**R**

18 Dyke Parade Cork Co Cork
Seats 40   Meal for 2 approx £70

Style and quality are the keynotes here, in terms not only
of cooking but also of service and decor. The building itself, once
the civic library, is Georgian, but the whole place has been
elegantly modernised, and Michael and Deirdre Clifford's
collection of contemporary Irish art adorns the walls. The dining
area is striking in its simplicity, with comfortable high-back chairs,
high-quality linen and single flowers floating in glass bowls.
Michael's cooking is controlled and confident, with inventive use
of the best of local produce. The dinner menu changes monthly,
though some specialities put in regular appearances. Typifying his
style are a warm salad of grilled scallops with an aubergine
mousse, Clonakilty black pudding with poached free-range egg,
cabbage and smoked kassler, velouté of celeriac and wild
mushrooms, monkfish tails 'en papillote' with ginger and spring
onions and pan-fried fillet of beef with braised salsify and a rich
Fleurie sauce. There's always a fresh fish of the day, plus game
in season and some very hard-to-resist chocolate desserts.
Set L £13.50 Set D £29. L 12.30-2.30 D 7.30-10.30. Closed L Sat
& Mon, all Sun, Bank Holidays, 2 weeks Aug. AMERICAN EXPRESS Diners,
Mastercard, Visa.

★

Around Cork

Shanagarry	**Ballymaloe House**	
Tel (21) 652531 Fax (21) 652021		**HR**

Shanagarry Co Cork
Rooms 30   Double room from £120

Part of an old castle that became a farmhouse, modernised through
the centuries, but with the 14th-century keep remaining in its
original form. The hotel is situated in the middle of a 400-acre
farm, both owned and run by Ivan and Myrtle Allen. Two miles
from the coast, near the small fishing village of Ballycotton, the
main house provides the day rooms, a large drawing room with
an open fire and a TV room, complete with video recorder.
Throughout, there's an interesting collection of modern Irish
paintings with works by Jack B Yeats in the dining room.
Thirteen bedrooms in the main building are traditionally
furnished, and a further five modern, garden rooms open
on to a lawn. Another eleven rooms, more cottagey in character,
surround the old coachyard, with some on ground level suitable
for wheelchairs. Ballymaloe is a warm and comfortable family
home, especially welcoming to children of all ages (high tea
is served at 5.30pm), who can rely on the Allen (grand)children
to relay the latest news from the farm or share the sandpit and
pool. For the delightful breakfasts, all the ingredients are local
or home-made, with even the oatmeal used for porridge ground
in an old stone mill down the road. *Garden, croquet, outdoor
swimming pool, tennis, golf (9), children's outdoor play area.
Closed 24-26 Dec.* AMERICAN EXPRESS *Diners, Mastercard, Visa.*

Restaurant
Seats 90   Meal for 2 approx £80

Perhaps more than anyone else in the country, Myrtle Allen has
nurtured, encouraged and cajoled chefs from her kitchen to spread
their wings further afield after first achieving high standards here.
Wherever you go in Ireland, you're likely to come across
an individual who at some time has cooked alongside this doyenne
of Irish chefs. There are several smallish interconnecting dining
rooms, any of which can be used privately, all furnished with
antiques, and a conservatory with a black-and-white tiled floor,
Lloyd Loom furniture and lots of greenery. With the bread home-
baked, the fish caught locally (sometimes the menu is deliberately
late to see what the fishing boats have brought in), and the salads
and vegetables picked that day, you can certainly rely on the
ingredients being fresh and wholesome – indeed, much produce   ★
comes from their own farm. With Irish and French as the main
influences, the cooking is simple, enhancing the quality of the raw
materials. Typically, nightly-changing menus might feature
Ballycotton fish soup, hot dressed crab, brill *en papillote* with fresh
herbs, a selection of patés, hot buttered lobster, fillet of sole with
spinach butter sauce, roast stuffed loin of Shanagarry pork with
apple sauce and red cabbage, or roast chicken with *pipérade*. Ivan
Allen has built up a fine wine cellar over many years with some
exceptional vintage Bordeaux and an increasing awareness
of quality New World wines. Set Sun L £16.50. Set D £30.
L 12.30-2 (Sun buffet at 1) D 7-9.30 (Sun buffet at 7.30).

Republic of Ireland Index

Romania

Currency: Romanian Lei   **Exchange Rate:** £1 = approx Lei 2600
Not usually obtainable in UK. Travellers cheques/US dollars
recommended.

International dialing code: 010 40
(Bucharest + 1)

Passports/Visas: Visa required by British passport holders.
(Romanian Embassy 4 Palace Green W8 4QD Tel: 0171-937
9666/Consulate 937 9667)

British Embassy in Bucharest Tel: 1-312 0303

TRANSPORT
Airports:
Bucharest-Otopemi Tel: 1-615 2747 (flight info) / 1-212 0122 (general
info)
Railway Stations:
Contact Romanian Tourist Board Tel: 0171-224 3692.
Car hire in Bucharest:
Hertz Tel: 1-611 4365 (airport 1-212 0040) / Avis Tel: 1-614 0400
(airport 1-212 0011)
Speed Limits: 80 km/h on trunk roads, 60 km/h in towns.

Banks open: Mon-Fri 9.30am-5pm (Fri to 3pm).

Shops open: 9.30am-5pm Mon-Sat (variable).

National Holidays: 1 & 2 May, Orthodox Easter, 1 & 2 Dec,
Christmas Day.

Tourist Offices:
Romanian Tourist Board in London - Tel: 0171-224 3692
In Bucharest - Tel: 1-614 5160

American Express Travel Service Offices or Representative (R):
Bucharest - National Tourist Office
   Carpati (R)
   Boulevard Magheru Nr.7
   Tel: 1-3122596/3122594

Bucharest

Bucharest	La Gogosaru'

Tel (1) 617 3402	R

53 Strada Turda Bucharest 1

Seats 80   Meal for 2 approx $20

Not the best part of town and not the smartest of restaurants,
although tables do come with linen cloths and napkins, but this
is the place to experience real Romanian cooking and local colour.
Established in the late 19th-century, La Gogosaru' (it's old-
fashioned Romanian for sweet peppers) has been returned
to family ownership since the revolution. Eating options are in the
front room with its booth seating down each side and a TV
at each end (*Dallas* with Romanian subtitles on our last visit),
a slightly smarter back room (still with TV) or, best bet when the
weather is fine, outside on the green patio. Most of the dishes are
translated into some sort of English. For starters, for a whole table,
try the 'hot-plate' that will probably include little spicy sausages
from the Oktana region, *mici* (a mixture of minced pork and beef
grilled), chicken livers, mushrooms and deep-fried cheese – the
other one in batter will be calf's brain. If this does not fill you up,
try the *tochitura* (mixed meat stew served with a mould of soft
polenta topped with a fried egg). Customers are mostly local
so prices are low. The address is not helpful as the restaurant
is actually in a small back street called L'Autaru that runs parallel
to Strada Turda at its southern end. *Open noon-2am (Mon 2pm-
2am). No credit cards.*

Bucharest	Helvetia

Tel (1) 311 0566 Fax (1) 311 0567	H

13 Piata Aviatorilor Bucharest 1

Rooms 30   Double room from $235

Built a year ago, this hotel is close to the Aviatorilor Metro
Station, a couple of stops to the north of the city centre. The
exterior is white marble, which also covers all the floors of the
reception. This area with some stools at a bar counter and a couple
of leather armchairs, provides the only public space apart from the
restaurant. Air-conditioned bedrooms vary in size but all have
double beds, a couple of easy chairs, coffee table and low chest
of drawers. There is no desk or other usable work space but
a folding table can be provided on request. All the bathrooms have
tubs, except two rooms with showers only, and also hand-held
showers. The rooms do not have mini-bars. *24hr room service.
Satellite TV/air-con. Private parking.* AMERICAN EXPRESS *Diners,
Mastercard, Visa.*

Bucharest   Inter-Continental

Tel (1) 614 04 00   Fax (1) 312 04 86   HR

4 Boulevard Nicolae Balcescu Bucharest 1
Rooms 435   Double room from $235

Right in the centre of the city, this high-rise hotel was built in the
70s and now looks a little drab and dated. Spacious bedrooms,
however, are still acceptable with all the usual amenities, including
a mini-bar. Major refurbishment may take place if its state-owned
status changes. There are a pool and gym on the top floor (but
don't count on an early morning dip, as it doesn't open until
noon), which enjoys fabulous views. Excellent concierge service.
*24hr room service. Satellite TV/air-con/safe. Theatre-style conference
facilities for up to 500. Indoor swimming pool, sauna, gym.*
AMERICAN EXPRESS *Diners, Mastercard, Visa.*

Restaurant Balada
Seats 100   Meal for 2 approx $60

Of the hotel's two restaurants this one is billed as offering
Romanian cuisine, but what you will actually find is mostly the
likes of spaghetti milanese, vol-au-vent and chicken Kiev.
However, there *are* some Romanian dishes – if not all particularly
authentic – on the clearly comprehensible (in English) menu, like
turkey in jelly (it should strictly speaking be pork), minced pork
wrapped in cabbage leaves with *sauerkraut* and Romanian-style
soft polenta, and pheasant with mushrooms. Up on the 21st floor,
the views are splendid and a five-piece band, featuring a rather
good violinist, provides the entertainment. *L noon-4 D 6-midnight.
Closed Sun.*

Bucharest   Sofitel

Tel (1) 212 29 98   Fax (1) 211 5688   HR

2 Boulevard Expozitiei Bucharest 1
Rooms 203   Double room from $225

Far and away the best place to stay in Bucharest. Brand new (since
summer 1994), this French-managed hotel was built as part of the
new World Trade Centre, on the outskirts of the city centre
towards the airport. The airy, spacious reception rooms have
a touch of style, young Romanian staff are as keen as mustard
to provide good service, and well-designed bedrooms are
of international standard. A shuttle bus runs to the airport (about
10 minutes away) and will run to the hotel's own sports centre
being built right on the edge of a park lake, five minutes away.
Back at the hotel, attractions not generally expected in these parts
include a night club and a shopping arcade. Excellent buffet
breakfast, including *pain au chocolat* and marmalade. *Theatre-style
conference facilities for up to 400. Indoor swimming pool, gym, sauna,
indoor and outdoor tennis courts. Parking shared with World Trade
Centre.* AMERICAN EXPRESS *Diners, Mastercard, Visa.*

Restaurant Darclée

Seats 85   Meal for 2 approx $85

Not only the best place to stay but a pretty good bet for eating
too with a genuine French chef providing some sound Gallic
cooking. The likes of salmon mousse with a saffron cream sauce,
sea-scallops in champagne sauce, medallions of pork with morels
and fricassée of duck breast with tarragon come attractively
presented, if in sometimes rather nouvelle-sized portions. Desserts   ★
could include a 'tulip' of prune mousse and gratinated poached
pears with Sauternes. The setting is cool and comfortable and the
staff very willing. There's a short wine list on which the perfectly
drinkable Romanian wines provide the best value. *L 12.30-2.45
D 7.30-10.45.*

Bucharest   **Velvet**

Tel (1) 615 9241   Fax (1) 312 7004   R

2-4 Strada Stirbei-Voda Bucharest 2

Seats 60   Meal for 2 approx $85

One of the smartest restaurants in town, a comfortable, air-
conditioned basement with gilt-edged crockery, crystal glassware
and attentive service. The menu is essentially international, with
dishes such as salad niçoise, frogs' legs with tomato sauce, seafood
salad, pike-perch meunière, steak au poivre, breast of duck
bigarade and pork escalope with lemon sauce prepared by chef
Dobre Doru, who puts a lot of effort into attractive presentation.
The sweet trolley offers just a few desserts, like fruit tart, chocolate
gateau and cheesecake brought over from the Inter-Continental's
kitchens. They serve good coffee. *L 12-4 D 7-midnight. Closed
L Sat.* AMERICAN EXPRESS *Diners, Mastercard, Visa.*

Russian Federation

Currency: Russian Rouble   **Exchange Rate**: Liable to fluctuation Not obtainable in UK. Travellers cheques/US dollars recommended.

International dialling code: 010 7
(Moscow +095 St Petersburg +812)

Passports/Visas: Visa required by British passport holders.
(Russian Consulate 5 Kensington Palace Gdns W8 4QS Tel: 0171-229 8027)

British Embassies in Russia Moscow Tel: 095-231 8511 / St Petersburg Tel: 812-312 0072

TRANSPORT
Airports:
Moscow-Sheremetyevo Tel: 095-578 5753
St Petersburg-Pulkova Tel: 812-104 3180/104 3444
Railway Stations:
Main information centre for Russian railways Tel: 095-292 3786/292 2111
Car hire:
Moscow - Avis Tel: 095-240 9863 (airport 095-578 5646) Hertz Tel: 095-284 4391 (airport 095-578 7532) Innis Tel: 095-599 9222
St Petersburg - Avis Tel: (airport) 812 235 6444 Innis Tel: 812-210 5858
Speed limits: 90 km/h outside cities, 60 km/h in built-up areas.

Banks open: Russian State banks are usually open 9.30am-1pm. Many of the new private banks open from 10am to 6pm, and private exchanges in hotels are generally open 9am-6pm (sometimes to 8pm). Most banks are closed for lunch 1-3pm.

Shops open: Hours are variable. Food stores generally from 9/10am to 8pm (often closed between 2 & 3pm). Department stores generally 9am-8pm; others till 6pm.

National Holidays: New Year's Day, 8 Mar, 1, 2 & 9 May, 7 Oct, 7 & 8 Nov.

Tourist Offices:
Russian Embassy in London - Tel: 0171-229 3628
Tourist Board in Russia –
Moscow Tel: 095-923-5765/203 6962
St Petersburg Tel: 812-210 0905/210 0990/104 3465

(further information available from Intourist London - Tel: 0171-538 8600/538 5965)

American Express Travel Service Offices or Representative (R):
Moscow - AETS
   21a Sadovaya-Kudrinskaya
   103001
   Tel: 095-956 9000/9004 #

Moscow

Moscow	Azteca	
Tel 095 956 84 89		**R**

Intourist Hotel Ulitsa Tverskaya 3/5 Moscow
Seats 60   Meal for 2 approx $120

A tiny Mexican restaurant, which first opened in December 1993,
consisting only of five tables and a bar, crammed into a corner
of the 20th floor of the Intourist Hotel. Now it has opened
a second room with a spectacular view over the city. The lively
atmosphere provided by the Latin-American dance music ensures
a full house, so get here early as they do not take reservations.
A wide variety of Mexican food is served, ranging from prawn
quesadillas and *enchiladas* to beef marinated in tequila, all well
prepared and presented. Cocktails and Corona beer as well
as various wines are available. The main courses may start from
around $20, but the drinks are expensive. *Open 24hrs. Private
parking.* AMERICAN EXPRESS *Diners, Mastercard, Visa. Roubles.*

Moscow	Hotel Balkschug Kempinski Moskau	
Tel 095 230 95 00 Fax 095 230 65 02/3		**HR**

Ulitsa Balchug 1 113035 Moscow
Rooms 202   Double room from $450

In 1992 the building's Soviet-style interior was hollowed out,
leaving only the 19th-century facade and making way for the
latest Kempinski hotel – the first in Eastern Europe. Splendid
views of the Kremlin and Red Square can be seen from the
windows and Stalin's 1930s 'Wedding Cakes', the five towers that
dominate the Moscow skyline, are also clearly visible. The hotel
staff are mostly Western European and the rooms certainly match
up to Western standards; with marble bathrooms and elegant rust-
red furnishings. Each room has a safe and is double-glazed and
insulated against the extremes of Moscow's climate. A major
advantage is a number for reservations based in London for hassle-
free booking – 0800 89 85 88(toll free). *24hr room service. Theatre-
style conference facilities for up to 220. 4 interpreting booths.
Secretarial/translation services on request.* AMERICAN EXPRESS *Mastercard,
Visa.*

Restaurant   Le Romanoff
Seats 39   Meal for 2 approx $65

Here, traditional Russian specialities are given a new
contemporary twist, served with finer, much lighter sauces.
A roulade of Caucasian venison is served in a light juniper sauce
and sautéed fillet of monkfish with scallops comes in a saffron
sauce. But there are some classic combinations: Siberian-style meat
dumplings, tartar of home-marinated salmon and some delicious
zakuski (starters). Their Beluga Malossol caviar comes on crushed
ice, while the Siberian ravioli are solid pastry ravioli filled with
meat and cabbage. *Open 6am-11pm.*

Moscow   Carousel
Tel 095 200 57 63   `R`

Ulitsa Pervaya Yamskaya 7 Moscow
Seats 60   Meal for 2 approx $100

In a restaurant opened as recently as February 1994, Italian and
Russian cuisine is prepared under the direction of an Italian chef.
He tends to emphasise seafood, with oysters available at $18 per
half dozen. Main courses are expensive (from about $30) but very
well prepared. The wine list is long and mainly Italian, but does
include some French, Californian and South American bottles.
A modest bottle of Pinot Grigio costs $30. *Open noon-6am. Public
parking.* AMERICAN EXPRESS *Diners, Mastercard, Visa. Roubles.*

THE APARTMENT SERVICE
Tel in UK: (0181) 748 4207   Fax: (0181) 748 3972
The Apartment Service will find you the right apartment
worldwide to suit your needs, whether you are on a short or
long-term stay. A 96-page colour catalogue is free on request.
All budgets are catered for.

Moscow   El Rincón Español
Tel 095 292 28 93   `R`

Manezh Square Moscow
Seats 80   Meal for 2 approx $120

Located just inside the entrance of the Hotel Moscow, the
restaurant is actually quite independent from it. A wide variety
of imported Spanish dishes is served, with particularly good
starters, including smoked ham, *chorizo* and pickled herrings.
Main courses start at $22. The atmosphere is lively, without being
deafening. Service is fast by Moscow standards with English-
speaking waitresses. *Open noon-midnight. Private parking.*
AMERICAN EXPRESS *Diners, Mastercard, Visa. Roubles.*

Moscow   Glazur
Tel 095 248 44 38   `R`

Smolensky Bulvar 12 Moscow
Seats 50   Meal for 2 approx $150

For those determined to experiment with Russian cooking and
mix with an elite clientele at the same time, this is a relatively safe
bet. However, the promising menu, with dishes like steamed trout
in white wine sauce and pike-perch with king prawns,
is somewhat misleading as many items may be unavailable. Caviar
comes at $38 a portion, but there are much cheaper starters,
including stuffed tomatoes and mushroom julienne. Main courses
can be indeterminate, though perfectly edible slabs of meat,
accompanied by the inevitable Russian mixture of beetroot and
cabbage. A jazz band makes conversation only possible between
numbers. Wines start at about $18 a bottle. *Open noon-midnight.
Closed 1 week from 25 Dec. No parking.* AMERICAN EXPRESS *Diners,
Mastercard, Visa. No roubles.*

Moscow   Lili Wong's Chinese Restaurant

Tel 095 956 83 01	R

3/5 Ulitsa Tverskaya Moscow
Seats 200   Meal for 2 approx $105

Finally, good Chinese food has come to Moscow and the Oriental decor is unequalled in the rest of the city. The chefs are all from Hong Kong, and as a result the food is authentic. An assortment of appetisers, ranging from $8 to $18, includes spring rolls, sesame toasts and won ton soup. Main courses start at approximately $24 and include dishes like Szechuan prawns, chicken satay, pork with chili and crispy duck. Rice is shamelessly overpriced at $6 a portion; while vegetables are limited and dominated by onions. *Open noon-midnight. No parking.* AMERICAN EXPRESS *Diners, Mastercard, Visa. Roubles.*

Moscow   Metropol

Tel 095 927 60 00 Fax 095 92 76 01	H

Teatrainy Proyazd 1/4 Moscow
Rooms 403   Double room from $370

Originally built in 1903, it was fully restored to all its former art nouveau grandeur in 1991 by the Inter-Continental Group. Just a short walk from Red Square, many of the rooms look out on to the Bolshoi Theatre. The rooms are extremely well equipped and all have mini-bars, satellite TVs with 24 channels and personal databases. The conference facilities also make this an excellent place for businessmen with facilities for meetings for up to 600. Cars can be rented and all the cultural events going on in the city can be booked from here. For a little relaxation after the conferences, try the nightclub or fitness centre with its sauna and swimming pool. *24hr room service. Air-con. Conference facilities. Business centre. Travel agency. Sports centre. Secure private parking.* AMERICAN EXPRESS *Diners, Mastercard, Visa.*

Moscow   Moscow Aerostar Hotel

Tel 095 155 50 30 Fax 095 213 90 01	H

Leningradsky Prospekt 37 Korpus 9 Moscow
Rooms 415   Double room from $255

This hotel was intended to be ready for the 1980 Moscow Olympics but was never completed. It finally opened as a joint Russian-Canadian venture in May 1991 and is conveniently located on the main route to Sheremetiero Airport (a 30-minute journey), close to the Kremlin and just a bus, tram or metro ride away from the centre. The end result has been well-equipped rooms with satellite TV and a movie channel, voice-mail and air-conditioning. Apart from comprehensive conference facilities there is also a health club with a sauna, massage, aerobics and a gym and an important extra – an American medical centre. *24hr room service. Conference facilities. Business centre: secretarial/translation services. Sports facilities. Private parking.* AMERICAN EXPRESS *Diners, Mastercard, Visa.*

Moscow — Olympic Penta

Tel 095 971 61 01   Fax 095 971 61 01 [H]

Olympiski Prospekt 18/1 129110 Moscow
Rooms 500   Double room from $236

The location, outside Moscow's Garden Ring Road, near the
Olympic Stadium, may not be great, but it is well served
by public transport and the Prospekt Mira metro station is nearby.
There's a well-equipped business centre and various sports facilities
including a 22m indoor swimming pool, tennis courts, a gym,
sauna and solarium. The hotel is only three years old, so the rooms
are still quite modern, and equipped with a desk, coffee table and
television. There is also a variety of different food on offer: the
Café Vienna has the largest buffet in Moscow, while the *Bakery*
is a rare luxury – it bakes Danish pastries, croissants and baguettes
twice a day and the formal restaurant combines Russian and
Chinese cooking. *24hr room service. Business centre: theatre-style
conference facilities for up to 400. Secretarial/translation/fax/
photocopying services on request. Private parking.* AMERICAN EXPRESS®
Mastercard, Visa.

Moscow — Pirosmani

Tel 095 247 19 26 [R]

Novodevichy Prospekt 4 Moscow
Seats 113   Meal for 2 approx $110

For the more adventurous, this cosy restaurant with its Georgian-
style decor is the best of its kind in Moscow, illustrated by its
predominantly Georgian clientele. Violinists provide the musical
entertainment in the evenings. Rich, spicy dishes are accompanied
by freshly baked *lavash* (Georgian bread) and cheese pastries.
Georgian and French wines are available, but the choice is limited.
Some people may be put off by the presence of suspicious looking
characters, who offer to guard diners' cars – at a price. Best to pay
and keep tyres intact. No English is spoken. *Open noon-12.30am.
Parking.* AMERICAN EXPRESS® *Roubles.*

★

Black Sea   Krasnador

Radisson Hotel Lazurnaya

Tel 862 6 61 59 99   Fax 862 6 61 59 98   **H**

Kuroitny Prospekt 103 354024 Sochi
Rooms 300   Double room from $120

This 25-storey hotel sits on a bluff overlooking the Black Sea, in a
new, up-and-coming holiday resort which Russians visit to escape
the cold and enjoy the healing hot springs. Radisson bought the
building half-completed from a Turkish company and have spent
the last two years renovating it. The end result is an extremely
well-equipped hotel. Balconies look out across to the sandy
beaches. The sports facilities are also excellent. *24hr room service.*
Satellite TV/air-con. Theatre-style conference facilities for up to 300.
Simultaneous translation. 2 swimming pools (1 indoor)/Russian and
Turkish baths/private beach with water sports/tennis courts.
AMERICAN EXPRESS *Mastercard, Visa.*

St Petersburg

St Petersburg	**Bella Leone**	
Tel 812 113 16 70 Fax 812 11 30 73		**R**

Vladmirisky Prospekt 9 St Petersburg

Seats 50   Meal for 2 approx $70

The Swiss-trained chefs concentrate their efforts on combining traditional Russian fare with more European cooking. Siberian-style meat dumplings and traditional buckwheat blinis and smoked salmon are found alongside lobster soup and fried duck breast on the menu. The house specialities are Russian caviar (most caviar these days comes from Iran) and grilled lobster. Wines are Italian, French, German and Moldavian (very aromatic), but they aim to introduce more Commonwealth of Independent States wines. This is one of the few restaurants in St Petersburg that is quiet. *Open noon-midnight. Planning to accept* AMERICAN EXPRESS *at the time of going to press. Dollars and roubles only.*

St Petersburg	**Grand Hotel Europe**	
Tel 812 119 60 00 Fax 812 119 60 01		**HR**

Mikhailovskaya 1-7 St Petersburg

Rooms 301   Double room from $345

Right in the heart of St Petersburg, near the Gostini Dvor metro station, this 19th-century hotel is owned and run by a Swedish hotel group and all the staff have been through extensive training. In 1991 the whole building was renovated and the Benois stained-glass window, the facade by Carlo Rossi and the glass-roofed ballroom were all restored. The facilities are now very good: the health club has a gym, sauna and spa and there are excellent boardroom-style conference facilities for up to 250. The traditional features of the rooms have been restored and reproduction period furniture arranged elegantly in them. The *Sadko* bar is a popular meeting place, even though some claim the new Mafia of 'professionals' meet here. Despite this, the hotel receives our Best Hotel in Eastern Europe award. *24hr room service. Satellite TV/fax. Secretarial/translation services.* AMERICAN EXPRESS *Mastercard, Visa.*

See over for restaurant

Restaurant
Seats 96   Meal for 2 approx $80

A French chef who apprenticed with Troisgros at Roanne came
over from France and created a new style of cooking, now
universally known in the Russian Federation as the 'Renaissance
of Russia' cuisine: a combination of traditional Russian dishes and
modern gourmet cooking. Now he is a consultant and the menu
is not even so much as adapted without his blessing. Traditional
Russian raw ingredients like beetroot, pearl barley, mushrooms
and caviar are used more imaginatively than before. Sturgeon
is stuffed with cabbage and served with a rich smoked caviar   ★
sauce; salmon coulibiac and pigeon and beef borsch are traditional
dishes served here with new ingredients. 65 chefs prepare these
dishes, and almost as many waiters serve the customers in the
19th-century, stained-glass windowed-building, formerly used
by the Tsars, before becoming a hospital during the 900 Days
War. The wine list is surprisingly international, with Spanish
house reds and whites. On Sundays, they run a 'jazz brunch' with
free champagne. *D 6-11. Closed D Sun.*

St Petersburg   **Restaurant Troika**

| Tel 812 113 53 43   Fax 812 310 42 79 | **R** |

Zagorodnyy Prospekt 27 St Petersburg
Seats 160   Meal for 2 approx $90

Until the October Revolution, this place in the south of the city
was an old-style drinking house, but after 1917 it became
a restaurant in Swedish and Russian hands. All the cooking
is traditionally Russian (even though most of the dishes originate
from old Polish recipes). Sturgeon, cold hors d'oeuvre, steaks and
chicken Kiev are the backbone of the menu. There is an enormous
list of *zakuski* (cold appetisers). White French and Spanish red
wines are served. The tables rise up around a stage, where
traditional Russian dancing and European cabaret provide live
entertainment, Moulin Rouge-style. *D 8-12. Closed Mon.*
AMERICAN EXPRESS *Mastercard, Visa.*

Russian Federation Index

Recommended by

EGON RONAY'S GUIDES

1995

Hotels & Restaurants	Pubs & Inns
Europe	Just a Bite
Family Hotels & Restaurants	Paris
Oriental Restaurants	Ireland
New Zealand & South Pacific	Australia

Egon Ronay's Guides are available from all good bookshops or can be
ordered from Leading Guides, 35 Tadema Road, London SW10 0PZ
Tel: 071-352 2485 / 352 0019   Fax: 071-376 5071

Spain

Currency: Peseta   **Exchange Rate:** £1 = approx 200 Pts

International dialling code: 010 34
(Madrid + 1 Barcelona + 3 Malaga + 52 Seville + 5 Valencia + 6)

Passports/Visas: No visa required by British passport holders.

British Embassy in Madrid Tel: 1-319 0200   Fax: 1-319 0423

TRANSPORT
Airports:
Barcelona Tel: 3-478 5000
Madrid Tel: 1-305 8343
Malaga Tel: 52-24000
Seville 5-451 1159
Valencia Tel: 6-370 9500
Railway Stations:
Renfe Madrid Tel: 1-530 0202/1-323 4426 / Renfe Barcelona Tel: 3-490 0202
Car hire:
Madrid - Avis Tel: 1-305 4273 / Hertz Tel: (airport) 1-305 8452 / Budget Tel: 1-571 6660 (airport 1-747 7427)
Barcelona - Avis Tel: 3-209 9533/209 9354 / Budget Tel: (airport) 3-322 9012
Malaga - Avis Tel: (airport) 52-233 096/230 855 / Budget Tel: 52-447 078 (airport 52-239 449)
Speed limits: 100 km/h on trunk roads, 90 km/h on secondary roads, 120 km/h on motorways, 50 km/h in towns.

Banks open: 9am-2pm Mon-Fri (some Saturday opening).

Shops open: 10am-8pm (most are closed at lunchtime between 1-4pm).

National Holidays: New Year's Day, 6 Jan, 1 May, 15 Aug, 12 Oct, 1, 6 & 8 Nov & Christmas Day (+ four days varying by area).

Tourist Offices:
Spanish Tourist Board in London - Tel: 0171-499 0901
In Spain –
Madrid Tel: 1-429 4951
Barcelona Tel: 3-478 4704
Malaga Tel: 52-213 445

American Express Travel Service Offices or Representative (R):
Madrid - AETS
  Plaza De Las Cortes 2
  28014
  Tel: 1-322 5500 #

Madrid

Madrid   El Amparo

Tel (1) 431 64 56   Fax (1) 575 54 91   **R**

Callejón de Puigcerdá 8 28001 Madrid

Seats 70   Meal for 2 approx Pts16,000

Basque cooking meets French cuisine in happy harmony. *Huevos escalfados con salmón y caviar* (poached eggs served with salmon and caviar), *rollitos de langosta con salsa de soja* (rolls of lobster in a soya sauce) and *pichones deshuesados a las dos pimientas* (baby pigeon with two peppers). The excellent wine list boasts a Rioja Muga house wine. This place, in a narrow, quiet street in the Belgravia of Madrid, is visited by lunching businessmen, so the atmosphere is a little formal and even in liberal Spain is not recommended for children – so be warned. *L 12.30-3.30 D 9-11.30. Closed Aug.* AMERICAN EXPRESS *Mastercard, Visa.*

★

Madrid   Bajamar

Tel (1) 548 48 18   Fax (1) 559 13 26   **R**

Gran Vía 78 28013 Madrid

Seats 280   Meal for 2 approx Pts10,000

The Madrileños patronise this restaurant in their droves, filling the 130 seats in the main dining room and overflowing into the three smaller rooms. But, because it is big, modern and well air-conditioned, the atmosphere is relaxed and easy-going. Since it opened 28 years ago, the menu has remained traditionally Spanish, with the 13 chefs preparing a wide selection of regional specialities. Fish, whether it comes as *sopa* or *zarzuela* (fish casserole) or *paella*, is the order of the day. Their grand *paella de Bajamar* is famous throughout Madrid and so is their house speciality: the special extra ingredient is fresh lobster. Most of the wines are Riojas. *L 1-4 D 8-12.* AMERICAN EXPRESS *Mastercard, Visa.*

★

THE APARTMENT SERVICE

Tel in UK: (0181) 748 4207   Fax: (0181) 748 3972

The Apartment Service will find you the right apartment worldwide to suit your needs, whether you are on a short or long-term stay. A 96-page colour catalogue is free on request. All budgets are catered for.

Madrid   El Bodegón

Tel (1) 562 88 44   Fax (1) 562 34 15   **R**

Pinar 15 28006 Madrid

Seats 85   Meal for 2 approx Pts12,000

The elegant, stylish, old-world interior with its crisp linen and silver cutlery is a luxurious setting for regional Basque, Andalucian, Valencian and Madrid cooking. The nine chefs in the kitchen consistently stick to traditional dishes like cold Andalusian consommé and *menestra de verduras* (mixed green vegetables cooked in olive oil), plus numerous rice and fish dishes. *L 1.30-4 D 9-12. Closed National Holidays. Valet parking.* AMERICAN EXPRESS *Diners, Mastercard, Visa.*

Madrid   **Cabo Mayor**

Tel (1) 350 87 76   Fax (1) 359 16 21   **R**

Calle Juan Ramón Jiménez 37 Madrid 28036
Seats 300   Meal for 2 approx Pts10,000

Pedro Luarumbe came from Santander in Cantabria, Northern
Spain, to open this restaurant in 1981, and has not looked back
since. The Cantabrian food is excellent and quite renowned, with
plenty of fresh fish and seafood from the Northern sea ports.
Lobster, clams, monkfish and cod are cooked with a little olive oil
and served with a variety of sauces, from parsley with clams
to onion and olive oil sauce. There are some interesting
Cantabrian dishes other than fish: steak is served in a raisin and   ★
cheese sauce, asparagus mousse comes with a spinach sauce and
cured venison. Regional Spanish wines complement the regional
cooking. The five dining rooms are all decorated like different
parts of a ship, from the hull to the cabin. *L 1.30-3.30 D 9-11.30.
Closed D Sat, all Jul, Aug, Good Fri-Easter Mon.* AMERICAN EXPRESS®
Diners, Mastercard, Visa.

Madrid   **Café de Oriente**

Tel (1) 541 39 74   Fax (1) 547 77 07   **R**

Plaza de Oriente 2 28013 Madrid
Seats 90   Meal for 2 approx Pts12,000

In an old square, this place is on the site of a 17th-century
monastery and is surrounded by some of the oldest buildings
in Madrid. Opened 12 years ago, the restaurant started off a chain
that now extends from Seville to Washington DC. French
guidelines have been laid down for the Basque cooking, with
traditional house specialities like hake in a parsley and garlic sauce,
and other choices could include roasted duck in a raspberry sauce
and fried crayfish with a tomato fricassée. Wines come from
France as well as Spain. *L 1-4 D 9-12.* AMERICAN EXPRESS® *Diners,
Mastercard, Visa.*

Madrid   **Casa Lucío**

Tel (1) 365 32 52   Fax (1) 366 48 66   **R**

Calle Cava Baja 35 28005 Madrid
Seats 125   Meal for 2 approx Pts 10,000

Lucío Damian Blazquez Blasque is quite a local celebrity and very
popular; he started his working life as a jocular waiter in an old
Spanish inn that used to be here and in the 70s took the plunge
and opened this Basque/Castilian restaurant. The cooking is robust,
with plenty of rich fish and meat dishes. *Callos a la Madrileña*
(tripe cooked 'Madrid-style', with a rich tomato and garlic sauce),   ★
merluza a la Bilbaína (hake served 'Bilbao-style,' with a clam sauce)
are two favourites. The decor is as traditionally Castilian as the
menu, with dark wood panelling and heavy beams. *L 1.15-3.30
D 9-11.30. Closed Aug. Valet parking.* AMERICAN EXPRESS® *Diners, Visa.*

Madrid   Casa d'a Troya

Tel (1) 416 44 55   **R**

Calle Emiliano Barral 14 Madrid 28043
Seats 60   Meal for 2 approx Pts8000

A Galician family came from Santiago de Compostela 30 years
ago and started this restaurant, dedicated to *Comida Gallega*
(Galician food). *Caldo gallego* is a light, fragrant consommé, while
pulpo a la gallega is Galician-style octopus, sliced and then grilled
with slivers of potato and seasoned with paprika. Fish and seafood
make up most of the menu. Unusually, there is also a healthy
choice of desserts, all regional specialities from Santiago
de Compostela. If you fancy something lighter, try the traditional
tapas at the bar. The informal, homely atmosphere attracts parents
and their young offspring. *L 2-3.30 D 9-11. Closed Aug, National
Holidays. Mastercard, Visa.*

Madrid   Combarro

Tel (1) 553 50 17   Fax (1) 534 25 01   **R**

Calle Reina Mercedes 12 28020 Madrid
Seats 150   Meal for 2 approx Pts10,000

Manuel Domínguez Limares opened this restaurant 21 years ago,
specialising in Galician cooking, with plenty of seafood and fish.
They are cooked in every conceivable way from hake baked
in herbs, to their specialities, pasties stuffed with seafood and
grilled lobster. Another speciality is river eel cooked in its own
juices. The wine list is not extensive, but includes a good Galician   ★
house white. Since this place is in the business and banking district
during the day, most of the guests are power-lunching. *L 1-4.30
D 8-12. Closed Aug. Valet parking.* AMERICAN EXPRESS® *Diners,
Mastercard, Visa.*

Madrid   Las Cuatro Estaciones

Tel (1) 553 63 05   Fax (1) 553 32 98   **R**

Calle General Ibáñez de Íbero 5 Madrid 28003
Seats 110   Meal for 2 approx Pts10,000

True to its name, this restaurant changes its menu every three
months, but always serves international dishes slanted towards
Mediterranean cooking, with plenty of light fish, vegetable, salad
and rice dishes. What we would consider paella is in fact any
composite rice dish, like *arroz a la marinera* (black rice with baby
squid). Or try one of the interesting non-rice dishes: *filetes
de lenguado y salmón al cava* (fillets of sole and salmon in a
champagne sauce) and the *gazpacho con bogavante 'Las Cuatro
Estaciones'* (an Andalucian cold soup made with salad vegetables   ★
and lobster). The wine list is well balanced, with some superb
French and German wines. The restaurant's central location
attracts businessmen during the day and dining couples at night,
when the colourful mirrored interior comes alive. *L 1.30-4 D 9-
12. Valet parking. Closed Aug, Thur-Sun over Easter.* AMERICAN EXPRESS®
Diners, Mastercard, Visa.

Madrid   **La Dorada**

Tel (1) 570 20 04   Fax (1) 571 854 04   **R**

Calle Orense 64-66 28020 Madrid

Seats 440   Meal for 2 approx Pts10,000

In this new building, in a busy street in the city, a vast number
of people pack in to eat; and it is worth joining them, eating
in either of the two dining rooms, or the large bar. Mediterranean
fish and seafood is the big speciality and fish is flown in every day
by private plane from Andalucia in the South. Most of the fish
dishes are grilled with plenty of olive oil and accompanied
by regional Spanish wines. *L 1-4.30 D 8-12. Valet parking.*
AMERICAN EXPRESS *Diners, Mastercard, Visa.*

Madrid   **Grand Hotel Reina Victoria**

Tel (1) 531 45 00   Fax (1) 522 03 07   **H**

Plaza de Santa Ana 4 28012 Madrid

Rooms 201   Double room from Pts23,000

Madrid's patron saint is Isidro, whose name lends itself to the
April San Isidro bull fights that are put on in Madrid every year.
During April while all the proud bullfighters and their ardent
followers are conducting their campaigns, they stay here too. The
interior has been completely refurbished in 20s style, with lots
of plants everywhere. The rooms are equipped with satellite TV,
private safes and faxes on request. However, despite their most
popular guests, there are no keep-fit or sports facilities. This is a
very busy part of the city, but one is still able to reach the airport
in under 30 minutes. *Room service. Public parking.* AMERICAN EXPRESS
Diners, Mastercard, Visa.

Madrid   **Jockey**

Tel (1) 319 24 35   Fax (1) 319 24 35   **R**

Calle Amador de Los Rios 6 Madrid 28010

Seats 155   Meal for 2 approx Pts12,000

Aiming to be all things to all men, and succeeding, the Jockey is as
cosmopolitan as Madrid comes, with French cooking and English
decor, paintings of racehorses and jockeys and dark mahogany
wooden-panelled walls. Duck, partridge and pheasant are all
regularly served on the menu, while sea urchin soup is a house
speciality. Other regional dishes have been adapted to this more
versatile French kitchen: ragout of lobster is served with fresh
pasta, boned partridge with mushrooms is cooked *en croute* and
fillet of pork with honey and raisins comes on a bed of rice.
Burgundies and Bordeaux meet Riojas and Galicians. *L 1-4
D 9-12. Closed Sun, Thur-Sun at Easter, Aug. Private parking.*
AMERICAN EXPRESS *Diners, Mastercard, Visa.*

★

Opening times are often liable to change at short notice,
so it's always best to book.

Madrid   Lúculo

Tel (1) 319 40 29   Fax (1) 319 40 29   R .

Calle Génova 19 Madrid 28004
Seats 75   Meal for 2 approx Pts12,000

This 19th-century mansion, with its pretty flowering gardens and
flowing fountains, used to be the home of the famous Spanish
liberal, Sagasta, before becoming a restaurant. Nowadays in the
summer people sit and eat in the gardens. The chef, an old hand
in the kitchen, cooks French dishes with a definite Mediterranean
bias. All kinds of fish come grilled, and there are plenty of rice
and pasta dishes. His speciality is black pudding lasagne served
with a cream of green peppers. The 80 different bottles on the
Spanish and French wine list have been hand-picked with much
deliberation and great results. *Valet parking. L 1.30-4.30 D 9.30-
12. Closed L Sat, all Sun.* AMERICAN EXPRESS *Diners, Visa.*

Madrid   Moaña

Tel (1) 548 29 14   Fax (1) 541 65 98   R

La Calle Hileras 4 28013 Madrid
Seats 100   Meal for 2 approx Pts10,000

A chain, Patanovo A.A., opened this Galician and traditional
Spanish restaurant back in 1970 and the three chefs have been here
since it opened. On the menu is the set dish of the day and
a speciality dish, not normally on the à la carte menu. *Jamón iberico*
(slices of cured ham, like Parma ham, wrapped in Galician pastry),
gazpacho and smoked salmon are typical dishes. There is also
a wide selection of seafood: large and small crabs, lobster, king
prawns, mussels, eels and oysters. The restaurant is named after
their speciality *bacalao Moana* (cod cooked in breadcrumbs). It is
right at the centre of Madrid, yet the small dining rooms here are
quiet and relaxed, with simple wooden tables and chairs. *L 1-4
D 9-10.30. Private parking.* AMERICAN EXPRESS *Mastercard, Visa.*

Madrid   El Olivo

Tel (1) 359 15 35   Fax (1) 345 91 83   R

Calle General Gallegos 1 Madrid 28036
Seats 80   Meal for 2 approx Pts10,000

Everything is Mediterranean about this place: the name – The
Olive Tree – is the symbol of Andalucia, the largest region
of Spain, deep in the South, and the menu is traditionally
Mediterranean. Andalucian consommé is cool and refreshing,
lobster is grilled in olive oil and monkfish is cooked in a black
olive sauce. Many of their dishes are cooked in olive oil, with
salmon and cod marinated in olive oil from Baena. They have
over 1500 wines, mostly Spanish, but the house speciality
is sherry. Down below are 25 sherry cellars, open to guests who
would like a mini-tasting before their meal. *L 1-4 D 9-12. Closed
Aug, Good Friday-Easter Mon. Valet parking.* AMERICAN EXPRESS *Diners,
Mastercard, Visa.*

Madrid   La Paloma

Tel (1) 576 86 92   Fax (1) 576 86 92   **R**

Calle Jorge Juan 39 28001 Madrid

Seats 70   Meal for 2 approx Pts10,000

This restaurant has only been open for two years, yet has already
made its culinary mark amongst Madrid's plethora of restaurants.
The food is all plain traditional Spanish home cooking. Pig's
trotters are cutleted and served in a rich sauce, cod comes in a
melon salad (a house speciality) and kidneys are served in their
own juices. There are lots of other offal dishes on the menu,
like brains and liver, all traditional Spanish fare. The regional wines
stretch from Rioja and Galicia to Catalonia and Valencia. It is very
quiet inside, with simple wooden tables and lots of plants, but
outside, the busy shopping streets of Goya are only a stroll away.
*L 1.30-4.30 D 9-11.45. Closed L Sat, all Sun, Aug, National
Holidays.* AMERICAN EXPRESS *Mastercard, Visa.*

Madrid   El Pescador

Tel (1) 402 12 90   **R**

Calle José Ortega y Gasset 75 Madrid 28006

Seats 90   Meal for 2 approx Pts10,000

Evaristo García Gomez is famous throughout Madrid, not only
for his two restaurants, the *O'Pazo* and this one, but also because
he supplies most of the fish eaten in Madrid. Any fish that can
be caught on the Cantabrian coast (in Northern Spain) is on the
menu and cooked in a traditional Northern Spanish way: grilled,
baked or casseroled and served with light sauces. Cantabrian
seafood soup is made from sea bream, sole, lobster and baked
turbot, while *merluza al horno* (baked hake) is a house speciality.
This well-known street attracts lunching executives during the
day, but is relatively quiet at night. *L 1-4 D 8.30-12. Closed Aug.
Valet parking. Mastercard, Visa.*

★

Madrid   Príncipe de Viana

Tel (1) 457 15 49   Fax (1) 457 52 83   **R**

Calle Manuel de Falla 5 Madrid 28036

Seats 80   Meal for 2 approx Pts12,000

Jesús María Oyarbide has passed his culinary secrets down to his
son, Javier, who manages this restaurant, which is as famous, but
much cheaper and more accessible than his father's restaurant,
Zalacaín. Here, he specialises in cooking from the Navarre
(a region in Northern Spain) with its emphasis on fresh fish. Cod
is prepared in a multitude of different ways; fresh hake is cooked
with clams; prawn and cod croquettes come with a tarragon
sauce. House specialities are hake in a garlic and herb sauce and
salmon cooked with green peppers. Like his father's restaurant, this
place is in the most exclusive part of town. *L 1.15-4 D 9-12.
Closed Aug, National Holidays. Valet parking.* AMERICAN EXPRESS *Diners,
Mastercard, Visa.*

★

Madrid   Príncipe y Serrano

Tel (1) 457 28 52   Fax (1) 558 86 76   **R**

Calle Serrano 240 Madrid 28016
Seats 150   Meal for 2 approx Pts12,000

Part of a new Spanish wave of cooking, this plush place in an
exclusive shopping street has an emphasis on light, cholesterol-free
dishes. Fresh fish like monkfish or hake is lightly grilled with
some lemon and garlic. The extensive wine list combines French
and Spanish bottles. As well as the main dining room, there is a
wine cellar where guests can eat. *L 1.30-4 D 9-12. Closed Aug,
Good Fri-Easter Mon. Private parking.* AMERICAN EXPRESS *Diners,
Mastercard, Visa.*

Madrid   Ritz Hotel

Tel (1) 521 28 57   Fax (1) 532 87 76   **H**

Plaza de la Lealtad 5 28014 Madrid
Rooms 154   Double room from Pts49,000

Busy and bustling, the Madrid Ritz is at the heart of the capital,
right next to the famous *Gran Vía*. The building is early 20th-
century, but has been totally renovated in keeping with the *Belle
Epoque* style. The classical, sweeping entrance leads up to some
good-sized double rooms and 29 suites, all very well equipped.
At the time of going to press, they did not have any sports
facilities, but were in the process of building a gym. *24hr room
service. Cable TV/fax. Theatre-style conference facilities for up to 300.
Public parking.* AMERICAN EXPRESS *Diners, Mastercard, Visa.*

Madrid   Señorío de Alcocer

Tel (1) 345 16 96   **R**

Avenida de Alberto Alcocer 1 28036 Madrid
Seats 80   Meal for 2 approx Pts12,000

Outside, it is a quiet avenue in central Madrid, inside it looks more
like an English country home with dark mahogany furniture and
rich, cluttered furnishings with hunting and fishing paintings.
Señor Martán still runs it with his wife. They have stuck to a
successful menu of Basque and Navarre cooking. Salmon salad,
fresh asparagus, lentils served with *chorizo* (spicy red sausage
flambéed in alcohol) and black pudding and *almejas con arroz* (rice
with clams) are all regular menu favourites. The regional Spanish
wine list is boosted by some good French wines. *L 1-4 D 9-12.
Valet parking. Closed Thur-Sun over Easter, Aug.* AMERICAN EXPRESS
Mastercard, Visa.

Madrid   El Torito

Tel (1) 573 48 14   **R**

Alcalde Sainz de Baranda 80 Madrid 28007
Seats 60   Meal for 2 approx Pts12,000

Down a quiet street, this seafood restaurant offers every
conceivable combination of fresh fish: *pulpo a la gallega* (octopus
grilled with potatoes and paprika), *navajas* (razor shells), fillets
of hake, king prawns. Many of the dishes are simply grilled and
served with Spanish Riojas. The name means little bull, so the

walls are lined with pictures and souvenirs of famous fights and bullfighters. *L 1.30-4.30 D 8.30-11.30. Closed National Holidays.* AMERICAN EXPRESS® *Mastercard, Visa.*

Madrid   La Trainera

Tel (1) 576 05 75   Fax (1) 575 06 31   **R**

Calle Lagasca 60 Madrid 28001

Seats 300   Meal for 2 approx Pts10,000

Miguel García still takes personal charge of his restaurant (right next to Calle Velázquez, one of the most elegant streets in Madrid) 28 years after he opened it. The plain wooden bistro-style tables add to the simple look inside, where the only decorations are the fishing motifs and nets on the walls in keeping with their Northern Spanish connections. The food is Cantabrian (Northern Spanish) with grilled hake served with fresh lemon, *mariscada* (a mixed grill of seafood) and *jamón de Jabugo* (an exquisite cured ham, like Parma ham). A house speciality is *merluza a la vasca* (hake Basque-style, cooked with clams, prawns and white wine). Most of the regional wine list is from Rioja. *L 1-4 D 8-11. Public parking. Mastercard, Visa.*

★

Madrid   Villa Magna

Tel (1) 578 20 00   Fax (1) 431 22 86   **HR**

Paseo de la Castellana 22 Madrid 28046

Rooms 182   Double room from Pts58,000

This hotel is as famous as the road outside, and is filled throughout the year with businessmen and politicians, who have conferences and meetings here. Facilities are good, with theatre-style seating for up to 230 people and satellite TV and faxes in the bedrooms. There are also 18 extra suites all decorated, like the rooms, with mahogany furniture and carpets. *24hr room service. Secretarial/ translation services. Sauna. Private parking.* AMERICAN EXPRESS® *Diners, Mastercard, Visa.*

Restaurant Berceo

Seats 65   Meal for 2 approx Pts10,000

In the banking centre of Madrid, this fish restaurant is naturally more formal during the day, when long client lunches fill the tables, but in the evening becomes more relaxed with tables also laid out on the terrace. Grilled sole, hake, lobster, clams, squid and crayfish are definitely the staples of the menu, with the choice changing every week. Typical Spanish stews are also served in winter: try *fabada* (a bean stew), or *judías blancas* (white bean soup). The dishes are lighter in the summer, with plenty of salads and rice. The choice of Riojas, Bordeaux and burgundies is good. *L 1-4 D 8.30-12. Private parking.*

To dial overseas from the UK, 010 will change to 00 on 16th April 1995.

Madrid   Viridiana

Tel (1) 523 44 78   Fax (1) 532 42 74   R

Calle Juan de Mena 14 28014 Madrid

Seats 50   Meal for 2 approx Pts12,000

A family-run, truly Spanish restaurant right in the heart of the
city, near the *Plaza de Cibeles* and *Gran Vía*. The menu has a large
number of the chef's own personal creations, along with more
traditional dishes: courgettes stuffed with tuna mousse, tongue in a
red wine sauce and brioche served with duck paté in a Pedro
Jimenez wine sauce. The decor is dedicated to Luis Buñuel's film
Viridiana, hence the name, and the walls are covered with black
and white film stills. *L 1.30-4 D 9-12. Closed Sun, 1-4 April, Aug,
24, 25 & 31 Dec, 1 Jan. No credit cards.*

Madrid   Zalacaín

Tel (1) 561 47 32   Fax (1) 561 47 32   R

Calle Álvarez de Baena 4 Madrid 28006

Seats 100   Meal for 2 approx Pts18,000

This restaurant was opened by Jesús María Oyarbide in 1973
to commemorate the centenary of the birth of the Spanish
novelist, Pio Baroja, and the people of Madrid have been
celebrating ever since. From the Basque area, his food is rooted
in Basque traditions, but his head chef, Benjamin Urdiaín, who
is renowned across Spain, also draws on French techniques and
ingredients to create his magical menu. Duck is roasted and served
with a light cream of black olives; lasagne is layered with foie gras
and asparagus; pig's trotters are stuffed with lamb and served in a   ★
mustard sauce. House specialities to look out for are the *ensalada
de bogavante* (lobster salad) and *menestra de verduras* (mixed fresh
vegetables cooked in olive oil). The wine list is as exclusive as the
place in general, which serves Madrid's rich and famous. But
do not let that put you off; if you can afford it, you will have
a splendid meal and superb service. *L 1-4 D 9-12. Closed 24 Dec-
1 Jan, Aug, National Holidays. Private parking.* AMERICAN EXPRESS
Diners, Mastercard, Visa.

Around Madrid

Moralzarzal   El Cenador de Salvador

Tel (1) 857 77 22   Fax (1) 857 77 80   R

Avenida de España 30 28411 Moralzarzal

Seats 80   Meal for 2 approx Pts14,000

High up in the mountains, on the outskirts of Madrid, the family
opened this village restaurant in an old Sierra-style residence (grey
stone mountain house). The venue may not be very cosmopolitan,
but the cooking is. There is an emphasis on meat and poultry,
with some fish as well, all served fresh in season. *Merluza al pil pil*
(hake served in its own stock) and *tartar de bonito con salmon* (tuna
tartare with salmon) are two examples. Unusually for Spanish
restaurants they also have some tasty desserts: *arroz emperatriz* (rice
pudding served with almonds and fruit). This place is very relaxed
and full of families at weekends. *L 2-4.30 D 9-1. Closed D Sun, all
Mon, 15-30 Oct. Private parking.* AMERICAN EXPRESS *Diners, Mastercard,
Visa.*

Barcelona

Barcelona	**Hotel Arts**

Tel (3) 221 10 00   Fax (3) 221 10 70   **HR**

Calle de la Marina 19-21 08005 Barcelona

Rooms 455   Double room from Pts20,000

This newly opened de luxe hotel in the very heart of the Olympic
Village (15 minutes from the airport) offers the very latest
facilities; the rooms have televisions, CD players, videos and huge
Italian marble bathrooms complete with saunas. The decor
is modern, with light Mediterranean colours throughout and
casual wooden furniture. As well as a large number of bedrooms,
there are 56 suites. SOGO, the Japanese company who bought the
hotel, has organised everything very thoroughly, including the
conference facilities. *24hr room service. Satellite TV/fax. Theatre and
boardroom-style conference facilities for 50/1000. Outdoor swimming
pool/gym/jacuzzi. Valet/private parking.* AMERICAN EXPRESS *Diners,
Mastercard, Visa.*

Newport Restaurant

Seats 80   Meal for 2 approx Pts12,400

A refreshing change from the typically Spanish restaurants that are
everywhere in Barcelona, this place is Californian; the chef spent
12 years out there and returned with a modern Californian menu.
Marinated salmon is served on a pistachio blini, with lime cream
and caviar; warm shrimp salad is served with roasted aubergine
and a mango sauce, while San Francisco crab cakes are served with
a roasted pepper coulis. Their warm chocolate cake served with
espresso zabaglione is irresistible. They have some good
Californian wines. *D only 8-12.30. Closed Sun.*

Barcelona	**El Asador De Aranda**

Tel (3) 417 01 15   Fax (3) 212 24 82   **R**

Avenida del Tibidabo 31 08022 Barcelona

Seats 250   Meal for 2 approx Pts9000

Set on a hill in a residential district of Barcelona, this restaurant,
is quiet during the week, despite its size, but frantic and noisy
at weekends. The *Modernist* 19th-century building still has its
original wooden floors and old tables. The Castilian cooking
is very traditional, with the head chef (known as the *maestro
asador*, head spit-roaster) preparing huge spit-roasts. Lamb is also
roasted in traditional wooden ovens. This is certainly a place for
committed carnivores, with house specialities like *picadillo* (minced
meat served with asparagus), *chorizo* (spicy sausage) and *jamón
de Jabugo* (rich cured ham). *L 1-4 D 9-12. Closed Sun, Thur-Mon
over Easter, National Holidays. Valet parking.* AMERICAN EXPRESS *Diners,
Visa.*

To dial overseas from the UK, 010 will change to 00
on 16th April 1995.

Barcelona   **Balmes Hotel**

Tel (3) 451 19 14   Fax (3) 415 00 49   **H**

Calle Mallorca 216 08008 Barcelona
Rooms 100   Double room from Pts17,000

Unlike so many of Barcelona's hotels, this one is shiny and new
and was purpose-built four years ago. Naturally, the rooms are
very modern and well equipped, but the conference facilities are
limited to one boardroom that can house a maximum of 40
people. The outdoor swimming pool provides a soothing way
to relax at the end of a sweltering hot day. The airport is an easy
20 minute drive away, while the city centre is only a 10 minute
walk, or short bus ride. *Satellite TV/fax. Secretarial/translation
services on request. Outdoor swimming pool. Private parking.*
AMERICAN EXPRESS *Diners, Mastercard, Visa.*

Barcelona   **Bel Air**

Tel (3) 237 75 88   Fax (3) 237 95 26   **R**

Corcega 286 08008 Barcelona
Seats 120   Meal for 2 approx Pts10,000

Situated in the very centre, off the Diagonal, the restaurant has
stuck to a creative Mediterranean menu since it opened back in the
early 80s. Most of the dishes served are fish, with hake, tuna,
squid, monkfish and John Dory regularly appearing on the menu.
Paella and other dishes with rice are popular house specialities.
The varied wine list has a good selection of Catalan, Rioja and
Galician wines. There are two private rooms (for up to 30). *L 1-4
D 9-12. Closed Sun, National Holidays. Public parking.*
AMERICAN EXPRESS *Diners, Mastercard, Visa.*

Barcelona   **Beltxenea**

Tel (3) 215 30 24   Fax (3) 487 00 81   **R**

Calle Mallorca 275 Centresvelos 08008 Barcelona
Seats 160   Meal for 2 approx Pts16,000

Well-heeled Catalans walk in off the affluent Paseo de Gracia into
this elegant wood-panelled enclave with its fine china displays.
The owner-chef is Basque and his dishes are loyal to his roots.
Lobster and game are particular specialities. He also collects wines
and boasts some very old Riojas. *L 1.30-3.45 D 8.30-11.45. Closed
L Sun, all Sat, 25 & 26 Dec.* AMERICAN EXPRESS *Diners, Mastercard, Visa.*

Barcelona   **Botafumeiro**

Tel (3) 218 42 30   Fax (3) 415 58 48   **R**

Gran de Gràcia 81 08012 Barcelona
Seats 300   Meal for 2 approx Pts12,000

Since the 70s, when this restaurant opened as a modest place
known only for its reliably good food, it has grown and
developed into a major eaterie where businessmen power-lunch
behind discreet screens, their tones muffled by the wooden
panelling. But despite this change, it is still a very good place for
simply prepared fish; perhaps grilled with a little garlic, onion and
olive oil, but never served with sauces. They offer a fantastic
variety of seafood, with unusual sea dates, sea cucumbers and spiny

lobster. Their wine list is very comprehensive, with a selection of up-and-coming Galician wines. *Open 1pm-1am. Closed Aug. Private parking.* AMERICAN EXPRESS *Diners, Mastercard, Visa.*

Barcelona   Can Travi Nou

Tel (3) 428 03 01   Fax (3) 428 19 17   **R**

Calle Jorge Manrique 08035 Barcelona
Seats 300   Meal for 2 approx Pts10,000

Vast terraces seat an extra 300 people in the summer, when business lunches run late into the afternoon. During the winter, diners have to content themselves with the 17th-century dining room, still with its original decor. The menu is traditionally Catalan, with a variety of baked and grilled fish and some interesting house specialities: aubergines are stuffed with anchovies, grilled chicken is served with lobster and meatballs are cooked with squid and tomatoes. Wines are Spanish, with a Catalan house red, but there are also champagnes. *L 1-4.30 D 8.30-12. Closed D Sun.* AMERICAN EXPRESS *Diners, Mastercard, Visa.*

Barcelona   Hotel Colón

Tel (3) 01 14 04   Fax (3) 17 29 15   **H**

Avenida de la Catedral 7 08002 Barcelona
Rooms 147   Double room from Pts21,000

Families are attracted to this family-run hotel as it is relaxed and easy-going, yet right in the centre of the city (definitely not a place for businessmen). The hotel spreads out onto a terrace – and seven of the double rooms have private terraces – but there are no gardens or sports facilities. However, for those keen on exercise, the Olympic Village is easily reached from here. The rooms are comfortably decorated in flowery fabrics, with satellite TV and faxes on request. *Private parking.* AMERICAN EXPRESS *Diners, Visa.*

Barcelona   Condes de Barcelona

Tel (3) 484 86 00   Fax (3) 488 06 14   **H**

Passeig de Gràcia 73-75 08008 Barcelona
Rooms 183   Double room from Pts15,000

One of Barcelona's many architectural attractions, this hotel is a listed monument and an artistic landmark. Despite being in one of the city's busiest boulevards, all the rooms are quiet as they are double-glazed. The health facilities are also appealing, especially in the heat of the midday sun. *Cable & satellite TV/fax. Theatre-style conference facilities for up to 220. Secretarial/translation services on request. Health club/spa/solarium. Private parking.* AMERICAN EXPRESS *Diners, Mastercard, Visa.*

Meal prices for 2 are based on à la carte menus.
When set menus are available, prices will often be lower.

Barcelona   **La Dama**

Tel (3) 202 06 86   Fax (3) 200 72 99   **R**

Avenida Diagonal 423 08036 Barcelona
Seats 58   Meal for 2 approx Pts14,000

Like many buildings in Barcelona, this is an architectural delight;
the *Modernist* (Catalan art nouveau) structure still remains, with
the columns, old glass and sculptures skilfully restored. The
Diagonal is one of the largest, busiest boulevards in Barcelona, but
inside, the four quiet dining rooms provide the perfect retreat for
power-lunching politicians. The chef sticks basically to Catalan
cooking, but throws in French and Italian ideas and ingredients.
Salads, terrines, fish and meats come together with game when
it is in season. Try the house speciality: baked potatoes filled with
king prawns. Unusually, they have a patissier in the kitchen and
so have plenty of good desserts: apple tart, lemon mousse and puff
pastry tarts filled with wild strawberries and fresh cream. *L 1-4
D 8.30-12. Valet parking.* AMERICAN EXPRESS *Diners, Mastercard, Visa.*

Barcelona   **El Dorado Petit**

Tel (3) 204 51 53   Fax (3) 280 57 02   **R**

Dolores Monserdá 51 08017 Barcelona
Seats 90   Meal for 2 approx Pts13,000

Luís Cruañas and his wife have run this restaurant, 15 minutes
from the centre of Barcelona, for ten years, successfully combining
an extensive modern Mediterranean menu with some unusual, old
Catalan-style fish and rice dishes: sea bass is cooked with seaweed
and served with a sea urchin sauce, John Dory is casseroled
in white wine and rosemary, while sea bream comes baked
in rock salt. Some of the interesting Mediterranean dishes include
baby octopus sautéed with garlic and parsley, and potato cake   ★
served with lamb's brains in a white butter sauce. Other unusual
specialities are the Ampurdan regional dishes, including lobster
grilled and glazed with a garlic and olive oil marinade. The menu
de Picoteo is very good value, offering eight dishes for Pts 4500
(per person). The decor is as sophisticated and interesting as the
food, with large mirrors, paintings and antique sideboards
cluttering the three dining rooms like a cosy home. *L 1.30-4
D 9-12. Closed Sun. Valet parking.* AMERICAN EXPRESS *Mastercard, Visa.*

Barcelona   **Finisterre**

Tel (3) 439 55 76   Fax (3) 430 91 14   **R**

Avenida Diagonal 469 08036 Barcelona
Seats 80   Meal for 2 approx Pts18,000

The decor matches the atmosphere with rich velvet-clad chairs
and heavy brocade curtains. The dishes are, however,
a combination of regional Catalan and classic international
cooking. Paella, cannelloni and black rice are served along with
a good choice of fish, from salmon to cod and sole. Most of the
fish dishes are baked and served with simple sauces like
hollandaise. The extensive wine cellar has not only a broad
selection of German and French wines, but also 120 Riojas, from
1946 onwards. *L 1-4 D 9-12. Private parking.* AMERICAN EXPRESS *Diners,
Visa.*

Barcelona	**Florián**	
Tel (3) 212 46 27 Fax (3) 418 72 30		**R**

Calle Bertrán y Serra 20 08022 Barcelona
Seats 70   Meal for 2 approx Pts10,000

Here, it is Rosa who cooks in the kitchen, while her husband,
Javier Garcia Ruano, runs the dining room, in a simple restaurant
out on the Northern outskirts of Barcelona. The modern building
is nothing special, but the Mediterranean cooking is, with a light
seasonal choice of fish, seafood and beef. Mushrooms are Gran's
speciality, with whole dishes devoted exclusively to them. Other
house specialities include oxtail in a Cabernet Sauvignon sauce.
L 1-4 D 9-11.30. Closed Aug. Valet parking. AMERICANEXPRESS *Diners,
Mastercard, Visa.*

★

Barcelona	**Jaume de Provença**	
Tel (3) 430 00 29 Fax (3) 439 29 59		**R**

Provença 88 08029 Barcelona
Seats 70   Meal for 2 approx Pts14,000

Owner and head chef Jaime Bargués is largely self-taught, inspired
partly by his mother, a good Catalan cook, and also by his trips
around France. The menu mixes Catalan with Mediterranean
cooking. *Canelones a la barcelonés* is cannelloni filled with chicken,
ham or pork and topped with a béchamel sauce and *callos a la
catelana* is tripe fried with onions, garlic, chorizo, ham and
tomatoes, Catalan-style. Mediterranean dishes include *chipirones*
(baby squid fried in olive oil) and fried red mullet. Reds, whites
and rosés come from all over Spain, and there's a healthy selection
of Italian and French wines. They have also just introduced their
own label, a Bordeaux. A private dining room for 16 people gives
added privacy for parties, even though the atmosphere here
is never raucous. *L 1-4 D 9-11.30. Closed D Sun, all Mon.*
AMERICANEXPRESS *Diners, Mastercard.*

★

Barcelona	**La Masía**	
Tel (3) 371 00 09 Fax (3) 372 84 00		**R**

Avenida Països Catalans 58 08950 Esplugues de Llobregat
Seats 100   Meal for 2 approx Pts11,000

Right on the edge of the official outer limits of Barcelona, this
restaurant is full of locals, who fill the garden during the summer,
when there are 50 more tables available. The same family have
been running this place for 45 years and still serve a blend
of traditional Catalan and French cuisine. Light dishes like cold
cream of fig soup, artichoke and asparagus salad, and lobster salad
share the menu with roast kid in a black mushroom sauce and
grilled salmon with herbs. House favourites are roast baby chicken
and turbot in crab sauce, but the menu changes constantly. The set
menu for Pts8000 for two is extremely good value. *L 12-4
D 8.30-11.30. Closed D Sun. Public parking.* AMERICANEXPRESS *Diners,
Mastercard, Visa.*

Barcelona   Neichel

Tel (3) 203 84 08   Fax (3) 205 63 69   R

Beltran i Rózpide 16 bis 08034 Barcelona
Seats 50   Meal for 2 approx Pts16,000

Jean-Louis Neichel is the chef and owner of this Mediterranean
restaurant; all the cooking has strong and interesting French ideas
applied to local ingredients and regional recipes – Neichel actually
trained with Alain Chapel in France. There is a healthy emphasis
on fish dishes with lobster and prawns served with home-made
noodles in a seafood sauce and supreme of sea bass with tomatoes,
capers and mustard. House specialities include beef tournedos
served with foie gras and port, truffle and white grape sauce, and
roasted lobster. The 'designer' interior is modern, with a handsome
array of bottled preserves on display and large windows looking
out on to a garden filled with lemon trees, only 4km from the
centre of Barcelona. Chic, and definitely a relaxed place to savour
great cuisine. *L 1-3.30 D 8.30-11.30. Closed L Sat, all Sun, Aug.
Valet parking.* AMERICAN EXPRESS *Diners, Mastercard, Visa.*

Barcelona   L'Oliana

Tel (3) 201 32 82   Fax (3) 414 44 17   R

Santalo 54 08021 Barcelona
Seats 140   Meal for 2 approx Pts8000

Part of the 80s explosion of new restaurants, this place was
purpose-built in a tree-lined street just above the *Plaza Calvo
Jatelo*. The cooking is traditionally Catalan with plenty of meat
and fish dishes and fresh vegetable salads. The fish dishes are
particularly appetising: fresh salmon comes marinated in dill and
grain mustard, steamed lobster is served in a tarragon sauce and
there is a gratin of Cadaqués sea urchins. The wine list
is dominated by regional bottles like Rueda and Rioja with
a Parnas 1993 house wine, but there are also a few French clarets.
L 1-4 D 8.30-12. Closed D Sun. Valet parking. AMERICAN EXPRESS
Mastercard, Visa.

Barcelona   Oliver y Hardy

Tel (3) 419 31 81   R

Diagonal 593-595 08014 Barcelona
Seats 120   Meal for 2 approx Pts10,000

Young 20-somethings hang out in this modern restaurant-cum-
bar-cum-disco, surrounded by black and white photos of the
place's namesakes, Laurel and Hardy. The menu is as international
as the place, with choices like clam and crab risotto and monkfish
baked with prawns. A particular house speciality is fillet of steak
served with duck's liver and a truffle sauce. Wines range from
regional Spanish to traditional French bottles. *L 1.30-4.30 D 9-1am
(Sat till 2am). Closed L Sat, all Sun. Private parking.* AMERICAN EXPRESS
Diners, Visa.

Barcelona	**Paradis Roncesvalles**

Tel (3) 209 01 25   Fax (3) 209 12 95   R

Vía Augusta 201 08021 Barcelona
Seats 500   Meal for 2 approx Pts9000

Ten minutes out of Barcelona, this restaurant is part of a chain
which now extends from Madrid to New York. The cooking
is mostly Mediterranean with figs served with Iberian ham,
carpaccio of salmon and prawns and lobster served with noodles.
There are also several Catalan dishes: hake baked with tomatoes,
cod stuffed with Colbert prawns. The house specialities are always
rather interesting like *fiden* (foie gras and boletus mushrooms) and
sirloin steak cooked in a crust of rock salt. *L 1-4 D 9-12. Closed
Sun, Aug. Private parking.* AMERICAN EXPRESS *Mastercard, Visa.*

Barcelona	**Quirze**

Tel (3) 371 10 84   Fax (3) 371 65 12   R

Laureá Miró 202 Esplugues de Llobregat 08950 Barcelona
Seats 80   Meal for 2 approx Pts10,000

This restaurant 2km out of Barcelona has a chequered past: it was
an inn, an outdoor cinema and then a casino. Now it is a beamed,
large-windowed restaurant, with modern, hand-crafted furniture,
serving a wonderful variety of game, mushrooms and fish, all
constantly changing with the seasons. Artichoke hearts are stuffed
with monkfish and mushrooms; sea bass is cooked in a chive
sauce. There are also some tasty meat dishes: kidneys served in a
truffle sauce and magret of duck à la Campari. An excellent choice
of Catalonian white wines and Spanish champagnes is available.
L 1-4 D 9-11.30. Closed D Sun, all Sun in summer. Private parking.
AMERICAN EXPRESS *Mastercard, Visa.*

Barcelona	**El Racó D'En Freixa**

Tel (3) 209 75 59   Fax (3) 209 79 18   R

Sant Eliés 22 08006 Barcelona
Seats 50   Meal for 2 approx Pts14,000

Señor Freixa has been working in restaurants since he was 14 and
eight years ago opened this Catalan restaurant in the San Gervano
district, near the city centre. His menu has been influenced by his
time in France, with dishes like monkfish in an aromatic juniper
sauce with roasted onions and *paeg*, wild rabbit stuffed with raisins
and pine nuts and served with a garlic cream sauce. The house
speciality is Catalonian chicken crisp-cooked with cardamon. The
regional wine list includes good Penedés and Rioja wines, with
several French Bordeaux and Alsace wines. The main dining hall,
which holds 36, gives a superb view of the kitchen through a glass
window. *L 1-3.45 D 9-11.45. Closed D Sun, all Mon, 1-29 Aug.
Private parking.* AMERICAN EXPRESS *Mastercard, Visa.*

Barcelona   Reno

Tel (3) 200 91 29   Fax (3) 414 41 14   R

Tuset 27 Barcelona 08006
Seats 190   Meal for 2 approx Pts12,000

The chef, Pedro Gonzalez, is renowned for his imaginative
creations, adapting and mixing French and Catalan cooking. One
of his house specialities is an excellent example of that: *ensalada
de gourmet* (green bean salad served with truffles and foie gras).
Other dishes are more traditionally Catalan, like fillet of sole in a
white wine sauce, squid stew served with rice and fillet steak
grilled with honey. For those searching for a lighter meal, the
terrine of goose liver and the smoked salmon soufflé are worth   ★
trying. The European wine list boasts 400 different bottles, with
Spanish house wines. Not surprisingly, the restaurant, with its
discreet wooden panelling and plush leather chairs, attracts a select
clientele: businessmen by day and smart tourists at night. *L 1-4
D 8.30-11.30. Closed Sat. Private/valet parking.* AMERICAN EXPRESS
Diners, Mastercard, Visa.

Barcelona   Ritz

Tel (3) 18 52 00   Fax (3) 17 36 40   H

La Gran Vía de las Cortes Catalanas 668 08010 Barcelona
Rooms 155   Double room from Pts43,000

The Barcelona Ritz opened 75 years ago and the classically
designed building remains largely unchanged, inside and out. The
double rooms and seven suites were, however, renovated back
in 1991 and now have cable and satellite TV and faxes. But,
mirrors, lamps, plants and mahogany still fill the bedrooms. Right
in the city centre, only 15 minutes by car from the airport, they
have no gardens or sports facilities. *Theatre-style conference facilities
for up to 400. Secretarial/translation services. Private parking.*
AMERICAN EXPRESS *Diners, Mastercard, Visa.*

Barcelona   Restaurante las Siete Puertas

Tel (3) 319 30 33   Fax (3) 319 3046   R

Paseo Isabel Sugunod 14 (Planta Baja) 08003 Barcelona
Seats 350   Meal for 2 approx Pts10,000

Government ministers and local fisherman might well sit side
by side in this vast, unpretentious restaurant which, after 150
years, is considered something of an institution in Barcelona (the
town hall gave them a plaque to commemorate 150 years
of service to the city). Situated right on the port, the restaurant is
nonetheless well connected to the city centre, and the Olympic
Village is right next to it. The menu remains cheerfully Catalan,
providing hearty plates of paella, stew and grilled fish. *Paella
zarzueles* (paella with shellfish) is a house speciality. Game is on the
menu in season. All the major Spanish wine-producing areas are
on the list, which also has some excellent French wines. *Open 1pm-
1am. Public parking.* AMERICAN EXPRESS *Diners, Mastercard, Visa.*

Barcelona   Tikal

Tel (3) 302 22 21   `R`

Rambla de Catalunya 5 08002 Barcelona
Seats 60   Meal for 2 approx Pts8000

The chef arrived recently from the Barcelona Hilton and has
tended to concentrate on traditional Catalan cooking. The
emphasis on fish here, however, seems more typically
Mediterranean with cod, hake, and shellfish all grilled with plenty
of olive oil. The menu changes constantly, using fresh, typically
Iberian ingredients: *Jabugo* (cured ham) and wild mushrooms are
often served. The food here is very reasonably priced, so too the
wines – look out for the excellent house Rioja. *L 1-4 D 8-11.30.
Closed Sun, National Holidays. Public parking.* AMERICAN EXPRESS
Mastercard, Visa.

Barcelona   El Tragaluz

Tel (3) 487 01 96   Fax (3) 487 19 16   `R`

Pasaje de la Concepción 5 08008 Barcelona
Seats 150   Meal for 2 approx Pts12,000

This original art nouveau building, with its glass ceiling, was
converted into a restaurant four years ago by the famous Catalan
designer, Moriscal, who also designed the logo for the Olympics.
Everything in the restaurant, from the plates to the different
shaped fish on the walls, is designed by him. However, the Catalan
cooking is less avant garde, with traditional fish dishes: *merluza*
(hake), *gambas de Palamos* (prawns from the Costa Brava), lobster,
clams and shrimps. Game is served in season. The well-thought-out
wine list with regional Riojas, Ribera del Dueros and Catalan
Penedés also, unusually, has some Californian bottles. *L 1.30-4
D 9-12. Closed Sun, National Holidays. Public parking.*
AMERICAN EXPRESS *Mastercard, Visa.*

Barcelona   Via Veneto

Tel (3) 200 72 44   Fax (3) 201 60 95   `R`

Calle Ganduxer 10-12 08021 Barcelona
Seats 80   Meal for 2 approx Pts14,000

José Moniesa worked all over Spain and around France before
returning home to Barcelona 12 years ago and opening his now
famous Belle Epoque-style restaurant in a smart residential district.
His cooking is a perfect blend of traditional Catalan and French
cuisine: lobster Cardinal, smoked goose with radish sauce, baked
monkfish with crisp vegetables and oxtail with red wine and   ★
mousseline potatoes. Heavy emphasis is placed on red wines, with
French burgundies and Bordeaux. The house wines are Catalan.
L 12.30-4 D 8.30-12. Closed L Sat, all Sun. Valet parking.
AMERICAN EXPRESS *Diners, Mastercard, Visa.*

Around Barcelona

Sant Celoni   **El Racó de Can Fabes**

Tel (3) 867 28 51   Fax (3) 867 38 61   **R**

Sant Joan 6 Sant Celoni 08470 Barcelona
Seats 40   Meal for 2 approx Pts11,000

Husband-and-wife team, Santi Santamaria and Angels Serra,
opened 13 years ago in the industrial town of Sant Celoni, 45km
from Barcelona, without ever having had specific culinary
training. Now, they have an experienced chef in the kitchen, who
applies French culinary disciplines to local Catalan produce and
methods. Crayfish brochettes are served in a curry sauce and
"coriandered" vegetables, lobster broth comes with vegetables and
cod fillets are served with *butifarra* (a kind of black sausage). There
are also some traditional French dishes dotted around the menu:
baby pigeon *à la crapaudine* (split from the breast to the wings,
grilled with butter and black pepper and served with artichokes
and cardamon seeds) and veal sweetbreads come on a bed of salad.
The wife still makes the most extraordinary ice creams like lemon
verbena. A special set menu (*menu de les herbes i espècies*) is priced
on Pts8950. *L 1.30-3.30 D 8.30-11.30. Closed D Sun, all Mon,
1-14 Feb, 26 Jun-12 Jul.* AMERICAN EXPRESS *Diner, Mastercard, Visa.*

★

Vall Doreix   **La Reserva**

Tel (3) 589 21 21   Fax (3) 674 21 00   **H**

Rambla Mossen Jacinto Verdeguer 41 08190 Vall Doreix
Rooms 16   Double room from Pts22,000

Barcelona blossomed after the 1992 Olympic Games and this
is one of the results: a 1920s private mansion converted into yet
another new hotel, set in a tiny hamlet ten minutes drive out
of Barcelona. It is a perfect retreat from the humidity, up in the
hills above the city. The hotel has its own spacious grounds,
an outdoor swimming pool and a view down over the valley.
Most of the furniture in the original house is still in the rooms, but
satellite TV, mini-bars and faxes are modern touches. Small
business conferences can be arranged for up to 30 people, and the
original library, full of antique books, is still open for general use.
*24hr room service. Secretarial/translation services on request. Swimming
pool. Public parking.* AMERICAN EXPRESS *Diners, Mastercard, Visa.*

Malaga/Marbella

Malaga   Café de Paris

| Tel (5) 222 50 43   Fax (5) 222 50 43 | R |

Calle Vélez 8 Malaga 29016
Seats 60   Meal for 2 approx Pts8000

Inside this wooden reproduction Moorish building, with a tower
rising up out of the middle, the owner-chef has been producing
an eclectic mix of French cuisines and regional Basque cooking.
He goes on a sabbatical every year to work in kitchens in France
and Luxembourg and is constantly trying to update his techniques
and ideas. So, cold lasagne with anchovies and a gazpacho-style
sauce graces the menu along with foie gras salad with a truffle
sauce, an assortment of typically Spanish rice dishes and a vast
selection of local seafood baked with a little rock salt, Galician-
style. The set menu (Pts3975) is excellent value with choices like
grilled lobster, entrecote and profiteroles. *L 1.30-4 D 8.30-12.
Closed Sun, Aug. Public parking.* AMERICAN EXPRESS *Diners, Mastercard,
Visa.*

Marbella   Cenicienta

| Tel (5) 277 43 18 | R |

Avenida Cánovas del Castillo 52 29600 Marbella
Seats 40   Meal for 2 approx Pts9000

The oak-panelled dining room decorated with presentation plates,
bells and Chinese porcelain seats only 40, but in summer tables for
another 20 are put out on the patio. A German-trained chef and
her husband have run the restaurant since the 70s, serving
typically French food. The house speciality is fondues, including
fish and *bourguignon*. The menus change regularly with several
vegetarian dishes such as ravioli on offer. *D only 8-late.*
AMERICAN EXPRESS *Mastercard, Visa.*

Marbella   La Fonda

| Tel (5) 277 25 12 | R |

Plaza de Santo Cristo 9-10 29600 Marbella
Seats 60   Meal for 2 approx Pts7000

In the old part of Marbella, full of balconied Andalucian mansions,
this building is a couple of hundred years old. Originally it was
an inn, then a school, and became a restaurant 18 years ago. The
main menu is fish-orientated with modern Spanish dishes.
However, the specials tend to be traditional regional dishes like
veal escalopes and gilthead. The wine list concentrates on Riojas.   ★
If it makes full use of its patio space in summer, the restaurant can
seat up to 120. *D only 8-12.30. Closed Sun. Public parking.*
AMERICAN EXPRESS *Diners, Mastercard, Visa.*

Marbella	**La Hacienda**	
Tel (5) 283 12 67		**R**

Carretera de Cádiz 29600 Marbella
Seats 140   Meal for 2 approx Pts6500

The death of Paul Schiff, the owner-chef for 25 years, two months
before we went to press, has been a severe blow to Spanish haute
cuisine. However, his daughter, who has taken over and is now
head chef, has worked in the kitchen for over 13 years. The menu
is still very creative, adapting traditional Andalucian raw materials
to produce original dishes. Whitebait is stuffed with Serrano ham
and spinach; a tartare of swordfish and Iranian caviar comes in a
sour sauce; potted duck is cooked in puff pastry with Muscat and
marrow. Only Southern Spanish wines are served. La Hacienda
is only 15 minutes drive from Marbella on the road to Fuengirola,
so escape out to this old Andalucian farmhouse on a sweltering
summer evening. *L 1.30-3.30 D 8.30-11.30. Closed L Jul-Aug, all
mid Nov-mid Dec. Private parking.* AMERICAN EXPRESS *Diners, Mastercard,
Visa.*

★

Marbella	**Marbella Club**	
Tel (5) 277 13 00 Fax (5) 282 98 84		**H**

Boulevard Principe Alfonso Bon Hohanlohe 29600 Marbella
Rooms 100   Double room from Pts22,000

Only a 3km taxi ride from Marbella Central Railway Station, this
sumptuous hotel is surrounded by large grounds, sub-tropical
gardens, lakes, streams and waterfalls. It has been the palatial
retreat of many a celebrated star, from Ava Gardner and Brigitte
Bardot to the King of Spain and the Duke of Windsor. As one
would expect, being very near the beach, the hotel has two
swimming pools and tennis courts. As well as the well-equipped
rooms, there are five bungalows for four to six people. The decor
is modern and light, with rattan and pine furniture in the recently
redecorated bedrooms. *24hr room service. Satellite TV/safe. Theatre-
style conference facilities for up to 160. Secretarial/translation services
on request. Private parking.* AMERICAN EXPRESS *Diners, Mastercard, Visa.*

Marbella	**Meliá Don Pepe**	
Tel (5) 277 03 00 Fax (5) 277 99 54		**HR**

José Meliá 29600 Marbella
Rooms 204   Double room from Pts20,700

Right in the centre of the most popular tourist area, this place gets
very busy during the summer. The hotel itself is modern and
surrounded by 30,000 square metres of sub-tropical gardens, only
200m from the beach. All the facilities are up to date and the
bedrooms are well equipped. *24hr room service. Satellite TV/safe.
Theatre-style conference facilities for up to 500. Secretarial/translation
services. Gym/spa/Turkish baths/2 tennis courts. Private parking.*
AMERICAN EXPRESS *Diners, Mastercard, Visa.*

Grill La Farola
Seats 60   Meal for 2 approx Pts12,000

The experienced chef cooks modern Spanish food featuring
a multitude of grilled and roasted fish and poultry dishes. Veal
cutlets are grilled with tarragon; lobster is roasted with melted
butter; swordfish and monkfish are skewered and grilled with red
peppers. House specialities are the huge paella and the hake grilled
with ham and cheese. The wines are French and Spanish, with
a Rioja Siglo de Oro house wine. *D only 8.30-12.30 am.*
AMERICANEXPRESS *Diners, Mastercard, Visa.*

Marbella   **La Meridiana**

| Tel (5) 277 61 90   Fax (5) 282 60 24 | **R** |

Camino de la Cruz 29600 Marbella
Seats 80   Meal for 2 approx Pts16,000

In this typically Andalucian setting – a road, edged with palm
trees, winds up out of Marbella to a low terracotta-coloured
restaurant – the chef, who previously worked at the renowned
Jockey restaurant in Madrid, prepares an equally typical
Mediterranean French menu: warmed breast of duck salad comes
with foie gras and sour cherry vinaigrette, fillet of sole is served
in a wine sauce with Sanlucar spiny lobster and glazed onions and
skate is cooked in black butter and capers. Their house specialities
are also typically French with dishes like Bresse capon stuffed with
foie gras and truffles. Crepes and soufflés make up the dessert
menu for those with space left. The wine list, however, is mainly
Spanish with plenty of Rioja, Navarra and Penedés bottles
to choose from. In the summer, this place has another 60 seats out
on the leafy-green terraces. *L 1.30-3.30 (not between 15 Jun and 15
Sept) D 8.30-12. Closed 15 Jan-15 Feb. Private parking.*
AMERICANEXPRESS *Diners, Mastercard, Visa.*

★

Marbella   **Los Monteros**

| Tel (5) 277 17 00   Fax (5) 282 58 46 | **H** |

Carretera de Cádiz 29600 Marbella
Rooms 169   Double room from Pts17,000

Only 4km from Marbella, this traditional hotel has excellent
sports facilities, including ten tennis courts, five squash courts,
a gym, two swimming pools (one indoor/one outdoor), an 18-hole
golf course and water sports. *24hr room service. Theatre-style
conference facilities for up to 80. Private parking.* AMERICANEXPRESS
Diners, Mastercard, Visa.

> The Golden Eurostar [★] denotes our pick of the
> restaurants. Cooking is the major consideration, but
> other factors are also taken into account, including
> ambience, comfort and service.

Marbella   **Puente Romano**

| Tel (5) 277 01 00   Fax (5) 277 57 66 | H |

Carretera de Cádiz 29600 Marbella

Rooms 220   Double room from Pts27,000

Set in a lush Andalucian garden, with a lake and stream, the hotel is right on the beach, which is great for those keen on water sports. Inside, it is simply decorated with Andalucian wood and cool Mediterranean colours. The atmosphere is very relaxed, partly because of the climate, but also because most of the staff have been here since it opened in 1979. Malaga Airport is only 35 minutes away. *24hr room service. Satellite TV/safe. Theatre-style conference facilities for up to 160. 2 swimming pools (water sports/tennis courts. Private parking.* AMERICAN EXPRESS *Diners, Mastercard, Visa.*

Marbella   **Villa Tiberio**

| Tel (5) 277 17 99   Fax (5) 82 47 72 | R |

Carretera de Cádiz 29600 Marbella

Seats 150   Meal for 2 approx Pts14,000

Only 100m away from the Marbella Club hotel, this Italian restaurant is run by the Italian brothers who own *Barbarella* in London. The building, then a dilapidated house, was converted into a restaurant in the late 80s, with Roman statues and columns inside and a huge sub-tropical garden and waterfall outside. One chef makes the pasta, served with shellfish and spiny lobster. The menu changes seasonally, but look out for baby lamb and roast suckling pig, as they are particular house specialities. They have a wide selection of French, Italian and Spanish wines. The terrace can seat an extra 100. *D only 7.30-2.30. Closed Sun (except Aug), National Holidays. Private parking.* AMERICAN EXPRESS *Mastercard, Visa.*

Around Malaga/Marbella

Fuengirola   **Byblos Andaluz**

| Tel (5) 247 30 50   Fax (5) 247 67 83 | H |

Mijas Golf Apartado 138 29640 Fuengirola

Rooms 144   Double room from Pts25,000

A hotel built right on two 18-hole international golf courses (Par 72/Par 71), designed by Robert Trent Jones, will naturally attract some serious golf professionals. However, with every conceivable facility from heli-transfer to Malaga International Airport and simultaneous translation services to express dry-cleaning and laundry, this is also a great place for mixing work and pleasure. The rooms are lavishly but tastefully decorated in Arabian, Andalusian, Roman or rustic style. They are air-conditioned, double-glazed and equipped with satellite TV and private safes. *24hr room service. Theatre-style conference facilities for up to 150. 5 tennis courts (hard/grass), gym, French bowls, 3 swimming pools (1 outdoor). Hairdresser/beauty salon. Private parking.* AMERICAN EXPRESS *Diners, Mastercard, Visa.*

Puerto Banús — Taberna del Alabardero

Tel (5) 281 2794   Fax (5) 281 86 30   R

Muelle Benabola 29660 Puerto Banús
Seats 170   Meal for 2 approx Pts10,000

The restaurant, part of a small chain based in Madrid, looks out
over the marina. Inside, it is designed like a yacht, complete with
portholes, and serves new Basque cuisine (traditional Basque
cooking with French ideas added). Plenty of fish is served, like
hake and Cantabrian clams topped with puréed parsley sauce,
shellfish soup and spiny lobster (chosen from the tank). The menu
changes with the seasons. *L 1-4 D 8-12. Closed Feb.* AMERICAN EXPRESS
Diners, Mastercard, Visa.

Sotogrande — Club Maritimo Cabo Mayor

Tel (5) 679 03 90   Fax (5) 679 03 77   R

Puerto Sotogrande 11310 Sotogrande (Cádiz)
Seats 80   Meal for 2 approx Pts12,000

Approximately 8 miles east of Gibraltar and 45 miles west
of Marbella, the restaurant is managed by husband and wife team
Paco and Manoli Teodoro – she cooks, he fronts. Operated by the
Madrid-based Cabo Mayor group, it also serves as the dining
room for the hotel and apartments in the same building. Fully air-
conditioned, the restaurant has wonderful views of the harbour
and you can also dine outside on pretty terraces. The relatively
short menu specialises in fish dishes and includes some of Manoli's
Cantabrian specialities and her home-baked bread, alongside items
from the parent restaurant in Madrid: Jabugo ham with foie gras,
and poached eggs with prawns and fresh pasta. Other starters
include a delicious salad of avocado and anchovies in a delicate
olive oil dressing with fresh herbs, tiny roasted peppers stuffed
with fish in a red pepper cream sauce, and a medley of sautéed
crayfish, shrimps, and langoustines served with fresh spinach. For
a main course you could choose squid in a black sauce with
tomato petals, sea bream with thyme and a red and green pepper
sauce, and an excellent breast of duck with a honey sauce. Fine
desserts include a parfait of white chocolate with Cointreau
or Manoli's speciality: a pastel of fresh fruits on a raspberry coulis
and a caramel sauce. A few champagnes apart, an almost exclusive
Spanish wine list at quite reasonable prices. Though staff are
generally friendly, their service skills do not always match the
standard of food. *L 1-4 D 8-12. Closed Sun.* AMERICAN EXPRESS *Diners,
Mastercard, Visa.*

Seville

Seville	**Alfonso XIII**	
Tel (5) 422 28 50 Fax (5) 421 6033		**H**

San Fernando 2 41004 Seville
Rooms 146   Double room from Pts39,000

The Italian hotel chain, CIGA, this hotel along with many others
in Venice, Milan and Madrid; and owns the opulence of the 20s
has been maintained, with its original decor and impressive facade.
Despite being in the centre of the city, three minutes walk from
the Giralda, the hotel is very tranquil as it is surrounded
by Arabian-style flower gardens. As in all CIGA hotels, the rooms
are well equipped. *24hr room service. Theatre-style conference
facilities for up to 500. Secretarial/translation services on request.
Private parking.* AMERICAN EXPRESS *Diners, Mastercard, Visa.*

Seville	**El Burladero**	
Tel (5) 422 29 00 Fax (5) 422 09 38		**R**

Canalejas 1 41001 Seville
Seats 100   Meal for 2 approx Pts10,000

On the Plaza de la Magdalena, in the heart of the old city, the
restaurant has been run by the Spanish company Trip, who have
owned hotels and restaurants all over Spain, for the last 27 years.
The name, El Burladero, refers to 'the bull-ring' and the restaurant
is strong on beef dishes. House specialities include oxtail stewed with
vegetables. But there are plenty of other dishes: rice is served
with prawns and clams and hake is served in the traditional way
with boiled potatoes and onions. Not surprisingly, the place
is decorated with bulls' heads and portraits of famous bullfighters.
L 1.30-3.45 D 9-11.45. Closed 15 Jul-15 Aug. AMERICAN EXPRESS *Diners,
Mastercard, Visa.*

Seville	**Egaña Oriza**	
Tel (5) 422 72 54 Fax (5) 421 04 29		**R**

San Fernando 41 41004 Seville
Seats 170   Meal for 2 approx Pts14,000

The husband-and-wife team who have been running this
restaurant for the last seven years started cooking in their home
town of Guipúzcoa, before moving to Madrid and eventually
further south to Seville. Like many migrating Spaniards, they have
brought their home culinary delights with them and have
an extensive, intricate Basque menu with a few local specialities
thrown in. Hake is prepared *pil-pil* Basque-style, fried in olive oil
and garlic and served with the oil. Scallops are served *au gratin*.
There are some interesting Basque meat dishes too: rare steak
is served with small red peppers, foie gras with a light grape sauce.
Txangurro (spider crab), pig's trotters and *salmorejo* (Andalucian
garlic soup) are house specialities to look out for. All the wine
regions of Spain are well represented, with some excellent vintage
Riojas. *L 1.30-4 D 9-11.30. Closed L Sat, all Sun, Aug. Private
rooms for up to 80.* AMERICAN EXPRESS *Diners, Mastercard, Visa.*

Seville   Florencia

Tel (5) 453 35 00   Fax (5) 453 23 42   R

Hotel Occidental Portacoeli Avenida Eduardo Dato 49 41018 Seville
Seats 48   Meal for 2 approx Pts12,000

The restaurant is in the Occidental Hotel but most of the diners
come here specially to eat as Florencia has, since opening seven
years ago, developed quite a reputation for itself. Juan Martin
Ruiz' dishes are international, but with light Spanish touches: ham
salad is laced with sweet sherry, potatoes are stuffed with sea bass,
monkfish and lobster in an aromatic wine sauce with red peppers.
Their house speciality is foie gras with raisins in a *Pedro Jimenez*
sauce. The wine list covers all major wine-producing areas
of Spain, but has no international offerings. *L 1.30-4 D 9-12.
Closed Aug. Private parking.* AMERICAN EXPRESS *Diners, Mastercard, Visa.*

Seville   Florencia Pórtico

Tel (5) 458 20 00   Fax (5) 458 46 15   R

Avenida Kansas City 41018 Seville
Seats 30   Meal for 2 approx Pts12,000

Opposite the railway station and ten minutes from the centre
of Seville, this modern restaurant has a small dining room with
wooden tables, classic candles and subdued salmon-pink tones. The
menu leans heavily towards French cuisine with home-made foie
gras, lobster and king prawn salad with a black truffle sauce, duck
magret with camomile honey vinegar and Muscat. Other
appetising house specialities include rockfish soup with *rouille* and
chicken stuffed with truffles and leeks in a foie gras sauce. The
patissier makes fresh desserts well worth ordering. There is an
impressive list of Rioja reds including 1970, 1976 and 1978
vintages. *L 1.30-3.30 D 8.30-11.30. Closed Sun, Aug. Public
parking.* AMERICAN EXPRESS *Diners, Mastercard, Visa.*

Seville   Pello Roteta

Tel (5) 427 84 17   R

Farmaceútico Murillo Herrera 10 41010 Seville
Seats 62   Meal for 2 approx Pts8000

Pello Roteta, the Basque owner-chef, opened this family-run
restaurant eight years ago when he decided Seville needed
somewhere a little different from the typical Andalucian
restaurant. Despite his training at the Hilton in London, he cooks
traditional Basque food, with dishes like hake topped with *salsa
verde*, sirloin steak in a mushroom sauce and seaweed salad. Their
house speciality is also straight Basque: hake fillets stuffed with
seafood. The restaurant is out of the centre of the city, across the
river in Triana, the traditionally working class area. Inside, it is
quite extraordinary: the two dining rooms are divided by huge
bookcases full of cookery books which guests are encouraged
to peruse. Note, too, the collections of crockery and old rugs
covering the bare wooden floors. *L 1.30-4 D 9-11. Closed Sun,
15 Jul-15 Aug.* AMERICAN EXPRESS *Diners, Mastercard, Visa.*

Seville   **Taberna del Albardero**

| Tel (5) 456 06 37 | **RR** |

Zaragoza 20 41001 Seville
Seats 170   Meal for 2 approx Pts12,000

This 17th-century palatial mansion in the centre of Seville was,
until recently, a private home, but has just been converted into
a restaurant and ground-floor bar. The Taberna del Albardero
chain of restaurants who run it have turned two rooms into
dining rooms, while keeping all the antiques and wooden
furniture in place. The chef, who has been here since it opened,
cooks quite a few Northern Spanish dishes, including seafood
soups, hake Basque-style (served with a garlic, onion and parsley
purée), sirloin steak in red wine and breast of duck in a mandarin
orange sauce. Their *delicias* (desserts) are elaborate and constantly
changing. They also have seven suites, each with its own jacuzzi
and old fireplace (from Pts12,000). *L 1-4 D 9-12. Closed Aug.
Private parking.* AMERICAN EXPRESS *Diners, Mastercard, Visa.*

Around Seville

Carmona   **Casa de Carmona**

| Tel (5) 414 33 00   Fax (5) 414 37 52 | **H** |

Plaza de Lasso 1 Carmona 41410 Seville
Rooms 30   Double room from Pts15,000

It took five years for the Medina family to convert this 16th-
century palace into a hotel, having bought it in 1986; previously,
it had been in the hands of the Lasso de Lavega family for four
centuries. Despite keeping the antiques and old furniture, they
have introduced Laura Ashley-style printed furnishings and new
mahogany furniture. The rooms are of a good size; there is even
a 200 square-metre suite. For an old hotel in the centre of a town
(only three minutes from the railway station) this has excellent
sports facilities: an outdoor swimming pool, gym, sauna and
massage parlour. *24hr room service. Satellite TV/CD player. Theatre-
style conference facilities for up to 150. Secretarial/translation services
on request. Hairdresser. Private parking.* AMERICAN EXPRESS *Diners,
Mastercard, Visa.*

Sanlúcar la Mayor   **Hacienda Benazuza**

| Tel (5) 570 33 44   Fax (5) 570 33 44 | **H** |

Valle de las Nieves 41800 Sanlúcar la Mayor Seville
Rooms 44   Double room from Pts31,000

On a hill overlooking the River Guadiamar valley in the small
town of Sanlúcar la Mayor (15km from Seville), the only noise
to disturb you is the sound of birds. The history of the hotel
encapsulates Spain's history: built as a farmhouse in the 5th
century by the Moors, it passed to King Alfonso X 'The Wise',
and then to the religious order of Santiago, before passing into the
hands of the renowned 19th-century bull-rearers the Pablo
Romero family. Since then, the drama may have lessened, but the
simple, glistening white Moorish arches and fountains remain. The
rooms are still full of antiques, frescoes and works of art that were
present in the original Andalucian grange, but they also have
excellent modern facilities. In keeping with its past, the hotel still

rears Andalusian and Arabian horses, which are available for guests to ride. Traditional Spanish hunts and partridge shoots can also be organised on the hotel's 3000-hectare game reserve, which has a landing strip for those arriving in a private jet. Around the hotel are 10,000 hectares of the *Donana* nature reserve with more than 250 species of wild boar, cat, fowl and deer. *24hr room service. Satellite TV/air-con/safe/jacuzzi. Theatre-style conference facilities for up to 350. Outdoor swimming pool/tennis courts/pitch & putt. Closed 15 Jul-31 Aug. Private parking.* AMERICAN EXPRESS *Diners, Mastercard, Visa.*

Valencia

Valencia   Eladio

| Tel & Fax (6) 384 22 44 | | R |

Chiva 40 46018 Valencia

Seats 70   Meal for 2 approx Pts8000

Eladio Rodríguez worked as a chef in Zurich for 20 years, before
returning home to Valencia, where he now specialises in Galician
cooking. Every single dish is a house speciality, including grilled
hake, baked and grilled turbot and chargrilled salmon. A salad
of scallops with prawn tails is served in a mustard-seed vinaigrette
and octopus is served with cabbage, ham and *chorizo* (spicy
sausage) fried in olive oil with garlic and pepper. There are some
good Spanish regional wines. Eat in one of two dining rooms, each
with oak panelling and marble floors. *L 12.30-4 D 8.30-12. Closed
Sun, Aug.* AMERICAN EXPRESS *Diners, Mastercard, Visa.*

Valencia   Galbis

| Tel (6) 380 94 73   Fax (6) 380 06 54 | | R |

Marvá 28-30 Valencia 46007

Seats 90   Meal for 2 approx Pts8000

The Galbis family have owned taverns and inns in and around
Valencia for generations, culminating in the opening of this
restaurant in the centre of the city. Carlos Galbis cooks traditional
Valencian dishes in the evening with plenty of fried hake, spiny
lobster and spider crab, but sticks to more universal Spanish dishes
at lunchtime. The decor is as traditional as the food, with hand-
crafted wooden furniture and still-life paintings on the walls.
*L 1-4.30 D 8.30-11.30. Closed L Sat, all Sun, 8 Aug- 4 Sept.
Private parking.* AMERICAN EXPRESS *Visa.*

Valencia   Monte Picayo

| Tel (6) 142 01 00   Fax (6) 142 21 68 | | H |

Urbanización Monte Picayo 46530 Valencia

Rooms 83   Double room from Pts13,350

Set on a hillside surrounded by orange groves, with views over
the sea, the hotel is owned by the Occidental Hotels Group, but
still family-run. All the rooms have terraces from which to take
in the view and five of the rooms actually have their own outdoor
swimming pools. There are 11 swimming pools in total, tennis
courts, mini-golf and riding. All the rooms have traditional
Castilian furniture – all hand-crafted – and are very well equipped.
The hotel is about 20km from Valencia in the direction of
Barcelona. *Room service. Satellite TV/air-con. Restaurant
(International). Theatre-style conference facilities for up to 1000.
Secretarial/translation services on request. Private parking.*
AMERICAN EXPRESS *Diners, Mastercard, Visa.*

Valencia   Oscar Torrijos

| Tel (6) 373 29 49   Fax (6) 373 29 49 | | R |

Dr. Sumsi 4 46005 Valencia

Seats 55   Meal for 2 approx Pts5000

Set in a 70-year-old house in the centre of Valencia, with elegant
oak panelling and hand-carved wooden furniture, this restaurant

serves typically Spanish food with a wide selection of rice: served with among other things, spiny lobster, artichokes, anglerfish and John Dory. They have some great speciality desserts like *hojaldre* (puff pastry) dishes. The wine list has a particularly comprehensive selection of Riojas and Catalan wines. *L 12-3.45 D 8-11. Closed Sun, 15 Aug-15 Sept. Public parking.* AMERICAN EXPRESS *Diners, Visa.*

★

Valencia   Rías Gallegas

Tel (6) 357 20 07   **R**

Matemático Marzal 11 46007 Valencia

Seats 90   Meal for 2 approx Pts7000

Here in this family-run restaurant, it is the wife who is in the kitchen, while her husband charms the guests. Like many other popular Spanish restaurants, run by Northern Galicians who have moved south in the last 50 years, the Rías Gallegas has stuck to its own, more robust, rustic Galician style of cooking. They cook a great deal of seafood like spiny lobster, hake, haddock and octopus *a la gallega* (briefly boiled in salty water and served with boiled potatoes and a mild stock sauce). Their simple cooking belies the amount of work that goes into choosing the fish: the catch comes up fresh from La Corúba and only the best are accepted. The extensive wine collection is reasonably priced, starting at the equivalent of £6; despite their reserves of vintage bottles, the best-selling one is made by a neighbour. *Open noon-2am. Closed Aug. Private parking.* AMERICAN EXPRESS *Visa, Mastercard.*

★

Valencia   Valencia Palace

Tel (6) 393 55 33   Fax (6) 393 55 32   **H**

Paseo de la Alameda 32 46023 Valencia

Rooms 199   Double room from Pts25,000

Part of the Sol international hotel chain, this hotel, their 150th, opened last year. Despite being right in the centre of Valencia, it has a terrace with an open-air swimming pool and a range of sports facilities. The rooms have many modern accessories: private safe, fax, CNN, British, French and Italian channels. The banqueting and conference facilities in this modern place are also excellent. *24hr room service. Conference facilities for up to 600. Secretarial/translation services on request. Outdoor swimming pool/gym/sauna/jacuzzi/massage. Public parking.* AMERICAN EXPRESS *Diners, Mastercard, Visa.*

Valencia   Versalles

Tel (6) 342 37 38   Fax (6) 342 18 04   **R**

Dolores Alcayde 14 46007 Valencia

Seats 100   Meal for two approx Pts12,000

The chef serves a variety of fish prepared Basque-style: in their own juices with rich sauces. The house speciality is a big Basque traditional dish, *cocotxas* (hake fillets fried with prawns, white wine and clams with a parsley, onion and garlic purée served on top of the fish). The wine list is limited, but has a dry red Rioja and white Castillo de Liria house wine. The building was a private house and still has antique furniture in the restaurant. The tables spread out on to the terrace in the summer. *L 1-3.30 D 9-11. Closed Sun, Aug.* AMERICAN EXPRESS *Diners, Mastercard, Visa.*

Elsewhere in Spain

San Sebastian   Arzak

Tel (43) 27 84 65   Fax (43) 27 27 53   R

Alto de Miracruz 21 20015 San Sebastian

Seats   Meal for two approx Pts20,000

A picturesque city in the heart of Basque country, a celebrated
restaurant, an elegant dining room with lots of antiques, old
painings, fine porcelain, gleaming silver and lovely floral
arrangements: an apt setting for Basque Juan Maria Arzak's
inventive cooking that owes everything to his origins – the
restaurant has been in the family since 1895. The *menu degustacion*
at 8,600 Pts presents a good example of the dishes on offer,
starting perhaps with soup of baby crayfish or lobster with fried
vegetable strips, langoustines with morels and an almond purée,
green pasta with mushrooms and foie gras, or a mixture of
smoked salmon, cheese and fresh herbs. A fish course might
comprise fillets of fresh cod served with a chive vinaigrette and
squid-infused olive oil, or monkfish sautéed with white wine and   ★
fresh herbs, and served with an assortment of seasonal vegetables.
Meat-eaters could enjoy calf's liver with a corn purée or
medallions of lamb with garlic, herbs and turnips. For a dessert
try the chocolate and greengage tart with a sweet basil and
rhubarb sauce or a galette of oranges served with fromage blanc
ice cream. The wine list includes the best riojas (Arzak 89 Rioja
Alta), Julian Chivite's refreshing Gran Fuedo rosé from Navarra,
and the local white Txakoli Txomin Etxaniz – now there's a
mouthful! *L 1-3.30 D 8.30-11. Public parking. Closed D Sun, all
Mon, 2 weeks end-June, Nov.* AMERICAN EXPRESS *Diners, Mastercard,
Visa.*

Spain Index

Recommended by

EGON RONAY'S GUIDES

1995

YOUR GUARANTEE
OF
QUALITY AND INDEPENDENCE

- Establishment inspections are anonymous

- Inspections are undertaken by qualified
  Egon Ronay's Guides inspectors

- The Guides are completely independent
  in their editorial selection

- The Guides do not accept advertising,
  hospitality or payment from listed
  establishments

Hotels & Restaurants   Pubs & Inns
Europe   Just a Bite
Family Hotels & Restaurants   Paris
Oriental Restaurants   Ireland
New Zealand & South Pacific   Australia

Egon Ronay's Guides are available from all good bookshops or can be
ordered from Leading Guides, 35 Tadema Road, London SW10 0PZ
Tel: 071-352 2485 / 352 0019 Fax: 071-376 5071

Sweden

Currency: Swedish Kronor   **Exchange Rate:** £1 = approx SKr11.50

International dialling code: 010 46
(Gothenburg + 31 Stockholm + 8)

Passports/Visas: No visa required by British passport holders for stay of less than 3 months.

British Embassy in Stockholm Tel: 8-667 0140

TRANSPORT
Airports:
Stockholm-Arland Tel: 8-797 8557/797 6000
Stockholm-Bromma Tel: 8-797 6874
Railway Stations:
Gothenburg Tel: 31-10 3000
Stockholm Tel: (international) 8-696 7509 (domestic) 8-696 7540
Car hire in Stockholm:
Budget Tel: 8-33 4383 (airport 8-593 62100)
Avis Tel: 8-34 9910
Speed limits: 70 km/h on trunk roads, 90-110 km/h on motorways, 50 km/h in towns.

Bank open: Mon-Fri 9.30am-3pm (& 4-5.30pm on Thursdays). Some banks stay open till 5.30pm daily.

Shops open: Generally 9am-6pm (1-4pm Sat). Some stores stay open till 8/10pm in large cities + 12-4pm some Sundays.

National Holidays: New Year's Day, 6 Jan, 1 & 4 April, 1, 12 & 23 May, 25 Jun, 5 Nov, Christmas Eve, Christmas Day, Boxing Day & New Year's Eve.

Tourist Offices:
Swedish Tourist Board in London - Tel: 0171-935 9784
In Stockholm - Tel: 8-789 2000/789 2400 / Gothenburg Tel: 31-81 8200

American Express Travel Service Offices/or Representative (R):
Stockholm - AETS
   Birger Jarlsgatan 1
   PO Box 1761
   S 111 87
   Tel: 8-6795200/6797880 #

Stockholm

Stockholm   **Berns**

Tel (8) 614 07 00   Fax (8) 611 51 75   **H**

Näckströmsgatan 8 Berzelii Park 111 47 Stockholm
Rooms 60   Double room from SKr1590

Even though the hotel is in the centre of town, close to the city's
most popular shopping district, it enjoys a quiet location by the
edge of Berzelii Park, almost opposite the Halwyl Museum.
A beautiful art deco building, it is also close to the harbour and
old town. The hotel was totally refurbished a couple of years ago,
using the original Italian art deco style, with cedarwood
furnishings and marble and wooden floors. This is an extremely
pleasant and hospitable hotel with a good selection of conference
facilities accommodating a small meeting of up to 15 in a VIP
suite, or large conferences in the banqueting rooms. *24hr room
service. Cable/satellite TV/fax. Theatre-style conference facilities for
up to 800. Business centre: secretarial/translation services. Closed 23
Dec-3 Jan. Valet parking.* AMERICAN EXPRESS *Diners, Mastercard, Visa.*

> ### THE APARTMENT SERVICE
> Tel in UK: (0181) 748 4207   Fax: (0181) 748 3972
> The Apartment Service will find you the right apartment
> worldwide to suit your needs, whether you are on a short or
> long-term stay. A 96-page colour catalogue is free on request.
> All budgets are catered for.

Stockholm   **Eriks**

Tel (8) 23 85 00   Fax (8) 796 60 69   **R**

Österlånggatan 17 111 31 Stockholm
Seats 60   Meal for 2 approx SKr1400

The old town of Stockholm dates from the 14th and 15th
centuries and is remarkably well preserved. There used to be
a 15th-century inn in The Green House where Eriks now occupies
elegant premises (including a small hotel), three minutes walk
from the Royal Palace. The chef-patron, Erik Lallerstedt, was
famous for his cuisine in his previous restaurant on a barge in the
harbour. The *menu dégustation* includes a truffle and potato salad   ★
with air-dried duck breast and a terrine of goose liver; main
courses are lobster, turbot and halibut poached in a chervil and
champagne sauce. To finish, try his delicious ice cream made with
Arctic raspberries, tangy and tasty. *L 11.30-2.30 D 6-11. Closed
Sun, Jul and National Holidays.* AMERICAN EXPRESS *Diners, Mastercard,
Visa.*

Stockholm   **Esplanade**

Tel (8) 663 07 40   **H**

Strandvägen 7A 114 56 Stockholm

Rooms 33   Double room from SKr1200

This is an informal but smart family hotel in a good residential
area, only minutes from the city centre. A few rooms have a very
good view but many face a quiet courtyard. The decor is in art
nouveau style. All rooms are comfortable and well maintained but
with only 33, it is best to book well ahead. There is no restaurant
but a good full English breakfast buffet is available. Tall guests are
even provided with extra long beds. *No room service. Cable TV.*
AMERICAN EXPRESS *Diners, Mastercard, Visa.*

Stockholm   **Grand Hotel**

Tel (8) 22 10 20   Fax (8) 611 86 86   **HR**

Södra Blasieholmshamnen 8 103 27 Stockholm

Rooms 306   Double room from SKr2117

When the Nobel prize winners come to Stockholm to receive
their awards from the King of Sweden, they always stay here,
in Sweden's premier hotel. The hotel is set on the waterfront,
facing the Royal Palace, and if you are lucky enough to have
a room at the front, you can watch the tourist boats come and go.
Well-equipped bedrooms have all been luxuriously redecorated
recently with pale blue fabric and light Swedish wood. Bathrooms
are fitted with Italian marble and underfloor heating. The
marvellous pillared lobby reflects the elegance of the entire
establishment. *24hr room service. Cable/satellite TV. Theatre-style
conference facilities for up to 600. Secretarial/translation services.
Private garage.* AMERICAN EXPRESS *Diners, Mastercard, Visa.*

Restaurant Franska Matsalen

Seats 70   Meal for 2 approx SKr2000

The Grand Hotel really is extremely grand and the Franska
Matsalen (which means the French Dining Room) is also elegant
and prestigious. It has been popular and well known for some
time now, with many tables looking out over the water and the
Royal Palace beyond, and the cooking continues to improve. The
19th-century decor with its beautiful wall panelling makes   ★
a lovely background to chef Roland Persson's many fine dishes
based on French classic cuisine. Service is first class and the wine
list extensive. In the Grand Veranda restaurant, you can enjoy
a typical simple Swedish *smörgåsbord. D only 6-11. Closed July.*

> Meal prices for 2 are based on à la carte menus.
> When set menus are available, prices will often be lower.

Stockholm   **Den Gyldene Freden**

Tel (8) 24 97 60   Fax (8) 21 38 70   **R**

Österlånggatan 51 103 17 Stockholm

Seats 700   Meal for 2 approx SKr700

This historic restaurant with its stone steps and deep cellar vaults
has an illustrious past; in the early part of the 18th century it was
the most famous of the 790 taverns in old Stockholm. The good
citizens of Stockholm enjoyed their ale and sausages in these cellars
until recently, when the Swedish Literary Academy became the
owners and the tavern became a restaurant. In the last few years,
new kitchens have been installed and one of the country's best
chefs, Ulf Kappen, has taken over the stoves. While sticking
to Swedish food, he offers some interesting dishes such as Arctic
char braised in cream with chives, dill and anchovy – a real treat.
Other fish on the menu are angler fish, brill, whitebait and
a steaming, aromatic shellfish casserole with saffron and fennel.
A popular meat dish is brisket of beef with potatoes. *L 11-3
D 6-11. Closed Sun, Jul. No parking.* AMERICAN EXPRESS *Diners,
Mastercard, Visa.*

Stockholm   **KB**

Tel (8) 679 60 32   Fax (8) 611 82 83   **R**

Smålandsgatan 7 111 46 Stockholm

Seats 60   Meal for 2 approx SKr800

KB is a Stockholm institution and one of the most popular places
to lunch in town. The central location and the swift and relaxed
service combined with good, mostly Swedish food, ensures a full
house. Chef-proprietor Örjan Klein is responsible for KB's
development into a well-regarded restaurant. Dishes to try are
parsley-baked cod with shiitake mushrooms and rack of lamb
with savoy cabbage. A notable dessert is almond parfait with
apricots and caramel sauce. *L 11.30-5 (Aug till 2) D 7-10.30.
Closed L Sat, all Sun, 22 Jun-6 Aug, National Holidays.*
AMERICAN EXPRESS *Diners, Mastercard, Visa.*

Stockholm   **Operakällaren**

Tel (8) 676 58 00   Fax (8) 20 95 92   **R**

Operahuset S-111 86 Stockholm

Seats 200   Meal for 2 approx SKr1100

Operakällaren is unique. Classified as a historic monument and
part of the Royal Opera House, it dates back to 1787. Today it is
a complex of three linked restaurants at different price levels. The
main dining room has a magnificent view of the Royal Palace
across the water. Appropriately, head chef, Swiss-born Werner
Vögeli, is a culinary adviser to the King and Queen of Sweden.
As a visitor to Stockholm it is almost mandatory to sample the
gigantic Swedish *smörgåsbord* or table of hors d'oeuvre, which you   ★
can visit as many times as you like – there are more than 50
dishes, hot and cold, fish and meat, cheese and fruit. A speciality
is Janssons Temptation (baked layers of sliced potatoes, anchovies,
minced onions and cream). Operakällaren has one of the best wine
lists in the country. *L 11.30-2 D 5-11. Closed L Sun, Jul. Private
parking.* AMERICAN EXPRESS *Diners, Mastercard, Visa.*

Stockholm   **Paul & Norbert**

| Tel (8) 663 81 83 | **R** |

Strandvägen 9 114 56 Stockholm

Seats 32   Meal for 2 approx SKr1000

With only eight tables and a location on the fashionable
Strandvägen, this is a very exclusive restaurant. More importantly
the German proprietors, Paul Beck and chef Norbert Lang, serve
some of the finest food available in Sweden. Reservations are
a must if you want to sample their classic specialities, such
as lobster bisque with armagnac or sautéed sweetbreads in a nettle
sauce. In winter Swedish game is the best and do not miss the   ★
Bresse pigeon with a calvados sauce. Desserts include hot soufflés
and several fruit variations. Paul keeps the service to a high
standard and helps you select the wine, which can also be ordered
by the glass – very useful in pricey Sweden. *L 11.45-2.30 D 5.30-
10.30. Closed Sat, Sun, Jul, 24 Dec-1 Jan.* AMERICAN EXPRESS *Diners,
Mastercard, Visa.*

Stockholm   **SAS Strand Hotel**

| Tel (8) 678 78 00   Fax (8) 611 24 36 | **H** |

Nybrokajen 9 103 27 Stockholm

Rooms 120   Double room from SKr1890

The SAS Strand is a very good and popular first-class hotel used
to a large extent by businessmen. The location is superb – on the
pleasure harbour where the white boats from the Archipelago
dock. Rooms are modern and well equipped. The Italian-style
patio is a very pleasant place to have a breakfast buffet
or afternoon tea. SAS airline passengers can check in for their
flights in the hotel before leaving. *24hr room service. Cable TV.
Theatre-style conference facilities for up to 50. Private parking/garage.*
AMERICAN EXPRESS *Diners, Mastercard, Visa.*

Stockholm   **Sergel Plaza**

| Tel (8) 22 66 00   Fax (8) 21 50 70 | **H** |

Brunkebergstorg 9 103 27 Stockholm

Rooms 394   Double room from SKr1395

An attractive modern hotel in the very centre of Stockholm's
business district. It was completed in 1984 and was originally
intended for the Swedish Parliament. It features a stunning atrium
lobby with a piano bar. In the hotel there is also a casino and the
gourmet restaurant, Anna Rella. For the business traveller there
is a 42-roomed Executive Floor with its own check-in and
breakfast lounge. For the health-conscious, the hotel provides
a sauna and jacuzzi with Swedish massage. *24hr room service.
Satellite/cable TV. Theatre-style conference facilities for up to 200.
Closed 23-25 Dec. Private parking.* AMERICAN EXPRESS *Diners, Mastercard,
Visa.*

Stockholm   Ulla Winbladh

Tel (8) 663 05 71   Fax (8) 663 05 73   **R**

Rosendalsvägen 8 Djurgården 115 21 Stockholm
Seats 50   Meal for 2 approx SKr900

The excellent location, in a park on the island of Djurgården only
minutes from the city centre, makes Ulla Winbladh the perfect
place for a meal in the summer. The high standard of food and
service makes a visit worthwhile anytime. The restaurant is named
after the girlfriend and muse of the 18th-century Swedish poet
and composer, Carl Mikael Bellman, and his spirit watches over
the diners. The menu is strong on Swedish dishes and is very
reasonably priced. You might start with bleak roe (Sweden's
answer to caviar) and potato pancakes with crème fraiche.
A popular main course is reindeer fillet with lingonberry cream
sauce. The light dessert, elderflower and blackcurrant mousse,
is another local speciality. There is a small but reasonably priced
wine list. *Open 11.30am-11pm (Sat & Sun from noon). Private
parking.* AMERICAN EXPRESS *Diners, Mastercard, Visa.*

Stockholm   Victory Hotel

Tel (8) 14 30 90   Fax (8) 20 21 77   **H**

Lilla Nygatan 5 111 28 Stockholm
Rooms 44   Double room from SKr1790

This is one of Stockholm's top hotels, as famous for buried treasure
(part of which is exhibited in the City Museum, with the rest
in the hotel) as it is for elegance and style. Located in the old city,
the hotel was built in 1642 for Pastor Primarius Olav Laurelius.
The bedrooms are well furnished, with modern bathrooms, but
no mini-bar, and are decorated with maritime and Swedish folk
antiques. Their design is unfussy, but full of character. Swedish
colour schemes are used and a typical room has exposed beams
and pine floors and a blue-and-white-striped bedspread with a pine
headboard. The sparkling white, well-equipped bathrooms have
tiled floors and large white spa baths. The suites, in contrast, are
old-fashioned and luxurious with chandeliers and old-style cabinets
and writing desks. For those wishing to relax, there is also
a swimming pool and cold water spa, with sauna. On the small
rooftop terrace, tables are arranged around a fountain and provide
an excellent place for a summer snack. *Cable/satellite TV. Theatre-
style conference facilities for up to 90. Sports facilities. Closed 24 & 31
Dec. Valet parking.* AMERICAN EXPRESS *Diners, Mastercard, Visa.*

Stockholm   Wedholms Fisk

Tel (8) 611 78 74   **R**

Nybrokajen 17 111 48 Stockholm
Seats 72   Meal for 2 approx SKr1100

Chef-patron Bengt Wedholm is justly famous in Sweden for his
mastery in selecting and cooking the best fish. Red-bellied lake
trout and turbot are cooked to perfection and served in large
portions. Located on the quayside, this bistro-style restaurant has
a simple decor and very pleasant staff. The wine list is good but,
as always in Sweden, prices are high. *Open 11.30am-11pm (Mon-
Fri), (Sat from 2). Closed Sun, Jul, National Holidays.* AMERICAN EXPRESS
Diners, Mastercard, Visa.

★

Gothenburg

Gothenburg   **Gothia**

Tel (31) 40 93 00 Fax (31) 18 98 04   **H**

Mässans Gata 24 S-402 26 Gothenburg

Rooms 290   Double room from SKr1250

The hotel is in the same building as the Svenska Mässan Exhibition and Congress Centre, which opened in 1984; not a particularly quiet location, since the Lisebergs Amusement Park is next door. The rooms are modern and well equipped, but the only health facility is the Scandinavian sauna. *Satellite/cable TV. Theatre-style conference facilities for up to 200. Closed 20 Dec-2 Jan. Private parking.* AMERICAN EXPRESS *Diners, Mastercard, Visa.*

Gothenburg   **The Place**

Tel (31) 16 03 33 Fax (31) 16 78 54   **R**

Arkivgatan 7 411 34 Gothenburg

Seats 25   Meal for 2 approx SKr1300

A small team have owned and run this place for the last eight years, preparing a classic French menu with a sprinkling of Swedish dishes. Starters like baked garlic snails are served in a brioche with crisp salad, followed by Norwegian salmon baked with spinach and served with a yellow pepper sauce, fillets of sole stuffed with ratatouille and a crayfish sauce, pasta with fillet of beef and a Dijon mustard sauce or honey-roast chicken on a skewer with a ginger sauce and peanut butter. The house dessert sounds more American than anything else, but that does not detract from its calorific attractiveness: Toblerone parfait served with an almond muffin. With the *menu dégustation*, a different glass of wine is served with each of the five courses (SKr595) from the 700 bottle-strong wine cellar. *D only 5-12. Closed mid Jun-mid Jul, 25 Dec. Public parking.* AMERICAN EXPRESS *Mastercard, Visa.*

★

Gothenburg   **Riverton**

Tel (31) 10 12 00 Fax (31) 13 08 66   **H**

Stora Badhusgatan 26 411 21 Gothenburg

Rooms 191   Double room from SKr1150

Despite being a large international hotel, this place is family-run and still has a cosy, relaxed feel about it. It is 3km from the main railway station and has rooms which are modern in a glitzy 60s, rather over-the-top-kind of way but are equipped with all the expected amenities. *Cable/satellite TV. Theatre-style conference facilities for up to 300. Sauna, solarium, jacuzzi. Private parking.* AMERICAN EXPRESS *Diners, Mastercard, Visa.*

Opening times are often liable to change at short notice, so it's always best to book.

Gothenburg   **Sheraton Göteborg**

| Tel (31) 80 60 00   Fax (31) 15 98 88 | **H** |

Södra Hamngatan 59-65 401 24 Gothenburg

Rooms 344   Double room from SKr1790

5000 different rose bushes are a feature of the Gothenburg
Horticultural Gardens which also has a Butterfly House. These are
a short walk away from the hotel across the canal. The hotel also
has the advantage for travellers of being opposite the main railway
station. The rooms are classically decorated and well equipped.
An indoor swimming pool, sauna, gym and health club give keep-
fit fanatics plenty of choice. *24hr room service. Satellite/cable TV.
Theatre-style conference facilities for up to 500. Closed 23 Dec. Valet
parking.* AMERICAN EXPRESS® *Mastercard, Visa.*

Gothenburg   **Sjömagasinet**

| Tel (31) 24 65 10   Fax (31) 24 55 39 | **R** |

Klippans Kulturreservat 414 51 Gothenburg

Seats 300   Meal for 2 approx SKr500

This old shipping warehouse was converted into a restaurant in
the summer of 1994 and specialises in fish and shellfish. One
delicious shellfish dish has a crisp pastry crust with fresh woodland
mushrooms and young vegetables and is served with a crayfish
sauce flavoured with tarragon. Main courses stick to poached or
fried seafood, featuring a number of sole dishes. The wines are
mainly regional French. The surrounding area is beautiful, with
old houses and a gorgeous view over the river and the harbour.
Open 11.30am-11pm. Closed 24 & 25 Dec, 1 Jan. AMERICAN EXPRESS®
Diners, Mastercard.

Gothenburg   **Victors Hotel**

| Tel (31) 17 41 80   Fax (31) 13 96 10 | **H** |

Skeppsbroplatsen 1 411 18 Gothenburg

Rooms 44   Double room from SKr1150

Three women own and manage this hotel right in the city centre,
with the harbour outside. There are only 15 doubles, so booking
is essential. The furniture in the rooms has a minimalist Swedish
touch. *24hr room service. Theatre-style conference facilities for up to
40. Private parking.* AMERICAN EXPRESS® *Diners, Mastercard, Visa.*

Gothenburg   **Westra Piren**

| Tel (31) 51 95 55   Fax (31) 23 99 40 | **R** |

Eriksberg (Pier 4) 402 79 Gothenburg

Seats 80   Meal for 2 approx SKr1500

This used to be an old service house for the floating docks until
four years ago, when it was converted into a restaurant. The food
is an eclectic mix of French and Swedish, with starters like superb
noix de St Jacques en deux façons and main courses such as grilled
turbot with fried herbs and a lobster vinegar, baked halibut with
parsley, mustard and horseradish sauce and medallions of fried
monkfish served with a paprika vinaigrette. The house speciality
is crayfish. The restaurant is six kilometres from the city, so phone
for directions when booking. The main restaurant is on the 2nd
floor and a brasserie on the first offers slightly simpler food which
can be enjoyed on a terrace in fine weather. *Open 11.30am-11pm
(Sat from 6.30). Closed L Sat, all Sun. Public parking.* AMERICAN EXPRESS®
Diners, Mastercard, Visa.

Solna

Solna	Ulriksdals Wärdshus

Tel (8) 85 08 15   Fax (8) 85 08 58   **R**

Ulriksdal S-170 71 Solna
Seats 140   Meal for 2 approx SKr1000

If you arrive early for dinner you can witness a traditional
Swedish ceremony when the blue and yellow Swedish flag
is lowered in front of the dining room veranda. This lovely old
country inn, in a suburb of Stockholm, in a Royal Park has been
transformed into a first-class restaurant by its owner-host Lauri
Nilsson and chef Karl-Heinz Krücken. The centrepiece of the
dining room at lunchtime is the lavish Swedish *smörgåsbord*, which
features many varieties of herring preparations and other Swedish
fish dishes. Follow this with ham and beef, patés and meatballs and
finally a variety of cheeses. The perfect drink to accompany this
is chilled Swedish *aquavit* with a beer chaser. In the evening choose
between a set or à la carte menu with dishes such as medallions
of venison. The wine cellar is one of the finest in Sweden and
is the venue for regular tasting sessions conducted by Mr Nilsson.
Open noon-10pm (Sat from 12.30, Sun 12.30-6.30) Closed D Sun.
AMERICAN EXPRESS *Diners, Mastercard, Visa.*

Sweden Index

Switzerland

Currency: Swiss Franc   **Exchange Rate:** £1 = approx Fr2

International dialing code: 010 41
(Zürich + 1 Geneva + 22 Basle + 61)

Passports/Visas: No visa required by British passport holders.

British Embassy in Zürich Tel: 1-47 1520   Fax: 1-252 8351

TRANSPORT
Airports:
Geneva-Cointrin Tel: 22-799 3111/717 7711
Zürich-Kloten Tel: 1-816 2211/816 3511
Basle-Mulhouse Tel: 61-325 2511
Railway Stations:
Geneva Tel: 22-738 5200
Zürich Tel: 1-211 5010
Basle Tel: (Swiss) 61-272 6767 (French) 61-271 5033 (German) 61-691 5511
Car hire:
Geneva - Hertz Tel: 22-798 2202 (airport 22-734 3134) Avis Tel:
(airport) 22-798 2300 Budget Tel: (airport) 22-732 5252
Zürich - Hertz Tel: 1-814 0511 (airport 1-242 8484) Avis Tel: 1-809
1818 (airport 1-813 0084) Europcar Tel: (airport) 1-813 2044 Budget
Tel: 1-813 3131
Basle - Hertz Tel: 61-325 2780 (airport 61-271 5822) Avis Tel:
(airport) 61-325 2840 Budget Tel: (airport) 61-325 2936
Speed limits: 80 km/h on trunk roads 120 km/h on motorways,
50 km/h in towns.

Banks open: Mon-Fri 8.30am-4.30pm

Shops open: Mon-Fri 8am-12pm & 1.30-5.30pm (Sat till 4pm). Many
shops close Monday mornings.

National Holidays: New Year's Day, 6 Jan, 14, 16 & 17 April, 1 & 25
May, 4, 5 & 15 Jun, 1 & 15 Aug, 1 Nov, 8 Dec, Christmas Day &
Boxing Day.

Tourist Offices:
Swiss Tourist Board in London - Tel: 0171-7341921
In Switzerland –
Geneva Tel: 22-310 5031
Zürich Tel: 1-211 4000
Basle Tel: 61-261 5050

American Express Travel Service Office:
Zürich - AETS
    Bahnhofstrasse 20
    PO Box 5231   Ch-8022   Tel: 1-2118370 #

Basle

Basle   **Basel**

| Tel (61) 261 24 23   Fax (61) 261 25 95 | **H** |

Münzgasse 12 4051 Basle

Rooms 72   Double room from Fr295

Buried deep in the heart of the old Renaissance part of Basle, the
Cathedral and Museum of Fine Arts are a short strolling distance
away. The building itself was a renowned 18th-century brewery
with oak shutters and sandstone window frames. There are only
18 rooms in the old part, while the rest are in a 70s extension.
By January 1995, all the rooms will have been redecorated, with
lithographs and some original paintings on the walls. *24hr room
service. Safe/fax. Conference facilities for up to 30.
Secretarial/translation services on request. Private/valet parking.*
AMERICAN EXPRESS *Diners, Mastercard, Visa.*

> THE APARTMENT SERVICE
> Tel in UK: (0181) 748 4207   Fax: (0181) 748 3972
> The Apartment Service will find you the right apartment
> worldwide to suit your needs, whether you are on a short or
> long-term stay. A 96-page colour catalogue is free on request.
> All budgets are catered for.

Basle   **Le Bourguignon**

| Tel (61) 281 14 10   Fax (61) 281 14 20 | **R** |

Bachlettenstrasse 1 4054 Basle

Seats 65   Meal for 2 approx Fr220

Herr Holzmann and his French chef started this restaurant ten
years ago, since when they have developed and refined
an imaginative French menu, constantly re-interpreting traditional
French dishes. Examples are *crapaudine de poussin roti désossé
au vinaigre de balsamico* (de-boned poussin grilled on a skewer with
balsamic vinegar) or *ragout de saumon poelé minute façon stroganoff*
(ragout of salmon stroganoff). The 150 wines are mainly from
France. *L 11.30-3 D 6.30-12. Closed Sun, Jul, Aug. Private parking.*
AMERICAN EXPRESS *Diners, Mastercard, Visa.*

Basle   **Hotel Drei Könige**

| Tel (61) 261 52 52   Fax (61) 261 21 53 | **HR** |

Blumenrain 8 4001 Basle

Rooms 88   Double room from Fr420

This Napoleon-style house, also known as the Hotel Trois Rois,
overlooking the Rhine stands on a site dating back to 1026. For
the last 150 years it has been a hotel, and has been visited
by Napoleon, Voltaire and Dickens. The high-ceilinged rooms are
full of antiques, valuable furniture and carpets, yet they have all
recently been renovated and are well equipped. The reception
is particularly impressive, with tall columns leading up to a ceiling
hung with antique chandeliers, which throw light down on to the
wood-panelled walls. The location is extremely convenient too:
right in the city centre near all the main museums and the zoo.

24hr room service. Safe. Conference facilities for up to 100.
Secretarial/translation/fax services on request. Private garage.
AMERICAN EXPRESS *Mastercard, Visa.*

Rotisserie des Rois

Seats 65   Meal for 2 approx Fr180

In the winter, huddle up to the blazing fires, surrounded by Louis
XV furniture, and in the summer try the terrace overlooking the
river. The menu is rather eclectic, with fish and meat dishes
cooked in a variety of unusual ways. Turbot is poached in spices
and served on a bed of wild rice, while noisettes of lamb are
served with a basil and garlic sauce. Have a light starter, like
gravlax with horseradish sauce, and keep room for one of the
many rich French desserts. *L 11.30-2 D 6.45-9.30.*

Basle   **Europe**

Tel (61) 691 80 80   Fax (61) 691 82 01   **HR**

Clarastrasse 43 4058 Basle
Rooms 170   Double room from Fr260

Smooth, shiny and ultra-modern hotel in a small city-centre park
near the Basle Trade Fairs. It was built in the 1970s, but has
recently seen much updating and renovation. Seats in blue-and-
black leather provide relaxation in the lobby, while features in the
bedrooms include pastel decor and wardrobes designed by Colane.
Plenty of mirrors in the bathrooms. *24hr room service. Video/air-
con. Theatre-style conference facilities for up to 150.*
Secretarial/translation services on request. Private garage. AMERICAN EXPRESS
Mastercard, Visa.

Les Quatre Saisons

Seats 80   Meal for 2 approx Fr280

The head chef, previously at *Stucki* – Basle's leading gastronomic
venue – has developed a strong French menu along similar lines.
Starters such as *bouillabaisse* of saltwater crayfish and *foie gras
de canard* can be followed by one of the light, well-balanced fish
dishes: *filet de loup de mer grillé au jus de fenouil* (grilled fillet of sea
bass in a fennel-scented jus), or *turbotin roti aux fines herbes et purée
d'artichauts* (roasted baby turbot with herbs and artichoke purée).
A large list of house wines includes Italian, Californian and French.
L 11.30-2 D 6.30-10. Closed Sun, 2 weeks Aug. Private parking.

Basle   **Schweizerhof**

Tel (61) 271 28 33   Fax (61) 271 29 19   **H**

Centralbahnplatz 1 4002 Basle
Rooms 75   Double room from Fr265

The railway station is next to this 19th-century hotel and the
airport a 15-minute taxi ride away. Also the shops, museums and
zoo are within walking distance. Some rooms have 60s furniture,
the rest original pieces from the 1860s. The marble-floored
reception is arranged like a cosy living room with sofas and
armchairs. *24hr room service. Conference facilities for up to 100.*
Secretarial services on request. Private parking. AMERICAN EXPRESS *Diners,
Mastercard.*

Basle	**Stucki Bruderholz**

Tel (61) 361 82 22 Fax (61) 361 182 03	R

Bruderholzallee 42 4059 Basle

Seats 70   Meal for 2 approx Fr200

Hans Stucki and his wife Susi have been running this French
restaurant in a residential district of Basle for over 35 years. His
menu is constantly evolving, drawing in a large crowd of lovers of
good food, but always has some interesting duck and veal dishes.
The new fish menu is worth trying, with starters like vichyssoise
served with smoked salmon and caviar or langoustine tails fried
with a ragout of vegetables and basil, and main courses like fillet   ★
of fresh sea fish cooked in coriander and served with vegetables
and saffron. On a warm evening, try the mint ice cream parfait
with bitter chocolate. 500 wines (including his beloved Swiss
wines) from all over the world make for an impressive and
diverse list. *L 12-2 D 7-10. Closed 24 Dec-7 Jan. Private parking.*
AMERICAN EXPRESS *Diners, Mastercard, Visa.*

Basle	**Der Teufelhof**

Tel (61) 261 10 10 Fax (61) 261 10 04	R

Leonhardsgraben 47 Heuberg 30 4051 Basle

Seats 60   Meal for 2 approx Fr175

The 19th-century building, now a restaurant (and also a hotel),
is filled with contemporary art. A theatre downstairs holds regular
art exhibitions. Five years ago a husband-and-wife team bought
and renovated it, bringing in a competent chef from Germany.
Since then, he has developed some strong French and international
specialities, and even adds the occasional Asiatic dish. Dishes to try
include: *Grouse mousse mit Gänseleber und Weinbeerensosse* (grouse
mousse and roasted goose liver with grape sauce), *steinbuttfilet
im Mangoldblatt mit Périgord-Trübchen in Chambertinjus* (fillet
of turbot wrapped in Swiss chard with Périgord truffles) and
crépinette vom Täubchen in Chambertinjus (boned, stuffed pigeon
in wine gravy). The 450 wines come from Italy, France and
Switzerland with a New World wine highlighted every month.
L 12-2 D 7-10. Closed Sun, Mon. AMERICAN EXPRESS *Mastercard, Visa.*

Around Basle

Binningen	**Schloss Binningen**

Tel (61) 421 20 55 Fax (61) 421 06 35	R

Schlossgasse 5 4102 Binningen

Seats 56   Meal for 2 approx Fr260

This remarkable 13th-century castle is only 2km out of Basle;
formerly the meeting place for local noblemen, it was converted
into a restaurant back in 1895, and many of the original paintings,
furniture and tables still exist. It may feel as if you are eating in a
museum, but the menu is modern and imaginative, adapting
traditional Swiss-French dishes: foie gras is served with a light port
jelly and a cold consommé, veal sweetbreads and lobster are baked
in a pastry pie and guinea fowl is presented with a fricasse of
baby vegetables. The desserts, like the rest of the menu, change
only four times a year, but are, nevertheless, mouthwatering:
choux are filled with chocolate *crème patissière* and oranges
marinated in 20 different spices. Unusually, all the wines on the
wine list are available by the glass. *Open 11.30am-11.30pm. Private
parking.* AMERICAN EXPRESS *Diners, Mastercard, Visa.*

Geneva

Geneva   L'Arlequin

Tel (22) 311 13 44   Fax (22) 311 1350   **R**

34 Quai Général-Guisain 1204 Geneva
Seats 45   Meal for 2 approx Fr300

This 19th-century building, across from the *Jardin Anglais*, was
restored after the people of Geneva voted not to knock it down.
The old facade remains, but the restaurant was completely rebuilt,
keeping the high-ceilinged rooms, which provide an excellent
setting for the modern French cooking. The chef has been greatly
influenced by his training and experience in top French restaurants
and is inspired by the work of Georges Blanc and Joël Robuchon.
He concentrates on fish dishes, like *navarin de homard aux pates   ★
fraiches et chanterelles* (a navarin of lobster with mushrooms,
vegetables and wine sauce served with fresh pasta). A particularly
refreshing combination is *filet de loup avec sauce au basilic
et quenelles de crabe* (sea bass fillet with a basil sauce and crab
quenelles). *L 12-2 D 7-10.30. Closed Aug.* AMERICAN EXPRESS *Mastercard,
Visa.*

Geneva   Le Béarn

Tel (22) 321 00 28   Fax (22) 381 31 15   **R**

4 Quai de la Poste 1204 Geneva
Seats 60   Meal for 2 approx Fr300

The two dining rooms in this old stone and wood restaurant
on the banks of the Rhone in the very centre of Geneva are very
different: *Empire* has rich period furniture and glistening glass and
cutlery, while *Rustique* is smaller, with simpler wooden chairs and
tables. Whichever you choose, the menus offered are the same:
traditionally French. The *Menu Printemps* has some
straightforward dishes: red mullet served with a Provençal caper,
anchovy, olive and tuna purée; salmon in puff pastry; duckling
with seasonal vegetables. *L 12-2 D 7.30-10. Closed Sat (but open
D Sat Oct-Jun), Sun, mid Jul-end Aug, 3 days Christmas, National
Holidays.* AMERICAN EXPRESS *Diners, Mastercard, Visa.*

Geneva   Hotel des Bergues

Tel (22) 731 50 50   Fax (22) 732 19 89   **H**

33 Quai des Bergues 1201 Geneva
Rooms 123   Double room from Fr390

Switzerland's oldest hotel sits in neo-classical splendour on the edge
of Lake Geneva, near the Rhone. Despite its idyllic location, it is
still very accessible: 6km from the airport and 500m from the
railway station (a vital option in a clock-conscious country). The
rooms are still decorated with original Louis Philippe furnishings
and they all have marble bathrooms; there are also ten spacious
suites. The reception hall, with its shiny grey marble, is as dazzling
as the six lounges, which can also be used as conference rooms.
24hr room service. Cable TV/fax. Private parking. AMERICAN EXPRESS
Diners, Mastercard, Visa.

Geneva   **La Cigogne**

Tel (22) 311 42 42   Fax (22) 31 40 65   **HR**

17 Place Longemalle 1204 Geneva

Rooms 52   Double room from Fr370

A place long on history and short on facilities; the house dates
back some 100 years and has some splendid frescoes, original stone
floors and fireplaces. Three lifts have been installed. All the
bedrooms were renovated and individually designed in 1985:
some have Louis XV or XVI furniture, others are stripped down
to simple pine. Located in a quiet square in the centre of Geneva's
commercial district, it is midway between the cathedral and the
lakeside gardens. *Video/safe. Conference facilities for up to 25.*
AMERICAN EXPRESS *Diners, Mastercard, Visa.*

Restaurant

Seats 36   Meal for 2 approx Fr230

This elegant mahogany-panelled dining room was opened back
in 1900 and was very fashionable during both World Wars. In the
last five years, it has seen a new lease of life with the arrival of a
chef who worked with Guérard in Eugénie-les-Bains in France.
His classical French culinary upbringing expresses itself in dishes
like *salade de mesclun et caille rotie avec croutons à la mousse de cèpes*
(roasted quail served on a bed of mixed salad with croutons and
wild mushroom mousse) and *pintadeau poelé aux chanterelles
et fleurs de courgettes farcies aux légumes et tomates panées* (sautéed
guinea fowl served with chanterelles and stuffed courgettes
flowers). The à la carte menu changes every week but always has
a good choice of fish dishes. However, the nine desserts are
different creations every day. *L 12-2 D 7-10.*

Geneva   **Hostellerie de la Vendée**

Tel (22) 792 04 11   Fax (22) 792 05 96   **HR**

28 chemin de la Vendée Petit-Lancy 1213 Geneva

Rooms 33   Double room from Fr200

This small hotel in a residential suburb 3km out of Geneva
is dedicated to all things gastronomic, with regular *dégustations*
drawing in the guests. It was recently renovated and the bedrooms
have modern, wooden furniture and pastel decor. *Private parking.*
AMERICAN EXPRESS *Diners, Mastercard, Visa.*

Restaurant

Seats 50   Meal for 2 approx Fr260

The menu is faithfully French, traditional to its core. Staple dishes
are *coquelet en croute, champagne et truffe* (chicken pie with
a champagne and truffle sauce) and *rouget entier désareté, tagliatelle
de courgette et pistou aux saveurs d'anchois* (red mullet with
courgette ribbons and an olive oil, lime, basil, anchovy and
tomato sauce). The set business lunch menu changes every week,
while the à la carte varies with the seasons. The finale is definitely
grand with such desserts as *symphonie autour des fruits rouges*
(a compote of red fruits served with strawberry mousse and red
fruit ice cream). *L 12-1.45 D 7-9.45. Closed L Sat, all Sun,
24 Dec-5 Jan.*

Geneva   Inter-Continental

Tel (22) 919 39 39   Fax (22) 919 38 38   **H R**

7 Chemin du Petit-Saconnex 1211 Geneva
Rooms 358   Double room from Fr460

This 1960s skyscraper has a total of 18 floors with the top floor
used for conferences. The views from some of the rooms are
splendid, so try to get a room near the top if possible. Like all
Intercontinentals, they have a constant renovation policy and
regularly update the rooms and the facilities. The hotel is only five
minutes from the very centre of Geneva and the airport and right
next to all the headquarters of international organisations like the
UN. *24hr room service. Satellite TV/fax. Theatre-style conference
facilities for up to 700. Outdoor swimming pool/sauna/massage.
Private/valet parking.* AMERICAN EXPRESS *Diners, Mastercard, Visa.*

Restaurant Les Continents
Seats 80   Meal for 2 approx Fr160

The Irish chef here has had a classical French training, but true
to his more lyrical, creative roots, experiments with his menu,
mixing ingredients that do not traditionally appear together.
Thick slices of lobster are served with a *bouillabaisse* and ratatouille
is garnished with fresh basil; sautéed fillet of red mullet, potatoes
and young leeks is served with truffles and savoury carrots.
L 12-2.30 D 7-10.30. Closed Sat, Sun.

Geneva   Parc des Eaux-Vives

Tel (22) 735 41 40   Fax (22) 786 87 65   **R**

82 Quai Gustave-Ador 1207 Geneva
Seats 250   Meal for 2 approx Fr220

Close to the edge of Lake Geneva and surrounded by a 14-hectare
city park, this restaurant is in an idyllic location. Like many old
Swiss buildings, the listed 18th-century restaurant is owned by the
City of Geneva; it's run by a husband-and-wife team. Inside it is
typically Swiss, but the menu is modern French: fillet of red
mullet is sautéed with garlic and served with a tomato and
courgette flan; warm duck liver comes with a confit of potatoes
cooked with rosemary. Seasonal changes are rigidly observed with
game, fish, asparagus and truffles all served at the right time of the
year. House specialities are quite an art: *noisettes de lotte aux pétales
de tomates séchées, beurre blanc aux graines de sésame* (monkfish in a   ★
white butter sauce with sesame seeds and sun-dried tomato) and
pigeon cuit en vessie façon demi-deuil (boned pigeon with truffle
inserted under the skin stuffed with a foie gras, truffle and
vegetable mixture and cooked in a bladder). The cellar is stocked
with 1000 different wines, including an impressive array of Italian
and Californian bottles. *L 12-2 D 7.30-10. Closed Sun, (except
L Easter-Sept), Mon, Jan. Private parking.* AMERICAN EXPRESS *Mastercard,
Visa.*

Geneva   La Perle du Lac

Tel (22) 731 79 35   Fax (22) 731 49 79   **R**

128 Rue de Lausanne 1202 Geneva
Seats 45   Meal for 2 approx Fr250

Set in a 1920s building, bought by the town council to ensure its
heritage would be preserved, this restaurant is on the left bank of
the Lake in the business district. 11 chefs prepare a carefully
thought-out and balanced à la carte menu and two set menus,
which all change every two to four months. The dishes are
determinedly French, but use an interesting mix of raw
ingredients, bringing new inventiveness to regional favourites. Try   ★
escalope de loup de mer poelée à l'émulsion de beurre noisette et capres
(escalope of sea bass sautéed in browned butter with capers), *blanc
de turbot roti aux épices et moutarde de Meaux* (spicy roast turbot) or
aiguillettes de caneton au miel d'acacia et figues (slices of duck breast
with acacia honey and figs). Amongst their 300 different wines,
there are some strong New World contenders. *L 12-2 D 7-10.
Closed Mon, Jan. Private parking.* AMERICAN EXPRESS *Mastercard, Visa.*

Geneva   Hotel du Rhone

Tel (22) 731 98 31   Fax (22) 732 45 58   **H**

Quai Turrettini 1201 Geneva
Rooms 214   Double room from Fr430

The Rafael Group owns hotels in Germany, France and the
United States, as well as this large hotel in the heart of Geneva's
commercial centre, only ten minutes from the airport, with
superb views over Lake Geneva. Despite being built in the 50s,
it is up-to-date, having been renovated a couple of years ago. The
rooms are in art deco style, with plain bedcovers and curtains and
marble bathrooms. *24hr room service. Video. Theatre-style conference
facilities for up to 180. Business centre: fax/secretarial/translation
services. Private parking.* AMERICAN EXPRESS *Mastercard, Visa.*

Geneva   Hotel Le Richemond

Tel (22) 731 14 00   Fax (22) 731 67 09   **H**

Jardin Brunswick 1201 Geneva
Rooms 98   Double room from Fr550

The Armleder family have run this hotel, which overlooks Lake
Geneva with the Alps beyond, for 120 years, never ceasing
to strive for absolute perfection. It is the pinnacle of luxury with
expensive prices to match – but they stint on nothing. Rooms and
suites (there are over 30 of the latter category with the 'Colette'
suite designed in memory of the famous writer who often stayed
here) are lavishly decorated in elegant style with 19th-century
furniture, and spacious bathrooms that are sumptuously equipped.
Enjoy afternoon tea in the gracious lounge and hall, or sip
a cocktail in the art deco Jardin terrace, served by effusively
helpful staff; room service is not to be missed – it's the best you'll
find anywhere. *24hr room service. Theatre-style conferences for up to
250. Fax/secretarial/translation services on request. Garage.*
AMERICAN EXPRESS *Diners, Mastercard, Visa.*

Around Geneva

Bellevue   **La Réserve**

Tel (22) 774 17 41   Fax (22) 774 25 71   **HR**

301 Route de Lausanne 1293 Bellevue
Rooms 114   Double room from Fr270

Situated minutes away from the motorway to Lausanne and the
airport and just ten minutes outside the centre of Geneva, this
modern mansion hotel, with its glittering outdoor pool,
is surrounded by acres of park, and is near the lakeside marina.
American Presidents (landing their helicopters on the lawn) and
even the Davis Cup team have stayed here – the latter, doubtless,
because of the splendid keep-fit facilities available, from gym
to tennis. The concierge also doubles as tennis coach for the less
expert players. The bedrooms are all quite similar: ultra-modern,
decorated in light, creamy pastels with new fireplaces taking pride
of place. The shiny metal and matt-black bar is a striking spot for
pre-dinner cocktails. *24hr room service. Video. Theatre-style
conference facilities for up to 200. Two swimming pools (indoor and
outdoor), gym, sauna, 4 tennis courts (1 indoor).* AMERICAN EXPRESS *Diners,
Mastercard, Visa.*

Restaurant Tsé Fung
Seats 60   Meal for 2 approx Fr200

The formal Chinese setting, with its low lanterns and revolving
tables, is the perfect place for the very refined Chinese cooking
that the small kitchen produces. Steamed and grilled meat-filled
ravioli are accompanied by sweet and sour pancakes. The six
menus vary a little every day, but a regular and popular house
speciality is *canard laqué péquinois* (Peking duck served with
pancakes and a plum and black bean sauce). The *dégustation* menus
have some interesting nibbles: tiny egg rolls with mint, shrimps
served with a spicy lime sauce and stuffed crab claws. *L 12-2.30
D 7-10.30.*

Carouge   **Auberge de Pinchat**

Tel (22) 342 30 77   Fax (22) 300 22 19   **HR**

32 Chemin de Pinchat 1227 Carouge
Rooms 5   Double room from Fr130

Outside Geneva, in a small town in the countryside, this early
20th-century beamed house is full of plants and paintings. The
owners opened it as a hotel and restaurant in 1981, after their
restaurant and club in Geneva became too hard to manage. Clearly
they do not have room for many people, with just four double
rooms and one single (with showers and toilets but not baths), but
most people stay here because of the food, rather than the
accommodation provided. *24hr room service. Closed 21 Dec-1 Jan,
15-31 Oct. Mastercard, Visa.*

See over for restaurant

Restaurant
Seats 12   Meal for 2 approx Fr200

The small lounge, with its arched ceiling and rustic decorations,
is the understated setting for some elegant meals for small parties
of friends. The chef was born and bred in Normandy and cites
Escoffier's cookery book as his bible. Every three weeks he changes
the menu, but his regular favourites include *foie gras de canard aux
morilles avec Baumes de Venise* (duck foie gras with wild
mushrooms and Baumes de Venise), *langoustines au beurre
de poivron doux* (langoustines in a red pepper butter) and *rognon
de veau avec sauce moutarde à l'ancienne* (calf's kidneys served in a
classic French mustard sauce). *L 12-3 D 7-9.30.*

Cologny   **Auberge du Lion d'Or**

Tel (22) 736 44 32   Fax (22) 786 74 62   **R**

5 Place Pierre Gauthier 1223 Cologny
Seats 70   Meal for 2 approx Fr360

This delightful inn, filled with Louis XVI furniture and large bay-
windows, sits on a hill overlooking Lake Geneva. Henri Large has
been faithfully cooking French food here for the last 40 years,
tending to concentrate his efforts and imagination on Mediterranean
fish dishes: *bouillabaisse* (made from ten different fish, from conger
eel to crab, and laced with saffron), *filet de rouget aux agrumes* (red
mullet cooked with citrus fruits), *turbot au four* (baked turbot).
Wines are international, with a good selection from the New
World. A separate bar seats 40 people and has a small hearty menu
with a Fr25-35 dish of the day. *L 12-2 D 7.30-10. Private parking.*

Peney-Dessus   **Domaine de Chateauvieux**

Tel (22) 753 15 11   Fax (22) 753 1924   **HR**

16 Chemin de Chateau Peney-Dessus 1242
Rooms 17   Double room from Fr155

Formerly an inn, then a farm, now on its third life, as a hotel, this
establishment is only 11km from Geneva and five minutes from
Satigny Railway station. Vines surround the building and run
down to the Rhone. It only has 17 double rooms, mostly used
by gourmets who eat in the splendid restaurant. All the rooms are
decorated in Laura Ashley style and filled with reproduction
wooden furniture. *Cable TV. Closed 31 Jul-15 Aug, 23 Dec-15
Jan. Private parking.* AMERICAN EXPRESS® *Mastercard, Visa.*

Restaurant
Seats 60   Meal for 2 approx Fr320

Monsieur Chevrier has been running this place for eight years and
cooking his modern creative dishes in the kitchen. He has
an impressive résumé, having worked with Girardet, but he still
feels his main influence has been his mother's home cooking. His
raw ingredients are always interesting and used in an exciting
way. *Feuilleté aux oignons confits et fricassée d'amourette aux queues
d'écrevisses* (a confit of sweet onions cooked in puff pastry and
served with bone-marrow and crayfish tails); *filet de dorade royale
rotie aux aromates et matelote de suppions au vin rouge* (fillet of sea
bream roasted with herbs and served with an inkfish and red wine
stew). As well as some excellent French bottles, there are also some
good New World wines. *L 12-2 D 7-10.*

Lausanne (Crissier)

Crissier	**Girardet**

Tel (21) 634 05 05	**R**

1 Rue d'Yverdon 1023 Crissier Lausanne
Seats 65   Meal for 2 approx Fr500

Frédy Girardet has worked in this restaurant since 1959, when his
father ran it as a small café. In 1971 he bought the whole mansion
(formerly the old town hall) and opened it as a restaurant proper.
Since then, he has been a leading gastronomic light, blazing a path
that many all over the world try to follow. He has written,
among other things, a book on 'Spontaneous Cooking', which
encapsulates his aims and style at Girardet. His repertoire, and that
of his chef, Rochat, who has been with him for 15 years, is based
on the freshest raw ingredients and inventive combinations.
Bavaroise d'artichaut en salade de homard breton (artichoke bavaroise   ★
served with lobster salad), *canette sauvagine confite au zeste de citron*
(confit of wild duck with lemon) and *saumon sauvage juste tiède au
sel de Guérande, émulsion de fenouille à l'huile de Maussane* (warm
wild salmon served with Guérande salt and a fennel mousse with
Maussane olive oil). Girardet is as meticulous and creative with his
wines as his cooking, with 700 to 800 different distinguished
bottles, including local crus, to choose from. *L 12-3.15 D 7-8.30.
Closed Sun, Mon, 3 weeks from last Sat Jul, 3 weeks from 23 Dec.
No credit cards.*

Around Lausanne

Vufflens-le-Chateau	**Hotel de l'Ermitage**

Tel (21) 802 21 91 Fax (21) 802 22 40	**HR**

1134 Vufflens-le-Château
Rooms 9   Double room from Fr300

Bernard Ravet and his wife opened this cosy country house five
years ago, as a resting place for satiated gourmets. Since then, the
place itself has taken on a character of its own (even though they
will not allow someone to stay who is not eating in the
restaurant). The beamed rooms are simply appointed in a homely
style, but are, nevertheless, equipped with mini-bars and
televisions. Situated just outside Vufflens-le-Chateau village with
its vineyards and rolling farmland, the grounds are spacious with
gardens and a lake. However, Lausanne is only fifteen minutes
away by car and Geneva half an hour. *Closed 22 Dec-10 Jan, Aug.
Private parking. Mastercard, Visa.*

Restaurant
Seats 50   Meal for 2 approx Fr200

Bernard Ravet may have uprooted himself from his native
Burgundy but his cooking remains true to his origins. His
imaginative French menu is fresh and seasonal, helped by his
extensive vegetable and herb gardens. In his two old kitchens,
which he has recently modernised, he also has a bakehouse where
fresh bread is baked every day. His house speciality is fresh foie
gras smoked along with meat and fish in their old-fashioned   ★
smokehouse. The old stone wine cellar has over 650 bottles from
all over the world and notably, some rare local wines from the
Cote Vaudoise. *L 10.30-3 D 7.30-12. Closed Sun, Mon, first
3 weeks Aug, 22 Dec-10 Jan.*

Montreux

Montreux   **L'Ermitage**

Tel (21) 964 44 11   Fax (21) 964 70 02   **HR**

75 Rue du Lac 1815 Clarens
Rooms 7   Double room from Fr250

This late-19th-century house surrounded by flowery gardens near
Lake Geneva used to be an old family bed and breakfast and now
belongs to a husband and wife, who have tended to concentrate
on their restaurant, rather than the hotel. The seven bedrooms are
all en suite with comfortable cane furniture and modern fabrics.
*Room service. Closed Mon, Sun, 3 weeks Christmas from 24 Dec.
Private parking.* AMERICAN EXPRESS *Diners, Mastercard, Visa.*
Restaurant
Seats 60   Meal for 2 approx Fr100

Monsieur cooks, while Madame takes the orders, but despite this
cosy set up, the set and à la carte menus are professional and
inventive. The *roulade de sole* is layered with artichokes, crayfish
and sole spread with tomatoes and olive oil; while the *filet de loup
de mer* is cooked with mousserons and served with a chive and
lemon sauce. Meat dishes also combine some interesting
ingredients, like cutlet of veal, served in a kidney, red wine and
celery sauce. The wine list is predominantly Swiss and French
with a few token bottles from the New World. *L 12-1.45 D 7-9.*

Brent   **Le Pont de Brent**

Tel (21) 964 52 30   Fax (21) 964 55 30   **R**

1817 Brent Sur Montreux
Seats 50   Meal for 2 approx Fr200

The *croquant aux framboises* (crunchy almond pastry boats filled
with wild raspberries) is enough reason for eating here. The
comprehensive choice of French main courses, is another: *marbre
de ris de veau* (veal sweetbreads) and *saumon sauvage à la barigoule
d'artichaut* (wild salmon with olive oil, artichoke and a basil sauce).
The menu changes quite often, but the extra *menu surprise*
is different every day. This really is rather a grand place for such
a small village (only 300 inhabitants), with Louis XV furniture,
marble floors and stucco walls, making an elegant dining room
for a refined French menu. *L 12-2 D 7-9.30. Closed Sun, Mon, 25-
31 July, 23 Dec-6 Jan. Mastercard, Visa.*

Around Montreux

Glion-sur-Montreux   **Hotel Victoria**

Tel 21 963 31 31 . Fax 21 963 13 51   **H**

1823 Glion-sur-Montreux
Rooms 50   Double room from Fr200

Only 12 minutes from Montreux overlooking Lake Geneva, this
small family-run hotel is a real retreat; the early 20th-century
house is surrounded by acres of woodland without a building in
sight and has an outdoor swimming pool and tennis courts.
However, despite its feeling of isolation the *funiculaire* easily takes
you down the hill to the lakeside and from there, the railway
station is minutes away. The rooms are cosily cluttered with old-
fashioned furniture, with chandeliers hanging from the ceiling and
oil paintings on the walls. *24hr room service. Theatre-style conference
facilities for up to 100. Secretarial services. Private parking.*
AMERICAN EXPRESS *Diners, Mastercard, Visa.*

Zürich

Zürich   **Restaurant Agnès Amberg**

Tel (1) 251 26 26   Fax (1) 252 50 62   **R**

Hottingerstrasse 5 8032 Zurich

Seats 40   Meal for 2 approx Fr130

Oozing elegance, this place is decorated with chandeliers, leather
upholstery and English silverware, with a few menu cards and oil
paintings on the walls. Its location, next to the famous
Schauspielhaus Theatre and Kunsthaus Art Gallery, is equally
auspicious; so is the cooking. The chef has been home-trained
in the Amberg kitchens and serves a well-balanced choice of fish,
seafood and meat. Lightly warmed calf's tongue served on celery
with vinaigrette, is followed by a ragout of baby lamb and
crushed herbs. He has a particular penchant for terrines, with
terrine de foie de canard a regular feature on the menu. The dessert
delight must be the vanilla pancakes served with a rhubarb
compote. *Open 11am-midnight. Closed Sun, Mon, 1 Jul-3 Aug, 24
Dec-1 Jan. Public parking.* AMERICAN EXPRESS *Diners, Mastercard, Visa.*

★

Zürich   **Baur au Lac**

Tel (1) 220 50 20   Fax (1) 220 50 44   **H**

Talstrasse 1 8022 Zürich

Rooms 140   Double room from Fr560

Idyllically located, bordering Lake Zurich with a park on one side
and the Schanzengraben canal on the other, this hotel has been run
by the Kraft family for over 150 years. Paradeplatz, Zürich's
commercial centre, is only five minutes walk away, but in another
direction the hotel offers superb views of the Alps. At the
moment, the rooms are being dramatically expanded and will
be finished in 1996. The alterations will leave the hotel with only
50 rooms, even more spaciously arranged, with Louis XV or
modern furniture. *Cable TV. Theatre-style conference facilities for
up to 180. Secretarial/translation services on request. Hairdresser/dry
cleaning service.* AMERICAN EXPRESS *Mastercard, Visa.*

Zürich   **Dolder Grand Hotel**

Tel (1) 251 62 31   Fax (1) 251 62 31   **HR**

Kurhausstrasse 65 8032 Zürich

Rooms 184   Double room from Fr490

This hotel is architecturally unique: the architect, Jacques Gros,
a famous exponent of the German Art Nouveau movement,
Jugendstil, built it with spires and turrets, and nooks and crannies.
The extraordinary building is set in an equally extravagant park,
with 20 acres of woods and gardens. The rooms are painted and
decorated in pale colours, with fitted furniture and fine curtains.
Balconies look out over the park, Zürich and the Lake. They are
all very well equipped in meticulous Swiss style, with faxes, safes
and satellite and cable TV in all the rooms. *24hr room service.
Theatre-style conference facilities for up to 500. Secretarial/translation/
valet services on request. Hairdresser/doctor. Outdoor swimming pool,
tennis courts, 9-hole golf, ice skating. Private garage.* AMERICAN EXPRESS
Visa, Mastercard.

Restaurant La Rotonde

Seats 80   Meal for 2 approx Fr230

Long sash windows give diners a panoramic view over the park
and across the lake. Inside, this large dining room is very light,
with bronze furniture, white curtains and pale seasonal
arrangements of flowers. Despite adhering to traditional French
cooking, there are always interesting nuances and new ingredients
to look out for. Home-made ravioli are filled with artichokes and
pine nuts, brook char (salmon-trout) fillets are topped with morels   ★
and a Swiss white wine and walnut sauce and grilled fillets of sole
come with a rich white butter and fennel seed sauce. Fresh peaches
served with a vanilla almond parfait are an excellent way to end
this feast. The wine list is sizeable, but still tends to concentrate
on Swiss and French wines. *L 12-2.30 D 7-10.30.*

Zürich   Eden au Lac

Tel (1) 261 94 04   Fax (1) 261 94 09   **HR**

ıUtoquai 45 8023 Zürich

Rooms 56   Double room from Fr480

This sumptuous neo-classical hotel, with Roman statues and
wrought-iron balconied French windows, looks like an elegant
opera house, sitting, like so many of the pristine Swiss hotels, right
on the Lake. The interior design, with light, chintz sofas, glass-
topped tables and tall palm trees dotted around the lobby,
is sophisticated and stylish. The rooms are individually furnished
in sunny, crisp colours with modern marble bathrooms. Any
problems (highly unlikely), then see the concierge, who has been
here for the last 32 years. *Fax/safe. Theatre-style conference facilities
for up to 50. Secretarial/translation services. Sauna.* AMERICAN EXPRESS
Mastercard, Visa.

Restaurant

Seats 50   Meal for 2 approx Fr200

A classic dining room, with rich red velvet chairs and heavy
curtains swathed around the windows which give a view out over
the Lake. The cuisine is also traditional, concentrating on French
and international. So a chicken Madras sits alongside *steak de veau
sur fondue de champignons* (veal cutlet on a bed of mushrooms),
emincé de volaille (sliced chicken with herbs in a cream sauce) and
chateaubriand. Among the chef's favourites is *blanc de turbot braisé
au champagne.* The wine list is heavily weighted towards regional
offerings (both house wines are Swiss), but has some good French
wines. *Open noon-11pm.* AMERICAN EXPRESS *Mastercard, Diners, Visa.*

Zürich   Hotel Europe

Tel (1) 261 10 30   Fax (1) 251 03 67   **H**

Dufourstrasse 4 8008 Zürich

Rooms 41   Double room from Fr350

From whichever angle you look at it, this hotel is well located:
only five minutes from the main railway station, near the Opera
House and the Bernhard Theatre and close to the world-renowned
shopping street, the Bahnhofstrasse. In spite of this, the family-run
hotel is quiet with an imposing entrance, furnished in a traditional
manner with wooden furniture and old paintings. The flowery

rooms have recently been renovated and now have air-
conditioning, electrically adjustable beds and telephones in the
bathrooms. There are only 12 doubles, the rest of the rooms being
suites or singles. *24hr room service. Secretarial/translation services
on request. Public parking.* AMERICAN EXPRESS *Diners, Mastercard, Visa.*

Zürich	Königstuhl	
Tel (1) 261 52 87 Fax (1) 252 61 78		**R**

Stussiofstatt 3 8001 Zürich
Seats 50   Meal for 2 approx Fr300

The French chef has created an interesting modern French bistro
menu with no tendencies to veer towards local Zürich specialities.
The menu *dégustation*, with steak tartare, bass soup with saffron,
fillets of John Dory with giant prawns, and pigeon breast stuffed
with turnip and cabbage and served with tomato gnocchi, is well
balanced and light, completed by a fluffy pear soufflé. The chef
loves fish, and his menu shows it. Good burgundies and Bordeaux.
L 12-3 D 6-12. Closed Sun, Mon, 19 Jun-29 Aug. AMERICAN EXPRESS
Diners, Mastercard, Visa.

Zürich	Wirtschaft Flühgass	
Tel (1) 381 12 15 Fax (1) 422 75 33		**R**

Zollikerstrasse 214 8008 Zürich
Seats 50   Meal for 2 approx Fr150

This 16th-century listed inn outside Zürich is typically Swiss with
its cosy 'villagey' bistro tables, painted wooden chests, and
traditional Swiss-German food. A husband-and-wife team have
run this place for eight years, sticking mainly to classical dishes:
(home-made goose liver paté and veal schnitzel with rösti) but
also indulging in the occasional digression into Italian regional
dishes, such as *tripes à la milanaise. L 11.30-2 D 6.30-9.30. Closed
Sat, Sun, mid Jul-mid Aug. Private parking.* AMERICAN EXPRESS
Mastercard, Visa.

Zürich	Zunfthaus zur Schmiden	
Tel (1) 251 52 87 Fax (1) 261 12 67		**R**

Marktgasse 20 8001 Zürich
Seats 70   Meal for 2 approx Fr120

The wooden carvings and extensive wooden panelling are all over
600 years old and part of the original Blacksmiths Guild (still
alive today). The 16th-century hall on the second floor is still used
for banquets and parties. This rich setting is splendid for the chef's
well-rehearsed menu: classical French food, with a few local
specialities. Fish dishes depend on what's good in the market (trout
with white wine and herbs is a good dish) and there's a wide
selection of meat and poultry. They have their own patissier in the
kitchen, so try the *profiteroles glacés* on a very diverse dessert list.
*L 11.30-2 D 6-10. Closed Good Fri-Easter Mon, Whitsun, 23-27
Dec, mid Jul-Aug.* AMERICAN EXPRESS *Diners, Mastercard, Visa.*

Around Zürich

Gattikon   Sihlhalde

Tel (1) 720 09 27   **R**

Sihlhaldenstrasse 70 8136 Gattikon

Seats 65   Meal for 2 approx Fr150

This 200-year-old farmhouse, in a tiny village 3km from Zürich on the road to Chur, is a culinary haven. The chef-owner started operations in 1972 and is proud of his simple but well-executed French cooking. Home-made ravioli are filled with truffles, foie gras is served with fresh basil and pike-perch is baked in a potato pastry crust. *Crepes Suzette* and *tarte aux poires* offer a very fitting conclusion to a classic meal. *L 10-1 D 6-11.30. Private parking.* Mastercard, Visa.

★

Gockhausen   Cordon Rouge

Tel (1) 821 03 95 Fax (1) 822 17 23   **R**

Tobelhofstrasse 344 8044 Zürich Gockhausen

Seats 30   Meal for 2 approx Fr100

The menu in the main restaurant, ten minutes from the centre of Zürich, includes both French and German cooking, with *sauerbraten* (braised beef marinated in vinegar and served with a potato purée) sitting alongside baked pike-perch served with a mousseline sauce. The 500 different wines really do touch on every major wine-growing region. If you want a cheaper meal, try their bistro (next door) with a very similar menu. *L 11-1.30 D 7-10. Closed Sun, Mon, 20 Dec-7 Jan.* AMERICAN EXPRESS *Mastercard, Visa.*

Küsnacht   Petermann's Kunstube

Tel (1) 910 07 15 Fax (1) 910 04 95   **R**

Seestrasse 160 8700 Küsnacht

Seats 50   Meal for 2 approx Fr200

Ten minutes out of Zürich, on an idyllic roadside spot by the Lake, Horst Petermann started this restaurant back in 1982. Since then, his fame has spread through his cooking and the art gallery he runs in his traditional Zürich house, alongside the restaurant. Every day, there is a different fish menu alongside the other set and à la carte menus, with pike-perch, lobster, red mullet and many others. He readily blends together unusual ingredients; so veal chops are served wrapped in smoked bacon and baked under a lavender honey glaze and pigeon cooked with port comes with an asparagus gratin. For dessert, try the bitter apple tart served with a warm honey sauce. *L 12-3 D 7-12.30. Closed Sun, Mon, 3 weeks Aug, 2 weeks Feb. Private parking.* AMERICAN EXPRESS *Diners, Mastercard, Visa.*

★

Unterengstringen   **Witschi's**

Tel (1) 750 44 60   Fax (1) 750 19 68   **R**

Zürcherstrasse 55 8103 Unterengstringen

Seats 40   Meal for 2 approx Fr400

Herr Witschi moved his restaurant nine years ago from the centre
of Zürich to this quiet residential surburb. His classical French
menu is strongly dictated by the ingredients available in the
market and Witschi's personal emphasis on seafood. His specialities
– *filet de sandre aux racines de persil* (fillet of pike-perch cooked
with parsley roots), *crépinette de chevreuil aux cerises en aigre-doux*
(venison sausages in a sweet and sour cherry sauce) – are definitely
worth trying. 250 different wines include comprehensive choice
of French burgundies and a Macon house white. The decor is as
Mediterranean as much of the menu. *Open 11am-midnight. Closed
Sun, Mon, 24 & 25 Dec, 1 week Aug. Private garage.* AMERICAN EXPRESS®
Mastercard, Visa.

★

Switzerland Index

Ukraine

Currency: Ukranian Karbovanetc

Exchange Rate: £1 = approx Kar 75,000
Not obtainable in UK. US dollars recommended.

International dialing code: 010 7
(Kiev + 044)

Passports/Visas: Visa required by British passport holders.
(Ukranian Embassy in London - 78 Kensington Park Road W11 2PL
Tel: 0171-727 6312)

British Embassy in Kiev Tel: 044-228 0504

TRANSPORT
Airports:
Kiev-Borispol (International) Tel: 044-295 6701
Kiev-Zhulyany (Domestic) Tel: 044-272 1201
Railway Stations:
Kiev - Vokzalmaya Ploscha Tel: 044-223 3306
Car hire: enquire at airport
Speed limits: 90 km/h outside cities, 60 km/h in built-up areas.

Banks open: Hours vary, but banks are generally open between 10am
& 6pm. Exchange bureaux may stay open later.

Shops open: Shop hours vary, but are generally open between 9am &
6pm (some later) and many close for lunch.

National Holidays: New Year's Day, 7 & 13 Jan, 8 Mar, Orthodox
Easter, 6 Jun, 24 Aug, New Year's Eve

Tourist Offices:
Ukranian Embassy in London 0171 727 6312
In Kiev - Intourist Kiev Tel: 044-225 3243

(further information available from Intourist London - Tel: 0171-538
8600/538 5965)

Ukraine   Kiev

Kiev   Restaurant Lestniza

Tel 044 229 86 29   Fax 044 229 86 29   **R**

Baresha Grechenko Street 7 Kiev
Seats 50   Meal for 2 approx $15

A healthy product of the new liberal ownership laws, this
restaurant, near one of the city's main squares, is a private co-
operative. Its predictable Soviet-style facade greatly improves
inside, with parquet flooring, crystal chandeliers and paintings.
Regional Jewish and Ukranian dishes are the specialities of its
Ukranian chef; meat and poultry are stewed in peasant-style clay
pots; *vareniki* (Ukranian ravioli made of noodle dough) are filled
with a mixture of meat and cheese; while *pelmeni* (crispy pastry
ravioli originating from Siberia) come with rice and sour cream.
Pike-perch is a popular fish dish. Only Ukranian and Russian
wines are available. *Open 11am-midnight. No credit cards.*

THE APARTMENT SERVICE
Tel in UK: (0181) 748 4207   Fax: (0181) 748 3972
The Apartment Service will find you the right apartment
worldwide to suit your needs, whether you are on a short or
long-term stay. A 96-page colour catalogue is free on request.
All budgets are catered for.

Kiev   Rus Hotel

Tel 044 220 42 55   Fax 044 220 43 96   **H**

Ulitsz Gospitalnaya 4 Kiev
Rooms 486   Double room from $164

Technology has yet to fully reach this government-owned hotel
in the centre of the city (the local Intourist office provides all
secretarial and faxing facilities), but they are trying. Four of the
VIP suites do have satellite TV, a fax, hairdryer and trouser press;
the rest are more modestly equipped with an empty fridge and
local television and are rather functional. The beds are old-
fashioned and of wood. *24hr room service. Boardroom-style conference
facilities.* AMERICAN EXPRESS *Diners, Mastercard, Visa.*

United Kingdom

Currency: Pound Sterling
Dialling code from overseas: 44
(prefix number differs according to country from which call is being made)

TRANSPORT

Airports: England - London Tel: Heathrow 0181-759 4321 / Gatwick 01293 535353 / Stansted 01279 680500 / City 0171-474 5555. East Midlands Tel: Birmingham 0121 7675511
N.Ireland - Belfast International Tel: 01849 42 28 88
Wales - Cardiff-Wales International Tel: 01446 71 11 11
Scotland - Glasgow Internat'l Tel: 0141 887 1111 / Edinburgh Internat'l Tel: 0131 333 1000
Railway Stations: (General Rail Enquiries for UK)
England - London Tel: 0171-278 2477 (for Kings Cross) 262 6767 (for Paddington) 387 7070 (for Euston, St Pancras, Marylebone & Kings Cross Thameslink) 928 5100 (for all other London terminals)
N.Ireland - Belfast Tel: 01232 899 411
Scotland - Glasgow Tel: 0141 204 2844 / Edinburgh Tel: 0131 556 2451
Wales - Cardiff Tel: 01222 22 8000
Car hire:
Avis - Tel: 0181-848 8733 Hertz - Tel: 0181-679 1799 Budget - Tel: 0800 181181 Europcar - Tel: 01345 222525
Speed limits: 70 mp/h on motorways, 60 mp/h on dual carriageways, 50 mp/h on other main roads, 30 mp/h in built-up areas (unless otherwise indicated). Local speed limits.

Banks open: Standard hours 9.30am-3.30pm Mon-Fri. Individual banks and branches may stay open later and some main branches are also open on Saturdays. Some banks in Scotland stay open later on Thursdays (to 5/5.30pm, closing 12.30-2.30pm).
Shops open: Generally 9/9.30am-5.30/6pm Mon-Sat. Department stores, shopping centres and supermarkets are often open longer hours, and some larger stores and supermarkets also open on Sundays.
National Holidays: New Year's Day, Good Friday, Easter Monday, 8 & 29 May, 28 Aug, Christmas & Boxing Day (some holidays in Scotland and N. Ireland vary).

Tourist Offices:
British Tourist Association & Tourist Board Tel: 0181-846 9000

American Express Travel Service Offices or Representative:
London - AETS 6 Haymarket SW1Y 4BS Tel: 0171-930 4411 #
or - AETS 78 Brompton Road Knightsbridge SW3 1ER Tel: 0171-584 6182 /or 225 0055

London

London	**Aubergine**

Tel 0171-352 3449   Fax 0171-351 1770   **R**

11 Park Walk London SW10 0AJ

Seats 40   Meal for 2 approx £85

Chef-patron Gordon Ramsay trained most informatively with
Macro Pierre White but has also had stints with Roux restaurants,
in Paris with Savoy and Robuchon and finally a short spell with
Pierre Koffmann. Ramsay's dishes are extremely well conceived
and superbly, often brilliantly, executed: ballotine of foie gras is an
elegant disc with a port jelly perimeter, the foie gras rich but not
heart-stoppingly so, the jelly assertive but not bullying;
cappuccino of haricot blanc with truffle oil is at once subtle and
voluptuous; tortellini of lobster (a speciality) combines soft,
delicate pasta with a shellfish filling just strong enough in flavour
and a warm, entirely apt *vinaigrette crustacés*. To follow, a red
mullet dish comprises a little 'castle' of small fillets built up on
a foundation of aubergine caviar and topped with tiny braised
leeks and little beignets of sage; the castle is surrounded
by a punchy Mediterranean moat of olive oil, chopped olives,
anchovies and tomatoes that would get the better of many fish but
proves an excellent mate for the full-flavoured mullet. Completing   ★
the main-course picture might be a pavé of brill with duxelles
of girolles, steamed fillet of sea bass with braised fennel hearts and
a tarragon jus, pigeon 'poché grillé, with purée of swede, wild
mushroom ravioli and a tarragon jus, ribeye of Scotch beef, roast
rump of lamb niçoise with millefeuille of aubergine (at last!),
guinea fowl 'en cocotte' with tagliatelle of leeks and caramelised
calf's sweetbreads with a *navet* (turnip) confit. Tarte tatin of pears
makes a sensational ending to a great meal; other dessert choices
might include orange tart, crème brulée with 'jus Granny Smith',
millefeuille of vanilla with red fruit, *pavé chocolat* or French
cheeses; *assiette de l'Aubergine* (for two diners) is a little
of everything for the indulgent or the indecisive! Petits fours
served with coffee. Book well in advance, as this is currently one
of the capital's hot spots. *L 12-2.30 D 7-11. Closed L Sat, all Sun.
Set L £18 Set D £26.* AMERICAN EXPRESS *Mastercard, Visa.*

> THE APARTMENT SERVICE
> Tel in UK: (0181) 748 4207   Fax: (0181) 748 3972
> The Apartment Service will find you the right apartment
> worldwide to suit your needs, whether you are on a short or
> long-term stay. A 96-page colour catalogue is free on request.
> All budgets are catered for.

London	**Bombay Brasserie**

Tel 0171-370 4040   **R**

Courtfield Close Courtfield Road London SW7 4UH

Seats 175   Meal for 2 approx £70

The most glamorous Indian restaurant in town, and a hit since
opening its doors in 1982. The handsome room, with its Raj
pictures and paddle fans, is from a time past, evoking a grand hotel

of a century ago. Entrance is to a roomy bar area where mango
Bellini is a popular cocktail. One part of the restaurant proper
is a large and flowery conservatory, which despite its lack of views
manages to convey a garden feel. The kitchen garners its recipes
from all parts of the sub-continent and numbers seafood, 'coastal',
tandoori and vegetarian among its specialities. Some of the best
dishes are Bombay roadside and seaside snacks (*ragara pattice* and
sev batata puri), pomfret coated with mint chutney steamed
in a banana leaf, Goan fish curry, chicken biryani and lobster *peri
peri* (*very very* spicy). Lunchtime buffet. Evening pianist. *L 12.30-3
D 7.30-12 (Sun to 11.30). Closed 25 & 26 Dec. Set buffet from
£14.95. Diners, Mastercard, Visa.*

London	**The Canteen**	
Tel 0171-351 7330 Fax 0171-351 6189		**R**

Harbour Yard Chelsea Harbour London SW10 0XD

Seats 135   Meal for 2 approx £60

A stimulating and entertaining restaurant with agreeably accessible
prices (by making all the dishes at each stage one-price, the pricing
effectively offers a two-course £19 fixed-price menu). In a light
and airy atmosphere, with the bonus of marina views from much-
prized conservatory window tables, the interior offers plenty
of interest as well as a good buzz. In the large, L-shaped dining
room on two levels, begin, perhaps, with a velouté of celery with
poached egg and chervil, gazpacho with crab, saffron or squid ink
risotto, Savoy cabbage alsacienne, artichokes barigoule (stuffed
with duxelles) or parfait of foie gras and chicken livers with toast
poilane; papillote of smoked salmon 'Albert Roux' is served with
toasted brioche and roast sea scallops with sauce vierge attract
a small supplement. Fish is a favourite ingredient among the main
courses with seven or so dishes offered, ranging from smoked
haddock with poached egg and new potatoes to red mullet with
ratatouille provençale, beignets of sage and a tapénade sauce.
Carnivores may relish roast rump of lamb niçoise, pot-roast pork
with spices and ginger or honey-roast roast duck leg with pommes
fondant and a bittersweet sauce. Wines are sensibly priced with
over 20 bottles under £20; a list of fine wines is also available
on request. Easy parking in the Harbour complex's underground
car park, from where lifts can take you direct to the restaurant
area. *L 12-3 (12.30-3.30 Sun) D 6.30-12 (7-11 Sun).* AMERICAN EXPRESS
Mastercard, Visa.

★

The Golden Eurostar [★] denotes our pick of the
restaurants. Cooking is the major consideration, but
other factors are also taken into account, including
ambience, comfort and service.

London   **Chez Nico at Ninety Park Lane**

Tel 0171-409 1290   Fax 0171-355 4877   **R**

90 Park Lane London W1A 3AA

Seats 70   Meal for 2 approx £135

Nico's quest for perfection continues apace at Forte's *Grosvenor House*. The opulent dining room is elegantly appointed with honey-coloured panelling brightened by mirrors and discreet lighting and Jean-Luc Giguel leads front-of-house with aplomb, setting exemplary standards of service. Menus are written in refreshingly straightforward English and the choice is long, with over 10 dishes at each stage. Sensational signature dishes remain, as in a salad of foie gras on toasted brioche with caramelised orange – a glorious combination of flavour and texture – and deserve to stay on the menu until the next century! Nico's highly individual style of creativity evolves these days rather than explodes, and the pace is certainly less hectic than previously. Dishes are reworked, often simplifying but also subtly redefining and refining them; invention never takes a back seat, but we will see if the advertisement holds true: will a sun-dried tomato ever make it through the hallowed portals of King Nico's kitchen? Such delights as noisettes of pig's trotter stuffed with morels and sweetbreads and served with leeks, 'lasagne' of Dover sole fillets, or pressed foie gras and duck fillets with cherries, green peppercorns and toasted brioche are among the starters. The choice of fish main courses might include grilled red mullet or John Dory with celeriac chips, brill or steamed sea bass with fennel and basil purée, while eight meat and offal dishes range from veal sweetbreads with Parma ham and morel mushrooms to braised shin of veal in Madeira, and "confied" (confit-ed?) maize-fed chicken with grapes and foie gras pancakes. Sauces are simply sensational – glossy veal reductions that simply burst with flavour; there are no corners cut in these kitchens. A magnificent climax to a truly unforgettable meal is the grand plate of assorted mini-desserts (£6 supplement) – a tasting of many of the desserts including a slice of chocolate tart with orange-flavoured custard, honey ice cream with gratinated grapefruit, lemon tart with lemon sorbet and raspberry sauce and iced nougat with caramelised nuts. Cheeses, served from a trolley, are all French and accompanied by grapes – simple, straightforward, but, as throughout the restaurant, only the best, tip-top quality ingredients are used. Although many dishes on the lunch menu are simpler in construction and lighter in design, Nico's lunch is surely one of London's great bargains. Consistency is of supreme importance in a restaurant that heads the Premier Division (London) and Nico's watchful eye ensures that all is just as it should be. Mostly sky-high prices (though they are inclusive of VAT and service) on an excellent wine list that has a fair sprinkling of half bottles. *L 12-2 D 7-11. Closed L Sat, all Sun, 4 days Easter, L Bank Holiday Mondays, 11 days Christmas/New Year. Set L £25 Set D £46 (2 courses)/£54.* AMERICAN EXPRESS *Diners, Mastercard, Visa.*

London   **Hotel Conrad**

Tel 0171-823 3000   Fax 0171-351 6525   **HR**

Chelsea Harbour London SW10 OXG

Rooms 160   Meal for 2 approx £229

Though it might not have a central London location, the hotel has
many advantages, not least its quiet waterside setting overlooking
the marina (summer outdoor barbecues on the terrace), its superb
supervised leisure complex, comprehensive room service, and the
benefit of one of London's (and for that matter the UK's) best
hotel managers in Doreen Boulding. A further advantage is that
there's no traffic noise, in fact all the air-conditioned suites (there
are no ordinary bedrooms), some with balconies, have a lobby
insulating them from the corridor and this makes them even more
peaceful. Designed by David Hicks, the tastefully furnished rooms
offer every modern comfort: twin wardrobes, three telephones
with two lines, multi-channel TV with video, mini-bar and many
extras, such as fresh fruit, flowers, books and magazines, suit-
carriers and even an umbrella. In the luxurious marble bathrooms
you'll find a walk-in shower as well as a large tub, twin
washbasins, bidet, separate loo (some suites also have a guest loo),
bathrobes and quality toiletries. There's a cool and relaxing feel
in the spacious marble-floored public areas, where uniformed and
smartly-dressed staff are always on hand to offer a high standard
of service, including valet parking. In addition, there's a free Jaguar
limo service to Knightsbridge. Conference/banqueting facilities for
up to 200. *Terrace, indoor swimming pool, sauna, solarium, steam
room, gym, beauty & hair salon shop.* AMERICAN EXPRESS *Diners,
Mastercard, Visa.*

Brasserie

Seats 45   Meal for 2 approx £60

The à la carte menu in this elegant dining room is supplemented
by set menus both at lunchtime (2/3 courses) and in the evenings
(3/4 courses) – some typical dishes: terrine of duck and duck
breast with an orange dressing, medallions of venison with broad
beans, and layered apple tart with cinnamon ice cream. From the
grill you could choose Dover sole or rack of lamb, off the à la
carte wild mushroom and Parmesan risotto, tournedo of monkfish
with a smoked butter sauce, guinea fowl with lentils and ceps, and
a classic *tarte au citron* to finish. *L 12.30-3 D 7-10.30.*
Set L £13.50/16.50 (Sun champagne brunch £28.50)
Set D £22.50/26.50.

> Meal prices for 2 are based on à la carte menus.
> When set menus are available, prices will often be lower.

London   **The Dorchester**

Tel 0171-629 8888   Fax 0171-409 0114   **HR**

Park Lane London W1A 2HJ

Rooms 247   Meal for 2 approx £298

Since opening its doors in 1931, the Dorchester has been among
the world's top hotels, renowned for its enviable standards
of service, comfort and food. The grand oval foyer, with its rug-
strewn black-and-white marble floor, bustles with the comings
and goings of smartly attired porters, page boys and guests. The
splendid, long Promenade, complete with enormous floral display
at one end and rows of faux-marble columns with ornate gilt
capitals, is very much the heart of the hotel and a wonderful place
to take traditional English afternoon tea. Another focal point is the
bar, where an Italian menu is served daily at lunch and supper
time. Bedrooms have an essentially English style with fine fabrics
varying from striking floral prints and delicate damasks to heavy
tapestries; the bed linen is, of course, real linen. All rooms are
triple-glazed and have white Italian marble bathrooms with bidets
and hand showers in addition to powerful showers over the
bathtubs; many even have separate shower cubicles and twin
washbasins, while most have natural light (a real luxury in a hotel
bathroom). Four superb roof garden suites, all restored to their
original splendour, put the icing on the cake. Standards of service
throughout the public areas are superlative and are matched on the
bedroom floors following the implementation of the call button
system for valet, maid and waiter room service (the hotel boasts
an amazing ratio of three staff to each room). Breakfasts, as one can
expect from a hotel with such an outstanding culinary history, are
first-rate, covering English (a superior fry-up, poached haddock,
grilled kippers, coddled egg with smoked salmon or chives),
Continental (excellent baking includes croissants and apple scones)
or low-fat and low-cholesterol options; served from 7am (7.30am
Sun) in the Grill Room. Among the many elegant public rooms,
opulent banqueting and conference facilities (for up to 550) feature
over 1500 square metres of gold leaf gilding and are among
London's finest. The Dorchester Spa offers thermal therapy as well
as the more usual relaxations. *Gym, sauna, spa bath, steam room,
solarium, beauty & hair salon, shopping gallery.* AMERICAN EXPRESS *Diners,
Mastercard, Visa.*

Terrace Restaurant

Seats 81   Meal for 2 approx £120

It is currently only possible to eat in the Terrace on a Friday and
Saturday night. Booking is essential to ensure a table in a room
that is decorated with great style: there are mirrored columns,
Chinese-inspired painted wall panels, a central gazebo where four
couples can dine in relative seclusion, and a band which strikes
up from mid-evening till late (around 1am), the singer inviting
diners to face the music and dance. The menu offers a fixed-price
meal of either three or four courses of imaginative, modern,   ★
sophisticated dishes and there is also a very extensive vegetarian
menu, its dishes a very creditable and worthwhile alternative, and
a result of increased demand. The orthodox menu begins with
a super appetiser of, say, a slice of delicate salmon mousse wrapped
in smoked salmon and continues with superb pan-fried red mullet
served with a perfectly balanced Sauternes wine sauce and a purée

of potato and celery or white and green lasagne leaves filled with
a melting piece of pan-fried foie gras and accompanied
by a deliciously creamy wild mushroom sauce. A granité of, say,
dry white wine, follows and for a main dish the choice could
be a beautifully fresh fillet of halibut with mussels and vegetables
cooked in their own juices, tender and succulent roast duck breast
with petits pois or baked rack of lamb, superbly trimmed and
accompanied by goat's cheese wrapped in a crispy filo pastry.
Typical dessertsare a wonderful three chocolate mousse, each layer
flavoured with a different liqueur, and pears poached in red wine
and spices served with a caramel granité. Service is superbly
professional. The wine list is, naturally, grand and offers some
of the best growers from both Europe and the New World. Prices
are on the high side, but not too unreasonable, and there's plenty
of good drinking around £25. *D only 7-11.30. Closed Sun-Thurs,
Aug. Set D £38/£42.*

Grill Room
Seats 81   Meal for 2 approx £130

Largely unchanged since the hotel first opened in 1931; although
the decor is grand Spanish, the menu is firmly and splendidly
English. Tables are widely spaced, which is just as well given the
numerous trolleys that bring not just the traditional roast rib
of beef and Yorkshire pudding and the side of smoked salmon – to
be sliced at the table – but also the dish of the day (Monday's
boiled silverside and caraway dumplings, Friday's fish pie) the
wide range of breads, 'bespoke' salads, good desserts and the
notably wide selection of British cheeses. *L 12.30-2.30 D 6-11
(Sun & Bank Holidays 7-10.30). Set L £23.50 Set D £28.*

Oriental Room
Seats 79   Meal for 2 approx £120

London's most exclusive Chinese restaurant and almost certainly
the most expensive, too. Some dishes work better than others
on a mainly Cantonese menu with many luxurious items.
Specialities include deep-fried crispy pigeon with pickled
vegetables and steamed fresh eel with black bean sauce. Staff are
smart, charming and knowledgable under a suave and
accomplished manager. No children under 12. Lovely private
rooms (Indian-themed, Chinese, Thai). *L 12-2.30 D 7-11.
Closed L Sat, all Sun, Aug. Set L £20 (dim sum) & £25 Set D £28.*

To dial overseas from the UK, 010 will change to 00
on 16th April 1995.

London   **47 Park Street**

Tel 0171-491 7282   Fax 0171-491 7281   **H**

47 Park Street Mayfair London W1Y 4EB
Rooms 52   Meal for 2 approx £326

Even the youngest budding gourmets can relax at 47 Park Street
as the suites at this gracious Edwardian town house are spacious,
can be equipped with extra beds or cots if need be and can provide
a baby sitting service on request. Perhaps this is a reflection of the
French attitude towards children and taking them to good
restaurants and hotels, ie it's perfectly normal and even to be
encouraged. For this most English of establishments is French
owned, and French designed (by Monique Roux, wife of Albert,
whose *Le Gavroche* (qv) is downstairs and provides the ultimate
in 24hr room service). Superlatives flow thick and fast –
sumptuous, elegant, tasteful – in describing the suites of rooms
themselves (generously proportioned, perfectly equipped) or the
standards of maintenance (impeccable). There's a concierge round
the clock, a business centre (during normal office hours), leisure
facilities adjacent, and the epitome of banqueting/conference
facilities for 20/30. *Hotel limousine, valeting (8am-5pm), baby-sitting,
hairdressing, shopping service.* AMERICAN EXPRESS *Diners, Mastercard, Visa.*

London   **Four Seasons Hotel**

Tel 0171-499 0888   Fax 0171-493 1895   **HR**

Hamilton Place Park Lane Mayfair London W1A 1AZ
Rooms 227   Meal for 2 approx £315

Although several storeys high the hotel, fronted by a small garden
with maturing sycamore trees, is somewhat overlooked by its
neighbours. Inside, the modernity of the exterior gives way
to a stylish elegance firmly rooted in classic good taste. The lobby
walls are clad in rich mahogany with a huge Venetian chandelier
suspended from the ceiling, while underfoot is a floor of polished
light brown and other matching coloured marbles. The lounge,
as well as being a place to meet and relax, is also where all-day
light meals and superb afternoon teas are served in gracious,
supremely civilised surroundings with colourful, springy carpets
and, as elsewhere in the public areas, vases of exquisite flowers
in grandiose arrangements. Among the finest of the already
splendid bedrooms are the 11 Conservatory rooms which are
especially bright and airy. There are 26 suites, including five
grand apartment suites. All these have CD players but all rooms
have stereo televisions, video players and satellite broadcasts in six
languages as well as a Reuters and an in-house channel, the latter
showing first releases on video. There's a library of 200 feature
films available for guests' use. Not only are the rooms beautifully
decorated in soft hues with fine furniture (some with marble tops),
spacious and well-equipped but the beds too are extremely
comfortable – queen-size in single rooms and king-size or twin
in double. Bathrooms in fine cream marble live up to expectations
with every facility provided including bidets (not in single
rooms), fine toiletries and ample thick towels. The Conservatory
fitness club on the second floor is for the exclusive use of residents
and is an up-to-date, light room with a comprehensive selection
of the latest exercise equipment each with individual TV monitors

and headphones. The hotel has fine banqueting suites including the magnificent Pine Room with its ornate 18th-century panelling. Breakfasts are, as one would expect, superb, not only for choice – a lenghty à la carte is supplemented by four set-price breakfasts including Japanese and healthy options – but also for quality. Staff are on the whole excellent, providing efficient, discreet and smiling service. Underground garage and valet parking. *Garden, gym, valeting, coffee shop (9am-1am).* AMERICAN EXPRESS *Diners, Mastercard, Visa.*

Four Seasons Restaurant

Seats 55   Meal for 2 approx £120

A room with a view (out to the small garden), hiding the hideous traffic of Park Lane during the summer months, is the sophisticated setting for Jean-Christophe Novelli's always exciting and innovative cooking. The room, florally decorated in shades of charcoal and pink, has a discreet elegance which is surpassed by the artistry of what emanates from the kitchens. Steamed scallop kebab wrapped in lettuce with a reduction of mixed peppers with olive oil or a warm sausage of poached lobster accompanied by a couscous with peppers, ginger and cardamom and a marbled terrine of foie gras and lentils wrapped in smoked salmon illustrate his style. A magnificent ragout of lobster, scallops, squid, langoustine and mussels flavoured with vanilla with broad beans and black noodles is typical of the main dishes he offers. Other choices are equally exciting: fillet of turbot poached in coconut milk with bazelle leaves and honey and light almond purée, pan-fried duck breast with a light carrot juice and mustard seeds served with chick pea chips, or a wonderful offal platter of veal trotter, sweetbreads and tail with poached ox tongue and oxtail accompanied by a potato and celeriac purée. Desserts such as a light rice pudding with star anise and cardamom with a poached pear in Sangria, a strawberry mousse with strawberry toffee and white peppercorn sauce or a hot bitter chocolate cake which when cut oozes rich dark chocolate and is accompanied by a white chocolate ice cream are just three of a superb selection that complete a marvellous three courses. A fine wine list features with many great names, lots of half bottles and several wines available by the glass. *L 12.30-3 D 7-10.30. Set L £25 (Sun £28) Set D £45.*

Lanes Restaurant

Seats 75   Meal for 2 approx £80

One of London's most stylish restaurants; although windowless, the room has a light and contemporary decor and features a central buffet with wonderful displays throughout the day. Executive chef Eric Deblonde offers a choice of fixed-price three-course lunch menus all including wine. Dinner menus are well laid out and simply priced: your pick of the buffet as first or main course, ditto for pasta, grills, or other main courses like braised lamb shank or roast salmon in a potato cake. Lanes' Alternative Cuisine offers light and vegetarian options. *L 12-3 D 6-12 (Sun 6.30-11). Set L from £22.75.*

London   Le Gavroche

Tel 071-408 0881   Fax 071-409 0939   **R**

43 Upper Brook Street Mayfair W1Y 1PF
Seats 60   Meal for 2 approx £160

Albert Roux passed on the mantle of head chef to his son Michel
Jr a few years ago and any changes have been imperceptible: the
menu is more or less the same with the restaurant's classic dishes
firmly in place; the staff, under the guiding hand of manager
Silvano Giraldin, are so smoothly professional and unobtrusive
that you hardly notice them, though at every turn they are there –
in force! The setting offers understated elegance, with the street-
level reception lounge calmly welcoming, and the plush,
basement, club-like dining room cleverly designed – a
combination of intimate booths, cosy corners and 'serious' tables
for important business discussions. With such surroundings and
quality, prices are inevitably stiff, and the archaic practice
of presenting only the host with priced menus is almost endearing.
On the other hand, the £36 per person lunch menu is a steal,
especially when you consider that this price is inclusive of half
a bottle of decent wine (*Chablis St Martin "Cuvée Albert Roux"
1993, Domaine Laroche* or the sublimely smooth *Chateau Clerc-
Milon 1983 Pauillac*) free *Evian*, service and VAT. Moreover,
there's a choice of three dishes at each stage, including the
wondrous trolley of French cheeses, always in tip-top condition,
and the ice-cream/sorbet trolley (pink grapefruit, raspberry and
apricot on the last visit). A typical lunchtime menu might feature
a starter of *roulade de saumon fumé au crabe et sauce verte,* followed
by *cuisse de poulet de Bresse sautée à la vigneronne,* with *peche pochée
au champagne et mousse à la framboise* to finish. A similar 3-course   ★
dinner menu (without wine) will cost you half as much again
(£48): *petite gelée de rouget à la tapénade, entrecote poelée canaille
(a tarragon sauce), oeufs à la neige au lait d'amande,* again
highlighting the tremendous value at lunchtime. You can always
expect to find two or three classic dishes from the Roux repertoire
on this menu, maybe a *petit ragout de homard parfumé au gingembre,
bouillon de légumes au foie gras et feuilles vertes,* and signature desserts
such as a sablé (depending on the season, raspberry, red fruits
or pears and chocolate) or a soufflé. Speaking of puddings, *l'assiette
du chef* – a tasting of various desserts – is certainly worth a punt.
Still riding high in the à la carte charts are the *soufflé suissesse,
mousseline de homard au champagne,* and *daube de boeuf à la
bourgeoise,* the latter showing that *cuisine bourgeoise* can go hand
in hand with haute cuisine. Before the meal you will be offered
a little tray of stunning canapés, and with the coffees or teas a stand
of exquisite petits fours that are almost a dessert in themselves for
those greedy and wise enough to consume the lot! The wine list
is exceptional though expensive, but to be fair, prices have not
increased over the last couple of years. From the New World,
only the best of California get a look in. And we repeat, no charge
for mineral water – other restaurants please note! Minimum
evening charge £50. *L 12-2 D 7-11. Closed Sat & Sun, Bank
Holidays, 23 Dec-3 Jan. Set L £36 Set D £48 & £75.*
AMERICAN EXPRESS *Diners, Mastercard, Visa.* 🐂

London **Hotel Inter-Continental London**

Tel 071-409 3131   Fax 071-409 7460   **HR**

1 Hamilton Place Hyde Park Corner W1V 1QY
Rooms 469   Meal for 2 approx £277

Always popular with Americans both on business and on holiday,
the hotel, located at Hyde Park Corner, has a vast, elegant foyer
leading to a stylish lounge well provided with supremely
comfortable seating. It's also a fine conference and banqueting
venue (1000/850 max) and the fully equipped business centre has
four private meeting rooms. There's also a purpose-built Video
Conferencing Suite. Bedrooms are sleek and airy with seating
areas, air-conditioning, double-glazing and mini-bars; bathrooms
provide quality towelling and good toiletries. Rooms extend over
eight floors, and those at the top enjoy fine views. The hotel offers
a luxury airport service – the chauffeur will telephone ahead
to advise reception of your arrival ensuring minimum delay when
checking-in. There's underground parking for 100 cars. *Plunge
pool, gym, sauna, spa bath, solarium, beauty salon, coffee shop
(7am-11pm).* AMERICAN EXPRESS *Diners, Mastercard, Visa.*

Le Soufflé Restaurant
Seats 70   Meal for 2 approx £150

In January 1994 Peter Kromberg was named chef-patron at this
very elegant, softly lit restaurant, 19 years after arriving. He and
his brilliant team continue in tip-top form, and that form
is nowhere better shown than in the stunning eight-course *choix
du chef*, a daily-changing display of artistry and balance. *Terrine
de lapereau, crème d'avocat; poelé de Saint Jacques au fumé et lys
de bois; sorbet de Bordeaux et framboises; pot au feu de saumon
d'Ecosse; cabecou de Périgueux grillé; flan brulée à la crème fraiche;*
and *palet aux deux chocolats glacé à la belle sandrine* made up a recent
choix, producing a meal of total satisfaction without repletion (you
can, nonetheless, order your choice of four courses from this
menu). Soufflés, the speciality, do not appear on the *choix*, but are
available on the splendid Sunday lunch menu and, of course,
on the carte. The latter offers two savoury varieties, perhaps
lobster with *sauce américaine* and tarragon, and spinach with Tete   ★
de Moine cheese, a softly boiled quail's egg in the middle, served
with a vinaigrette of black olives and anchovies. There may
be four for dessert, including poire William with its ice cream and
wild cranberries, or marbled bitter chocolate and orange flavoured
with Grand Marnier. Several of the starters and main courses
carry the healthy heart symbol, denoting a dish low in fat, calories
and carbohydrates and high in fibre. The sommelier's suggestions
on the predominantly French wine list represent good value,
otherwise it's quite pricey. A less formal menu, highlighted
by a serve-yourself buffet, is available in the Coffee House, open
long hours every day. *L 12.30-3 D 7-10.30. Closed L Sat, D Sun,
all Mon, August, 1 week Christmas, 2 weeks Jan. Set L £27.50 (Sun
£26) Set D £37.50/£43.*

London   Langan's Brasserie

Tel 0171-491 8822 · R

Stratton Street London W1X 5FD
Seats 220   Meal for 2 approx £85

Just off Piccadilly, Richard Shepherd's and Michael Caine's
enormous brasserie is on two floors and its walls are covered
in modern art. Langan's is legendary, not only for its ability
to pack in diners by the score but also for its ability to keep them
all satisfied. The long, long menu features around 80 dishes, from
snails, mussels or baked egg, cabbage and bacon hash to start,
followed by Langan's renowned cod and chips, black pudding
with kidneys and bacon, braised knuckle of gammon with butter
beans and roast duck with sage and onion stuffing and appple
sauce. The mix covers both traditional English and French –
spinach soufflé served with an anchovy sauce is the speciality   ★
on the ground floor, *carré d'agneau roti aux herbes de Provence*
upstairs. Among the 25 or so desserts you might find elderflower
sorbet, walnut ice cream with caramel sauce and *crepes des Alpes.*
Nursery food addicts could be well pleased with a meal of bangers
and mash with white onion sauce followed by rice pudding,
washed down, of course, with a favourite champagne. The ground
floor is always bustling with busy diners, while upstairs the
Venetian room has its own quieter charm. *L 12.30-3 D 7-11.45
(Sat 8-12.45). Closed L Sat, all Sun, Bank Holidays.* AMERICAN EXPRESS®
Diners, Mastercard, Visa.

London   Leiths

Tel 0171-229 4481 · R

92 Kensington Park Road London W11 2PN
Seats 75   Meal for 2 approx £115

Alex Floyd puts an innovative modern slant on classic British
dishes at this most civilised of restaurants, which at 25 is just two
years younger than the chef himself. Ravioli of duck livers and
Jerusalem artichokes with vegetable and tarragon broth, and sole-
wrapped fish mousseline with pea and clam sauce illustrate the
exciting aspect while roast (properly roast!) duckling and rib
of beef béarnaise still delight traditionalists. Note the splendid hors
d'oeuvre trolley, enticing desserts, British cheeses and terrific wine
list. *D only 7.30-11.30. Closed 2 days Aug Bank Holiday, 4 days
Christmas.* AMERICAN EXPRESS® *Diners, Mastercard, Visa.*

London   Restaurant Marco Pierre White

Tel 0171-259 5380   Fax 0171-235 4552 · R

66 Knightsbridge London SW1Y 7LA
Seats 50   Meal for 2 approx £175

Occupying part of the Hyde Park Hotel at street level, this is one
of the culinary high spots of London. Marco, once known as the
enfant terrible of British cooking, is now reaching far greater
heights and has begun to surround himself with the trappings
of great style and luxury. The interior of his restaurant has soft
cream-coloured walls hung with some exceptionally fine works
of art. These are set off by discreet lighting and grandly
extravagant arrangements of exotic blooms. Marco is a man
of growing stature with an immense, almost unbounded energy.

He is constantly striving for change with new and exciting concepts forever at his fingertips; a showman, certainly, but not one given to gimmickry or unnecessary accoutrements. Instead, he brings together ingredients in simple, supremely subtle fusions of flavour and texture. His menu offers a stunning selection of starters followed by an almost bewildering choice of main dishes and to finish a plate of wonderful French cheeses and/or exquisite desserts. Starters include an ultra-refreshing tian of crab layered with tomato and avocado served with a vinaigrette of tomato; soft grilled scallops sprinkled with best-quality sea salt and surrounded by a pool of intense squid ink sauce, or a fricassee of crayfish and chanterelles in a supremely light frothed-up creamy extract of the mushrooms. Fish is superbly handled, as in escalope of brill viennoise, the fish layered with spinach and with a crunchy crumb topping, buttered noodles and a sabayon of grain mustard. Offal is beautifully executed, caramelised calf's sweetbreads with almonds, fricassee of wild mushrooms and courgettes with a sherry vinegar sauce being typical. His roast fillet of lamb, cooked to almost melting tenderness, is surrounded by a mix of Provençal vegetables with roast garlic and a superb lamb jus; the most delicious Bresse pigeon with garlic confit, buttered cabbage with bacon and a thyme jus is another example of his affinity with taste and composition. Desserts such as the chocolate leaf 'box' filled with chocolate mousse and brandied cherries, hot raspberry soufflé or caramelised apple tart topped with vanilla ice cream and a dribbling of caramel are yet further demonstrations of his artistry. Serious wine list and mostly serious prices, though there are a few value-for-money bottles to be had. Small selection of really well chosen New World wines; half bottles a little thin on the ground; customers would benefit from a recommended house list. *L 12-2.30 D 7-11.30. Closed L Sat, all Sun, first 2 weeks in Aug, Bank Holidays. Set L £25 Set D £65. Mastercard, Visa.*

★

London   **Panda Si Chuen**

Tel 0171-437 2069   R

56 Old Compton Street London W1V 5PA
Seats 63   Meal for 2 approx £50

Just outside the traditional heart of Chinatown, Panda Si Chuen beacons as a bright Northern star in the firmament of London's Chinese restaurants. Decor is discreetly elegant with a few small ornate gilt carvings on the walls. However it is the food that is the magnet here. The cooking of Szechuan province is renowned for its generally spicy nature. Here it has reached an exalted level which produces dishes of often exquisite flavour. Grilled dumplings to begin burst with succulent meats and juices while Szechuan tea-smoked duck is imbued with a distinct and delicious flavour reminiscent of Lapsong Souchong. Deep-fried oysters are large with a moist, plump inside and crisp outside, kung-po chicken has the fieriness of chili and the sweet crunchiness of cashew nuts. The menu is not overlong but does include some of the more familiar dishes from the south such as sweet and sour pork. Staff are helpful, polite and friendly. *Meals 12-11.30. Closed Sun, Bank Holidays.* AMERICAN EXPRESS *Diners, Mastercard, Visa.*

London   **Le Pont de la Tour**

`Tel 0171-403 8403`   **H**

Butlers Wharf Building 36D Shad Thames Butlers Wharf London SE1
Seats 105   Meal for 2 approx £95

A beautiful setting on the south bank of the Thames right
by Tower Bridge and overlooking St Katharine's Dock across the
water. In fine weather the large canopied terrace allows for
alfresco dining with a very Continental air. Lunch is a fixed-price
affair, the menu offering half a dozen or so starters and main
dishes. In the evening a slightly more extensive à la carte applies.
Dishes are, as befits the cool, stylish elegance of the setting, very
fashionable, with strong Mediterranean influences. Tomato,
mozzarella and pesto tart, red mullet escabeche and rillettes
of pork with rhubarb and ginger pickle or a delicate warm sole
mousse topped with a soft, lightly poached oyster and
accompanied by a well-balanced butter sauce make superb starters.
These could precede chargrilled veal escalopes with a creamy
saffron risotto and zesty gremolata, pot-roast chump of lamb with
cannellini beans and rosemary for lunch while in the evening roast
duck with a foie gras croute and port sauce, fillet and crépinette
of venison with a potato and parsnip rösti or a sauté of scallops
with vermouth, leeks and caviar are typical of the more elaborate
style. Desserts are superb – passion fruit tart, white chocolate
truffle cake or a stunning blueberry and vanilla millefeuille.
Excellent espresso and chocolate coffee beans round off a splendid
meal. You may have difficulty choosing a wine from the
exceptional list here, so great is the choice. However, there's
a marvellously comprehensive house selection with tasting notes
alongside that might help you make up your mind. In addition
to the main restaurant there is a less formal bar and grill open
noon to midnight every day. *L 12-3 D 6-12 (Sun to 11). Closed
some Bank Holidays. Set L £25.* AMERICAN EXPRESS *Diners, Mastercard,
Visa.*

London   **Les Saveurs**

`Tel 0171-491 8919`   **R**

37a Curzon Street Mayfair London W1Y 8EY
Seats 55   Meal for 2 approx £120

A restaurant which has taken very little time to join the ranks of
London's best. In manager Emmanuel Menjuzan and sommelier
Yves Sauboua, both consummate professionals, Les Saveurs has
front-of-house staff fully worthy of the food. The restaurant itself,
an elegant and formal basement dining room, is reached down
a fine staircase from the smart reception area. Decorated in soft
creamy tones with subdued lighting, maple-panelled walls,
modern flower paintings and antique mirrors, there's an air
of sophistication, further enhanced by wonderful floral   ★
arrangements and exquisite place settings. And, what of the
cooking? Well, chef Joël Antunès firstly has an impeccable track
record with stints in the best restaurants in France, as well as a spell
in one of the world's great hotels, Thailand's Bangkok Oriental,
from where many of his innovative and creative touches, not
to mention the stunning presentation, come. Applying these
techniques to a sound classical training, he is able to infuse every

dish with perfectly balanced flavours, retain the textures of the raw materials to their optimum, and season with the lightest of touches. All the trappings of luxury eating are demonstrated by an appetiser before the first course, a pre-dessert *with* petits fours *and* a post-dessert platter of more petits fours and tuiles of every description, each a bit part to the main attraction. A variety of menus, all at exceptionally kind prices for such a high standard of cooking, is offered: a fixed price for either two or three courses, with the alternative of a fixed-price three-course lunch (four choices at each stage) or a no-choice five-course dinner menu. A spring version of the latter had oysters in aspic with horseradish cream to start, followed by a brochette of Dublin Bay prawns and mackerel with artichoke; a main course of risotto of pigeon with duck foie gras (risottos are something of a speciality here: the version with lobster, ceps and thyme butter has been on the menu since the outset, or mackerel with pistou); a selection of French cheeses in tip-top condition and a croustillant of nougatine with vanilla. Such an interesting menu is typical of the care and understanding that goes into producing the seasonally changing 'set' menu; dishes are well balanced and impeccably chosen. Alternatively, the inexpensive lunch – a steal at £21 – has reasonably-priced wine suggestions to accompany, say, fricassee of baby squid served à la niçoise, fillet of lamb flavoured with thyme, ending with a feuilleté of apples served with caramel. On the à la carte menu look out for specialities such as terrine of foie gras with aubergines, rabbit salad à la niçoise, fillet of red mullet served with potatoes and a sauce salmis (fish and liver), a pastilla (sort of crispy envelope) of pigeon served with semolina and cardamom butter, and sensational desserts such as hot chocolate madeleine served with almond cream or bitter chocolate sorbet surrounded by a tea syrup. Apart from the aforesaid wine suggestions, there are few bargains on the predominantly French wine list, that has many classics and some lesser-known wines from the South-West. *L 12-2.30 D 7-10.30. Closed all Sat & Sun, 2 weeks Aug, two weeks Christmas/New Year. Set L £21 Set D £34.* AMERICAN EXPRESS® *Diners, Mastercard, Visa.*

The Golden Eurostar [★] denotes our pick of the restaurants. Cooking is the major consideration, but other factors are also taken into account, including ambience, comfort and service.

Opening times are often liable to change at short notice, so it's always best to book.

London   **The Savoy**

Tel 0171-836 4343   Fax 0171-240 6040   **HR**

The Strand London WC2R 0EU

Rooms 200   Meal for 2 approx £260

One of the world's finest hotels, with tip-top standards of service
under the direction of General Manager Herbert Striessnig.
There's an international feel to the public areas – contrast the
genteel Englishness of the peaceful drawing room with the
brashness of the American Bar, or the grandeur of the ornate and
marble-pillared Thames Foyer (afternoon tea and light snacks)
with the 'Upstairs' (see below). Bedrooms, many in the original
art deco style, include the much sought-after river suites, and boast
such luxuries as real linen bedding, huge cosseting bath sheets,
a nightly turn-down of beds and personal maid, valet and waiter
bell service. There are banqueting and conference facilities for
up to 500, plus a variety of stylish private rooms. The beautifully
designed Fitness Gallery, which benefits from natural daylight and
fresh air, was added during the rebuilding of the Savoy Theatre
over the last couple of years. The leisure centre's facilities are
complimentary for guests and include a rooftop swimming pool
(the pool atrium), his and hers saunas and steam rooms, warm-
up and workout rooms, and a massage room. Guests also have
temporary membership of the Wentworth Club, the renowned
golf and country club a short drive from London, which has
tennis courts and an outdoor pool in addition to several golf
courses (proof of handicap required). *Indoor swimming pool, gym,
sauna, steam room, beauty & hair salon, news kiosk, flower shop,
valeting.* AMERICAN EXPRESS *Diners, Mastercard, Visa*

River Restaurant

Seats 140   Meal for 2 approx £130

Busier and animated at lunchtime, in contrast to more sedate
evenings when there's dancing to a live band (playing old
chestnuts) and twinkling lights across the river providing further
attraction. Tables located by the picture windows, where the
Thames is in the background, are much sought after, but it's such
a grand room that you are well placed wherever you're seated.
Maitre chef des cuisines Anton Edelmann's daily-changing seasonal
dinner menu (five courses, £47) includes wines selected
by sommelier Werner Wissmann to complement each course.
Alongside this menu are an interesting list of à la carte dishes
(lobster and apple salad with light curry dressing, fillet of lamb
on aubergine purée, peach mousseline with pistachio tuiles) and
a less expensive *diner au choix*, which is similar to the lunchtime
déjeuner au choix – a recent menu offered haricot bean stew with
langoustines, pastry-wrapped breast of duck and crepes Suzette
among the choice of six or so dishes at each stage. *Régime naturel*
options offer carefully-conceived dishes for health-conscious diets.
Naturally, there's a grand and international wine list for such a
grand hotel, but there are a few bottles within the reach of mere
mortals! *L 12.30-2.30 D 6-11.15. Set L from £26.25 (Sun £23.50)
Set D £37 & £47.*

Grill Room
Seats 85   Meal for 2 approx £120

Booking is essential both lunchtime and evening in the Savoy
Grill, which many politicians and leaders of industry regard
almost as their dining club. *Maitre chef de cuisine* David Sharland's
classic favourites are the main attraction; from asparagus in season
and dressed crab to pea, pear and watercress soup, Caesar salad,
fishcakes, calf's liver with sage, lamb's kidneys with bacon and
straightforward grills. A daily lunchtime *plat du jour* might
be sausages with creamed potatoes and onions on Monday, roast
rib of beef with Yorkshire pudding on Thursday, or Cornish fish
pie on Friday; dinner dishes are more involved: beef Wellington,
duck with cherries or *poularde de Bresse grand-mère*. In addition,
roast saddle of lamb appears every day. Sweets from the trolley
include the likes of summer pudding, crème brulée and an unusual
chocolate pecan pie. The evening theatre menu (6-7pm) allows
you to have your first and main courses before the show,
returning for coffee and pastries in the Thames Foyer afterwards.
Service, under maitre d'hotel Angelo Maresca, is executed with
style and panache and shines as brightly as the beautiful polished
yew panelling of this mellow-toned, very grand hotel dining
room. *L 12.30-2.30 D 6-11. Closed all Sun, Aug. Set D (6-7.30pm)*
£26.75/£29.75

Upstairs at the Savoy
Seats 28   Meal for 2 approx £50

An ideal venue for an informal meal, overlooking the comings
and goings and hustle and bustle of The Savoy Courtyard – it's
a champagne, Chablis and oyster bar specialising in seafood dishes
(salmon kedgeree, fricassee of monkfish with wild rice, grilled cod
with a white bean stew) and fine wines by the glass.
12.30-midnight (Sat 5-midnight) Closed Sun.

London	Simpson's-in-the-Strand	

Tel 0171-836 9112   Fax 0171-836 1381   **R**

100 The Strand London WC2R 0EW
Seats 450   Meal for 2 approx £75

Even in a restaurant as staunchly traditional as Simpson's 'Grand
Divan Tavern' some changes occur, the latest here being that it's
now open for breakfast (7am-noon Mon-Fri). But it's the roast
joints that are still the bedrock of its fame, wheeled around
on silver trolleys as they have been since 1848. The same farm
in the north of Scotland has supplied the beef for 70 years, and
Simpson's gets through 25 loins each day (80% of customers order
it). Roast lamb (23 saddles) and roast Aylesbury duck (36 birds)
are other favourites, along with steak, kidney and mushroom pie,
Cumberland sausage with mashed potatoes and onion gravy, and
grilled lamb cutlets. Good-value lunch and pre-theatre menus; fish
and vegetarian dishes are also served. Fine British cheeses,
comforting puds, old-fashioned savouries. *L 12-2.30 D 6-11.*
Closed 25 & 26 Dec, Good Friday. Set L & D £10 (Sun L £17.50).
AMERICAN EXPRESS *Diners, Mastercard, Visa.*

London   The Square

Tel 0171-839 8787   **R**

32 King Street St James's London SW1 6RJ
Seats 75   Meal for 2 approx £80

A minimally decorated modern restaurant just off St James's
Square, its shop-like frontage adorned by large brass mobiles. Deep
blue, orange and ochre fabrics are used in the seat upholstery
to add a useful splash of colour to an otherwise creamy, well-lit
room. Philip Howard's daily-changing menus are firmly in the
best modern British style, showing a genuine flair for very well-
judged combinations and a keen eye for detail – the results on the
plate can be wonderful. Dishes are light and uncomplicated yet   ★
may comprise an amazingly wide variety of ingredients –
assembled to complement one another, utilising every flavour and
texture to the fullest and usually with many more facets than are
indicated by the terse menu descriptions: seared tuna, tartare
of vegetables, soy wilted greens; roast quail, *tarte fine* of wild
mushrooms; sauté of John Dory, ragout of leeks and mussels;
rump of lamb with aubergines and olive oil; praline parfait,
poached pear, honey madeleines. Splendid cooking and splendid
wines Service, under new restaurant manager John Davey
(previously at *Girardet* in Switzerland, *Guy Savoy* in Paris and
Mosimann's) is impeccable. *L 12-2 D 6-11.45. Closed L Sat, most
Bank Holidays. Mastercard, Visa.*

London   Le Suquet

Tel 0171-581 1785   **R**

104 Draycott Avenue London SW3 3AE
Seats 70   Meal for 2 approx £70

In surroundings inspired by the seafront at Cannes, fresh fish and
shellfish get traditional treatment on a menu whose only changing
element is the *plats du jour*. These often include sea bass (sold
by weight), sole grilled or meunière and seafood pot au feu.
Otherwise it's shellfish almost all the way, and the langoustines,
coquilles St Jacques, mussels and clams may be ordered in either
full or half-portions. For a major treat the mighty *plateau de fruits
de mer* (£16) is a must. Steaks are always available for meat-eaters.
Good salads and feuilletés. *L 12-2.30 D 7-12.30.* AMERICAN EXPRESS
Diners, Mastercard, Visa.

London   La Tante Claire

Tel 0171-352 6045   Fax 0171-352 3257   **R**

68 Royal Hospital Road London SW3 4HP
Seats 42   Meal for 2 approx £140

Quite simply, Pierre Koffmann is in top gear. Over the years,
superlatives about the cooking have been directed towards him
by the bucketload, so you could perhaps excuse the odd bout
of complacency. There is none. The meals we have eaten this year
have not disappointed, and even the change in front-of-house, with   ★
the arrival of new restaurant Manager Bruno Bellemère, has
occurred almost unnoticeably. You enter the restaurant via
a narrow corridor, separated from the dining room by etched glass
screens; those who do not wish to go straight to their tables can

have aperitifs in the comfortable reception area; the dining room itself is smallish, yet tables are not too close together, allowing intimate conversation. Decorated in pale wood and soft pastel colours with several fine modern paintings, it's an airy room. There's a distinct difference in the ambience at lunch and dinner: the former is more lively and animated with a real buzz, almost certainly due to the fact that customers cannot believe their good fortune in eating *déjeuner* of such a high standard at such a ridiculous giveaway price of only £25 for an *amuse-gueule* (perhaps an avocado mousse on a bed of finely chopped beetroot), three courses, coffee and delectable petits fours, not to mention a variety of excellent rolls. Dinner, on the other hand, is usually taken in reverent hushed, tones, as befits the minimum charge of £45 per person. What of the food? Pierre's signature dishes (*galette de foie gras au Sauternes et échalotes roties; coquilles St Jacques à la planche, sauce encre; pied de cochon aux morilles; filet de chevreuil au chocolat amer et vinaigre de framboise*) can always be enjoyed, but recent dishes that live in the memory were a ravioli of langoustines generously flavoured with truffles, the pasta probably coloured by the use of lobster eggs; a slice of marbled terrine of *bouillabaisse en gelée* with a colourful, artistic and quite fiery sauce rouille. Main courses included a perfectly cooked piece of halibut on a bed of lentils with baby onions and lardons, and a stuffed leg of tender young rabbit with wild mushrooms served with light, creamy mashed potato. Among notable desserts have been a tart of cherries topped with crumble and served with a sabayon and vanilla ice cream, and crisp caramelised pastry layers interspersed with fresh strawberries and cream on a fruit coulis. Excellent coffee, splendid French cheeses in tip-top condition, and a comprehensive French-only wine list (including many half bottles) with some quite fair prices. Sadly, most of the bin ends have been snapped up. Service purrs along efficiently and unobtrusively. *L 12.30-2 D 7-11. Closed Sat & Sun, Bank Holidays, 1 week Christmas, 3 weeks August. Set L £25.* AMERICAN EXPRESS® *Diners, Mastercard, Visa.*

To dial overseas from the UK, 010 will change to 00
on 16th April 1995.

Meal prices for 2 are based on à la carte menus.
When set menus are available, prices will often be lower.

Around London

Bray-on-Thames   **The Waterside Inn**

Tel 01628 20691   Fax 01628 784710   **RR**

Ferry Road Bray-on-Thames Berkshire SL6 2AT
Seats 75   Meal for 2 approx £165

"Un restaurant avec chambres". But *what* a restaurant with rooms!
The Thamesside setting is unsurpassed on a summer's day, when
drinks can be taken on the terrace or on the electric launch *The
Waterside Inn II*; and when the kitchen is on song the food
is truly memorable. Michel Roux bought the Waterside with his
brother in 1972, and his lieutenants – Head Chef Mark Dodson
and Restaurant Manager Diego Masciaga – have been at their
posts since 1988. Time-honoured French cooking skills have been
adapted to modern tastes, with the result that more dishes include
nage or *jus* as opposed to old-fashioned sauces. Classic ingredients
are still very much to the fore (foie gras, truffles, snails, lobster,
turbot, tournedos, Bresse pigeon, Challans duck) but you'll also
notice many herbs and spices making fresh, natural contributions
to dishes: lemon thyme with a mussel soufflé; chive flavouring
olive oil with grilled turbot; savory subtly enhancing *tournedos
poelé, persillade à l'échalote, cordon d'escargots.* Desserts like warm
raspberry soufflé or *ravioles au citrus et petit gratin de poires*   ★
et bananes put the finishing flourish on what should
be a magnificent meal. À la carte is always available, plus a *menu
gastronomique* at lunchtime during the week (priced very
reasonably at £28), an evening *menu printemps* between October
and April and a *menu exceptionnel* which (for 2 or more) offers
smaller portions of dishes taken from the carte. The à la carte
menu includes two main-course vegetarian dishes. The French-
only wine list – *'c'est magnifique'* – has all the great names, and
a few country wines. Surprisingly perhaps it's not all expensive,
especially noting that prices are inclusive of service. The room
is bright, elegant and inviting, though tables at the back do not
enjoy the best of the views. An army of smartly turned-out staff
provides constant, attentive service. *L 12-1.30 (Sun 12-2.30)
D 7-10. Closed all Mon, L Tue, D Sun Oct-April, Bank Holidays
(open L 25 Dec), 26 Dec-end Jan. Set L £28 Set D Oct-Apr £45
also Set L & D £62. Diners, Mastercard, Visa.*

Rooms
                                      Meal for 2 approx £110

Seven stylish and comfortable bedrooms, all en suite and some
with river views, could persuade you to forget the drive home,
and the fresh croissants will set you up for the day.

East Grinstead   **Gravetye Manor**

Tel 01342 810567   Fax 01342 810080   **HR**

Vowels Lane East Grinstead West Sussex RH19 4LJ
Rooms 18   Meal for 2 approx £200

The civilised hospitality and gracious charm of Peter Herbert and
staff (for whom nothing is too much trouble) continue to provide
an object lesson in how a country house hotel should be run. The
care and attention to every last detail both within the splendidly
transformed Elizabethan stone mansion (built in 1598) and in the

1000 acres of grounds is perfectly illustrated in the wing where four immaculate bedrooms were recently added and in the time and expense involved in restoring the William Robinson English garden to its former glory. Flower displays fill the gracious day rooms, which include a really delightful sitting room with oak panelling and an ornate moulded ceiling, and the entrance hall – now much brighter than in the past – with carefully selected chair patterns. Bedrooms, with their comfortable beds, antique furniture and sumptuous fabrics are models of good taste; books, magazines, post cards, bedside radios and TVs concealed behind tapestry screens are among a long list of thoughtful extras. The bathrooms, too, with his and her washbasins, bidet and power shower over the bath provide every conceivable need, and are havens of comfort. Fly fishing on the lake between May and September. The hotel stands 5 miles south-west of East Grinstead off the B2110 at the West Hoathly sign. *Garden, croquet, fishing. Mastercard, Visa.*

Restaurant

Seats 42   Meal for 2 approx £105

A comforting restaurant with an enviable reputation for consistently high standards, maintained over many years by a succession of talented chefs, the second chef generally inheriting the top job, thus ensuring a smooth transition. Add silky smooth service that is attentive without being overbearing and the room itself with mellow oak panelling under a Tudor ceiling and it all helps to create a memorable dining experience. A walled kitchen garden provides much of the produce in summer, their own smokehouse the smoked salmon, duck breast and the like and the spring which has served the Manor since 1598 is still providing water for the tables. Well-balanced à la carte and table d'hote menus offer dishes with a strong English flavour, though often with a modern twist, like home-smoked haddock with poached egg and mustard seed butter sauce, pan-fried black pudding with apples, frisée salad and sherry vinegar jus, fillet of cod in yeast batter with potatoes mashed with olive oil and sauce rouille, saddle of local venison served on spatzli with light and dark peppercorn sauces, and roast chump of English lamb with tomato and rosemary fondue and rich port sauce. Menu prices include service but not VAT. The wine list is one to drool over. All the big names and best vintages are there, but so are more unusual offerings, with often unseen bins from Australia, Germany and Italy – all well represented, as are half bottles. No smoking. *L 12.30-2 D 7.30-9.30 (Sun to 9). Closed D 25 Dec to non-residents. Set L £20 (+vat) (Sun £28 +vat) Set D £26 (+vat).*

To dial overseas from the UK, 010 will change to 00
on 16th April 1995.

Great Milton   Le Manoir aux Quat'Saisons

Tel 01844 278881   Fax 01844 278847   **HR**

Church Road Great Milton Oxfordshire OX44 7PD
Rooms 19   Meal for 2 approx £194

Now you see it, now you don't! The continuing saga of whether
the hotel should be allowed to display a sign in a field indicating
its presence just before (from London) Junction 7 of the M40
(from Birmingham, leave at Junction 8) could only happen in this
country. We should be shouting from the rooftops that Raymond
Blanc's country house hotel and restaurant is one of the finest
in the UK, and that it has just celebrated its tenth anniversary. The
15th-century manor house stands in beautifully tended landscaped
gardens (note the sculptured bronzes exhibited in the herb garden
and watery spots) and inside it's a model of refined elegance. The
flagstoned entrance hall leads into luxurious and comfortable
lounges that are immaculately furnished with antiques, fine
paintings and splendid flower arrangements and warmed in winter
by open fires. The theme continues in the individually decorated
bedrooms, which provide every conceivable luxury, from
a decanter of Madeira to a bowl of fresh fruit. Several garden-wing
rooms have their own private terrace with wrought-iron patio
furniture, while the medieval dovecote has been converted into
a romantic honeymoon suite. There are jacuzzi and whirlpool
baths in the magnificent bathrooms, not to mention huge towels,
generous bathrobes and exquisite toiletries. Of course, all this
would be wasted without service and excellent housekeeping
to match, and this, under the direction of new General Manager
Simon Rhatigan, proceeds smoothly and efficiently. Breakfasts,
naturally, are quite delicious. Small conferences (40). *Garden,
croquet, tennis, outdoor swimming pool, limousine, helipad.*
AMERICAN EXPRESS *Diners, Mastercard, Visa.*

Restaurant
Seats 95   Meal for 2 approx £195

Self-taught Raymond Blanc has come a long way since he first
opened his own restaurant in Summertown, Oxford. His accolades
are displayed in the hotel's foyer for everyone to see, and with his
TV series, cook books and cookery school *Le Petit Blanc* (courses
run by long-serving head chef Clive Fretwell), you wonder where
the man gets his energy from. Quite simply, he is a genius, his
cooking both creative and technically superb. He can't do it alone,
and doesn't, assisted as he is by Clive and the brigade, so the
kitchen is always in safe hands, as is the restaurant itself (in fact
three very different dining areas), under the guidance of Alain
Desenclos. The grounds and three-acre kitchen garden provide   ★
most of the quality produce used – whether it's organic herbs,
vegetables, or fruits – and head gardener Anne-Marie Owens gets
a well-deserved mention on the menu. The style has changed little
through the years – it has evolved, but still with the lightest
of touches, perhaps with more influences from the Far East than
before, adding exotic flavours to sound cooking practices. The
seasonal menus are written in French with English translations;
a three-course *menu du jour* offers two choices in each section,
following an appetiser; perhaps pressed terrine of duck with foie
gras and lentils, grilled fillet of John Dory in a light chicken jus

with rosemary, and a William pear charlotte on a raspberry coulis.
Or your table could be tempted by the eight-course *menu
gourmand* (a snip at £65!). Seriously, this offers you the chance
of sampling a selection of specialities (without having to make
up your mind), among which you might be served a charlotte
of aubergines and sweet peppers; quail's eggs, spinach, Parmesan
and black Périgord truffle ravioli; grilled fillet of brill; roasted
corn-fed Bresse pigeon; ending with three tasting desserts,
including, if you're lucky, an orange parfait wrapped in a fine
nougatine box. Push the boat out further and choose à la carte,
say, roasted medallion of sea bass filled with langoustines
or scallops on a bed of fennel, olive and cardamom sauce,
or roasted best end of Highgrove (guess where it comes from?)
lamb with pan-fried sweetbreads, kidneys and liver. Desserts (try
Le Café Crème) and farmhouse cheeses, from both France and
Great Britain, are a delight, petits fours and chocolates mini-
masterpieces. The wine list is a serious tome, with bucketfuls
of fine French wines, but also an excellent showing from
elsewhere, including a splendid selection of the best that the New
World has to offer. Good to see many lesser-known and value-for-
money French country wines on the list too. *L 12.15-2.15 (Sun
2.30) D 7.15-10.15. Set L £29.50 (not Sun) D £65.*

Meal prices for 2 are based on à la carte menus.
When set menus are available, prices will often be lower.

The Golden Eurostar [★] denotes our pick of the
restaurants. Cooking is the major consideration, but
other factors are also taken into account, including
ambience, comfort and service.

Shinfield   L'Ortolan

Tel 01734 883783   Fax 01734 885391   R

Old Vicarage Church Lane Shinfield nr Reading Berkshire RG2 9BY
Seats 65   Meal for 2 approx £140

As the address implies, the building is indeed the old vicarage,
now flanked by two conservatories (one an adjunct of the dining
room, the other a drawing room for pre-prandial drinks or after-
dinner coffee and exquisite petits fours – a fitting end
to memorable dining). The dining conservatory and the front
of the restaurant overlook a delightful garden and terrace, the
perfect spot on a balmy day. And yet the restaurant is only a few
minutes from Junction 11 of the M4, just an hour's drive from
London. What of John Burton-Race's cooking? Well, it's exciting
and creative, remarkable in fact, starting with perfect *amuse-gueule*
preparing the taste buds for what is to follow from a choice
of menus (check which are not available at weekends). Menu
dishes (two courses à la carte £45) are written in French with
descriptive English translations that actually inform you of what
you are about to eat. For instance, you are told that a *brandade
de morue, sauce vierge* is freshly salted cod, poached in milk, resting
on steamed potato, topped with thin strips of bacon and served
with a sauce vierge. Another starter, one of John's signature dishes,
unfortunately attracting a surcharge, is lasagne of langoustines
(layered langoustines in their mousse between fresh pasta leaves
with truffle oil). For a main course look no further than corn-fed   ★
squab pigeon roasted with honey, with sherry vinegar added to its
caramelised cooking juices, or a slice of sea bass steamed
in champagne with oyster jus and topped with a *paysanne* of leeks.
Desserts are truly mouthwatering – the delicate caramel mousse
served in a dome of toffee (*dome de mousse, caramel brulée*), a
L'Ortolan speciality, is still on the menu, as is the *assiette
chocolatière*, small portions of various chocolate desserts. Equally
impressive are the tarts (apple, bilberry, raspberry etc), all served
with delicious home-made ice creams. It's also worth noting that
many of the specialist suppliers are local (crayfish, fresh snails, eggs
etc) ensuring that the quality of raw materials is top-notch, so vital
to cooking as exceptional as this. The wine list is exemplary, but
you must search carefully for bargains, though the house selection
is both well chosen and fairly priced. Most wine-producing
countries get a look in, but the list is predominantly French, to be
expected at a restaurant which rivals the best in France. Staff are
smart, charming and always on the ball. *L 12-2.15 D 7-10.
Closed D Sun, all Mon, last 2 weeks Aug, last 2 weeks Feb.
Set L £22 (not Sun) and £32. Set D £32 & £40.* AMERICAN EXPRESS
Diners, Mastercard, Visa.

Birmingham

Birmingham   Chung Ying

`Tel 0121-622 5669`   **R**

16 Wrottesley Street Birmingham West Midlands B5 6RT
Seats 220   Meal for 2 approx £40

The Chinese flock to this well-established, traditionally appointed restaurant for its long Cantonese menu. The choice extends to well over 300 dishes, including more than 40 dim sum items and a 'special dishes' section with stuffed peppers, crabmeat on straw mushrooms, frog's legs and venison among the choice. Also of note are the casseroles: braised brisket with spices, belly pork with yam, lamb with dried bean curd, duck's webs and fish lips, chicken and liver. *Meals 12-11.30 (Sun to 11). Closed 25 Dec.*
AMERICAN EXPRESS *Diners, Mastercard, Visa.*

Birmingham   Hyatt Regency

`Tel 0121-643 1234   Fax 0121-616 2323`   **HR**

2 Bridge Street Birmingham West Midlands B1 2JZ
Rooms 319   Meal for 2 approx £140

A canalside setting in the heart of Birmingham for the impressive, mirrored 25-storey Hyatt Regency, which has a direct link to the International Convention Centre next door. Inside, the huge glazed atrium is the epitome of style and elegance, bedecked with plants, and awash with marble. The luxuriously appointed bedrooms include 12 suites; all are spacious and air-conditioned, featuring quality modern furniture and fashionably uncluttered decor, plus equally splendid, marble-floored bathrooms. Three rooms are adpated for the disabled, one floor of 17 rooms is reserved for non-smokers and three floors make up the Regency Club of superior rooms; the latter has its own Club Lounge on the 22nd floor. Excellent leisure facilities. Young, smart and willing staff. Conference facilities for up to 240, banqueting to 200. Charged, valet parking in the hotel's 24hr-manned car park nearby. *Garden, indoor swimming pool, gym, sauna, solarium, steam room, spa bath, business centre, café (6.30am-midnight).*
AMERICAN EXPRESS *Diners, Mastercard, Visa.*

Number 282
Seats 80   Meal for 2 approx £80

A Brasserie on Broad Street is the tag line here, though 'broadsheet' might be even more appropriate with the day's news headlines, weather, entertainment and even a personalised message on the paper place mat. The menu itself (on the same sheet) is equally international, and might offer an adventurous leek vichyssoise with jellied beef tea and marjoram tempura, magret of duck marinated with ginger and lavender honey served with stir-fried bamboo, bean sprouts, baby corn and sugar peas, or roast pork fillet glazed with gorgonzola and served with soft polenta and smoked tomato-olive stew. Puddings could be lime-chocolate terrine with citrus fruit salad, or apple cobbler with vanilla ice cream and cinnamon sauce. *L 12.30-2.30 D 6.30-11.30. Set L £12.75. Closed L Sat, all Sun.*

Birmingham   **Sloans**

Tel 0121-455 6697   Fax 0121-454 4335   **R**

**27 Chad Square Hawthorne Road Edgbaston Birmingham
West Midlands B15 3TQ**
Seats 66   Meal for 2 approx £60

Set in a small suburban shopping precinct, this smart, pale green,
split-level restaurant is run in exemplary fashion by owner John
Narbett and his friendly team. Lunch is a small-choice fixed-price
menu of two or three courses, with Simon Booth's cooking based
on English and French styles. Dishes are generally reasonably
straightforward, shown by game terrine, eggs florentine, mustard-
sauced breast of chicken and calf's liver with bacon and creamed
potato. The evening carte is lengthier, in a similar vein. *L 12-2.15
D 7-10. Closed L Sat, all Sun, Bank Holidays, 1 week Christmas.
Set L £11/£14.* AMERICAN EXPRESS *Diners, Mastercard, Visa.*

Birmingham   **Swallow Hotel**

Tel 0121-452 1144   Fax 0121-456 3442   **HR**

12 Hagley Road Five Ways Birmingham West Midlands B16 8SJ
Rooms 98   Meal for 2 approx £140

An imposing Edwardian building, strikingly transformed into
a quality luxury hotel. The foyer features sparkling Italian marble
floors, rich mahogany woodwork and crystal chandeliers; there
is a refined drawing room elegantly decorated with oil paintings,
a quiet, dignified library and a handsome bar with colourful floral
display throughout. The air-conditioned bedrooms are stylish,
well-proportioned and comfortable; one room is well equipped
for disabled guests. Beautiful fabrics are complemented by fine
inlaid furniture and bathrooms are impressive, with marble tiling
and a host of extras. An interestingly designed leisure club is based
around an Egyptian theme. Attentive, professional staff. Parking
for 70 cars. *Indoor swimming pool, gym, spa bath, steam room,
solarium, spa bath, hair & beauty salon.* AMERICAN EXPRESS *Diners,
Mastercard, Visa.*

Sir Edward Elgar Restaurant
Seats 55   Meal for 2 approx £96

High-class service fits comfortably into the luxurious surroundings
– murals and fine fabrics covering the walls, pianist/singer six
nights a week – of this split-level, Edwardian-themed restaurant.
Luxury is not hard to find on the menu, either, with the likes
of a caviar blini accompanying smoked salmon, lobster garnish
to roasted Dover sole with a pepper sauce and Provençal herbs,
and a bed of foie gras spätzle for the grilled maize-fed chicken.
Other dishes might include spaghetti of vegetables and truffles,
braised cod with red onions, potatoes and fresh thyme; a duo
of veal with a potato and herb millefeuille, and English duck
roasted with baby onions, lardons of bacon and small green lentils.
In addition to the à la carte and table d'hote menus there
is a special £25 post-theatre supper served until 10.45pm by prior
arrangement only. Some keenly-priced wines on a list that favours
France, but does less justice to other areas. No smoking.
*L 12.30-2.30 D 7.30-10.30. Closed L Sat. Set L £15.50/£19.50
(Sun £17.50) Set D £18.50/£25/£30 & £45.*

Langtry's

Seats 60   Meal for 2 approx £60

British cookery to traditional recipes produces daily lunchtime
dishes from around the country: Hampshire cottage pie
on Wednesday, boiled leg of Welsh mutton with caper sauce
on Thursday and east-coast beer-battered cod and chips on Friday.
Popular à la carte favourites also include Finnan haddock soup,
mixed grill, home-made fruit cake with Lancashire cheese and
English trifle. Outdoor seating in summer. *L 11.30-2.30
D 6.30-10.30. Closed Sun, Bank Holidays.*

Bristol

Bristol	**Bristol Marriott Hotel**

Tel 0117 9294281   Fax 0117 9225838   **H**

2 Lower Castle Street Bristol Avon BS1 3AD
Rooms 289   Meal for 2 approx £137

A city-centre high-riser that was once a Holiday Inn. Public areas
are spacious and well laid-out. Good-sized, air-conditioned
bedrooms offer large beds (two doubles in the twin-bedded
rooms) and ample work space. Executive floor rooms are similar
but with various extras – second telephone at the desk, mini-bar,
bathrobe – and an exclusive Executive lounge with
complimentary Continental breakfast and beverages. Three rooms
are equipped for disabled guests. Obliging staff and extensive 24hr
room service. The Conference venue caters for up to 600 theatre-
style; staffed business centre. Free parking in an adjacent multi-
storey car park. *Indoor swimming pool, gym, sauna, spa bath, steam
room, solarium, beauty salon, children's playroom, games room, news
kiosk; coffee shop 7am-11pm.* AMERICANEXPRESS *Diners, Mastercard, Visa.*

Bristol	**Harveys Restaurant**

Tel 0117 9275034   Fax 0117 9275003   **R**

12 Denmark Street Bristol Avon BS1 5DQ
Seats 120   Meal for 2 approx £80

The ancient cellars of Harveys Wine Merchants are home
to a comfortable, air-conditioned restaurant featuring the
accomplished cooking of Ramon Farthing, who brings
a contemporary touch to classic skills. Lunch and evening à la carte
are similar, both with a range of interesting dishes like slices
of calf's liver layered between sheets of pasta and creamed leeks
surrounded by a Madeira sauce; lightly crisped fillet of sea bass
on a bed of garlic and nutmeg spinach leaves sauced with a light
ratatouille butter infusion; and (a speciality) breast of pigeon sliced
on a bacon and potato rösti with roasted goose liver, glazed
shallots and a light sauce finished with grenadine. Other specialities
include home-cured bresaola in a splendid little salad and hot
orange soufflé served with a chocolate and Drambuie cream and
crisp biscuit twists. There's also a well-priced lunch table d'hote
and two fixed-price evening menus, the more expensive being
a surprise gourmet menu of six light courses "taking past and
current menu favourites, with an element of surprise". The
thoroughly comprehensive wine list is expertly laid out with each
section wisely prefaced. Note the exceptional clarets, sherries and
ports, but everything is worth drinking here. Adjoining the
restaurant is a fascinating wine museum. *L 12-1.45 D 7-10.45.
Closed L Sat, all Sun and Bank Holidays. Set L £16.50
Set D £28 & £38.* AMERICANEXPRESS *Diners, Mastercard, Visa.*

Bristol	**Restaurant Lettonie**

Tel 0117 9686456   Fax 0117 9686943   **R**

9 Druid Hill Stoke Bishop Bristol Avon BS9 1EW
Seats 24   Meal for 2 approx £80

Martin Blunos combines natural talent with true dedication
to produce the kind of dishes that makes the effort of finding this

small restaurant (just seven tables) in suburban Bristol well worthwhile. The house is in a shopping arcade, and the surroundings do not immediatley give a hint of the thought, skill and enterprise that go in to cooking. Everything on the menus bears the Blunos stamp of individuality, notably specialities like scrambled duck egg topped with Sevruga caviar served with blinis and a glass of iced vodka, roast rump of lamb scented with tarragon, and pumpkin ice cream. The set lunch menu offers three choices per course, the lower-priced dinner menu just two. Strong French showing on wine list, several bin ends (including vintage champagnes), otherwise only token representation from four countries. *L 12.30-2 D 7-9. Closed Sun & Mon, 2 weeks Aug, 2 weeks Christmas. Set L £15.95 Set D £19.50 (Tue-Thurs) & £29.95.* AMERICAN EXPRESS *Mastercard, Visa.*

Bristol   ## Swallow Royal Hotel

Tel 0117 9255100   Fax 0117 9251515   **HR**

College Green Bristol Avon BS1 5TA
Rooms 242   Meal for 2 approx £119

Reopened in 1991 after many years of neglect, the hotel occupies one of the most favourable locations in Bristol. Standing next to the cathedral and overlooking the neat lawns of College Green, it was built in 1863. The original Victorian grandeur has now been enhanced by a decor with firmly traditional leanings but which also encompasses an elegantly fashionable touch. The polished red marble-floored foyer has beautiful lounges on each side furnished in a comfortable country house style with deep-cushioned settees arranged in well-spaced groups. The cocktail bar features huge oriental murals at either end and a bar with gleaming glass and silverware. All the bedrooms apart from a few smaller inward facing rooms are spacious, with two armchairs and a writing desk. Every room has a whole host of the usual modern comforts from mini-bars with complimentary mineral water and fresh milk to irons and ironing boards for those who must press to impress. Coloured marble bathrooms have super-strong showers and most have bidets though a few have large corner baths instead where space is more limited. There are ten small suites with cosy sitting rooms and spa baths in the bathrooms. *Indoor swimming pool, sauna, solarium, spa bath, beauty & hair salons, keep-fit equipment. Closed 2 days Christmas.* AMERICAN EXPRESS *Diners, Mastercard, Visa.*

Palm Court Restaurant
Seats 80   Meal for 2 approx £70

The grand Palm Court extends up through three floors lined in Bath stone with curved balustrades and topped by stained-glass skylights. Menus follow the grand format, and might offer pan-fried red mullet on a lemon and tomato dressing, 'Brecon Court' venison cutlets with pear and sage chutney and iced raspberry parfait with raspberry sauce. Service is formal yet unfussy. *D only 7.30-10.30. Closed Sun, Bank Holidays. Set D £23.*

Manchester

Manchester	**Holiday Inn Crowne Plaza**

Tel 0161-236 3333   Fax 0161-228 2241   **H**

Peter Street Manchester Greater Manchester M60 2DS

Rooms 303   Meal for 2 approx £124

A grand town-centre hotel (adjacent to the G-Mex centre)
restored at great expense to its past glory with ornate ceilings,
arches and pillars. The foyer area is vast, with a glass roof and
hanging plants crowning white columns. Cane chairs and
comfortable couches adorn the adjoining terrace lounge. The high-
ceilinged Octagon, one of three bars, is decorated in similar style;
there are also three restaurants. Corridors that lead to the
bedrooms are wide and reminiscent of a former age of spacious
and luxurious hotels. Bedrooms, many recently refurbished, are
generously sized and have a high standard of decor, with tiled
bathrooms throughout; Extensive conference and banqueting
(including kosher) facilities for up to 700. *Indoor swimming pool,
sauna, solarium, spa bath, steam room, gym, squash, beauty & hair
salon, osteopath, news kiosk, shop (7am-8pm), coffee shop (11-3,
5.30-10.30).* AMERICAN EXPRESS *Diners, Mastercard, Visa.*

Manchester	**Market Restaurant**

Tel 0161-834 3743   **R**

**Edge Street/104 High Street Smithfield City Centre Manchester
Greater Manchester M4 1HQ**

Seats 42   Meal for 2 approx £55

Close to the city centre, in what is now the garment district, the
O'Gradys' friendly, homely restaurant has enormous appeal.
Decorwise it's like stepping back in time with everything from
the crockery and green wicker chairs to the light fittings and
background music dating back to the 1940s – even the wine
carafes are old-fashioned milk bottles. In contrast the monthly-
changing menu takes its inspiration from all over the place.
Starters might include middle-eastern tabouleh, air-dried ham
with melon, pitta bread with houmus and aubergine 'caviar' spiced
minced lamb with 'custard topping', while main dishes range from
duck breast with cranberry relish and port gravy, daube of beef,
and lamb kebab with Greek yoghurt and pine nuts to broccoli
and cheese ravioli with tomato and basil sauce (there are always
a couple of interesting vegetarian choices). Puds are important here
too, as is fitting for the home of the famous Pudding Club, whose
members meet six times a year to indulge in a feast of desserts like
steamed puddings, fruit pies, chocolate confection, syllabubs and
the like all helped down with lashings of real custard and extra
thick cream. *D only 6-9.30 (Sat from 7). Closed Sun, Mon, Tue,
1 week Christmas, 1 week Easter, Aug.* AMERICAN EXPRESS *Mastercard,
Visa.*

Manchester   **Victoria & Albert Hotel**

Tel 0161-832 1188   Fax 0161-834 2484   **HR**

Water Street Manchester Greater Manchester M3 4JQ
Rooms 132   Meal for 2 approx £141

Between their TV studios and the river Irwell, Granada's flagship
hotel is a cleverly converted mid-19th-century warehouse.
Original oak-timbered ceilings and cast-iron pillars feature in the
smart galleried reception area, 'Watsons' bar/lounge with its
comfortable Victorian drawing room atmosphere and
conservatory overlooking the river, and in the all-day French-style
café/bistro. Bedrooms, which vary in size and shape, also boast
timbered ceilings and some exposed brickwork; each is named
after, and subtly themed with stills from, a different Granada
TV drama or series. King- or queen-sized beds and a high level
of equipment – the TV offers account review, quick check-out and
breakfast ordering facilities – make for a comfortable stay aided
by keen staff offering an above average level of service.
Conference facilities for up to 250. *Garden, keep-fit equipment,
sauna, solarium, coffee shop (10am-midnight), news kiosk.*
AMERICAN EXPRESS *Diners, Mastercard, Visa.*

Sherlock Holmes Restaurant
Seats 130   Meal for 2 approx £65

John Benson-Smith cooks with style and wit throughout a menu
which never lacks interest. Some dishes are as simple as could be –
Yorkshire pudding with onion gravy, chicken liver paté, roast
beef carved from the trolley, poached salmon hollandaise – while
others are a good deal more elaborate, typified by a hot, spicy Thai
salad of prawns, mango, apricot and cashew nuts, or pan-fried grey
mullet with smoked salmon, mushrooms, cherry tomatoes and
a red wine sauce. Very good desserts, excellent home-baked bread.
*L 12-2 D 7-10. Closed L Sat. Set Sun L £14.95 Set D (pre-and
post-theatre) £15.*

Manchester   **Yang Sing**

Tel 0161-236 2200   Fax 0161-236 5934   **R**

34 Princes Street Manchester Greater Manchester M1 4JY
Seats 140   Meal for 2 approx £50

The class of cooking and the length of the menus make this the
most appealing Chinese restaurant in town, and its popularity
remains undiminished. Tanks of live carp, eels and lobsters testify
to the importance chef/proprietor Harry Yeung places on freshness
and quality of ingredients. Some 40 different dim sum (even more
on Sundays) can be chosen from trolleys parked in the middle
of the restaurant or ordered from the waiting staff. A selection
of pastries (all from their own kitchen) or fresh fruit for afters.
On the ground floor is a Chinese Fondue Restaurant where dishes
are cooked in a stock (rather than oil) that is drunk as a soup after
the main ingredients of the dish have been eaten. Banquets for
up to 200 guests can be held in the largest of several private
rooms. *Meals 12-11.30. Closed 25 Dec. Set meals from £27 for two.*
AMERICAN EXPRESS *Mastercard, Visa.*

Around Manchester

Longridge   **Paul Heathcote's Restaurant**

| Tel 01772 784969 | **R** |

104-106 Higher Road Longridge nr Preston Lancashire PR3 3SY

Seats 50   Meal for 2 approx £90

Paul Heathcote has by degrees gathered around him a coherent
team both in the kitchen and front of house who take pride
in excellence as a part of everyday life, yet apart from one none
of them has yet passed a 35th birthday. Exceptional among them
is Head Chef, Andrew Barnes, whose initiation to the stoves was
as "plongeur" in one of Heathcote's earlier kitchens. In Paul's
dynamic world of self-belief, here is proof positive that anything
is possible. And so it proves. Both the lunch and à la carte menus
change quite frequently so as to reflect the availability of seasonal
raw materials: duck and maize-fed chicken from nearby
Goosnargh, or beef from Dornoch. The Gourmet menu (still
a snip at £32.50) offers six set courses containing perhaps ten
times as many consituent parts. Breads of onion, sage and cheese
or walnut, dates and rosemary accompany a chilled tomato and
chervil juice of pure clarity and subtle complexity. A pig's trotter
filled with ham and sage has a pea purée, onion sauce and
a garnish of mange tout beignets. Roast red mullet lies over leaf
spinach and fondant potato with vegetable mirepoix and a red
pepper sauce. A sorbet is optional: flavoured with lemon and
rosemary, it transpires to be irresistible. The breast of Goosnargh
duck is a minor masterpiece of composition, encompassing
caramelised apples, cider potatoes and dumplings made from the
leg, with spring cabbage and a succulent, simple, translucent jus. ★
Alongside Swaledale and Jersey Blue is served Mrs Kirkham's local
3-day curd, leaf and ash-wrapped goat's cheese while, to finish,
an *assiette gourmande* might include a bread-and-butter pudding,
syrup sponge with crème anglaise, summer pudding with clotted
cream and a miniature strawberry shortcake. We have found
no fault this year with the kitchen's creativity translating into
simple, unqualified success on the plate. An almost complete
absence of traditionally-minded "classic" saucing contributes to an
appreciation of down-to-earth honest flavours obtained from
unquestionably fine, and predominantly local, ingredients. If,
as now appears plain, this is to be Heathcote's "stock in trade" then
there is no alternative than thoroughly to applaud it, as scarcely
a plate returns to the "plonge" with more than a crumb or two
on it. Half a mile past the White Bull pub (follow signs for Jeffery
Hill), this relaxed, sophisticated restaurant has entered another
dimension from where Paul Heathcote started out, only four years
ago. Well-chosen wines, and an excellent sommelier (Paul
Wiltshire) to tell you about them. *L 12-2 (Sun to 2.30) D 7-9.30.
Closed L Tues, Wed, Thurs, Sat (but open those L in Dec), all Mon.
Set L £20 (Sun £22.50) Set D £35.* AMERICAN EXPRESS *Mastercard,
Visa.*

Edinburgh

Edinburgh	**Atrium**

Tel 0131-228 8882   **R**

Cambridge Street Edinburgh Lothian EH1 2ED

Seats 60   Meal for 2 approx £60

Within the atrium of Saltire Court – a smart new office building
next to the Usher Hall in Edinburgh's Theatre district – the
restaurant's post-modern decor is quite stunning with railway
sleeper tables, linen-draped chairs and glass torches based on an
ancient glass drinking horn, set in wrought-iron sconces imparting
an almost medieval atmosphere. Some of the dishes on Andrew
Radford's twice-daily-changing menu (four or five choices at each
stage) are almost equally stunning; for example a brilliant dish
of lemon sole topped with a tomato gratin in a langoustine and
coriander broth. Other dishes that demonstrate Andrew's modern
style might include duck and salami salad with truffle oil; sausage
(spicy Italian) and mash with Parma ham and lentil jus; roast cod,
salsa gratin and spinach; and maize-fed chicken, with polenta,
mousserons and parsley. Puds tend to be variants of his old
favourites like sticky toffee pudding, lemon soufflé tart and apple,
pear and date crumble. Service is a happy blend of informality and
professionalism. There is also a short snack menu at lunchtime and
for pre-theatre diners between 6-7pm. There's not much order
on the wine list, though it has very well-chosen wines which are
keenly priced (3 *marque* champagnes under £30). *L 12-3
D 6-10.30. Closed L Sat, all Sun, 1 week Christmas. Diners,
Mastercard, Visa.*

Edinburgh	**The Balmoral**

Tel 0131-556 2414   Fax 0131-557 3747   **HR**

Princes Street Edinburgh Lothian EH2 2EQ

Rooms 189   Meal for 2 approx £171

At the top of Forte's tree in Scotland, the Balmoral wears its total
refurbishment from the early '90s very comfortably indeed.
Opulence, comfort, courtesy, elegance are the watchwords here –
definitely a place in which to be cosseted, and nothing is too much
trouble for the very professional staff. Bedrooms (with marble
bathrooms) and suites are excellently equipped and maintained,
modern conveniences blending discreetly with traditional
furnishings. There is good provision for non-smoking, lady
executive and disabled guests. We quote a standard price: there are
superior, deluxe and suites above that. Public areas are
of a similarly high standard, encompassing the Palm Court
Lounge, coffee shop, bars, brasserie and the main restaurant, so that
any style of refreshment can be provided. Room service
is available around the clock. There are ten function suites, the
largest taking 400, the total facility being for 800. *Indoor
swimming pool, gym, sauna, steam room, sunbeds, beauty & hair salon,
cashmere & crystal shop, coffee shop (9-5).* AMERICAN EXPRESS *Diners,
Mastercard, Visa.*

The Grill, No 1 Princes Street
Seats 45 | Meal for 2 approx £110

Very much the grand hotel dining room, where discretion and
attention to detail (both in decor and in food presentation) are
impeccable. Many dishes are indicated with a thistle device
as being a "Taste of Scotland". Try perhaps terrine of foie gras,
chicken and leeks, layered with spinach and surrounded by lamb's
lettuce, or a chartreuse of asparagus with a frisée salad, crispy
smoked duck and a walnut dressing, then for main courses roast
saddle of rabbit with a ragout of broad beans and a rabbit confit,
in a duo of champagne cream and Leith claret sauces, or courgette
flowers filled with a crab mousse served on a cushion of fresh
samphire. An extensive range of excellent quality fish and meat
can be simply grilled, and with eight hours' notice, two people can
share pressed Rouennais duck, its preparation finished at table.
Separate vegetarian menu. *L 12-2.15 D 7-10.30. Closed L Sat
& Sun. Set L £18.50/£21.50 Set D £35.*

Bridges Brasserie
Seats 80 | Meal for 2 approx £35

A brasserie in the Continental style, with an all-day menu of salads,
sandwiches, appetisers (stuffed mushrooms, quiche, paté) and main
courses (fish and chips, grilled rib-eye steak). Also a wide selection
of cakes and pastries, coffees and teas. *Meals 7am-11pm.*

Edinburgh   Caledonian Hotel

Tel 0131-225 2433   Fax 0131-225 6632   **H R**

Princes Street Edinburgh Lothian EH1 2AB
Rooms 239 | Meal for 2 approx £240

Built at the turn of the century by the Caledonian Railway
Company, the 'Caley' is virtually a national monument. In the
hands of Queens Moat Houses it has maintained traditional
standards of hospitality and service while moving with the times
in terms of comfort and amenities. The carpeted foyer leads
to a grand, gracefully proportioned and elegant lounge, furnished
with plush shot-silk sofas. Bedrooms are individually styled,
featuring well-chosen furniture and luxurious drapes; 5th-floor
rooms are smaller than some of the others; 41 rooms are reserved
for non-smokers. De luxe rooms and those with a view of the
Castle attract a supplement; there are also 22 suites. Towelling
robes are provided in all the bathrooms, which include a TV/radio
speaker; elegant antique-style fittings in Executive bathrooms. Plus
factors are the number of telephone extensions in the rooms, 24hr
lounge service and a turn-down service. Conference facilities for
up to 400; banqueting for 200+. Free parking for 40 cars.
AMERICAN EXPRESS *Diners, Mastercard, Visa.*

La Pompadour
Seats 70 | Meal for 2 approx £100

Opened in 1925 and named after Louis XV's mistress, the
Pompadour is elegant and formal; ornate plasterwork frames large
wall paintings of delicate flowers, a pianist plays soothing music
and excellent staff provide impeccable service. Chef Tony Binks
presents a menu of traditional Scottish dishes at lunchtime, while
in the evening there's an à la carte selection with a French slant:
oysters with creamed leeks and Brie glazed with a champagne
sabayon, fillets of Dover sole gratinated with a liaison of Chablis

and Dijon mustard, maize-fed poussin stuffed with Roquefort cheese, apple and Chateau de Born prunes. Chef Binks also offers a multi-course tasting menu with such dishes as creamed cauliflower and broad bean soup with Gruyère and almond dumplings; River Tay salmon stuffed with oyster mushrooms bound in natural yoghurt, with a panaché of fennel and corn with fine egg noodles; and pot-roast guinea fowl with root vegetables, spiced savoy cabbage and black-eye beans. Desserts from the trolley, Scottish and French farmhouse cheeses. *L 12.30-2 D 7.30-10.30. Closed L Sat, all Sun. Set L £27 Set D £35*

Carriages Restaurant
Seats 150   Meal for 2 approx £60

Carriages is open for breakfast, lunch and dinner seven days a week, serving a range of familiar, fairly straightforward dishes on à la carte and table d'hote menus. Chicken liver paté, avocado and prawn salad, seafood pasta and lamb hot pot accompany the day's roast at lunchtime, along with some Scottish favourites like haggis or Musselburgh pie. In the evening, steaks are a very popular choice (plain grilled, with bordelaise, pepper or chasseur sauce, or in classic entrées such as steak Diane and tournedos Rossini. *L 12-2.30 D 6.30-10. Set L £14.50/£17.25 (Sun £16.25) Set D £24.50.*

Edinburgh   Denzlers 121
Tel 0131-554 3268   **R**

121 Constitution Street Leith Edinburgh Lothian EH6 7AE
Seats 65   Meal for 2 approx £50

Externally forbidding former bank premises down amongst the bonded warehouses of Leith (5 minute taxi ride from the centre of Edinburgh); inside is bright and welcoming, while outside the parking is easy in the evening. Solidly traditional Swiss favourites like veal zurichoise, air-dried beef and ham (*bunderplatti*) and cheese fondues (minimum 2 persons) share the menu with the likes of smoked salmon served on toast with prawns in cream horseradish sauce and saddle of hare garnished with croutons, bacon and mushrooms, served with spätzli. Puds include *apfel strudel* and *coupe Nesselrode* (fresh chestnut purée piped over vanilla ice cream and meringue topped with cream). The set lunch offers very good value (*oeuf en cocotte*, pigeon pie) and includes a drink. Short, diverse wine list includes three Swiss wines. *L 12-2 D 6.30-10. Closed L Sat, all Sun, Mon, 1st week Jan. Set L £7.50* AMERICAN EXPRESS *Diners, Mastercard, Visa.*

Edinburgh   Ristorante Raffaelli
Tel 0131-225 6060   **R**

10 Randolph Place Edinburgh Lothian EH3 7TA
Seats 60   Meal for 2 approx £45

A sophisticated setting for all-day service of generally mainstream Italian cooking. Good home-made pasta features in a dish like tagliatelle with porcini mushrooms; other choices might include four-cheese or seafood risotto, grilled sea bass with barbecue sauce, medallions of venison with Barolo and polenta or grilled T-bone of veal with garlic and rosemary. Snacks in the wine bar next door. *Meals 12.15-9.30 (Sat from 6.30, Fri & Sat to 10). Closed L Sat, all Sun, Bank Holidays, 25 & 26 Dec, 1 Jan.* AMERICAN EXPRESS *Diners, Mastercard, Visa.*

Aberdeen

Aberdeen   **Ardoe House**

| Tel 01224 867355   Fax 01224 861283 | **H** |

South Deeside Road Royal Deeside Grampian AB1 5YP
Rooms 71   Meal for 2 approx £108

A few minutes' drive from the centre of Aberdeen, Ardoe House
enjoys a secluded setting at the end of a winding drive. Its style
is Scottish Baronial, and day rooms retain all their best original
features, with carved oak panelling and handsome ceiling work.
The drawing room and cocktail bar are warm and inviting, and
there's a choice of rooms available for conferences and banquets
(for up to 300/200). Bedrooms are comfortable and well
appointed, whether in the main building (some reached by a fine
oak staircase past a stained-glass window) or in the sympathetically
designed modern section, where the majority are located. *Garden,
croquet, putting.* AMERICAN EXPRESS *Diners, Mastercard, Visa.*

Aberdeen   **The Marcliffe at Pitfodels**

| Tel 01224 861000   Fax 01224 868860 | **HR** |

North Deeside Road Pitfodels Aberdeen AB1 9PA
Rooms 42   Meal for 2 approx £115

Aberdeen's latest and best hotel is set in six acres of landscaped
grounds on the western outskirts of the city, newly built, but
in traditional style, by experienced local hoteliers Stewart and
Sheila Spence. Day rooms like the rug-strewn, flagstoned lobby
and richly furnished lounge with its red walls, real fire and
scattering of antiques, demonstrate Sheila's flair for interior design.
Bedroom decor is particularly striking with innovative
combinations of floral patterns, checks and colourful
Mediterranean prints used to great effect. Well-designed and
spacious with quality furniture – antiques in the Master bedrooms
that boast such extras as video machines and decanters of sherry –
and comfortable armchairs, all rooms have desk as well as bedside
phones, mini-bars with fresh milk for the discreetly hidden
beverage kit (there's also 24hr room service) and trouser press
incorporating iron and ironing board. Good bathrooms feature
a third tap at the washbasin dispensing specially purified drinking
water. Immaculate staff, kitted-out in the hotel's own tartan, are
numerous and attentive, providing a high level of service. Good
breakfasts include 'Aberdeen Rowies', a local speciality a bit like
a flat croissant. No dogs. *Garden, snooker.* AMERICAN EXPRESS *Diners,
Mastercard, Visa.*

Conservatory Restaurant and Invery Room
Seats 100   Meal for 2 approx £90

A choice of eating here: the smart yet informal, split-level
(divided by stone balustrade) Conservatory with terrace offering
a short but varied à la carte – steak and mushroom pie with
Guinness, grilled salmon with sun-dried tomato and herb butter,
chargrilled steaks – and the opulent, formal, dinner-only Invery
Room. The latter, sporting a handsome antique sideboard, offers
a fixed-price, four-course menu that shares some dishes with the
Conservatory plus the likes of a warm salad of West Coast scallops

flavoured with tomatoes and balsamic vinaigrette, chargrilled halibut with chive butter sauce and medallions of beef with wild mushroom and Madeira sauce. Cooking generally is uncomplicated but not unsophisticated; and the raw materials are first-rate. Price quoted is for the no-smoking Invery Room. *Invery Room: D only 7-10. Closed Sun. Set D £33.50. Conservatory: L 12-2.15 D 6.30-10.*

Aberdeen	**Silver Darling**	
Tel 01224 576229		**R**

Pocra Quay North Pier Aberdeen Grampian AB2 1DQ
Seats 35   Meal for 2 approx £65

A French speciality 'barbecued seafood' restaurant overlooking the city and old port from the farthest point of the North Quay. Most of the fish is prepared in full view of diners through a large kitchen window, cooked on the barbecue and served with fennel, tomatoes and a herb butter sauce. Besides this there's a wide choice, from Mediterranean crab soup, pasta with seafood and basil, and a cold soufflé with smoked salmon and fromage blanc to trout poached in Sancerre, fried brill flambé with whisky and gigot of monkfish braised with smoked bacon, stuffed with wild mushrooms, garlic and thyme and served with a crab sauce. Booking is essential. *L 12-2 D 7-10. Closed L Sat & all Sun, 2 weeks Christmas.* AMERICAN EXPRESS *Diners, Mastercard, Visa.*

Glasgow

Glasgow	**Glasgow Hilton**

Tel 0141-204 5555 Fax 0141-204 5004	**HR**

1 William Street Glasgow Strathclyde G3 8HT
Rooms 319   Meal for 2 approx £140

Now comfortably established in the city, it's sometimes hard
to remember when the Hilton wasn't here. The eye-catching
decor, standards of service and watchpoints like Minsky's Deli –
not to mention the very shape of the tall, glass and granite
building – could almost make you believe you were Stateside
rather than Clydeside. Air-conditioned bedrooms (with sealed
windows) have standardised decor and furnishings, but an extra
£25 on the room-only rate brings Executive status with extras
like bathrobe and slippers, and use of the top-floor Executive
lounge with complimentary Continental breakfast, afternoon tea
and evening drink. One floor caters specifically for Japanese guests.
Extensive 24hr room service and conference/banqueting facilities
for up to 1100. Valet parking. *Indoor swimming pool, gym, sauna,*
steam room, solarium, beauty & hair salons, news kiosk, coffee shop
(6.30am-11pm). AMERICAN EXPRESS *Diners, Mastercard, Visa.* 🐂

Camerons Restaurant
Seats 60   Meal for 2 approx £95

Designed to resemble several interconnecting rooms from a grand
Scottish country house, the decor here is amongst the most
appealing of any modern hotel restaurant. There's plenty to like
about the menu too with dishes like a light broth of Western Isles
seafood and summer vegetables with seaweed pastry twists; cream
of snow pea soup with fresh ginger; warm foie gras salad with
grapes and raspberry vinaigrette; John Dory baked over dried
fennel with a light tomato dressing; a medley of Highland game
with forest mushrooms on a rich game jus; and lightly smoked
new season lamb with polenta, charred aubergine (the kitchen has
just acquired a brand new chargrill) and fresh vegetable tips,
combining a light, modern style with the best of Scottish produce.
The wine list is presented by grape variety and even includes
an Israeli kosher section. The New World is well represented,
there's a good house selection under £15 and plenty of half
bottles. *L 12-2 D 7-11. Closed L Sat, all Sun. Set L £16.50/£19.*

Glasgow	**One Devonshire Gardens**

Tel 0141-339 2001 Fax 0141-337 1663	**HR**

1 Devonshire Gardens Glasgow Strathclyde G12 0UX
Rooms 27   Meal for 2 approx £155

One Devonshire is one of a kind. Owned by Ken McCulloch and
superbly run by Beverly Payne, this is a hotel of real style and
distinction. It's an unusual spot at which to find such insulated
comforts, situated as it is at the junction of the Great Western and
Hyndland Roads; rooms at the rear are therefore quieter. Every
creature comfort imaginable (within a hotel context!) seems to be
available in bedrooms, bathrooms or public rooms as appropriate,
creating an air of opulence and luxury that somehow doesn't
overawe. Quality is evident throughout, whether it's the level
of service provided (courteous porterage, immaculate

housekeeping and cheerful turning-down of beds at night), the facilities offered in the bedrooms (hi-tech TV and CD player, mini-bar, fresh flowers, books, magazines, quality toiletries, and luxurious hooded bathrobes), or the standard and degree of comfort in the lounge and bar, where you can unwind and relax in serene splendour, surrounded by antiques and good paintings. You really feel valued and cosseted in a manner that only a truly professional hotelier and his staff can achieve. *Patio garden.* AMERICAN EXPRESS® *Diners, Mastercard, Visa.*

Restaurant
Seats 44   Meal for 2 approx £80

Sophisticated decor sees the crisp, spotlit whiteness of damask tablecloths set against a background of midnight blue with dense medieval-tapestry patterned drapes and wallpaper. There's a new chef, Andrew Fairlie, since last year but the market-driven, fixed-price menu format is unchanged except that there is now a little more choice. Very much in the modern idiom, typical dishes might include grilled and marinated vegetables with rocket, balsamic dressing and shaved Parmesan; crab ravioli; grilled goat's cheese with roasted egg plant; steamed turbot with potato salad and gazpacho sauce; breast of pigeon with shallot and garlic confit on a bed of Puy lentils and pan-fried calf's liver with sage-mashed potatoes and a green peppercorn sauce; all are based on first-rate ingredients cooked with flair and skill. Puds are fairly mainstream: lemon tart, chocolate marquise and gratin of strawberries. Good selection of home-made breads. Sunday lunch always includes prime roast joints of Scottish roast beef carved at yout table. *L 12.30-2 D 7-10.30. Closed L Sat. Set L £21.50 Set D £37.50.* 🐂

Glasgow   The Puppet Theatre
Tel 0141-339 8444   Fax 0141-339 7666   **R**
11 Ruthven Lane Glasgow Strathclyde G12 9BQ
Seats 72   Meal for 2 approx £75

Venture down a narrow lane opposite Hillhead Metro station in Glasgow's West End to find one of the city's newest and most chic restaurants. The first choice to make is whether to eat in the dark green, candle-lit, labyrinthine interior (one wall features a detail from the ceiling of the Sistine Chapel, another is mirrored, and there is an intimate padded booth) or the eccentrically-shaped conservatory to the rear of the early 19th-century building. Even more difficult is the decision about what to choose from a menu that is full of good things – skewered scallops with lentils and coriander; consommé of smoked salmon with langoustine and vegetable tortellinis; seared marinated beef fillet with radish, cucumber and roasted peanuts; steamed fillet of sea bass with hot and sweet peppers; calf's liver with lime and caramelised onions; rich venison pie; and side dishes like aubergine and polenta cakes, and carrot and celeriac mousse. Puds range from the exotic – roast baby pineapple with vanilla and cinnamon – to a jam tart with clotted cream custard. Just two dozen well-chosen wines on offer, almost all (except the fizz) at less than £20 a bottle. *L 12-2.30 D 7-11. Set L £11.95/£13.95 Set Sun L £15.95.* AMERICAN EXPRESS® *Diners, Mastercard, Visa.*

Glasgow   **Rogano**

Tel 0141-248 4055   Fax 0141-248 2608   R

11 Exchange Place Glasgow Strathclyde G1 3AN

Seats 55   Meal for 2 approx £75

Popular as ever and as firmly traditional as its setting of art deco
ocean-liner decor, Rogano is a Glasgow institution. Fish and
seafood feature very strongly on the menu – from fish soup,
oysters, mussels and sashimi to lobster, langoustines, salmon,
scallops and monkfish. Parma ham with fresh figs, fillet of Angus
beef with peppercorns and cognac, breast of duckling with
apricots, port and cinnamon, malt whisky parfait with prunes and
Earl Grey syrup complete the picture. Downstairs, the all-day *Café
Rogano* is more informal. *L 12-2.30 D 6.30-10.30 (Sun 6 to 10)
(Café 12-11, to midnight Fri & Sat, Sun 6-10 only). Closed L Sun,
all Bank Holidays. Set L £16.50.* AMERICAN EXPRESS *Diners, Mastercard,
Visa.*

Cardiff

Cardiff **Copthorne Hotel**

Tel 01222 599100   Fax 01222 599080   **H**

Culverhouse Cross Cardiff South Glamorgan CF5 6XJ
Rooms 135   Meal for 2 approx £119

A large new five-storey hotel to the west of town off the A48
(take Junction 33 M4) near the HTV studios. Lots of wood
panelling and rich autumnal colour schemes predominate
in appealing public areas, some of which overlook the hotel's own
small lake. All the good-sized bedrooms are well laid out with
large desks (to which the phone is easily movable) with
comfortable armchairs in addition to breakfast table and proper
armchair. Good bathrooms feature polished red-granite vanitory
units. Rooms on the Connoisseur Floor get extras like bathrobes
and slippers plus use of an Executive lounge with free soft drinks
and Continental breakfast. Banqueting/conference facilities for
200/300 (parking for 225). *Indoor swimming pool, gym, sauna, spa
bath, steam room, solarium, snooker.* AMERICAN EXPRESS *Diners, Mastercard,
Visa.*

Cardiff **Le Monde**

Tel 01222 387376   **R**

60 St Mary Street Cardiff South Glamorgan
Seats 70   Meal for 2 approx £40

One of a trio of atmospheric restaurants-cum-wine bars, this one
appeals primarily to fish-eaters with a wide array of shell, sea and
freshwater fish. Its siblings are *La Brasserie* (0222 372164)
specialising in grilled meats and seasonal game and offering a £5
set lunch, and *Champers* (0222 373363) with a Spanish slant
to both menu and wine list – over 100 Riojas! *Champers* is open
Sunday evening to 12.30am and seats about 150. *L 12-2.30
D 7-12. Closed Sun, 25 Dec.* AMERICAN EXPRESS *Diners, Mastercard, Visa.*

Cardiff **Park Hotel**

Tel 01222 383471   Fax 01222 399309   **H**

Park Place Cardiff South Glamorgan CF1 3UD
Rooms 119   Meal for 2 approx £113

Following the major refurbishment at the Park of all bedrooms
and function rooms (conferences for up to 300), the next to be
similarly treated are the ground-floor public rooms. The Park's
impressive stone-clad facade is a striking landmark on Cardiff's
pedestrianised Queen Street and today's lack of traffic is a bonus
for those occupying the best, front-facing bedrooms. Entry,
however, is from Park Place and vehicular access (to the rear)
is tricky. AMERICAN EXPRESS *Diners, Mastercard, Visa.*

Belfast

Belfast   **Roscoff**

Tel 01232 331532   Fax 01232 312093   **R**

Lesley House Shaftesbury Square Belfast Co Antrim BT2 7DB
Seats 70   Meal for 2 approx £75

Via Albert Roux in London plus spells in Canada and California,
Paul and Jeanne Rankin arrived in Belfast some five years ago and
opened the chicest restaurant in town. Since then it's been one
success after another, firstly maintaining standards and consistently
cooking the best food in the area, then bringing on young chefs
(witness the present sous chef, the very talented Jane McMeekin
who started here as an unpaid pastry commis and has gained
several internal promotions), presenting a TV series, and writing a
recipe book. Paul's style of cooking is modern and innovative and   ★
his influences are divers, producing dishes such as foie gras
wontons with wild mushrooms and wilted rocket, spiced sole
tempura with lobster and coriander aïoli, and fresh figs in Merlot
with honey almond ice cream. Complementing the good food
(the set lunch is a real bargain) is a most fairly priced and
interesting wine list; service is noticeably slick. *L 12.15-2.15
D 6.30-10.30. Set L £14.50 Set D £19.50. Closed L Sat, all Sun,
11 & 12 July, 24, 25 & 26 Dec, 1 Jan.* AMERICAN EXPRESS *Diners,
Mastercard, Visa.*

Belfast   **Stormont Hotel**

Tel 01232 658621   Fax 01232 480240   **H**

587 Upper Newtownards Road Stormont Belfast Co Down BT4 3LP
Rooms 106   Meal for 2 approx £127

Way out of town on the Newtownards Road, opposite Stormont
Castle, this modern hotel is always busy and bustling, having
various function rooms in addition to the Confex Centre with its
10 purpose-built trade and exhibition rooms. Public areas centre
around a sunken lounge (sometimes used as a conference 'break-
out' area) off which is a cosy cocktail bar. A mezzanine lounge has
huge glass windows overlooking the castle grounds. The majority
of bedrooms have been completely refurbished in recent times and
are spacious, comfortable and practical with satellite TV, good,
well-lit work space and modern easy chairs. Good bathrooms
feature marble tiling. Smart, helpful staff offer attentive lounge
service and there's a 24hr room-service menu. Good breakfasts are
served in the informal all-day brasserie. AMERICAN EXPRESS *Diners,
Mastercard, Visa.*

Scotch Beef Club Members: United Kingdom

ENGLAND
BUCKLAND: Buckland Manor
GREAT MILTON: Le Manoir aux Quat'Saisons
LONDON: Le Gavroche
LONDON: Hyatt Carlton Tower Rib Room
LONDON: Inter-Continental Hotel
LONDON: Tatsuso
ULLSWATER: Sharrow Bay

SCOTLAND
ABERFOYLE: Braeval Old Mill
AUCHTERARDER: Auchterarder House
AUCHTERARDER: Gleneagles Hotel
DUNBLANE: Cromlix House Hotel
DUNKELD: Kinnaird House
EDINBURGH: Balmoral Hotel
EDINBURGH: Caledonian Hotel
EDINBURGH: Sheraton Grand Hotel
FORT WILLIAM: Inverlochy Castle
GLASGOW: The Belfry
GLASGOW: Hilton International
GLASGOW: One Devonshire Gardens
GULLANE: La Potinière
INVERNESS: Culloden House Hotel
INVERURIE: Thainstone House Hotel
LANGBANK: Gleddoch House
LINLITHGOW: Champany Inn
MARKINCH: Balbirnie House Hotel
PEAT INN: Peat Inn
PORT APPIN: Airds Hotel
TURNBERRY: Turnberry Hotel

United Kingdom Index

FOR THE WIDEST RANGE OF SERVICED APARTMENTS WORLDWIDE

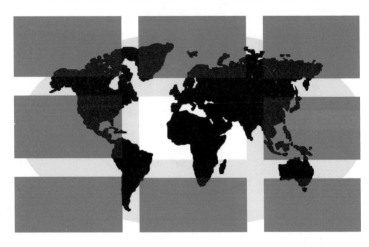

CALL THE SPECIALISTS

Serviced Apartments are the ideal alternative to hotel accommodation for holidays, business or as an interim housing solution.

Cost-effectively priced, all our apartments are serviced by maids, fully equipped and offer unrivalled luxury, space, privacy and security.

With over 25 international partners, The Apartment Service has unique representation in local markets who can help you choose the property that best suits your needs from the thousands of quality apartments throughout the World, from London to New York, from Paris to Sydney.

The Guide to Serviced Apartments containing details of over 3,000 apartments in Europe is available free of charge on request.

SERVICES APARTMENTS HAVE:-

- Lounges
- Kitchens
- Bathrooms
- Maid Service
- Baby Sitting Service
- Direct Dial Telephones

IDEAL FOR:-

- Holidays
- Training Courses
- Relocation
- Temporary Assignments
- Workbases
- Exhibitions
- Conference Presentations

CALL TODAY FOR MORE DETAILS OF OUR FREE SERVICE AND OUR BROCHURE

T H E   A P A R T M E N T   S E R V I C E
66 Dalling Road, London W6 0JA, U.K. Telephone: 081 748 4207 Facsimile: 081 748 3972

Call us toll free for our 96 page colour guide featuring apartments in 28 European cities on request

0800 243 163

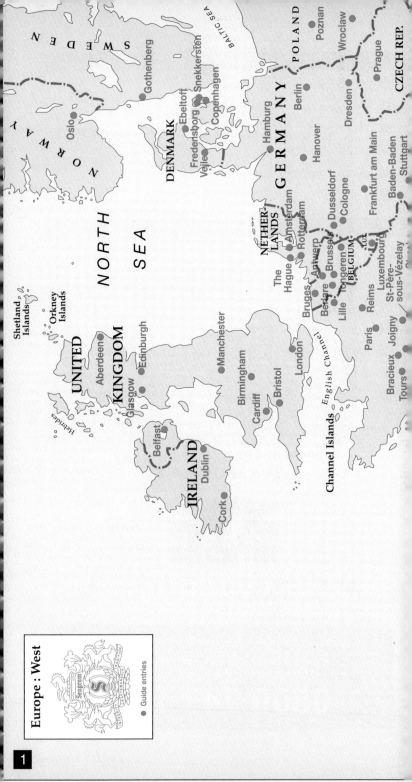

Europe : West

Seagram

• Guide entries

NORTH SEA

BALTIC SEA

NORWAY

Oslo

S W E D E N

Gothenberg

DENMARK

Ebeltoft
Fredensborg
Snekkersten
Vejle
Copenhagen

Hamburg

Berlin POLAND Poznan

Wroclaw

Hanover

Prague

CZECH REP.

Dresden

G E R M A N Y

NETHER-
LANDS
Amsterdam
Rotterdam
Dusseldorf
Cologne
Frankfurt am Main
Baden-Baden
Stuttgart

The
Hague
Antwerp
Bruges Brussels
Beloeil Tongeren BELGIUM LUX.
Lille Luxembourg
Reims St-Père-
sous-Vézelay

English Channel

Paris
Joigny
Bracieux
Tours

Shetland
Islands

Orkney
Islands

UNITED

Aberdeen

KINGDOM

Glasgow Edinburgh

Hebrides

Manchester

Birmingham
Cardiff Bristol

London

Belfast

IRELAND
Dublin

Cork

Channel Islands

1

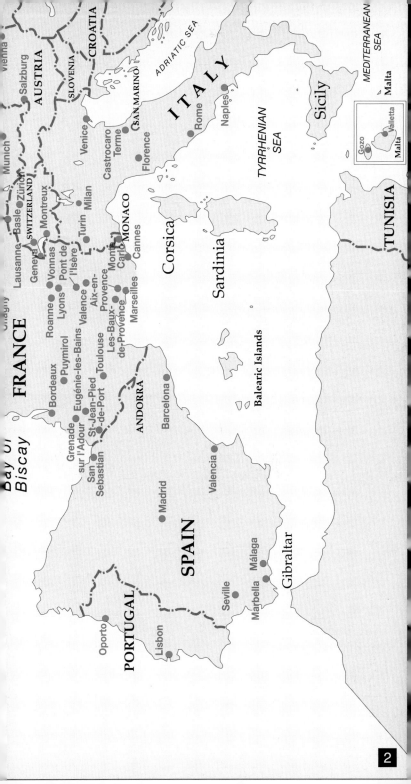

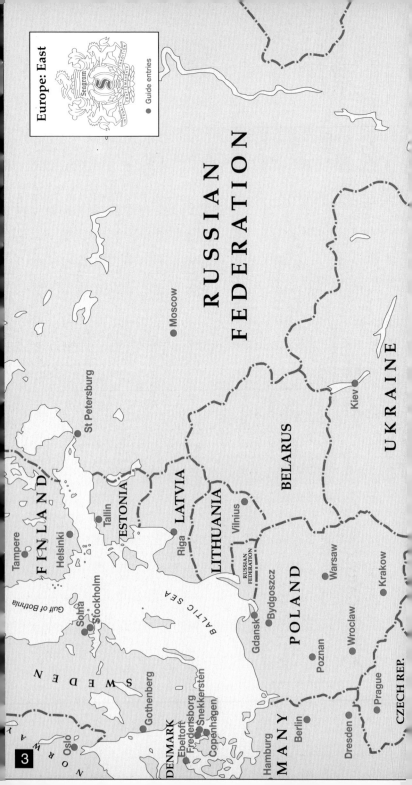

RUSSIAN
FEDERATION

● Moscow

UKRAINE

● Kiev

St Petersburg

BELARUS

FINLAND

Tampere

Helsinki

ESTONIA

Tallin

LATVIA

Riga

LITHUANIA

Vilnius

RUSSIAN
FEDERATION

Gulf of Bothnia

Stockholm

Sofia

BALTIC SEA

Gdansk

Bydgoszcz

POLAND

Warsaw

Krakow

SWEDEN

Poznan

Wroclaw

Gothenberg

Ebeltoft

Fredensborg

Snekkersten

Copenhagen

DENMARK

Prague

CZECH REP.

Hamburg

Berlin

MANY

Dresden

NORWAY

Oslo

3

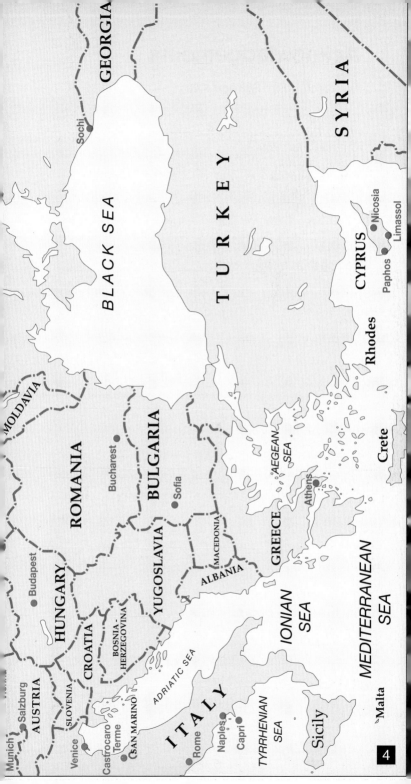

Acknowledgements

Research Editor **Shireen Jilla**

Contributors:
Mario Dix
Charles Florman
Zoltan Halasz
Sam le Quesne
Robin Lodge
Ian Wiesniewski

Egon Ronay's Guides would like to thank all those people who kindly supplied photographs to assist in the compilation of this book.

Index

READERS' COMMENTS

This first, new-style *Egon Ronay's Seagram Guide 1995 Europe*, concentrates on hotels and restaurants in major cities, plus others of note within reasonable driving distance. Inevitably, there are restaurants and hotels which we have not included, either because we don't know about them, or because they haven't yet been assessed by our inspectors. Please let us know of any establishments you think should be in the next edition and let us have your comments (both good and bad) on those which are included in this year's Guide. *(Europe 1995)*.

Name and address of establishment   **Your recommendation or complaint**

564

Readers' Comments continued

Name and address of establishment   **Your recommendation or complaint**

_____   _____

_____   _____

_____   _____

_____   _____

_____   _____

_____   _____

_____   _____

_____   _____

_____   _____

_____   _____

_____   _____

_____   _____

_____   _____

_____   _____

Your Name (BLOCK LETTERS PLEASE)

_____

_____

_____

_____

_____

READERS' COMMENTS

This first, new-style *Egon Ronay's Seagram Guide 1995 Europe*, concentrates on hotels and restaurants in major cities, plus others of note within reasonable driving distance. Inevitably, there are restaurants and hotels which we have not included, either because we don't know about them, or because they haven't yet been assessed by our inspectors. Please let us know of any establishments you think should be in the next edition and let us have your comments (both good and bad) on those which are included in this year's Guide. *(Europe 1995).*

Name and address of establishment	Your recommendation or complaint

Readers' Comments continued

Name and address of establishment   **Your recommendation or complaint**

_____   _____

_____   _____

_____   _____

_____   _____

_____   _____

_____   _____

_____   _____

_____   _____

_____   _____

_____   _____

_____   _____

_____   _____

Your Name (BLOCK LETTERS PLEASE)

_____

_____

_____

_____

_____

_____

READERS' COMMENTS

This first, new-style *Egon Ronay's Seagram Guide 1995 Europe*, concentrates on hotels and restaurants in major cities, plus others of note within reasonable driving distance. Inevitably, there are restaurants and hotels which we have not included, either because we don't know about them, or because they haven't yet been assessed by our inspectors. Please let us know of any establishments you think should be in the next edition and let us have your comments (both good and bad) on those which are included in this year's Guide. *(Europe 1995)*.

Name and address of establishment   **Your recommendation or complaint**

568

Readers' Comments continued

Name and address of establishment   **Your recommendation or complaint**

Your Name (BLOCK LETTERS PLEASE)

READERS' COMMENTS

This first, new-style *Egon Ronay's Seagram Guide 1995 Europe*, concentrates on hotels and restaurants in major cities, plus others of note within reasonable driving distance. Inevitably, there are restaurants and hotels which we have not included, either because we don't know about them, or because they haven't yet been assessed by our inspectors. Please let us know of any establishments you think should be in the next edition and let us have your comments (both good and bad) on those which are included in this year's Guide. *(Europe 1995)*.

Name and address of establishment   **Your recommendation or complaint**

570

Readers' Comments continued

Name and address of establishment   **Your recommendation or complaint**

Your Name (BLOCK LETTERS PLEASE)

READERS' COMMENTS

This first, new-style *Egon Ronay's Seagram Guide 1995 Europe*, concentrates on hotels and restaurants in major cities, plus others of note within reasonable driving distance. Inevitably, there are restaurants and hotels which we have not included, either because we don't know about them, or because they haven't yet been assessed by our inspectors. Please let us know of any establishments you think should be in the next edition and let us have your comments (both good and bad) on those which are included in this year's Guide. *(Europe 1995)*.

Name and address of establishment	Your recommendation or complaint

Readers' Comments continued

Name and address of establishment	Your recommendation or complaint

Your Name (BLOCK LETTERS PLEASE)

READERS' COMMENTS

This first, new-style *Egon Ronay's Seagram Guide 1995 Europe*, concentrates on hotels and restaurants in major cities, plus others of note within reasonable driving distance. Inevitably, there are restaurants and hotels which we have not included, either because we don't know about them, or because they haven't yet been assessed by our inspectors. Please let us know of any establishments you think should be in the next edition and let us have your comments (both good and bad) on those which are included in this year's Guide. *(Europe 1995)*.

Name and address of establishment	Your recommendation or complaint

Readers' Comments continued

Name and address of establishment	Your recommendation or complaint

Your Name (BLOCK LETTERS PLEASE)

READERS' COMMENTS

This first, new-style *Egon Ronay's Seagram Guide 1995 Europe*, concentrates
on hotels and restaurants in major cities, plus others of note within reasonable
driving distance. Inevitably, there are restaurants and hotels which we have
not included, either because we don't know about them, or because they
haven't yet been assessed by our inspectors. Please let us know of any
establishments you think should be in the next edition and let us have your
comments (both good and bad) on those which are included in this year's
Guide. *(Europe 1995)*.

Name and address of establishment   **Your recommendation or complaint**

Readers' Comments continued

Name and address of establishment	Your recommendation or complaint

Your Name (BLOCK LETTERS PLEASE)